ADAPTIVE ANTENNAS

Concepts and Performance

ADAPTIVE ANTENNAS

Concepts and Performance

R. T. Compton, Jr.

The Ohio State University

PRENTICE HALL
Englewood Cliffs, New Jersey 07632

Library of Congress Cataloging-in-Publication Data

Compton, R. T.

Adaptive antennas.

Includes index.

1. Adaptive antennas. I. Title.
TK7871.6.C627   1988   621.38′028′3   87-19307
ISBN 0-13-004151-3

Cover design: *Ben Santora*
Manufacturing buyer: *Richard Washburn*

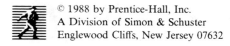 © 1988 by Prentice-Hall, Inc.
A Division of Simon & Schuster
Englewood Cliffs, New Jersey 07632

Printed in the United States of America
10   9   8   7   6   5   4   3   2   1

ISBN   0-13-004151-3

Prentice-Hall International (UK) Limited, *London*
Prentice-Hall of Australia Pty. Limited, *Sydney*
Prentice-Hall Canada Inc., *Toronto*
Prentice-Hall Hispanoamericana, S.A., *Mexico*
Prentice-Hall of India Private Limited, *New Delhi*
Prentice-Hall of Japan, Inc., *Tokyo*
Simon & Schuster Asia Pte. Ltd., *Singapore*
Editora Prentice-Hall do Brasil, Ltda., *Rio de Janeiro*

To Lorraine, Diane, Ted, and Chard

Contents

4 PERFORMANCE CHARACTERISTICS OF LMS AND APPLEBAUM LOOPS 185

5 ADVANCED WEIGHT CONTROL TECHNIQUES 282

6 STEERING VECTOR ARRAYS 335

7 REFERENCE SIGNAL GENERATION IN LMS ARRAYS 396

Preface

The purpose of *Adaptive Antennas: Concepts and Performance* is to present a unified treatment of adaptive antenna systems and to describe their capabilities and limitations. An additional purpose of the book is to acquaint the reader with the analytical techniques used to predict the performance of these systems in new applications.

The subject of adaptive antennas bridges several disciplines within electrical engineering. The author has found that engineers from different specialties tend to view adaptive antennas from quite different perspectives. Antenna engineers are inclined to ask about antenna patterns, sidelobe levels, null depths, the effects of element patterns, and polarization. Communications engineers tend to regard the adaptive antenna as a time-varying processor. They want to know how signal modulation and bandwidth, signal arrival angles, signal and noise powers, and the number of signals affect output signal-to-noise ratios, bit error probabilities, and the like. Control engineers usually ask about stability and rate of convergence of the adaptive weight control loops.

Our purpose in this book is to present adaptive array concepts in a way that incorporates all of these viewpoints. We freely mix together antenna, communication, and feedback control ideas in the presentation. Our goal is an integrated treatment that addresses all three aspects of the problem.

The book is essentially analytical in nature. We use mathematics as a tool to explain basic concepts and to study adaptive array performance. However, the reader will find that even though the approach is analytical, the emphasis in the book is on practical matters, not on theoretical problems. In fact, much of the material covered represents lessons learned (sometimes painfully!) from hardware development. But we do not go into detailed circuit questions. Instead, we describe the nature of the practical problems that occur and show how to determine the effects of these problems on system performance.

The overall plan of the book is as follows. After some introductory remarks in Chapter 1 about historical background, we begin in earnest in Chapter 2. Chapter 2 presents the adaptive array feedback concepts of Shor, Applebaum, and Widrow et al. and shows how to analyze these systems. The major emphasis in the chapter is on the least-mean-square (LMS) and Applebaum arrays, in both the continuous and discrete forms. Simple examples are given that show how an adaptive array accomplishes its major purpose: tracking a desired signal and nulling interference. Chapter 2 also serves to introduce analytic signal notation and the covariance matrix, shows how the array speed of response and stability are controlled by the covariance matrix eigenvalues, and proves that the maximum signal-to-interference-plus-noise ratio (SINR) criterion of Applebaum and the minimum mean square error criterion of Widrow are equivalent. The purpose of Chapter 2 is to introduce basic concepts and show how adaptive antennas work under idealized conditions.

Next, Chapters 3 and 4 discuss the practical effects that actually control the performance of adaptive antennas. Chapter 3 considers three factors important in all adaptive arrays, regardless of the weight control technique used: the number of degrees of freedom in the array, the signal bandwidths, and the element patterns. The concept of degrees of freedom is discussed from several viewpoints, and we show what happens when the number of signals exceeds the number of degrees of freedom. Bandwidth effects are analyzed in a general way to show how arbitrary desired signal and interference power spectral densities may be handled in an adaptive array analysis. To illustrate typical results, we compute the array performance for signals with flat, bandlimited spectral densities. Element pattern effects are also handled in a general way. Since element patterns cannot be defined without taking signal polarization into account, we also discuss polarization in the same section. We use the Poincaré sphere to characterize polarization. We show how to determine the performance of an adaptive array with arbitrary elements when it receives signals with arbitrary polarizations. Simple arrays of cross-polarized dipoles are used to illustrate typical results.

Chapter 4 continues the discussion of practical effects but concentrates on aspects particularly associated with the LMS array. Feedback loop bandwidth, feedback loop time delays, multiplier offset voltages, and weight saturation are described. The IF feedback loop is introduced as a method of avoiding multiplier offset voltages. Weight jitter is described and a method is presented for analyzing it. Finally, covariance matrix eigenvalue behavior is described. We show how eigenvalues depend on signal arrival angles, signal powers, signal bandwidths, number of signals, number of elements, element spacing, and element patterns. Chapter 4 summarizes many practical lessons learned in building LMS loops for adaptive arrays.

In Chapter 5 we turn to more advanced methods of weight control in adaptive arrays. Because of the pervasive problem of eigenvalue (or time constant) variation, researchers have tried to develop methods of weight control less sensitive to eigenvalues than the LMS array. Chapter 5 presents four of these methods: the modified LMS loop, the Gram-Schmidt processor, the recursive least-squares algorithm, and the sample matrix inverse method.

Next, Chapter 6 presents a variety of topics related to the steered beam, or Applebaum, array. We first describe the sidelobe canceler and discuss its relationship to the general Applebaum array. We show how the Applebaum array may be arranged into other equivalent forms by including a preweighting network in front of the adaptive processor. We examine the sensitivity of the Applebaum array to steering vector errors, a subject of some importance when an Applebaum array is used in a communication system. We present the Frost array, which is an adaptive array that incorporates constraints in its pattern or frequency response. Finally, we discuss the power inversion array, a special case of the Applebaum array.

We conclude the book in Chapter 7 by describing methods of using an LMS array in communication systems. The LMS array is attractive for communication applications because it can automatically track the arrival angle of an incoming desired signal. However, in order to do so, the array feedback must be supplied with a reference signal correlated with the desired signal and uncorrelated with interference. Since in general it is not obvious how such a reference signal may be obtained in a practical communication system, the purpose of Chapter 7 is to give a few examples of communication systems where this can be done. Unfortunately, the story is far from complete in this area, and research is continuing. Hopefully, the material in Chapter 7 will suggest additional ideas to the reader.

The book is intended to be used both as a graduate textbook and as a reference book for workers in the field. The manuscript was used twice as a text for a graduate course in the Electrical Engineering Department at Ohio State University. Students taking this course needed only an undergraduate background in electrical engineering. The book assumes the reader knows what a Hermitian matrix is, what the eigenvectors and eigenvalues of a matrix are, and what a coordinate transformation with matrices looks like. Also, a few elementary concepts in random variables and random processes are used. A student who has taken a course in matrices and one in random processes is ideally prepared. However, since only the simplest ideas from these fields are actually used, an instructor can easily fill in the desired background if necessary. The book uses feedback control terminology and discusses antenna patterns, but the presentation is self-explanatory, and no additional background in either controls or antenna theory is required. As noted previously, the Poincaré sphere is used to describe polarization. Since this concept will not be familiar to most electrical engineering students (unless they have specialized in electromagnetics), it is presented in such a way that no real background is required. The book includes homework problems to test the student's understanding of the subject matter and to give practice in analyzing array performance in various situations. A number of the problems discuss concepts or performance questions not covered in the text. Also, several of the problems require a programmable calculator or small computer to obtain numerical results.

For an engineer working in the field, the book can serve as a reference that unifies the antenna, communications, and feedback control aspects of the subject. An antenna engineer, for example, will find the book useful for learning how a reference signal is obtained for an adaptive array in a communication system, or for seeing how to take signal bandwidth into account in a performance study. A communications engineer will learn how element patterns and polarizations affect signal-to-noise ratios and array speed of response, as well as how to choose loop gains so the array does not modulate the signal. Our goal in this book has been to address the whole problem.

Writing a book is a humbling experience. One begins with grand ideas, but because of the immensity of the task, one is forced to compromise between the conflicting goals of perfection and getting the thing done. Moreover, because writing a book takes a few years, one has the unsettling experience of seeing new research papers continually appear while the book is being written. One can only watch nervously and hope that some novel paper will not throw the book out of date before it is even finished. Also, because at some point one must stop revising and simply finish, some things inevitably are not included. To my fellow workers in the field who find their favorite paper missing from the book, I can only apologize.

I am indebted to a large number of people for their help in this project. First and foremost I must thank Mr. Jim Willis and the Naval Air Systems Command, whose support has been absolutely essential. Many years of research support provided by Naval Air Systems Command made this project possible. In addition, I am indebted to Professor H. C. Ko, Chairman of the Electrical Engineering Department at Ohio State University, for allowing me time for this project and for making secretarial help available. My friends and colleagues in the ElectroScience Laboratory at Ohio State have contributed immeasurably by teaching me many things about adaptive arrays. In this regard, I am particularly indebted to Professor A. A. Ksienski, Dr. R. J. Huff, Dr. W. G. Swarner, and Dr. I. J. Gupta. I am greatly indebted to Ms. Emily Baird and Ms. Jacqueline Buckner for their diligent and professional job of typing the book from my cluttered manuscripts. Also, I am very grateful to the students in two classes who persevered through the manuscript, offered helpful suggestions for improvements, pointed out many typos and clumsy spots, and the like. Finally, I want to thank my wonderful wife and family for their encouragement and their patience during many long absences.

R. T. Compton, Jr.
Columbus, Ohio

ADAPTIVE ANTENNAS

Concepts and Performance

1

Introduction

An adaptive antenna is an antenna that *controls its own pattern*, by means of feedback control, while the antenna operates. Some adaptive antennas also control their own frequency response. All adaptive antennas to date have been arrays, rather than continuous aperture antennas, because the pattern of an array is easily controlled by adjusting the amplitude and phase of the signal from each element before combining the signals. Since adaptive antennas are in fact arrays, we shall use the terms *adaptive antennas* and *adaptive arrays* interchangeably in this book. Also, the adaptive antennas we discuss are receiving antennas. We do not consider transmitting antennas.

Adaptive antennas are useful in radar and communication systems that are subject to interference and jamming. These antennas change their patterns automatically in response to the signal environment. They do so in a way that optimizes the signal-to-interference-plus-noise ratio at the array output. Thus they are especially useful for protecting radar and communication systems from interference when the arrival direction of the interference is not known in advance. In communication systems, they are also useful when the desired signal arrival angle is unknown, since an adaptive array pattern can automatically track the desired signal direction. Adaptive arrays can operate with somewhat arbitrary element patterns, polarizations, and spacings. They do not require uniform element spacings or identical element patterns in the array. This feature is an advantage when an antenna system must be designed to operate on an irregularly shaped surface, such as that of an aircraft.

Adaptive antenna systems can be said to date from the 1950s. In 1956, Altman and Sichak [1] proposed the use of phase-lock loops for combining the

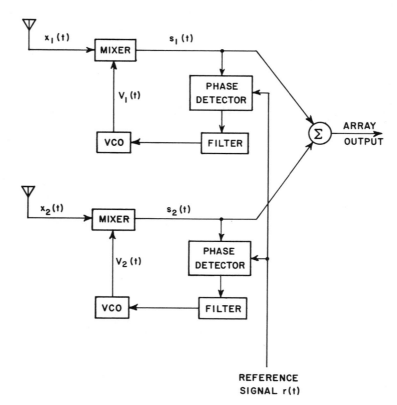

Figure 1.1 The phase-lock loop array.

signals from different receiving antennas in a diversity system. In the 1960s phase-lock loop arrays were extensively studied. Some typical phase-lock loop systems are described in a special issue on active and adaptive antennas of the *IEEE Transactions on Antennas and Propagation* in 1964 [2], edited by R. C. Hansen. See, for example, the papers by Ghose [3], Eberle [4], and Svoboda [5].

A phase-lock loop array operates by aligning the phase of the signal from each element with that of a reference signal, before summing the signals to produce the array output. A block diagram of a phase-lock loop array is shown in Fig. 1.1. The signal from each element is passed through a phase-lock loop[‡] that automatically aligns its phase with that of a reference signal. In Fig. 1.1, element signal $x_1(t)$, for example, is mixed with signal $v_1(t)$ from the voltage-controlled oscillator (VCO). The mixer output $s_1(t)$ appears at an IF frequency. The phase of $s_1(t)$ is determined by both $x_1(t)$ and $v_1(t)$. The phase difference between $s_1(t)$ and a reference signal $r(t)$ is derived in a phase comparator, and

---

[‡]Phase-lock loops are extensively discussed in Viterbi [6].

this phase difference is used to adjust the VCO until $s_1(t)$ is in phase with $r(t)$. The same reference signal $r(t)$ is used for all elements, so the signals $s_1(t)$, $s_2(t),\ldots$ from different elements are in phase and can be added to yield maximum array output signal power.

A phase-lock loop array is adaptive because the antenna pattern is controlled by the incoming signal direction. The array automatically forms a beam that tracks the signal. Moreover, amplitude control can be incorporated in a phase-lock loop array. Svoboda [5] discussed a method for making the gain behind each element proportional to the signal voltage and inversely proportional to the noise power. If this technique is used, the array becomes a maximal ratio combiner [7]. That is, it yields maximum possible signal-to-noise ratio at the array output.

However, the phase-lock loop array has a serious drawback: It is vulnerable to interference. Because the phase-lock loops can track only one signal at a time, the array is easily confused if more than one signal is received. If an interference signal arrives that is stronger than the desired signal, it can easily capture the beam of the antenna. Figure 1.2 (from Svoboda [5]) illustrates this problem in a typical situation with two signals. In this figure the vertical axis is the power ratio of the two signals. The horizontal axis is the frequency difference between the two signals. In the shaded region, the array will not track the desired signal properly. Suitable operation is obtained only if the interference falls in the unshaded region—that is, only if its power is too weak or if its frequency is too far off to capture the phase-lock loops.

Because phase-lock loop arrays are vulnerable to interference and jamming, interest in them has waned in favor of newer types of adaptive arrays,

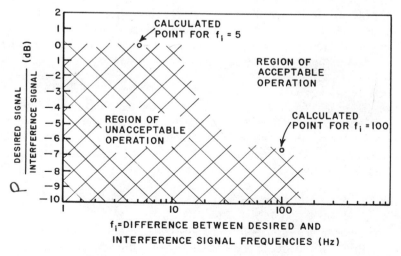

Figure 1.2   Regions of acceptable and unacceptable operation (reprinted from Svoboda [5] with permission, © 1964 IEEE).

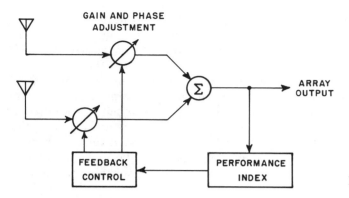

Figure 1.3   A general adaptive array.

such as the LMS and Applebaum arrays to be discussed in Chapter 2. These arrays not only can track a desired signal and maximize array output signal-to-noise ratio, they can null interference as well. The approach used in these arrays is more general than in the phase-lock loop array. The signal from each element is adjusted in both gain and phase, as shown in Fig. 1.3, and the adjustment of the gains and phases is treated as an adaptive optimization problem. That is, a performance index is defined, such as array output signal-to-interference-plus-noise ratio, and the gains and phases are controlled to maximize this performance index.

The performance index that should ideally be used depends on the application. If the array is used in a digital communication system, the ideal performance index is bit error probability. We should choose the array gains and phases to minimize this probability. If the array is used in a radar, we should maximize signal detection probability for a given false alarm probability. However, it turns out that these ideal performance indices are difficult to evaluate directly at the array output. In lieu of these, two other optimization criteria are actually used: (1) minimum mean-square error between the actual array output and the ideal array output and (2) maximum signal-to-interference-plus-noise ratio (SINR) at the array output. The first of these leads to the LMS array and the second to the Applebaum and Shor arrays. These performance indices are more fruitful than the ideal ones because they lead to useful forms of feedback for controlling the array pattern. Moreover, bit error probability always decreases with SINR and radar detection probability always increases with SINR, so these more practical criteria are essentially just as good.

It should be pointed out that with adaptive arrays we do not usually try to control certain conventional antenna characteristics, such as antenna gain, beamwidth, or sidelobe levels. These conventional characteristics are not useful as performance indices in the adaptive array problem. Consider the question of sidelobes, for example. Low sidelobes are desirable in a conventional antenna to minimize the effect of unwanted radiation coming from outside the main beam. However, an adaptive array eliminates unwanted radiation in an entirely different way. It places a pattern null on the interference. The pattern of an adaptive array will frequently have high sidelobes, but only in directions from which no interference comes. For that reason, these high sidelobes are of little consequence. In general, conventional antenna criteria are of less interest with adaptive arrays than more fundamental objectives, such as maximizing SINR.

With this background, we are ready to begin. In Chapter 2, we shall introduce the adaptive array concepts of Shor, Applebaum, and Widrow et al. and show how these antennas work under idealized conditions. In Chapters 3 and 4, we shall examine factors that affect their actual performance under nonideal conditions.

REFERENCES

1. F. J. Altman and W. Sichak, "A Simplified Diversity Communication System for Behind-the-Horizon Links," *IRE Transactions on Communications Systems*, CS–4 (March 1956): 50–55.

2. *IEEE Transactions on Antennas and Propagation*, AP–12, no. 2 (March 1964).

3. R. N. Ghose, "Electronically Adaptive Antenna Systems," *IEEE Transactions on Antennas and Propagation*, AP–12, no. 2 (March 1964): 161–169.

4. J. W. Eberle, "An Adaptively Phased, Four-Element Array of Thirty-Foot Parabolic Reflectors for Passive (Echo) Communication Systems," *IEEE Transactions on Antennas and Propagation*, AP–12, no. 2 (March 1964): 169.

5. D. E. Svoboda, "A Phase-Locked Receiving Array for High-Frequency Communications Use," *IEEE Transactions on Antennas and Propagation*, AP–12, no. 2 (March 1964): 207.

6. A. J. Viterbi, *Principles of Coherent Communications*, McGraw-Hill, New York, 1966.

7. D. G. Brennan, "Linear Diversity Combining Techniques," *Proceedings of the IRE*, 47, no. 6 (June 1959): 1075–1102; see sec. 2, para. 3, p. 1081.

2

Adaptive Array Feedback Concepts

In this chapter we describe several methods of controlling the pattern of an array adaptively. We limit the discussion in this chapter to basic concepts. In Chapters 3 and 4, we shall consider the performance capabilities and limitations of these techniques and describe practical problems that arise in implementing them.

The earliest work on the newer types of adaptive arrays was done in the 1950s by Howells [1] and Applebaum [2] at the General Electric Company. Unfortunately, their work was not published until 1966 as a report [3] and not until 1976 in the literature [1, 2]. Consequently, it was not widely known until the 1970s. Independently, an adaptive array concept was published by Shor [4] in 1966, and another, called the LMS (or least-mean-square) algorithm, appeared in 1967 in a paper by Widrow et al. [5]. These contributions constitute the beginning of the adaptive array field. In this discussion, we shall present the LMS algorithm first, then the Applebaum array, and finally Shor's array.

2.1 THE LMS ADAPTIVE ARRAY

Consider the N-element array shown in Fig. 2.1. The signal from the jth element is split with a quadrature hybrid into an inphase signal $x_{I_j}(t)$ and a quadrature signal $x_{Q_j}(t)$. Each of these signals is multiplied by a weight w_{I_j} or w_{Q_j}. The weighted signals are then summed to produce the array output signal $s(t)$. To make the array adaptive, a feedback system is used to control the

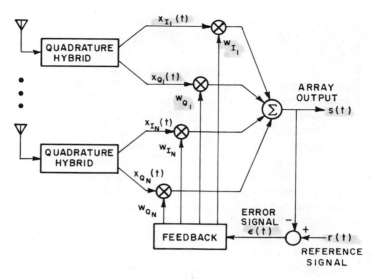

Figure 2.1   The LMS adaptive array.

weights, as shown in Fig. 2.1. The feedback system attempts to drive the weights toward their optimal values, which are defined as follows.

The LMS array of Widrow et al. [5] is based on a minimum mean-square error concept. An error signal $\varepsilon(t)$ is obtained by subtracting the array output $s(t)$ from another signal called the reference signal $r(t)$. The feedback adjusts the weights to minimize $E[\varepsilon^2(t)]$, where $E[\cdot]$ denotes expectation. The details of the feedback will be explained below.

First, however, let us consider why a minimum mean-square error criterion is useful. Suppose this array is used in a communication system. Assume the array output contains a desired signal, interference, and thermal noise; that is,

$$s(t) = \alpha s_d(t) + \beta s_i(t) + \gamma n(t), \qquad (2.1)$$

where $s_d(t)$ is the desired signal, $s_i(t)$ is the interference, $n(t)$ is the thermal noise, and α, β, and γ are constants representing the combined effect of the weights on these signals. We would like to adjust the weights in the array to maximize the desired signal and minimize the interference and thermal noise at the array output. To do so, suppose we let the reference signal $r(t)$ be a replica of the desired signal:

$$r(t) = s_d(t). \qquad (2.2)$$

Then $\varepsilon(t)$ will be

$$\varepsilon(t) = (1 - \alpha)s_d(t) - \beta s_i(t) - \gamma n(t), \qquad (2.3)$$

and the mean-square error is

$$E[\varepsilon^2(t)] = (1 - \alpha)^2 E[s_d^2(t)] + \beta^2 E[s_i^2(t)] + \gamma^2 E[n^2(t)]. \qquad (2.4)$$

Invalid for multipath ?!

(We assume the desired signal, interference, and thermal noise are all zero-mean processes uncorrelated with each other, so cross-product terms such as $E[s_d(t)s_i(t)]$ are zero.) We can see intuitively that $E[\varepsilon^2(t)]$ will be minimum when α is nearly unity and β and γ are small. Thus minimizing $E[\varepsilon^2(t)]$ corresponds approximately to fixing the desired signal power while minimizing the interference and thermal noise power at the array output.

Of course, the reader may be wondering how a replica of the desired signal can be obtained in a practical communication system. For one thing, it is a basic concept of information theory that a signal must be unknown in some respect if it is to convey information to the receiver [6]. For another, it would seem that if one knew the desired signal, one would not even need the antenna! However, it turns out that this reasoning is specious, because we will find that $r(t)$ does not, in fact, need to be a *perfect* replica of $s_d(t)$. It is only necessary that it be correlated with $s_d(t)$ and uncorrelated with $s_i(t)$ and $n(t)$. For certain kinds of communication signals, it is possible to obtain a suitable $r(t)$ by processing the array output signal. This subject will be discussed in Chapter 7. For the moment, let us assume that a suitable reference signal is available and determine the optimal weights.

The Optimal Weights

Before describing the feedback in Fig. 2.1, let us determine the weight settings that yield minimum $E[\varepsilon^2(t)]$. For an arbitrary set of weights, the array output is given by

$$s(t) = \sum_{\substack{j=1 \\ P=I,Q}}^{N} w_{P_j} x_{P_j}(t). \tag{2.5}$$

Therefore, the error signal is

$$\varepsilon(t) = r(t) - \sum_{\substack{j=1 \\ P=I,Q}}^{N} w_{P_j} x_{P_j}(t), \tag{2.6}$$

and the mean-square error is

$$E[\varepsilon^2(t)] = E[r^2(t)] - 2 \sum_{\substack{j=1 \\ P=I,Q}}^{N} w_{P_j} E[r(t)x_{P_j}(t)]$$

$$+ \sum_{\substack{j=1 \\ P=I,Q}}^{N} \sum_{\substack{l=1 \\ L=I,Q}}^{N} w_{P_j} w_{L_l} E[x_{P_j}(t)x_{L_l}(t)]. \tag{2.7}$$

This result may be written more simply by using matrix notation:

$$E[\varepsilon^2(t)] = E[r^2(t)] - 2\mathbf{W}_r^T \mathbf{S}_r + \mathbf{W}_r^T \mathbf{\Phi}_r \mathbf{W}_r, \tag{2.8}$$

where $\mathbf{W}_r$ and $\mathbf{S}_r$ are column matrices,[‡]

$$\mathbf{W}_r = \left[w_{I_1}, w_{Q_1}, w_{I_2}, w_{Q_2}, \ldots \right]^T, \tag{2.9}$$

$$\mathbf{S}_r = E \begin{bmatrix} x_{I_1}(t)r(t) \\ x_{Q_1}(t)r(t) \\ x_{I_2}(t)r(t) \\ x_{Q_2}(t)r(t) \\ \vdots \end{bmatrix}, \tag{2.10}$$

and $\mathbf{\Phi}_r$ is a $2N \times 2N$ matrix,

$$\mathbf{\Phi}_r = E \begin{bmatrix} x_{I_1}(t)x_{I_1}(t) & x_{I_1}(t)x_{Q_1}(t) & x_{I_1}(t)x_{I_2}(t) & x_{I_1}(t)x_{Q_2}(t)\ldots \\ x_{Q_1}(t)x_{I_1}(t) & x_{Q_1}(t)x_{Q_1}(t) & x_{Q_1}(t)x_{I_2}(t) & x_{Q_1}(t)x_{Q_2}(t)\ldots \\ x_{I_2}(t)x_{I_1}(t) & x_{I_2}(t)x_{Q_1}(t) & x_{I_2}(t)x_{I_2}(t) & x_{I_2}(t)x_{Q_2}(t)\ldots \\ x_{Q_2}(t)x_{I_1}(t) & x_{Q_2}(t)x_{Q_1}(t) & x_{Q_2}(t)x_{I_2}(t) & x_{Q_2}(t)x_{Q_2}(t)\ldots \\ \vdots & \vdots & & \end{bmatrix}. \tag{2.11}$$

Superscript T denotes the transpose.

It may be seen from Eq. (2.7) or (2.8) that $E[\varepsilon^2(t)]$ is a quadratic function of the weights. The extremum of this quadratic surface is clearly a minimum, because $E[\varepsilon^2(t)]$ can be made arbitrarily large by increasing $\mathbf{W}_r$. Thus for given values of $E[x_{P_j}(t)x_{L_i}(t)]$ and $E[x_{P_j}(t)r(t)]$, the surface obtained by plotting $E[\varepsilon^2(t)]$ versus the weights is a bowl-shaped surface, as illustrated in Fig. 2.2 for the case of two weights. The quadratic form of Eq. (2.8) is important, because it implies that the bowl has a well-defined minimum, and only one such minimum. Also, saddle points or relative minima are not possible. The optimal weight setting is at the bottom of the bowl.

The weight vector yielding minimum $E[\varepsilon^2(t)]$, which we denote by $\mathbf{W}_{r_{\mathrm{opt}}}$, may be found by setting

$$\nabla_{W_r} \left\{ E\left[\varepsilon^2(t) \right] \right\} = 0, \tag{2.12}$$

where ∇_{W_r} denotes the gradient with respect to $\mathbf{W}_r$. Since

$$\nabla_{W_r} \left\{ E\left[\varepsilon^2(t) \right] \right\} = -2\mathbf{S}_r + 2\mathbf{\Phi}_r\mathbf{W}_r, \tag{2.13}$$

[‡]We use the subscript r on $\mathbf{W}_r$, $\mathbf{S}_r$, and $\mathbf{\Phi}_r$ to indicate that these matrices are obtained from the real-valued weights w_{P_j} and signals $s_{P_j}(t)$ and $r(t)$. Later we shall define complex weights and signals, and we wish to reserve the use of the same symbols, without the subscript, for these quantities.

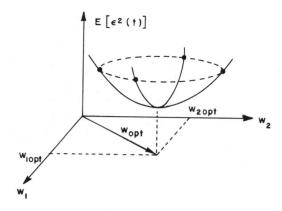

Figure 2.2   The $E[\varepsilon^2(t)]$ surface.

we find

$$\mathbf{\Phi}_r\mathbf{W}_{r_{\text{opt}}} = \mathbf{S}_r, \tag{2.14}$$

or

$$\mathbf{W}_{r_{\text{opt}}} = \mathbf{\Phi}_r^{-1}\mathbf{S}_r, \tag{2.15}$$

where it is assumed that $\mathbf{\Phi}_r$ is nonsingular so its inverse exists. (It will be seen below that $\mathbf{\Phi}_r$ is nonsingular whenever the element signals contain thermal noise.)

Let us now use Eq. (2.15) to determine the minimum value of $E[\varepsilon^2(t)]$. Suppose $\mathbf{W}_r$ has the value in Eq. (2.15). Then $E[\varepsilon^2(t)]$ will have its minimum value, $\varepsilon_{\text{min}}^2$, which is

$$\varepsilon_{\text{min}}^2 = \min_{\mathbf{W}_r} E[\varepsilon^2(t)] = E[r^2(t)] - 2\mathbf{W}_{r_{\text{opt}}}^T\mathbf{S}_r + \mathbf{W}_{r_{\text{opt}}}^T\mathbf{\Phi}_r\mathbf{W}_{r_{\text{opt}}}. \tag{2.16}$$

Using Eq. (2.14) to substitute for $\mathbf{S}_r$ gives

$$\varepsilon_{\text{min}}^2 = E[r^2(t)] - 2\mathbf{W}_{r_{\text{opt}}}^T\mathbf{\Phi}_r\mathbf{W}_{r_{\text{opt}}} + \mathbf{W}_{r_{\text{opt}}}^T\mathbf{\Phi}_r\mathbf{W}_{r_{\text{opt}}} \tag{2.17}$$

or

$$\varepsilon_{\text{min}}^2 = E[r^2(t)] - \mathbf{W}_{r_{\text{opt}}}^T\mathbf{\Phi}_r\mathbf{W}_{r_{\text{opt}}}. \tag{2.18}$$

Furthermore, this result may be used to rewrite the mean-square error for *arbitrary* weights in a useful form. Starting with Eq. (2.8) and using Eq. (2.18) to substitute for $E[r^2(t)]$ and Eq. (2.14) to substitute for $\mathbf{S}_r$, we find

$$E[\varepsilon^2(t)] = \varepsilon_{\text{min}}^2 + \mathbf{W}_{r_{\text{opt}}}^T\mathbf{\Phi}_r\mathbf{W}_{r_{\text{opt}}} - 2\mathbf{W}_r^T\mathbf{\Phi}_r\mathbf{W}_{r_{\text{opt}}} + \mathbf{W}_r^T\mathbf{\Phi}_r\mathbf{W}_r. \tag{2.19}$$

Finally, since $\mathbf{\Phi}_r$ is a symmetric matrix, we may replace $-2\mathbf{W}_r^T\mathbf{\Phi}_r\mathbf{W}_{r_{\text{opt}}}$ with

$$-2\mathbf{W}_r^T\mathbf{\Phi}_r\mathbf{W}_{r_{\text{opt}}} = -\mathbf{W}_r^T\mathbf{\Phi}_r\mathbf{W}_{r_{\text{opt}}} - \mathbf{W}_{r_{\text{opt}}}^T\mathbf{\Phi}_r\mathbf{W}_r. \tag{2.20}$$

Collecting terms, we find

$$E\left[\varepsilon^2(t)\right] = \varepsilon_{\min}^2 + \left(\mathbf{W}_r - \mathbf{W}_{r_{\text{opt}}}\right)^T \mathbf{\Phi}_r \left(\mathbf{W}_r - \mathbf{W}_{r_{\text{opt}}}\right). \qquad (2.21)$$

In this form the quadratic nature of $E[\varepsilon^2(t)]$ is clear. $E[\varepsilon^2(t)]$ will achieve its minimum value, $\varepsilon_{\min}^2$, when $\mathbf{W}_r = \mathbf{W}_{r_{\text{opt}}}$. For $\mathbf{W}_r \neq \mathbf{W}_{r_{\text{opt}}}$, the second term on the right is nonzero and $E[\varepsilon^2(t)] > \varepsilon_{\min}^2$. In general, the mean-square error surface is bowl shaped, as illustrated in Fig. 2.2 for the case of two weights. Because off-diagonal terms in $\mathbf{\Phi}_r$ are usually nonzero, the principal axes of the bowl are not parallel to the weight axes. (Nonzero off-diagonal terms will occur in $\mathbf{\Phi}_r$ whenever the signals in two array elements have nonzero correlation—that is, whenever any directional signals are incident on the array.) A coordinate system *Normal* with axes parallel to the principal axes of the bowl may be found by substituting *coords of*

$$\mathbf{W}_r = \mathbf{R}_r \mathbf{V}_r, \qquad (2.22)$$

$E[\vec{\varepsilon}^2(t)]$

where $\mathbf{R}_r$ is a $2N \times 2N$ coordinate rotation matrix and $\mathbf{V}_r$ is a $2N$-element column matrix:

$$\mathbf{V}_r = \left[v_1, v_2, \dots\right]^T. \qquad (2.23)$$

Substituting Eq. (2.22) into Eq. (2.21) gives

$$E\left[\varepsilon^2(t)\right] = \varepsilon_{\min}^2 + \left(\mathbf{V}_r - \mathbf{V}_{r_{\text{opt}}}\right)^T \mathbf{R}_r^T \mathbf{\Phi}_r \mathbf{R}_r \left(\mathbf{V}_r - \mathbf{V}_{r_{\text{opt}}}\right). \qquad (2.24)$$

If $\mathbf{R}_r$ is chosen so $\mathbf{R}_r^T \mathbf{\Phi}_r \mathbf{R}_r$ is diagonal—that is, so

$$\mathbf{R}_r^T \mathbf{\Phi}_r \mathbf{R}_r = \text{diag}\left(\lambda_{r_1}, \lambda_{r_2}, \dots, \lambda_{r_{2N}}\right)$$

$$= \begin{bmatrix} \lambda_{r_1} & 0 & 0 & \cdots \\ 0 & \lambda_{r_2} & 0 & \\ 0 & 0 & \lambda_{r_3} & \\ \vdots & & & \ddots \end{bmatrix} \qquad (2.25)$$

where the λ_{r_j} are the eigenvalues of $\mathbf{\Phi}_r$, then the v_j are the normal coordinates of the bowl. Since the extremum of $E[\varepsilon^2(t)]$ is a minimum, the eigenvalues λ_{r_j} are nonnegative and $\mathbf{\Phi}_r$ is nonnegative definite.

The LMS Algorithm

For any given array-element geometry, the shape, location, and orientation of the $E[\varepsilon^2(t)]$ surface depend on the signals incident on the array. If the number of these signals, their arrival angles, or their power levels change with time, the bowl and hence $\mathbf{W}_{r_{\text{opt}}}$ will move around in the weight plane. The problem of the adaptive array is to control the weight vector $\mathbf{W}_r$ to make it track the bottom of the bowl.

In the LMS array, the weights are controlled according to a gradient algorithm. Specifically, we let

$$\frac{d\mathbf{W}_r}{dt} = -k\nabla_{W_r}\{E[\varepsilon^2(t)]\}, \tag{2.26}$$

where $k > 0$. Since the gradient on the $E[\varepsilon^2(t)]$ surface is a vector pointing in the maximum uphill direction, and $k > 0$, this equation forces the weights to move in the steepest downhill, or steepest-descent, direction. Moreover, this equation makes the time rate change of $\mathbf{W}_r$ proportional to the slope of the $E[\varepsilon^2(t)]$ surface. Since the slope of a quadratic surface increases linearly with distance from its minimum point, Eq. (2.26) makes the weights change rapidly when they are far from the bottom of the bowl, but only slowly when they are close to the bottom.

The motivation for using Eq. (2.26) to control the weights may be viewed in several ways. For example, given a certain $\mathbf{W}_r$ in the array, with a corresponding $E[\varepsilon^2(t)]$, we would like to insure that $E[\varepsilon^2(t)]$ decreases with time. Since $E[\varepsilon^2(t)]$ is a function of the weights, we can use a chain rule to write

$$\frac{d}{dt}\{E[\varepsilon^2(t)]\} = \sum_{\substack{j=1 \\ P=I,Q}}^{N} \frac{\partial E[\varepsilon^2(t)]}{\partial w_{P_j}} \frac{dw_{P_j}}{dt}. \tag{2.27}$$

To ensure that $dE[\varepsilon^2(t)]/dt < 0$, we can choose

$$\frac{dw_{P_j}}{dt} = -k\frac{\partial E[\varepsilon^2(t)]}{\partial w_{P_j}}, \tag{2.28}$$

because then

$$\frac{dE[\varepsilon^2(t)]}{dt} = -k \sum_{\substack{j=1 \\ P=I,Q}}^{N} \left\{\frac{\partial E[\varepsilon^2(t)]}{\partial w_{P_j}}\right\}^2 \tag{2.29}$$

is automatically negative.

Additionally, imagine that the vector $\dot{\mathbf{W}}_r = d\mathbf{W}_r/dt$ has a given length:

$$\dot{\mathbf{W}}_r^T\dot{\mathbf{W}}_r = |\dot{\mathbf{W}}_r|^2 = \text{constant}. \tag{2.30}$$

Then we may ask what direction the vector $\dot{\mathbf{W}}_r$ should have in order to make $dE[\varepsilon^2(t)]/dt$ as negative as possible. Since

$$\frac{dE[\varepsilon^2(t)]}{dt} = \sum_{j,P} \frac{\partial E[\varepsilon^2(t)]}{\partial w_{P_j}} \frac{dw_{P_j}}{dt} = \nabla_{W_r}\{E[\varepsilon^2(t)]\}^T\dot{\mathbf{W}}_r, \tag{2.31}$$

$dE[\varepsilon^2(t)]/dt$ will clearly have its most negative value, for a given $|\dot{\mathbf{W}}_r|$, if $\dot{\mathbf{W}}_r$ is antiparallel to $\nabla_{W_r}\{E[\varepsilon^2(t)]\}$:

$$\dot{\mathbf{W}}_r = -k\nabla_{W_r}\{E[\varepsilon^2(t)]\}. \tag{2.32}$$

Thus a steepest-descent equation yields the fastest rate of decrease of $E[\varepsilon^2(t)]$ for a given rate of change $|\dot{\mathbf{W}}_r|$.

Now let us substitute for $E[\varepsilon^2(t)]$ in Eq. (2.26). Using Eq. (2.7) for $E[\varepsilon^2(t)]$, we find

$$\frac{\partial E[\varepsilon^2(t)]}{\partial w_{P_j}} = -2E[x_{P_j}(t)r(t)] + 2\sum_{\substack{l=1 \\ L=I,Q}}^{N} w_{L_l}E[x_{P_j}(t)x_{L_l}(t)]$$

$$= -2E\left(x_{P_j}(t)\left[r(t) - \sum_{\substack{l=1 \\ L=I,Q}}^{N} w_{L_l}x_{L_l}(t)\right]\right)$$

$$= -2E[x_{P_j}(t)\varepsilon(t)]. \tag{2.33}$$

Therefore Eq. (2.26) yields

$$\frac{dw_{P_j}}{dt} = 2kE[x_{P_j}(t)\varepsilon(t)]; \quad 1 \le j \le N, P = I, Q. \tag{2.34}$$

Implementing Eq. (2.34) in this form is difficult because of the expectation operator on the right side. The signals $x_{P_j}(t)$ and $\varepsilon(t)$ are available in the array, but there is no way to obtain $E[x_{P_j}(t)\varepsilon(t)]$ in a real-time processor. Hence it is necessary to use some type of estimate of $E[x_{P_j}(t)\varepsilon(t)]$ instead. Although several types of estimates might be used, we adopt the simplest estimate of all, namely, we replace $E[x_{P_j}(t)\varepsilon(t)]$ with $x_{P_j}(t)\varepsilon(t)$. The weight control equation in the LMS array then becomes

$$\frac{dw_{P_j}}{dt} = 2kx_{P_j}(t)\varepsilon(t). \tag{2.35}$$

This equation is known as the LMS algorithm‡ of Widrow et al. [5]. It is equivalent to the feedback loop shown in Fig. 2.3. Since w_{P_j} is just one of the quadrature weights in the adaptive array, two such loops are needed behind each antenna element, one for the inphase channel and one for the quadrature channel, as shown in Fig. 2.4.

The feedback loop shown in Fig. 2.3 is often called a *correlation* loop. This terminology is used because the loop forms the product of $x_{P_j}(t)$ and $\varepsilon(t)$ and

---

‡This feedback rule was first published in discrete form [5], where the use of the word "algorithm" is appropriate. According to *Webster's Seventh New Collegiate Dictionary*, an algorithm is "a rule of procedure for solving a recurrent mathematical problem." Hence, Eq. (2.35) should probably not be called an algorithm. However, this terminology is commonly used.

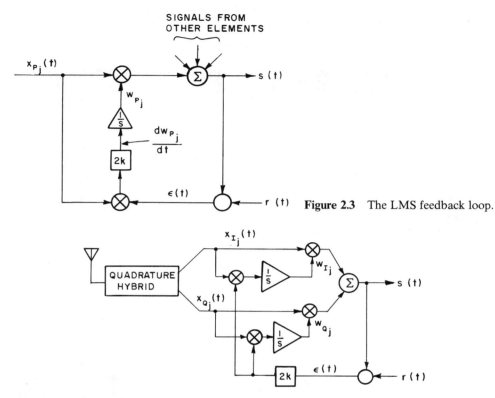

Figure 2.3 The LMS feedback loop.

Figure 2.4 LMS feedback for one element.

integrates the result. That is, the weight $w_{P_j}(t)$, which is

$$w_{P_j}(t) = 2k \int_{-\infty}^{t} x_{P_j}(\eta)\varepsilon(\eta) \, d\eta, \qquad (2.36)$$

may be viewed as an estimate of the correlation between $x_{P_j}(t)$ and $\varepsilon(t)$.

The Effect of Dropping $E(\cdot)$

Now let us examine the effect of eliminating the expectation operator in Eq. (2.34). We observe that, without the $E(\cdot)$ operator, the weights follow a steepest-descent path on the instantaneous $\varepsilon^2(t)$ surface. Since in general the signals $x_{P_j}(t)$ [and hence also $\varepsilon(t)$] are stochastic signals, the instantaneous $\varepsilon^2(t)$ surface is a stochastically varying surface. $E[\varepsilon^2(t)]$ is the mean of this surface. If $x_{P_j}(t)$ and $\varepsilon(t)$ are stationary random processes, the $E[\varepsilon^2(t)]$ surface does not change with time. The instantaneous $\varepsilon^2(t)$ surface, on the other hand, varies with time around its mean. As time progresses, the gradient $\nabla_{W_r}\{\varepsilon^2(t)\}$ fluctuates

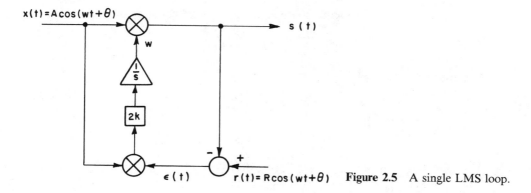

Figure 2.5 A single LMS loop.

randomly about its mean, $\nabla_{W_r}\{E[\varepsilon^2(t)]\}$. As a result, each weight in the array becomes a random process.

With the algorithm based on the gradient of the instantaneous $\varepsilon^2(t)$ surface, instead of the $E[\varepsilon^2(t)]$ surface, the weights fluctuate about their mean values. We can keep the variance of the weights small only by choosing the gain constant k small enough that the weights average out the stochastic variations. This is the price we pay for removing the $E(\cdot)$ operator. With the $E(\cdot)$ included, as in Eq. (2.34), an arbitrarily large value of k could be used. The speed of response of the weights could be made as fast as desired. With Eq. (2.35), however, the speed of response must be kept slow enough (i.e., k must be small enough) that the variance of the weights is acceptable. With k small, Eq. (2.35) yields a weight response equal to that of Eq. (2.34) plus a small weight "jitter."

Let us illustrate these remarks with a simple example. Consider a single LMS loop, as shown in Fig. 2.5. Suppose the input signal to this loop is a CW signal,

$$x(t) = A \cos(\omega t + \theta), \tag{2.37}$$

and suppose also the reference signal is

$$r(t) = R \cos(\omega t + \theta). \tag{2.38}$$

(A single LMS loop has no ability to adjust the phase of an incoming signal. Hence we purposely choose the reference signal in phase with the incoming signal.) Let the carrier phase θ in Eqs. (2.37) and (2.38) be a uniformly distributed random variable, with probability density function

$$p(\theta) = \begin{cases} \dfrac{1}{2\pi}, & 0 \leqslant \theta \leqslant 2\pi, \\ 0, & \text{elsewhere.} \end{cases} \tag{2.39}$$

We will determine the transient response of this loop with and without the expectation operator in the loop equation.

If the $E(\cdot)$ is included, the weight in Fig. 2.5 satisfies the equation

$$\frac{dw}{dt} = 2kE[x(t)\varepsilon(t)]. \tag{2.40}$$

The output signal is

$$s(t) = wx(t) = Aw\cos(\omega t + \theta), \tag{2.41}$$

so the error signal is

$$\varepsilon(t) = (R - Aw)\cos(\omega t + \theta). \tag{2.42}$$

Therefore

$$E[x(t)\varepsilon(t)] = E[A(R - Aw)\cos^2(\omega t + \theta)] = \tfrac{1}{2}A(R - Aw). \tag{2.43}$$

Thus, from Eq. (2.34), w satisfies

$$\frac{dw}{dt} = kA(R - Aw) \tag{2.44}$$

or

$$\frac{dw}{dt} + kA^2w = kAR. \tag{2.45}$$

The solution to this differential equation is

w/ $E[\cdot]$

$$w(t) = \left[w(0) - \frac{R}{A}\right]e^{-kA^2t} + \frac{R}{A}, \tag{2.46}$$

where $w(0)$ is the initial value of $w(t)$ at $t = 0$. Thus, with the $E(\cdot)$ operator included, we obtain a simple exponential response for the weight. This result is plotted in Fig. 2.6 for the case $k = A = R = 1$ and $w(0) = 0$. Note that the time constant of the response is

$$\tau = \frac{1}{kA^2}. \tag{2.47}$$

Thus, the smaller k, the longer the response time of the weight.

Now consider what happens when the expectation is omitted. In this case w satisfies

$$\frac{dw}{dt} = 2kx(t)\varepsilon(t) \tag{2.48}$$

$$= 2kA(R - Aw)\cos^2(\omega t + \theta)$$
$$= kA(R - Aw)[1 + \cos(2\omega t + 2\theta)], \tag{2.49}$$

or

w/o $E[\cdot]$

$$\frac{dw}{dt} + kA^2[1 + \cos(2\omega t + 2\theta)]w = kAR[1 + \cos(2\omega t + 2\theta)]. \tag{2.50}$$

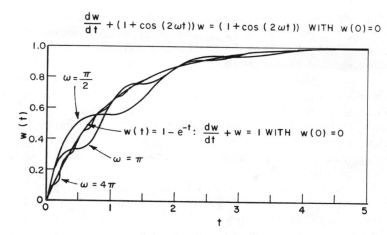

$$\frac{dw}{dt} + (1 + \cos(2\omega t))w = (1 + \cos(2\omega t)) \quad \text{WITH} \quad w(0) = 0$$

Figure 2.6   Solutions to Eqs. (2.45) and (2.50).

A formal solution to this equation may be obtained by an integrating factor method [7]. However, this solution is in the form of an integral difficult to evaluate. Instead, we present a few solutions to Eq. (2.50) obtained numerically. (A fourth-order Runge-Kutta method [8] was used.) Figure 2.6 shows some typical results computed for the case $k = A = R = 1$, $w(0) = 0$ and $\theta = 0$. [Note that we must assume a specific value for θ in this case. In Eq. (2.45), θ disappears from the analysis because the $E(\cdot)$ operator averages over θ. In a real-time processing loop, however, only one member of the ensemble of possible waveforms $A\cos(\omega t + \theta)$ will be present at a time.] Figure 2.6 shows the solutions for $\omega = \pi/2$, π, and 4π.

It is seen that as ω increases, these solutions approach the simple exponential. The reason is easy to see. Consider Eq. (2.44) for the case where the $E(\cdot)$ operation is included. Equation (2.44) shows that with $w(0) = 0$, the initial slope dw/dt at $t = 0$ is kAR. As time progresses, $w(t)$ increases and dw/dt drops. The result is the simple exponential in Fig. 2.6. On the other hand, consider Eq. (2.49) for the case without the $E(\cdot)$ operator. In this case dw/dt is given by the same expression as in Eq. (2.44), except that now an extra factor $1 + \cos(2\omega t + 2\theta)$ appears on the right. This function, which oscillates periodically between 2 and 0, modulates the gain k of the loop. Since $\theta = 0$, the transients in Fig. 2.6 have twice the slope of the exponential at $t = 0$. As time progresses, the factor $1 + \cos(2\omega t + 2\theta)$ drops to zero, then returns to 2, and so on. The result is that the solutions to Eq. (2.49) oscillate around the simple exponential curve. Also, the duration of one period of $1 + \cos(2\omega t + 2\theta)$ decreases as ω increases. Hence, as ω increases, the solution departs less and less from the simple exponential. For the example shown, the time constant of the exponential [see Eq. (2.47)] is $\tau = 1$. For $\omega = 4\pi$, the period of $1 + \cos(2\omega t + 2\theta)$ is $\frac{1}{4}$ second. If ω is increased to 10π, the period becomes $\frac{1}{10}$ second, and the solution without the $E(\cdot)$ operator is essentially the same as the exponential curve. Thus the solution of Eq. (2.50) is essentially the same as that to Eq. (2.45) as long as the weight time constant is about 10 times longer than the period of the fluctuations.

In practice, the signals $x_{P_j}(t)$ received by the array will usually contain envelope and phase modulation. In this case the instantaneous $\varepsilon^2(t)$ surface fluctuates not only at twice the carrier frequency, as in the above example, but also at baseband frequencies determined by the modulation spectra. In order for the weight response in Eq. (2.35) to approximate that of Eq. (2.34), it will then be necessary that the speed of response of the weights be slow compared to these modulation rates.

In order to study the behavior of the weights in an adaptive array mathematically, it is common to assume that the weight transients are slow compared to the fluctuations in the $\varepsilon^2(t)$ surface. This assumption allows one to use the weight differential equations with the $E(\cdot)$ operator included, as in Eq. (2.34). Doing so is helpful because it simplifies the analysis. If the $E(\cdot)$ is included, and if the signals are stationary, the weights satisfy differential equations with constant coefficients, as in Eq. (2.45), rather than with time-varying coefficients, as in Eq. (2.50). Equations with constant coefficients are, of course, easier to solve. An analysis that includes the $E(\cdot)$ operator predicts the exponential weight behavior but ignores weight variance caused by the fluctuations in $\varepsilon^2(t)$. We shall discuss weight variance further in Chapter 4.

Complex Notation

Let us now consider another means of simplifying the analysis of an adaptive array, namely, the use of analytic signal notation with complex weights. Readers who are unfamiliar with analytic signal notation or with quadrature hybrids may wish to read Appendices A and B before proceeding. Appendix A introduces the analytic signal concept, and Appendix B shows how to represent a quadrature hybrid with analytic signal notation.

Figure 2.7 shows a quadrature hybrid and one pair of weights, as would be used behind one element of the adaptive array. Since we have denoted the

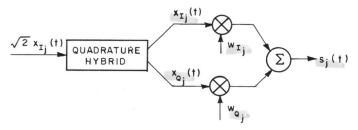

Figure 2.7   Quadrature hybrid processing for one element.

output signals from the quadrature hybrid by $x_{I_j}(t)$ and $x_{Q_j}(t)$, the input signal to the quadrature hybrid will be $\sqrt{2}\, x_{I_j}(t)$, as shown.[‡] Also, we denote the total output from this single element by $s_j(t)$.

The quadrature hybrid is assumed to be a broadband quadrature hybrid. Therefore,

$$x_{Q_j}(t) = \hat{x}_{I_j}(t), \tag{2.51}$$

where the caret denotes the Hilbert transform [9]. We may define the complex signal $\tilde{x}_j(t)$,

$$\tilde{x}_j(t) = x_{I_j}(t) + jx_{Q_j}(t) = x_{I_j}(t) + j\hat{x}_{I_j}(t), \tag{2.52}$$

which is an analytic signal; that is, its spectrum is zero for negative frequencies. Also, we define the complex weight w_j,[§]

$$w_j = w_{I_j} - jw_{Q_j}, \tag{2.53}$$

and for $s_j(t)$, $s(t)$, $r(t)$, and $\varepsilon(t)$, we define the associated analytic signals:

$$\tilde{s}_j(t) = s_j(t) + j\hat{s}_j(t), \tag{2.54}$$

$$\tilde{s}(t) = s(t) + j\hat{s}(t), \tag{2.55}$$

$$\tilde{r}(t) = r(t) + j\hat{r}(t), \tag{2.56}$$

and

$$\tilde{\varepsilon}(t) = \varepsilon(t) + j\hat{\varepsilon}(t). \tag{2.57}$$

Now consider the output from the jth element, as shown in Fig. 2.7,

$$s_j(t) = w_{I_j}x_{I_j}(t) + w_{Q_j}x_{Q_j}(t). \tag{2.58}$$

The Hilbert transform of $s_j(t)$ is

$$\hat{s}_j(t) = w_{I_j}\hat{x}_{I_j}(t) + w_{Q_j}\hat{x}_{Q_j}(t). \tag{2.59}$$

However,

$$\hat{x}_{I_j}(t) = x_{Q_j}(t) \tag{2.60}$$

and

$$\hat{x}_{Q_j}(t) = \hat{\hat{x}}_{I_j}(t) = -x_{I_j}(t) \tag{2.61}$$

‡As explained in Appendix B, the factor $\sqrt{2}$ is necessary to account for conservation of power in the hybrid. Also, a practical quadrature hybrid provides not only a 90° phase shift between $x_{I_j}(t)$ and $x_{Q_j}(t)$, but also a fixed phase shift and a small time delay between the input signal and $x_{I_j}(t)$. Our assumption neglects this fixed phase shift and time delay. We can neglect these effects in the analysis because it is assumed that each element in the array uses an identical quadrature hybrid. Thus any fixed phase shifts and time delays in the hybrids are the same for every element of the array and can be absorbed into the definition of the time origin and the carrier phase of the incoming signals.

§Complex w_j could be defined as either $w_{I_j} - jw_{Q_j}$ or $w_{I_j} + jw_{Q_j}$. We have chosen the definition in Eq. (2.53) because it ultimately results in fewer conjugate signs in subsequent equations.

[the signals $x_{I_j}(t)$ and $x_{Q_j}(t)$ are assumed zero-mean], so,

$$\hat{s}_j(t) = w_{I_j} x_{Q_j}(t) - w_{Q_j} x_{I_j}(t). \tag{2.62}$$

Therefore, the analytic signal $\tilde{s}_j(t)$ is

$$\tilde{s}_j(t) = s_j(t) + j\hat{s}_j(t)$$

$$= w_{I_j} x_{I_j}(t) + w_{Q_j} x_{Q_j}(t) + j\left[w_{I_j} x_{Q_j}(t) - w_{Q_j} x_{I_j}(t)\right]. \tag{2.63}$$

But this is just

$$\tilde{s}_j(t) = w_j \tilde{x}_j(t), \tag{2.64}$$

as may be seen from the definitions of w_j and $\tilde{x}_j(t)$ in Eqs. (2.52) and (2.53). For the entire array, the analytic output signal is

$$\tilde{s}(t) = \sum_{j=1}^N \tilde{s}_j(t) = \sum_{j=1}^N w_j \tilde{x}_j(t). \tag{2.65}$$

By defining a complex weight vector $\mathbf{W}$,

$$\mathbf{W} = \left[w_1, w_2, \ldots, w_N\right]^T, \tag{2.66}$$

and a complex signal vector $\mathbf{X}$,

$$\mathbf{X} = \left[\tilde{x}_1(t), \tilde{x}_2(t), \ldots, \tilde{x}_N(t)\right]^T, \tag{2.67}$$

Eq. (2.65) may be written

$$\tilde{s}(t) = \mathbf{W}^T \mathbf{X} = \mathbf{X}^T \mathbf{W}. \tag{2.68}$$

The Complex LMS Algorithm

Next let us determine the LMS algorithm in complex form.[‡] The LMS algorithm in real form is given by

$$\frac{dw_{I_j}}{dt} = 2kE\left\{x_{I_j}(t)\varepsilon(t)\right\} \tag{2.69}$$

and

$$\frac{dw_{Q_j}}{dt} = 2kE\left\{x_{Q_j}(t)\varepsilon(t)\right\}. \tag{2.70}$$

Consider the quantity

$$\tfrac{1}{2}E\left\{\tilde{x}_j^*(t)\tilde{\varepsilon}(t)\right\} = \tfrac{1}{2}E\left\{\left[x_{I_j}(t) - jx_{Q_j}(t)\right]\left[\varepsilon(t) + j\hat{\varepsilon}(t)\right]\right\}$$

$$= \tfrac{1}{2}E\left\{x_{I_j}(t)\varepsilon(t) + x_{Q_j}(t)\hat{\varepsilon}(t)\right.$$

$$\left. + j\left[x_{I_j}(t)\hat{\varepsilon}(t) - x_{Q_j}(t)\varepsilon(t)\right]\right\}. \tag{2.71}$$

[‡] A discussion of the complex LMS algorithm has been given by Widrow, McCool, and Ball [10]. Their treatment assumes a complex weight $w_j = w_{I_j} + jw_{Q_j}$, which is conjugate to ours.

This expression may be simplified by making use of Eq. (2.51) and two Hilbert transform relations,

$$E[\hat{x}(t)\hat{y}(s)] = E[x(t)y(s)] \tag{2.72}$$

and

$$E[\hat{x}(t)y(s)] = -E[x(t)\hat{y}(s)], \tag{2.73}$$

which are valid when $x(t)$ and $y(t)$ are stationary, zero-mean random processes[‡] [11]. Using these relations, the term $E[x_{Q_j}(t)\hat{\varepsilon}(t)]$ in Eq. (2.71) may be replaced with

$$E\left[x_{Q_j}(t)\hat{\varepsilon}(t)\right] = E\left[\hat{x}_{I_j}(t)\hat{\varepsilon}(t)\right] = E\left[x_{I_j}(t)\varepsilon(t)\right], \tag{2.74}$$

and the term $E[x_{I_j}(t)\hat{\varepsilon}(t)]$ with

$$E\left[x_{I_j}(t)\hat{\varepsilon}(t)\right] = -E\left[\hat{x}_{I_j}(t)\varepsilon(t)\right] = -E\left[x_{Q_j}(t)\varepsilon(t)\right]. \tag{2.75}$$

Therefore, Eq. (2.71) is the same as

$$\tfrac{1}{2}E\{\tilde{x}_j^*(t)\tilde{\varepsilon}(t)\} = E\{x_{I_j}(t)\varepsilon(t) - jx_{Q_j}(t)\varepsilon(t)\}. \tag{2.76}$$

Now consider the feedback equation

$$\frac{dw_j}{dt} = 2k\tfrac{1}{2}E\{\tilde{x}_j^*(t)\tilde{\varepsilon}(t)\}. \tag{2.77}$$

Substituting for $\tfrac{1}{2}E\{\tilde{x}_j^*(t)\tilde{\varepsilon}(t)\}$ with Eq. (2.76), we find that this is the same as

$$\frac{dw_{I_j}}{dt} - j\frac{dw_{Q_j}}{dt} = 2kE\{x_{I_j}(t)\varepsilon(t) - jx_{Q_j}(t)\varepsilon(t)\}, \tag{2.78}$$

that is, it is equivalent to both Eqs. (2.69) and (2.70) together. Thus, canceling the factors of 2 in Eq. (2.77) gives us the *complex LMS algorithm*:

$$\frac{dw_j}{dt} = kE\{\tilde{x}_j^*(t)\tilde{\varepsilon}(t)\}. \tag{2.79}$$

Equation (2.79) may be represented by the block diagram in Fig. 2.8.

The differential equation for the weight vector in complex form is easily found. Using the vectors defined in Eqs. (2.66) and (2.67), we write Eq. (2.79) in the form

$$\frac{d\mathbf{W}}{dt} = kE\{\mathbf{X}^*\tilde{\varepsilon}(t)\}. \tag{2.80}$$

However, $\tilde{\varepsilon}(t)$ may be written

$$\tilde{\varepsilon}(t) = \tilde{r}(t) - \mathbf{X}^T\mathbf{W}, \tag{2.81}$$

[‡]See Appendix A.

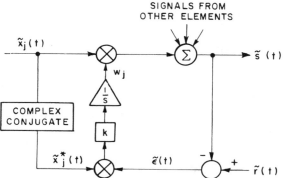

Figure 2.8 The complex LMS loop.

so Eq. (2.80) is

$$\frac{d\mathbf{W}}{dt} = kE\{\mathbf{X}^*[\tilde{r}(t) - \mathbf{X}^T\mathbf{W}]\}, \tag{2.82}$$

or

$$\frac{d\mathbf{W}}{dt} + kE(\mathbf{X}^*\mathbf{X}^T)\mathbf{W} = kE[\mathbf{X}^*\tilde{r}(t)]. \tag{2.83}$$

We define the *covariance matrix* $\boldsymbol{\Phi}$,

$$\boldsymbol{\Phi} = E(\mathbf{X}^*\mathbf{X}^T) = E\begin{bmatrix} \tilde{x}_1^*(t)\tilde{x}_1(t) & \tilde{x}_1^*(t)\tilde{x}_2(t) & \cdots \\ \tilde{x}_2^*(t)\tilde{x}_1(t) & \tilde{x}_2^*(t)\tilde{x}_2(t) & \\ \vdots & \vdots & \end{bmatrix} \tag{2.84}$$

and the *reference correlation vector* $\mathbf{S}$,

$$\mathbf{S} = E[\mathbf{X}^*\tilde{r}(t)] = E\begin{bmatrix} \tilde{x}_1^*(t)\tilde{r}(t) \\ \tilde{x}_2^*(t)\tilde{r}(t) \\ \vdots \end{bmatrix}. \tag{2.85}$$

(Note that $\boldsymbol{\Phi}$ is a Hermitian matrix.) The differential equation for $\mathbf{W}$ is then

$$\frac{d\mathbf{W}}{dt} + k\boldsymbol{\Phi}\mathbf{W} = k\mathbf{S}. \tag{2.86}$$

As long as $\boldsymbol{\Phi}$ is nonsingular (which will be the case whenever there is element noise in the array), the steady-state weight vector is given by

$$\mathbf{W} = \boldsymbol{\Phi}^{-1}\mathbf{S}. \tag{2.87}$$

To obtain the transient solution, we make a rotation of coordinates of the weights in the standard manner. Let

$$\mathbf{W} = \mathbf{RV}, \tag{2.88}$$

where $\mathbf{R}$ is an $\mathbf{N} \times \mathbf{N}$ unitary matrix with elements

$$\mathbf{R} = \begin{bmatrix} r_{11} & r_{12} & \cdots \\ r_{21} & r_{22} & \\ r_{31} & & \ddots \\ \vdots & & & \ddots \end{bmatrix} \tag{2.89}$$

and $\mathbf{V}$ is a column vector of new weights v_i,

$$\mathbf{V} = [v_1, v_2, \ldots]^T. \tag{2.90}$$

Substituting Eq. (2.88) into Eq. (2.86) and multiplying on the left by $\mathbf{R}^{-1} = \mathbf{R}^\dagger$ (where "$\dagger$" denotes transpose conjugate) we obtain

$$\frac{d\mathbf{V}}{dt} + k(\mathbf{R}^\dagger\mathbf{\Phi}\mathbf{R})\mathbf{V} = k\mathbf{R}^\dagger\mathbf{S}. \tag{2.91}$$

If $\mathbf{R}$ is chosen so $\mathbf{R}^\dagger\mathbf{\Phi}\mathbf{R}$ is diagonal,

$$\mathbf{R}^\dagger\mathbf{\Phi}\mathbf{R} = \mathbf{\Lambda} = \text{diag}\,(\lambda_1, \lambda_2, \ldots, \lambda_N), \tag{2.92}$$

where the λ_j are the eigenvalues of $\mathbf{\Phi}$, then the differential equations for the $v_j(t)$ are uncoupled. The solution for $v_j(t)$ will be

$$v_j(t) = \left[v_j(0) - \frac{q_j}{\lambda_j}\right]e^{-k\lambda_j t} + \frac{q_j}{\lambda_j}, \tag{2.93}$$

where $v_j(0)$ is the initial value of $v_j(t)$ and q_j is the jth component of the column vector $\mathbf{R}^\dagger\mathbf{S}$. The solution for $\mathbf{W}(t)$ may then be obtained from $\mathbf{V}(t)$ by means of Eq. (2.88). Multiplying the matrix $\mathbf{R}$ onto $\mathbf{V}$ will, in general, mix all the exponential terms into each weight w_j. Thus, $\mathbf{W}(t)$ will be of the form

$$\mathbf{W}(t) = \sum_{j=1}^{N} \mathbf{C}_j e^{-k\lambda_j t} + \mathbf{\Phi}^{-1}\mathbf{S}, \tag{2.94}$$

where the $\mathbf{C}_j$ are constant vectors determined from the initial value of $\mathbf{W}(t)$ at $t = 0$.

Now let us apply this formalism to a specific example.

Example 1

Consider an LMS array consisting of two isotropic elements, as shown in Fig. 2.9. A CW desired signal at frequency ω_d propagates into the array from angle θ_d relative to broadside. Let the elements be one-half wavelength apart at frequency ω_d. Also, assume each signal $\tilde{x}_j(t)$ contains thermal noise as well as desired signal. Thus,

$$\tilde{x}_1(t) = \tilde{d}_1(t) + \tilde{n}_1(t) \tag{2.95}$$

and

$$\tilde{x}_2(t) = \tilde{d}_2(t) + \tilde{n}_2(t), \tag{2.96}$$

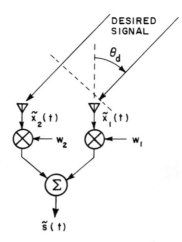

Figure 2.9 A two-element LMS array.

where $\tilde{d}_j(t)$ and $\tilde{n}_j(t)$ are the desired signal and thermal noise components, respectively. For a CW desired signal, $\tilde{d}_1(t)$ and $\tilde{d}_2(t)$ will be given by

$$\tilde{d}_1(t) = A_d e^{j(\omega_d t + \psi_d)} \tag{2.97}$$

and

$$\tilde{d}_2(t) = A_d e^{j(\omega_d t + \psi_d - \phi_d)}, \tag{2.98}$$

where A_d is the desired signal amplitude, ψ_d is the carrier phase angle at element 1 and ϕ_d is the interelement phase shift. We assume ψ_d is a uniformly distributed random variable; its probability density is

$$p(\psi_d) = \begin{cases} \dfrac{1}{2\pi}, & 0 \leqslant \psi_d \leqslant 2\pi, \\ 0, & \text{elsewhere.} \end{cases} \tag{2.99}$$

Since the element spacing is one-half wavelength, ϕ_d is given by

$$\phi_d = \pi \sin \theta_d. \tag{2.100}$$

The thermal noises are assumed to be zero-mean random processes, statistically independent of each other and the desired signal, each of power σ^2. Thus,

$$E\{\tilde{n}_i^*(t)\tilde{n}_j(t)\} = \sigma^2 \delta_{ij}, \tag{2.101}$$

where δ_{ij} is the Kronecker delta,

$$\delta_{ij} = \begin{cases} 1, & i = j, \\ 0, & i \neq j, \end{cases} \tag{2.102}$$

and

$$E\{\tilde{d}_i^*(t)\tilde{n}_j(t)\} = 0. \tag{2.103}$$

Finally, we suppose the reference signal is a CW signal correlated with the desired signal,

$$\tilde{r}(t) = \text{Re}^{j(\omega_d t + \psi_d)}. \tag{2.104}$$

Before proceeding, we note that for the desired signal assumed in Eqs. (2.97) and (2.98), the signal power received from each element (at the input to the quadrature hybrid) is A_d^2. For example, consider $\tilde{d}_1(t)$ in Eq. (2.97). The inphase and quadrature signals produced on element 1 by this desired signal are

$$x_{I_1}(t) = A_d \cos(\omega_d t + \psi_d), \tag{2.105}$$

and

$$x_{Q_1}(t) = A_d \sin(\omega_d t + \psi_d), \tag{2.106}$$

so the input signal to the quadrature hybrid (see Fig. 2.7) is

$$\sqrt{2}\, x_{I_1}(t) = \sqrt{2}\, A_d \cos(\omega_d t + \psi_d). \tag{2.107}$$

Thus the average input power is

$$E\left\{ \left[\sqrt{2}\, x_{I_1}(t) \right]^2 \right\} = A_d^2. \tag{2.108}$$

Furthermore, from Eq. (2.101) the noise power on each element is σ^2, since

$$E\{ \tilde{n}_i^*(t) \tilde{n}_i(t) \} = E\left[n_{I_i}^2(t) \right] + E\left[n_{Q_i}^2(t) \right] = \sigma^2. \tag{2.109}$$

Thus the input signal-to-noise ratio (SNR) on each element, ξ_d, is

$$\xi_d = \frac{A_d^2}{\sigma^2} = \text{input SNR per element.} \tag{2.110}$$

Let us now compute the steady-state array weights and examine the performance of the array. For the $\tilde{x}_j(t)$ in Eqs. (2.95) and (2.96), the signal vector may be written

$$\mathbf{X} = \mathbf{X}_d + \mathbf{X}_n, \tag{2.111}$$

where

$$\mathbf{X}_d = \begin{bmatrix} \tilde{d}_1(t) \\ \tilde{d}_2(t) \end{bmatrix} = A_d e^{j(\omega_d t + \psi_d)} \begin{bmatrix} 1 \\ e^{-j\phi_d} \end{bmatrix} = A_d e^{j(\omega_d t + \psi_d)} \mathbf{U}_d \tag{2.112}$$

with

$$\mathbf{U}_d = \begin{bmatrix} 1 \\ e^{-j\phi_d} \end{bmatrix} \tag{2.113}$$

and

$$\mathbf{X}_n = \begin{bmatrix} \tilde{n}_1(t) \\ \tilde{n}_2(t) \end{bmatrix}. \tag{2.114}$$

To solve for the array weights, we must first compute $\boldsymbol{\Phi}$ and $\mathbf{S}$ in Eqs. (2.84) and (2.85).

Consider first the covariance matrix; $\boldsymbol{\Phi}$ may be written

$$\boldsymbol{\Phi} = E(\mathbf{X}^*\mathbf{X}^T) = E\left(\mathbf{X}_d^*\mathbf{X}_d^T\right) + E\left(\mathbf{X}_n^*\mathbf{X}_n^T\right). \tag{2.115}$$

From Eq. (2.112), we find

$$E\left(\mathbf{X}_d^*\mathbf{X}_d^T\right) = A_d^2\mathbf{U}_d^*\mathbf{U}_d^T = A_d^2\begin{bmatrix} 1 & e^{-j\phi_d} \\ e^{+j\phi_d} & 1 \end{bmatrix} \tag{2.116}$$

and from Eqs. (2.101) and (2.114), we find

$$E\left(\mathbf{X}_n^*\mathbf{X}_n^T\right) = \sigma^2\mathbf{I} = \begin{bmatrix} \sigma^2 & 0 \\ 0 & \sigma^2 \end{bmatrix} \tag{2.117}$$

where $\mathbf{I}$ is the identity matrix. Therefore $\boldsymbol{\Phi}$ is

$$\boldsymbol{\Phi} = A_d^2\mathbf{U}_d^*\mathbf{U}_d^T + \sigma^2\mathbf{I}. \tag{2.118}$$

The vector $\mathbf{S}$ is given by Eq. (2.85). Since $\tilde{r}(t)$ is statistically independent of $\mathbf{X}_n$, we have

$$\mathbf{S} = E[\mathbf{X}^*\tilde{r}(t)] = E[\mathbf{X}_d^*\tilde{r}(t)] = A_d R\mathbf{U}_d^*. \tag{2.119}$$

The weight vector $\mathbf{W}$ is the solution to Eq. (2.86),

$$\frac{d\mathbf{W}}{dt} + k\boldsymbol{\Phi}\mathbf{W} = k\mathbf{S}. \tag{2.120}$$

Consider first the steady-state part of the solution,

$$\mathbf{W} = \boldsymbol{\Phi}^{-1}\mathbf{S}. \tag{2.121}$$

Writing out $\boldsymbol{\Phi}$ in Eq. (2.118) gives

$$\boldsymbol{\Phi} = \begin{bmatrix} A_d^2 + \sigma^2 & A_d^2 e^{-j\phi_d} \\ A_d^2 e^{j\phi_d} & A_d^2 + \sigma^2 \end{bmatrix}. \tag{2.122}$$

The inverse of $\boldsymbol{\Phi}$ is

$$\boldsymbol{\Phi}^{-1} = \frac{1}{\sigma^2\left(2A_d^2 + \sigma^2\right)}\begin{bmatrix} A_d^2 + \sigma^2 & -A_d^2 e^{-j\phi_d} \\ -A_d^2 e^{j\phi_d} & A_d^2 + \sigma^2 \end{bmatrix}. \tag{2.123}$$

Therefore, from Eqs. (2.113), (2.119), and (2.121),

$$\begin{aligned} \mathbf{W} &= \frac{A_d R}{\sigma^2\left(2A_d^2 + \sigma^2\right)}\begin{bmatrix} A_d^2 + \sigma^2 & -A_d^2 e^{-j\phi_d} \\ -A_d^2 e^{j\phi_d} & A_d^2 + \sigma^2 \end{bmatrix}\begin{bmatrix} 1 \\ e^{j\phi_d} \end{bmatrix} \\ &= \frac{A_d R}{2A_d^2 + \sigma^2}\begin{bmatrix} 1 \\ e^{j\phi_d} \end{bmatrix}. \end{aligned} \tag{2.124}$$

It will be helpful to write the coefficient in $\mathbf{W}$ in terms of ξ_d:

$$\mathbf{W} = \frac{\left(\dfrac{A_d^2}{\sigma^2}\right)\left(\dfrac{R}{A_d}\right)}{2\left(\dfrac{A_d^2}{\sigma^2}\right) + 1}\begin{bmatrix} 1 \\ e^{j\phi_d} \end{bmatrix}$$

$$= \frac{\xi_d\left(\dfrac{R}{A_d}\right)}{2\xi_d + 1}\begin{bmatrix} 1 \\ e^{j\phi_d} \end{bmatrix}. \tag{2.125}$$

The variable ξ_d is the input signal-to-noise ratio on each element of the array.

Equation (2.125) is the steady-state weight vector. We note that the two complex weights w_1 and w_2 have the same amplitude,

$$|w_1| = |w_2| = \frac{\xi_d(R/A_d)}{2\xi_d + 1} \tag{2.126}$$

but differ in phase by ϕ_d. This phase difference is just the proper amount to make the weighted signals $w_1\tilde{x}_1(t)$ and $w_2\tilde{x}_2(t)$ add in phase.

Consider next the pattern of the array with this weight vector. To compute the pattern, we suppose a unit amplitude signal propagates into the array from angle θ (as in Fig. 2.9). This signal produces a signal vector in the array

$$\mathbf{X} = e^{j\omega_d t}\begin{bmatrix} 1 \\ e^{-j\phi(\theta)} \end{bmatrix} \tag{2.127}$$

where

$$\phi(\theta) = \pi \sin\theta. \tag{2.128}$$

If the array weight vector is given by Eq. (2.124), the output signal from the array will be

$$\mathbf{W}^T\mathbf{X} = \frac{A_d R}{2A_d^2 + \sigma^2}\begin{bmatrix} 1 & e^{j\phi_d} \end{bmatrix}\begin{bmatrix} 1 \\ e^{-j\phi(\theta)} \end{bmatrix}e^{j\omega_d t}$$

$$= \frac{A_d R}{2A_d^2 + \sigma^2}\left\{1 + e^{j[\phi_d - \phi(\theta)]}\right\}e^{j\omega_d t}. \tag{2.129}$$

The magnitude of this signal is

$$|\mathbf{W}^T\mathbf{X}| = \frac{A_d R}{2A_d^2 + \sigma^2}\left|1 + e^{j[\phi_d - \phi(\theta)]}\right|. \tag{2.130}$$

The voltage pattern of the array is the factor

$$P(\theta) = \left|1 + e^{j[\phi_d - \phi(\theta)]}\right|. \tag{2.131}$$

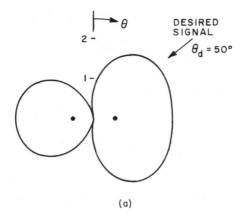

(a)

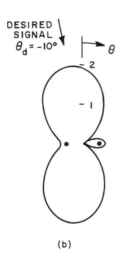

(b)

Figure 2.10   Voltage pattern for a two-element adaptive array. (a) $\theta_d = 50°$; (b) $\theta_d = -10°$.

Note that the maximum of $P(\theta)$ always occurs when $\theta = \theta_d$ (i.e., when $\phi = \phi_d$). Thus the LMS weight vector automatically steers the pattern maximum in the direction of the desired signal. Figure 2.10 shows $P(\theta)$ for two specific cases, (a) $\theta_d = 50°$ and (b) $\theta_d = -10°$.

Next let us examine the signal and noise powers at the array output. Note first that a *real* signal $s(t)$ has average power

$$P = E\{s^2(t)\}. \tag{2.132}$$

In terms of the associated *analytic* signal $\tilde{s}(t)$, P is given by

$$P = \tfrac{1}{2}E\{|\tilde{s}(t)|^2\}, \tag{2.133}$$

since

$$E\left[\hat{s}^2(t)\right] = E\left[s^2(t)\right]. \tag{2.134}$$

Now consider the desired signal and thermal noise powers at the array output. Since the signal vector $\mathbf{X}$ is given by Eq. (2.111), the array output signal $\tilde{s}(t)$ may be written

$$\tilde{s}(t) = \tilde{s}_d(t) + \tilde{s}_n(t), \tag{2.135}$$

where

$$\tilde{s}_d(t) = \mathbf{W}^T \mathbf{X}_d, \tag{2.136}$$

and

$$\tilde{s}_n(t) = \mathbf{W}^T \mathbf{X}_n. \tag{2.137}$$

Substituting for $\mathbf{W}$ from Eq. (2.124) and $\mathbf{X}_d$ from Eq. (2.112), we find that the output desired signal is

$$
\begin{aligned}
\tilde{s}_d(t) &= \frac{A_d R}{2A_d^2 + \sigma^2} \begin{bmatrix} 1 & e^{j\phi_d} \end{bmatrix} A_d e^{j(\omega_d t + \psi_d)} \begin{bmatrix} 1 \\ e^{-j\phi_d} \end{bmatrix} \\
&= \frac{2A_d^2 R}{2A_d^2 + \sigma^2} e^{j(\omega_d t + \psi_d)}.
\end{aligned}
\tag{2.138}
$$

Therefore, the desired signal power at the array output is

$$
\begin{aligned}
P_d = \tfrac{1}{2} E\left\{ \left| \tilde{s}_d(t) \right|^2 \right\} &= \frac{2A_d^4 R^2}{\left(2A_d^2 + \sigma^2 \right)^2} \\
&= \frac{\left(2\xi_d \right)^2 P_r}{\left(2\xi_d + 1 \right)^2},
\end{aligned}
\tag{2.139}
$$

where

$$P_r = \frac{R^2}{2} \tag{2.140}$$

is the power in the reference signal. Note that at high input signal-to-noise ratios, the output desired signal power equals the reference signal power.

In general, we observe that the LMS feedback does not actually match the desired signal at the array output to the reference signal. The output desired signal is given in Eq. (2.138), whereas the reference signal is given by Eq. (2.104). Comparing these two we see that

$$\tilde{s}_d(t) = \alpha \tilde{r}(t), \tag{2.141}$$

where α is

$$\alpha = \frac{2A_d^2}{2A_d^2 + \sigma^2} = \frac{1}{1 + \left(2\xi_d \right)^{-1}}. \tag{2.142}$$

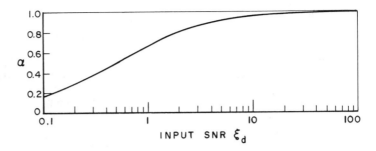

Figure 2.11 The ratio α versus input SNR.

The ratio α depends on the input SNR as shown in Fig. 2.11. When the input SNR is high, $\tilde{s}_d(t)$ is essentially equal to $\tilde{r}(t)$, but for low SNR, $\tilde{s}_d(t)$ is less than $\tilde{r}(t)$. The reason is that the LMS weights minimize the mean-square error signal $E\{\varepsilon^2(t)\}$. When the input SNR is high, the noise contributes only negligibly to $E\{\varepsilon^2(t)\}$, and minimizing mean-square error corresponds to matching $\tilde{s}_d(t)$ to $\tilde{r}(t)$. When the input SNR is low, however, noise is the largest part of $E\{\varepsilon^2(t)\}$. In this case $E\{\varepsilon^2(t)\}$ is minimized by lowering the weights to reduce the noise and allowing some mismatch between $\tilde{s}_d(t)$ and $\tilde{r}(t)$.

Next consider the noise. The output noise signal is

$$\tilde{s}_n(t) = \mathbf{W}^T\mathbf{X}_n = w_1\tilde{n}_1(t) + w_2\tilde{n}_2(t);\tag{2.143}$$

so the output noise power is

$$P_n = \tfrac{1}{2}E\{|\tilde{s}_n(t)|^2\} = \frac{\sigma^2}{2}\left[|w_1|^2 + |w_2|^2\right].\tag{2.144}$$

Substituting in w_1 and w_2 from Eq. (2.124) gives

$$P_n = \frac{A_d^2R^2\sigma^2}{\left(2A_d^2 + \sigma^2\right)^2} = \frac{2\xi_d P_r}{\left(2\xi_d + 1\right)^2}.\tag{2.145}$$

The noise power P_n depends on ξ_d as shown in Fig. 2.12.

Now consider the output signal-to-noise ratio from the array, SNR_{out}. From Eqs. (2.139) and (2.145),

$$\text{SNR}_{\text{out}} = \frac{P_d}{P_n} = 2\xi_d.\tag{2.146}$$

The output SNR is twice the input SNR. This is the maximum output SNR that can be obtained from two elements. (The two elements are acting as a two-element maximal ratio combiner [see reference 7 in Chapter 1].) The array yields the optimum output SNR regardless of the value of R, so the reference signal amplitude does not affect the optimality of the LMS weights. Also, the array yields maximum output SNR for any desired signal arrival angle θ_d.

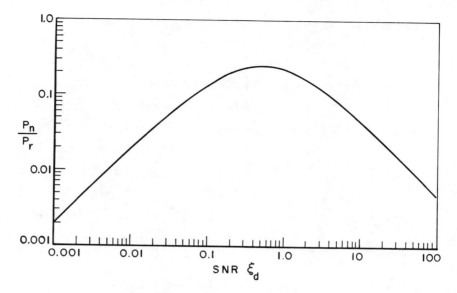

Figure 2.12 P_n/P_r versus input SNR.

Finally, let us consider the transient behavior of the weights in this array. In general, the weights start from arbitrary initial values at $t = 0$ and undergo a transient of the form in Eq. (2.94). Using Eq. (2.124), we have

$$\mathbf{W}(t) = \mathbf{C}_1 e^{-k\lambda_1 t} + \mathbf{C}_2 e^{-k\lambda_2 t} + \frac{A_d R}{2A_d^2 + \sigma^2}\begin{bmatrix} 1 \\ e^{j\phi_d} \end{bmatrix}, \qquad (2.147)$$

where λ_1 and λ_2 are the eigenvalues of $\mathbf{\Phi}$. These eigenvalues may be found by solving

$$|\mathbf{\Phi} - \lambda\mathbf{I}| = \begin{vmatrix} A_d^2 + \sigma^2 - \lambda & A_d^2 e^{-j\phi_d} \\ A_d^2 e^{+j\phi_d} & A_d^2 + \sigma^2 - \lambda \end{vmatrix} = 0, \qquad (2.148)$$

which yields

$$\lambda_1 = 2A_d^2 + \sigma^2, \qquad \lambda_2 = \sigma^2. \qquad (2.149)$$

(Note that because of the thermal noise term σ^2, both λ_1 and λ_2 are positive, so $\mathbf{\Phi}$ is positive definite.) To determine specific weight transients, one must evaluate the vector constants $\mathbf{C}_1$ and $\mathbf{C}_2$, which depend on the initial value of $\mathbf{W}(t)$. Applying Eq. (2.147) at $t = 0$ gives

$$\mathbf{C}_1 + \mathbf{C}_2 = \mathbf{W}(0) - \frac{A_d R}{2A_d^2 + \sigma^2}\begin{bmatrix} 1 \\ e^{j\phi_d} \end{bmatrix}. \qquad (2.150)$$

This is one equation in the two unknowns $\mathbf{C}_1$ and $\mathbf{C}_2$. To get another equation, one may use the differential equation for the weights,

$$\frac{d\mathbf{W}(t)}{dt} + k\boldsymbol{\Phi}\mathbf{W}(t) = k\mathbf{S}, \tag{2.151}$$

to express $d\mathbf{W}/dt$ at $t = 0$ in terms of $\mathbf{W}(0)$:

$$\dot{\mathbf{W}}(0) = k[\mathbf{S} - \boldsymbol{\Phi}\mathbf{W}(0)]. \tag{2.152}$$

Equation (2.147) yields for $\dot{\mathbf{W}}(0)$,

$$\dot{\mathbf{W}}(0) = -k\lambda_1\mathbf{C}_1 - k\lambda_2\mathbf{C}_2. \tag{2.153}$$

After combining Eqs. (2.152) and (2.153) and canceling the factor k one finds

$$-\lambda_1\mathbf{C}_1 - \lambda_2\mathbf{C}_2 = \mathbf{S} - \boldsymbol{\Phi}\mathbf{W}(0). \tag{2.154}$$

Multiplying Eq. (2.150) by λ_1 and adding it to Eq. (2.154) gives

$$\mathbf{C}_2 = \frac{1}{\lambda_1 - \lambda_2}\left\{\lambda_1\mathbf{W}(0) - \frac{\lambda_1 A_d R}{2A_d^2 + \sigma^2}\begin{bmatrix} 1 \\ e^{j\phi_d} \end{bmatrix} + \mathbf{S} - \boldsymbol{\Phi}\mathbf{W}(0)\right\}. \tag{2.155}$$

Multiplying Eq. (2.150) by λ_2 and adding it to Eq. (2.154) gives

$$\mathbf{C}_1 = \frac{1}{\lambda_1 - \lambda_2}\left\{-\lambda_2\mathbf{W}(0) + \frac{\lambda_2 A_d R}{2A_d^2 + \sigma^2}\begin{bmatrix} 1 \\ e^{j\phi_d} \end{bmatrix} - \mathbf{S} + \boldsymbol{\Phi}\mathbf{W}(0)\right\}. \tag{2.156}$$

An arbitrary value of $\mathbf{W}(0)$ can be inserted into these two equations and $\mathbf{C}_1$ and $\mathbf{C}_2$ computed. The values of $\mathbf{C}_1$ and $\mathbf{C}_2$ can then be put in Eq. (2.147) and the transient $\mathbf{W}(t)$ computed.

Figure 2.13 shows a set of typical weight transients computed in this manner for the following assumed parameter values,

$$k = A_d = R = \sigma^2 = 1, \tag{2.157}$$

and

$$\theta_d = 50°, \tag{2.158}$$

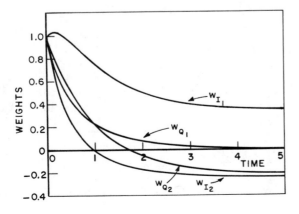

Figure 2.13 Weight transients for two-element array: $k = A_d = R = \sigma^2 = 1$, $\theta_d = 50°$, $w_1(0) = w_2(0) = 1 - j1$.

and also for the initial conditions

$$w_1(0) = 1 - j1,$$
$$w_2(0) = 1 - j1. \tag{2.159}$$

(That is, the initial values for the quadrature weights are $w_{I_1} = w_{Q_1} = w_{I_2} = w_{P_2} = 1$.)

We note that there are two exponential terms in the $\mathbf{W}(t)$ transients. (Because we have a two-element array, Φ is a 2×2 matrix, so it has two eigenvalues.) For the numerical values assumed in Eq. (2.157), we have

$$\lambda_1 = 2A_d^2 + \sigma^2 = 3 \tag{2.160}$$

and

$$\lambda_2 = \sigma^2 = 1; \tag{2.161}$$

therefore, the exponentials have time constants

$$\tau_1 = \frac{1}{k\lambda_1} = \tfrac{1}{3} \tag{2.162}$$

and

$$\tau_2 = \frac{1}{k\lambda_2} = 1. \tag{2.163}$$

In general, we observe that when the signal power A_d^2 is large, λ_1 will be essentially determined by the signal power, and λ_2 will be determined by the noise power. Therefore, at high signal-to-noise ratio, the two time constants will have a ratio equal to twice the SNR:

$$\frac{\tau_2}{\tau_1} \cong \frac{2A_d^2}{\sigma^2} = 2\xi_d. \tag{2.164}$$

This ratio is called *time constant spread* (or *eigenvalue spread*). The fact that time constant spread in the LMS array depends on signal power causes design problems when one must accommodate a wide range of signal powers in the array. This problem will be discussed in Chapter 4.

While the weights are going through the transients in Fig. 2.13, the array pattern is also changing with time. The pattern at any given time may be computed using the same method as in Eqs. (2.127) through (2.131). Figure 2.14 shows a series of such patterns computed at various times for the weight transients in Fig. 2.13. Figure 2.14(a) shows the initial pattern at $t = 0$; Figs. 2.14(b) through (g) show the patterns at $t = 0.15$, 0.3, 0.6, 1, 2, and 3; and Fig. 2.14(h) shows the final pattern. [Figure 2.14(h) is the same as the steady-state pattern computed in Fig. 2.10(a).] The plots in Fig. 2.14 are all voltage patterns drawn to the same absolute scale. Note that not only does the shape of the pattern change with time, but so does its absolute magnitude. The magnitude of

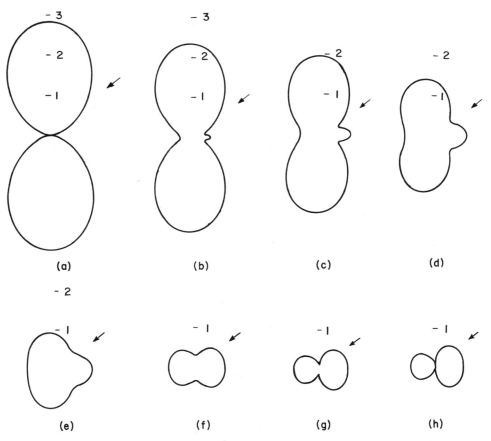

Figure 2.14 Transient patterns of a two-element array. (a) Initial pattern, $t = 0$; (b) $t = 0.15$; (c) $t = 0.3$; (d) $t = 0.6$; (e) $t = 1.0$; (f) $t = 2.0$; (g) $t = 3.0$; (h) final pattern, $t = \infty$.

the initial pattern is determined by the (arbitrary) choice of $\mathbf{W}(0)$, whereas the magnitude of the final pattern is determined by the values of A_d, R, and σ^2.

Example 2

Consider the same two-element array as in Example 1. However, assume the array now receives a CW interference signal as well as the desired signal. Let the interference signal arrive from angle θ_i with respect to broadside, as shown in Fig. 2.15. Now the element signals are given by

$$\tilde{x}_1(t) = \tilde{d}_1(t) + \tilde{i}_1(t) + \tilde{n}_1(t) \tag{2.165}$$

and

$$\tilde{x}_2(t) = \tilde{d}_2(t) + \tilde{i}_2(t) + \tilde{n}_2(t). \tag{2.166}$$

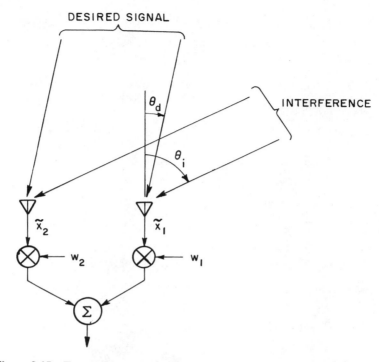

Figure 2.15   Two-element array with desired signal and interference.

The signals $\tilde{d}_1(t)$ and $\tilde{d}_2(t)$ are the same as in Eqs. (2.97) and (2.98). The interference signals $\tilde{i}_1(t)$ and $\tilde{i}_2(t)$ are assumed to be

$$\tilde{i}_1(t) = A_i e^{j(\omega_d t + \psi_i)} \tag{2.167}$$

and

$$\tilde{i}_2(t) = A_i e^{j(\omega_d t + \psi_i - \phi_i)}, \tag{2.168}$$

where A_i is the amplitude, ϕ_i is the interelement phase shift,

$$\phi_i = \pi \sin \theta_i, \tag{2.169}$$

and ψ_i is a uniformly distributed random variable with probability density function

$$p(\psi_i) = \begin{cases} \dfrac{1}{2\pi}, & 0 \leqslant \psi_i \leqslant 2\pi, \\ 0, & \text{elsewhere.} \end{cases} \tag{2.170}$$

We assume ψ_i is statistically independent of the desired signal phase ψ_d and of the thermal noise $\tilde{n}_1(t)$ and $\tilde{n}_2(t)$. The reference signal remains the same as in Eq. (2.104); it is correlated with the desired signal but not with the interference.

In Example 1, the input signal-to-noise ratio was

$$\xi_d = \frac{A_d^2}{\sigma^2}. \tag{2.171}$$

Similarly, the interference signal will have an input interference-to-noise ratio (INR) equal to A_i^2/σ^2. We define ξ_i to be the input INR,

$$\xi_i = \frac{A_i^2}{\sigma^2} = \text{input INR.} \tag{2.172}$$

The signal vector may be written

$$\mathbf{X} = \mathbf{X}_d + \mathbf{X}_i + \mathbf{X}_n, \tag{2.173}$$

where $\mathbf{X}_d$ is the same as in Example 1,

$$\mathbf{X}_d = A_d e^{j(\omega_d t + \psi_d)} \begin{bmatrix} 1 \\ e^{-j\phi_d} \end{bmatrix} = A_d e^{j(\omega_d t + \psi_d)} \mathbf{U}_d. \tag{2.174}$$

The interference signal vector $\mathbf{X}_i$ will be given by

$$\mathbf{X}_i = A_i e^{j(\omega_d t + \psi_i)} \begin{bmatrix} 1 \\ e^{-j\phi_i} \end{bmatrix} = A_i e^{j(\omega_d t + \psi_i)} \mathbf{U}_i, \tag{2.175}$$

where

$$\mathbf{U}_i = \begin{bmatrix} 1 \\ e^{-j\phi_i} \end{bmatrix}. \tag{2.176}$$

Finally, as before,

$$\mathbf{X}_n = \begin{bmatrix} \tilde{n}_1(t) \\ \tilde{n}_2(t) \end{bmatrix}. \tag{2.177}$$

The covariance matrix now becomes

$$\boldsymbol{\Phi} = E(\mathbf{X}_d^* \mathbf{X}_d^T) + E(\mathbf{X}_i^* \mathbf{X}_i^T) + E(\mathbf{X}_n^* \mathbf{X}_n^T). \tag{2.178}$$

The desired signal and noise terms were found previously in Example 1:

$$E(\mathbf{X}_d^* \mathbf{X}_d^T) = A_d^2 \mathbf{U}_d^* \mathbf{U}_d^T \tag{2.179}$$

and

$$E(\mathbf{X}_n^* \mathbf{X}_n^T) = \sigma^2 \mathbf{I}. \tag{2.180}$$

For the interference term, it is easily seen by analogy with Eq. (2.179) that

$$E(\mathbf{X}_i^* \mathbf{X}_i^T) = A_i^2 \mathbf{U}_i^* \mathbf{U}_i^T. \tag{2.181}$$

Therefore,

$$\boldsymbol{\Phi} = A_d^2 \mathbf{U}_d^* \mathbf{U}_d^T + A_i^2 \mathbf{U}_i^* \mathbf{U}_i^T + \sigma^2 \mathbf{I} \tag{2.182}$$

$$= \begin{bmatrix} A_d^2 + A_i^2 + \sigma^2 & A_d^2 e^{-j\phi_d} + A_i^2 e^{-j\phi_i} \\ A_d^2 e^{+j\phi_d} + A_i^2 e^{+j\phi_i} & A_d^2 + A_i^2 + \sigma^2 \end{bmatrix}. \tag{2.183}$$

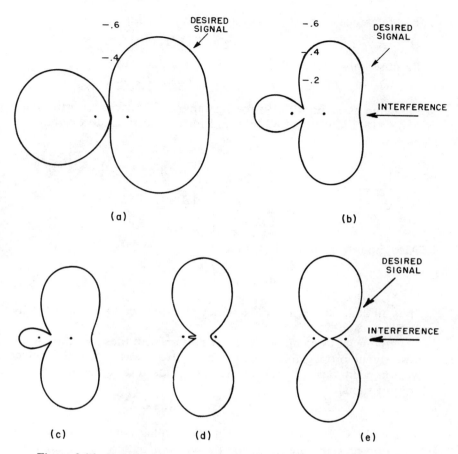

Figure 2.16 Voltage pattern for two-element array with interference: $\xi_d = 0\,\text{dB}$, $\theta_d = 50°$, $\theta_i = 90°$, $R/A_d = 1$. (a) $\xi_i = 0$; (b) $\xi_i = 1 = 0$ dB; (c) $\xi_i = 2 = 3$ dB; (d) $\xi_i = 10 = 10$ dB; (e) $\xi_i = 100 = 20$ dB.

The determinant of $\mathbf{\Phi}$ is[‡]

$$D = |\mathbf{\Phi}| = 4A_d^2 A_i^2 \sin^2\left(\frac{\phi_d - \phi_i}{2}\right) + 2A_d^2\sigma^2 + 2A_i^2\sigma^2 + \sigma^4. \qquad (2.184)$$

The inverse of $\mathbf{\Phi}$ is then found to be

$$\mathbf{\Phi}^{-1} = \frac{1}{D}\begin{bmatrix} A_d^2 + A_i^2 + \sigma^2 & -A_d^2 e^{-j\phi_d} - A_i^2 e^{-j\phi_i} \\ -A_d^2 e^{+j\phi_d} - A_i^2 e^{+j\phi_i} & A_d^2 + A_i^2 + \sigma^2 \end{bmatrix}. \qquad (2.185)$$

[‡]Note again that the thermal noise term $\sigma^2 \mathbf{I}$ in Eq. (2.182) causes $\mathbf{\Phi}$ to be positive definite. In Eq. (2.184), D cannot be zero unless $\sigma^2 = 0$.

The reference correlation vector **S** is given by Eq. (2.85),

$$\mathbf{S} = E[\mathbf{X}^*\tilde{r}(t)]. \tag{2.186}$$

Because only $\mathbf{X}_d$ correlates with $\tilde{r}(t)$, **S** reduces to

$$\mathbf{S} = A_d R \mathbf{U}_d^*, \tag{2.187}$$

the same as in Eq. (2.119) for Example 1. Therefore, substituting Eqs. (2.185) and (2.187) into Eq. (2.87), we find for the steady-state weights

$$\mathbf{W} = \frac{A_d R}{D} \begin{bmatrix} [A_i^2 + \sigma^2 - A_i^2 e^{j(\phi_d - \phi_i)}] \\ [A_i^2 + \sigma^2 - A_i^2 e^{j(\phi_i - \phi_d)}] e^{j\phi_d} \end{bmatrix} \tag{2.188}$$

$$= \frac{\xi_d(R/A_d)}{(D/\sigma^4)} \begin{bmatrix} [\xi_i + 1 - \xi_i e^{j(\phi_d - \phi_i)}] \\ [\xi_i + 1 - \xi_i e^{j(\phi_i - \phi_d)}] e^{j\phi_d} \end{bmatrix}. \tag{2.189}$$

Also, note from Eq. (2.184) that

$$\frac{D}{\sigma^4} = 4\xi_d\xi_i \sin^2\left(\frac{\phi_d - \phi_i}{2}\right) + 2\xi_d + 2\xi_i + 1; \tag{2.190}$$

thus all quantities in Eq. (2.189) may be expressed in terms of the signal-to-noise ratios ξ_d and ξ_i.

Now let us compute the array pattern with these weights. A unit amplitude test signal propagating into the array from angle θ will produce the signal vector **X** in Eqs. (2.127) and (2.128). This test signal will produce an array output signal

$$\tilde{s}(t) = \mathbf{W}^T\mathbf{X} \tag{2.191}$$

where **W** is given by Eq. (2.189). The voltage pattern is given by $|\tilde{s}(t)|$ as a function of θ. Figure 2.16 shows a series of patterns computed in this way for the parameters $\xi_d = 1$, $\theta_d = 50°$, $R/A_d = 1$, $\theta_i = 90°$, and for several values of input INR: $\xi_i = 0, 1, 2, 10,$ and 100.

These curves illustrate the ability of the LMS array to null an interference signal. As long as an interference signal is not correlated with the reference signal $\tilde{r}(t)$, the array feedback attempts to remove it from the array output by forming a pattern null on this signal. Moreover, as may be seen in Fig. 2.16, the depth of the null is a function of the interference power (or of ξ_i). This behavior is characteristic of the LMS array.

The fact that null depths depend on interference power in these arrays is both good and bad. It is good from the standpoint that a stronger interference signal automatically produces a deeper null; thus the amount of protection afforded by the array increases with interference power. However, it is bad from a different standpoint. When null depths depend on interference power, an interference signal whose power changes with time (such as one with envelope modulation) causes the weights to vary with time. Time-varying weights are not good because they may modulate the desired signal [12].

For this example, it is also instructive to compute the desired signal power, interference power, and thermal noise power and the desired signal-to-inter-ference-plus-thermal-noise ratio at the array output. Given the weight vector in Eq. (2.189), the output desired signal is

$$
\tilde{s}_d(t) = \mathbf{W}^T \mathbf{X}_d
$$

$$
= \frac{\xi_d(R/A_d)}{D/\sigma^4} \begin{bmatrix} [\xi_i(1 - e^{j(\phi_d - \phi_i)}) + 1] \\ [\xi_i(1 - e^{j(\phi_i - \phi_d)}) + 1]e^{j\phi_d} \end{bmatrix}^T A_d e^{j(\omega_d t + \psi_d)} \begin{bmatrix} 1 \\ e^{-j\phi_d} \end{bmatrix}
$$

$$
= \frac{2\xi_d R}{D/\sigma^4} e^{j(\omega_d t + \psi_d)} \left[1 + 2\xi_i \sin^2\left(\frac{\phi_d - \phi_i}{2}\right) \right]. \tag{2.192}
$$

The output desired signal power is then given by

$$
P_d = \tfrac{1}{2} E\{|\tilde{s}_d(t)|^2\}
$$

$$
= \frac{2\xi_d^2 R^2}{(D/\sigma^4)^2} \left[1 + 2\xi_i \sin^2\left(\frac{\phi_d - \phi_i}{2}\right) \right]^2. \tag{2.193}
$$

Similarly, the output interference signal is

$$
\tilde{s}_i(t) = \mathbf{W}^T \mathbf{X}_i
$$

$$
= \frac{\xi_d(R/A_d)}{D/\sigma^4} \begin{bmatrix} [\xi_i(1 - e^{j(\phi_d - \phi_i)}) + 1] \\ [\xi_i(1 - e^{j(\phi_i - \phi_d)}) + 1]e^{j\phi_d} \end{bmatrix}^T A_i e^{j(\omega_d t + \psi_i)} \begin{bmatrix} 1 \\ e^{-j\phi_i} \end{bmatrix}
$$

$$
= \frac{\xi_d(R/A_d)A_i}{D/\sigma^4} e^{j(\omega_d t + \psi_i)} \left[1 + e^{j(\phi_d - \phi_i)} \right]. \tag{2.194}
$$

The output interference power is

$$
P_i = \tfrac{1}{2} E\{|\tilde{s}_i(t)|^2\}
$$

$$
= \frac{\xi_d^2(R/A_d)^2 A_i^2}{2(D/\sigma^4)^2} \left[1 + e^{j(\phi_d - \phi_i)} \right]\left[1 + e^{-j(\phi_d - \phi_i)} \right]
$$

$$
= \frac{2\xi_i \xi_d R^2}{(D/\sigma^4)^2} \cos^2\left(\frac{\phi_d - \phi_i}{2}\right). \tag{2.195}
$$

The output thermal noise voltage is

$$
\tilde{s}_n(t) = \mathbf{W}^T \mathbf{X}_n = w_1 \tilde{n}_1(t) + w_2 \tilde{n}_2(t), \tag{2.196}
$$

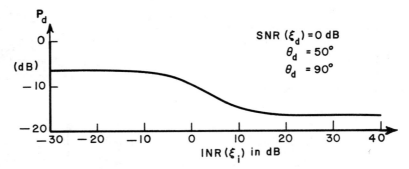

Figure 2.17 P_d versus ξ_i.

and the thermal noise power is

$$P_n = \tfrac{1}{2}E\{|\tilde{s}_n(t)|^2\} = \frac{\sigma^2}{2}\left[|w_1|^2 + |w_2|^2\right]$$

$$= \frac{\sigma^2\xi_d^2(R/A_d)^2}{2(D/\sigma^4)^2}\left[\left|\xi_i(1 - e^{j(\phi_d - \phi_i)}) + 1\right|^2 + \left|\xi_i(1 - e^{j(\phi_i - \phi_d)}) + 1\right|^2\right]$$

$$= \frac{\xi_d R^2}{(D/\sigma^4)^2}\{2\xi_i[\xi_i + 1][1 - \cos(\phi_d - \phi_i)] + 1\}. \qquad (2.197)$$

Finally, we define the output desired signal-to-interference-plus-thermal noise ratio, SINR:

$$\text{SINR} = \frac{P_d}{P_i + P_n} \qquad (2.198)$$

The powers P_d, P_i, P_n, and the SINR are plotted versus ξ_i in Figs. 2.17 through 2.20 for the same parameter values as in Fig. 2.16 ($\xi_d = 1$, $\theta_d = 50°$, $R/A_d = 1$, $\theta_i = 90°$). The curves show all quantities in dB, that is, P_d (dB) = $10\log_{10} P_d$, and so on. These curves illustrate several features of the adaptive array performance.

First, consider P_i versus ξ_i, shown in Fig. 2.18. It is seen that as the input interference power (or ξ_i) increases, P_i at first increases and then decreases. This behavior occurs for the following reason: When the interference is weak, it is too small to have any effect in the feedback loops controlling the weights. In this case the array pattern is dictated by the desired signal and is unaffected by the interference. The pattern of the array is essentially that shown in Fig. 2.16(a) for desired signal only. With the interference so weak that it does not affect the pattern, the output interference power is just proportional to the input interference power. This is the situation for $\xi_i < -10$ dB in Fig. 2.18.

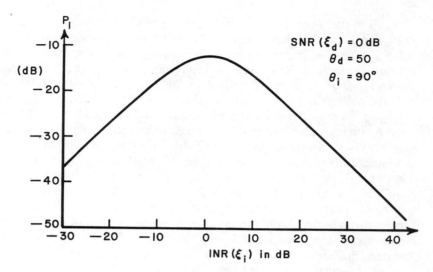

Figure 2.18 P_i versus ξ_i.

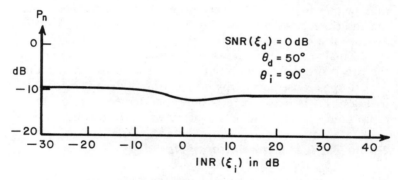

Figure 2.19 P_n versus ξ_i.

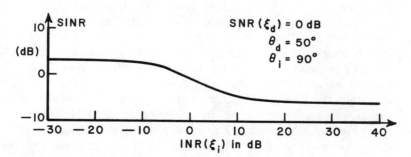

Figure 2.20 SINR versus ξ_i.

On the other hand, for strong interference signals, we already found in Fig. 2.16 that the null depth varies with interference power. Figure 2.18 shows that for $\xi_i > 10$ dB, increasing the interference power causes the null depth to drop twice as much as the increase in interference power. That is, increasing ξ_i by 10 dB causes P_i to drop 10 dB, which means the pattern response drops 20 dB. This behavior is characteristic of the LMS adaptive array.

Next consider the output desired signal power in Fig. 2.17. It is seen that as ξ_i increases, P_d drops. For weak interference P_d is -6.5 dB and as ξ_i increases P_d drops to about -16.5 dB. This drop occurs because a two-element adaptive array has only one degree of freedom[‡] in its pattern. That is, it is capable of pointing the pattern maximum in a given direction, or of pointing a null in a given direction, but not both. With no interference, the array forms a beam maximum on the desired signal. However, with strong interference present, the array nulls the interference instead, to minimize $E\{\varepsilon^2(t)\}$. Nulling the interference uses up the only degree of freedom, so that the array can no longer maximize its response on the desired signal. The output desired signal power is therefore reduced below its value without interference.

Next consider the output thermal noise power P_n as a function of ξ_i, as shown in Fig. 2.19. We find that P_n is almost constant as ξ_i varies. The reason is that $|w_1|^2 + |w_2|^2$ changes very little when interference is added. The effect of the interference is only to alter the phase of w_1, w_2 to produce a null at θ_i, instead of a beam maximum at θ_d.

Finally, Fig. 2.20 shows the output SINR. It is seen that as ξ_i increases, the SINR drops from an initial value of 3 dB to a final value of about -6 dB. This drop is caused primarily by the drop in desired signal power with ξ_i, shown in Fig. 2.17, because there is only one degree of freedom in the array. Using more than two elements in the array will alter this behavior of the SINR.

Some Typical Experimental Results

Now that we have considered the theoretical performance of a two-element LMS array, let us consider some typical experimental patterns measured with such an array. Figure 2.21 shows a sketch of an array of two monopoles mounted on a square ground plane. Such an array was used to measure experimental patterns at 2.1 gHz [13]. The monopoles were one-quarter wavelength long and were spaced a half wavelength apart. The output from each element was connected to a mixer, converted to 65 mHz, and put into two LMS processors, as shown in Fig. 2.22. A common local oscillator fed both mixers, to maintain the phase coherence of the signals, as shown. Also, the transmitted signal was used to generate the reference signal, as is also shown in Fig. 2.22.

Figures 2.23 through 2.25 show some experimental patterns obtained with this system. First, Fig. 2.23(a) illustrates a typical pattern obtained when a

[‡]Degrees of freedom will be discussed in Chapter 3.

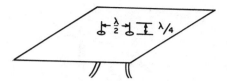

Figure 2.21 Two monopoles on a ground plane.

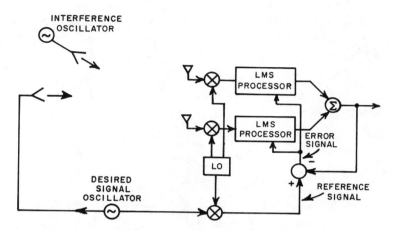

Figure 2.22 Experimental test setup for two-element array.

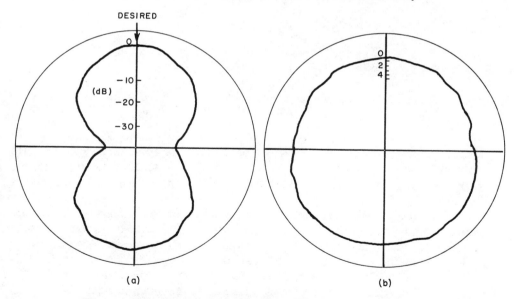

Figure 2.23 Two-element array with desired signal only. (a) Pattern with desired signal only (weights frozen after adaptation); (b) system response to desired signal as a function of arrival angle (weights tracking signal) (reprinted from [13] with permission, © 1973 IEEE).

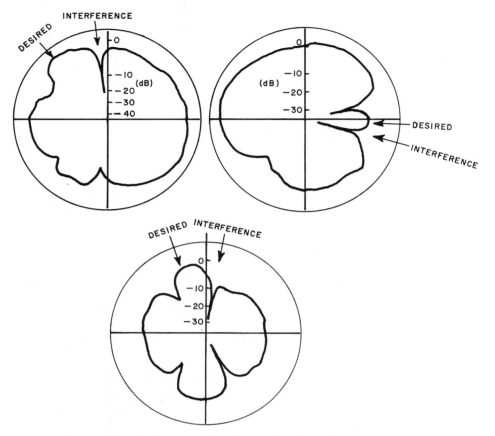

Figure 2.24 Final array patterns for various desired signal and inter-ference arrival angles (reprinted from [13] with permission, © 1973 IEEE).

desired signal is incident on the array from broadside. To obtain such a pattern, the weights are allowed to adapt, and after they have reached steady state, are frozen. With the weights frozen, the pattern is measured. Figure 2.23(a) shows the result.

Next, the same experiment is done, except that now the array weights are allowed to adapt as the pattern recorder turns. In this case the weights vary as the recorder turns, and the pattern maximum tracks the desired signal. Figure 2.23(b) shows the amplitude of the signal received as a function of angle. This plot is not an antenna pattern, of course, because the pattern changes as the antenna turns. Rather, it is a plot of the peak of the antenna beam as it tracks the desired signal around.

Next, Fig. 2.24 shows some typical patterns when both desired signal and interference are incident on the array. In Fig. 2.24, the weights are allowed to

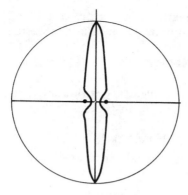

Figure 2.25 Interference null depth as a function of interference arrival angle (reprinted from [13] with permission, © 1973 IEEE).

adapt and are then frozen before the patterns are measured. Figure 2.24 shows three different patterns for three sets of incidence angles for the desired and interfering signals. It is seen how the adaptive feedback forces a null in the interference direction in each case.

Finally, Fig. 2.25 shows a plot of the null depth obtained on the interference signal, as a function of its arrival angle, when the desired signal is at broadside. (This is also not a pattern. It is a plot of null depth.) The curve essentially indicates the resolution ability of the two-element array.

The experimental patterns in Figs. 2.23 and 2.24 are not as smooth and symmetrical as the mathematically computed patterns shown earlier, such as those in Figs. 2.14 or 2.16. The reason is that the individual patterns of the monopole elements are not actually isotropic as assumed in the mathematical discussion. The pattern of a quarter wavelength monopole would be isotropic if it were mounted on an infinite ground plane. However, the square ground plane used in the experiments modifies the element patterns. In addition, each element operates in the presence of the other, so the mutual impedances between the elements also affect the patterns.

In Chapter 3, we shall discuss the effects of element patterns on adaptive array performance in a more complete way. Additional experimental pattern measurements for a four-element adaptive array may be found in reference [14].

2.2 THE APPLEBAUM ARRAY

The Applebaum array, also known as the Howells-Applebaum array [1, 2, 3], had its origins in the 1950s and thus predates the LMS array described in the last section. However, because the Applebaum array was not published in the open literature until 1976 [2], it was not widely known until that time. The Applebaum array is based on the concept of maximizing the desired-to-undesired (interference and noise) signal ratio at the array output. We shall first present Applebaum's derivation of the array, and then shall discuss the relationship between the Applebaum array and the LMS array.

The Optimization Criterion

Consider an N-element adaptive array with analytic signals $\tilde{x}_i(t)$ and complex weights w_i as shown in Fig. 2.26. In general the signal vector,

$$\mathbf{X} = \left[\tilde{x}_1(t), \tilde{x}_2(t), \ldots, \tilde{x}_N(t) \right]^T, \qquad (2.199)$$

may be split into a desired signal term, an interference term, and a thermal noise term,

$$\mathbf{X} = \mathbf{X}_d + \mathbf{X}_i + \mathbf{X}_n. \qquad (2.200)$$

The array output signal may be split in the same way,

$$\tilde{s}(t) = \mathbf{W}^T \mathbf{X} = \tilde{s}_d(t) + \tilde{s}_i(t) + \tilde{s}_n(t). \qquad (2.201)$$

The desired signal power, interference power, and thermal noise power at the array output will then be

$$P_d = \tfrac{1}{2} E\left\{ \left| \tilde{s}_d(t) \right|^2 \right\}, \qquad (2.202)$$

$$P_i = \tfrac{1}{2} E\left\{ \left| \tilde{s}_i(t) \right|^2 \right\}, \qquad (2.203)$$

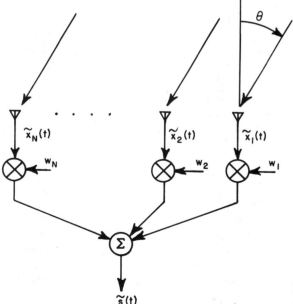

Figure 2.26 An N-element adaptive array.

and

$$P_n = \tfrac{1}{2}E\{|\tilde{s}_n(t)|^2\}.$$ (2.204)

We define the total *undesired* power at the array output P_u to be

$$P_u = P_i + P_n.$$ (2.205)

The adaptive array concept of Applebaum [2, 3] is based on a maximum signal-to-noise ratio concept. The optimization criterion used is to adjust the weights so that the quantity

$$\text{SINR} = \frac{P_d}{P_u} = \frac{P_d}{P_i + P_n}$$ (2.206)

is maximized. To see how this criterion may be applied to an adaptive array, we follow the development given by Applebaum [2, 3].

First, we assume the desired signal received by the array is "narrowband." If the signal is narrowband, the desired signal vector may be written in the form

$$\mathbf{X}_d = a\mathbf{U}_d,$$ (2.207)

where a is a scalar factor containing the amplitude and time dependence of the desired signal, and the vector $\mathbf{U}_d$ contains the interelement phase shifts and the element patterns. For example, consider the two-element array studied earlier in Fig. 2.9. We found in Eq. (2.112) that for a CW desired signal,

$$\mathbf{X}_d = A_d e^{j(\omega_d t + \psi_d)} \begin{bmatrix} 1 \\ e^{-j\phi_d} \end{bmatrix}.$$ (2.208)

This expression is in the form of Eq. (2.207), with

$$a = A_d e^{j(\omega_d t + \psi_d)},$$ (2.209)

and

$$\mathbf{U}_d = \begin{bmatrix} 1 \\ e^{-j\phi_d} \end{bmatrix}.$$ (2.210)

Or, if a desired signal contains narrowband amplitude or phase modulation,

$$\mathbf{X}_d = A_d(t) e^{j[\omega_d t + \psi_d + \phi_d(t)]} \begin{bmatrix} 1 \\ e^{-j\phi_d} \end{bmatrix}.$$ (2.211)

This expression is in the form of Eq. (2.207), with

$$a = A_d(t) e^{j[\omega_d t + \psi_d + \phi_d(t)]},$$ (2.212)

where $A_d(t)$ is the amplitude modulation, $\phi_d(t)$ is the phase modulation, and $\mathbf{U}_d$ is as given by Eq. (2.210). Finally, if the adaptive array contains N different elements, let the ith element pattern be $f_i(\theta)$. Then, if the signal has narrow-band amplitude and phase modulation, $\mathbf{X}_d$ will be given by Eq. (2.207) with a

defined in Eq. (2.212) and $\mathbf{U}_d$ given by

$$\mathbf{U}_d = \begin{bmatrix} f_1(\theta_d) \\ f_2(\theta_d)e^{-j\phi_{d2}} \\ \vdots \\ f_N(\theta_d)e^{-j\phi_{dN}} \end{bmatrix} \tag{2.213}$$

where ϕ_{di} is the interelement phase shift between element 1 and element i. Thus, $\mathbf{X}_d$ can be written in the form of Eq. (2.207) as long as the desired signal is narrowband.

The narrowband assumption is necessary in order that an interelement phase shift ϕ_{di} can be factored out for use in the vector $\mathbf{U}_d$. In general, the relative phase shift between two elements for an arriving signal is a function of frequency. If the desired signal has a wide bandwidth, the interelement phase shift will be different at different frequencies within its bandwidth. In that case one cannot factor out a single phase factor $e^{-j\phi_{di}}$ as in Eq. (2.213). The narrowband assumption means that ϕ_{di} is essentially constant across the bandwidth. (In Chapter 3 we shall treat the effects of bandwidth in more detail and shall evaluate quantitatively how performance depends on bandwidth.)

With $\mathbf{X}_d$ expressed as in Eq. (2.207), the output desired signal from the array is

$$\tilde{s}_d(t) = \mathbf{W}^T\mathbf{X}_d = a\mathbf{W}^T\mathbf{U}_d; \tag{2.214}$$

therefore, the output desired signal power may be written

$$P_d = \tfrac{1}{2}E\{|\tilde{s}_d(t)|^2\} = \tfrac{1}{2}E\{|a|^2\}|\mathbf{W}^T\mathbf{U}_d|^2. \tag{2.215}$$

Now consider the undesired output signal power P_u. In Eq. (2.84), we defined the covariance matrix $\mathbf{\Phi}$. If the signal vectors $\mathbf{X}_d$, $\mathbf{X}_i$, and $\mathbf{X}_n$ in Eq. (2.200) are statistically independent and zero mean, which we assume, then

$$\mathbf{\Phi} = E(\mathbf{X}^*\mathbf{X}^T) = E(\mathbf{X}_d^*\mathbf{X}_d^T) + E(\mathbf{X}_i^*\mathbf{X}_i^T) + E(\mathbf{X}_n^*\mathbf{X}_n^T) = \mathbf{\Phi}_d + \mathbf{\Phi}_i + \mathbf{\Phi}_n. \tag{2.216}$$

Note that $\mathbf{\Phi}$ can be written

$$\mathbf{\Phi} = \mathbf{\Phi}_d + \mathbf{\Phi}_u, \tag{2.217}$$

where

$$\mathbf{\Phi}_u = \mathbf{\Phi}_i + \mathbf{\Phi}_n. \tag{2.218}$$

For a given weight vector $\mathbf{W}$, the undesired signal at the array output $\tilde{s}_u(t)$ is

$$\tilde{s}_u(t) = \tilde{s}_i(t) + \tilde{s}_n(t) = \mathbf{W}^T(\mathbf{X}_i + \mathbf{X}_n) = (\mathbf{X}_i + \mathbf{X}_n)^T\mathbf{W}. \tag{2.219}$$

Therefore, the undesired output power is

$$P_u = \tfrac{1}{2}E\{|\mathbf{W}^T(\mathbf{X}_i + \mathbf{X}_n)|^2\} = \tfrac{1}{2}E\{\mathbf{W}^\dagger(\mathbf{X}_i^* + \mathbf{X}_n^*)(\mathbf{X}_i^T + \mathbf{X}_n^T)\mathbf{W}\}$$

$$= \tfrac{1}{2}\mathbf{W}^\dagger\left[E_{\!}(\mathbf{X}_i^*\mathbf{X}_i^T) + E(\mathbf{X}_n^*\mathbf{X}_n^T)\right]\mathbf{W}$$

$$= \tfrac{1}{2}\mathbf{W}^\dagger(\mathbf{\Phi}_i + \mathbf{\Phi}_n)\mathbf{W}$$

$$= \tfrac{1}{2}\mathbf{W}^\dagger\mathbf{\Phi}_u\mathbf{W}. \tag{2.220}$$

Thus, the quantity to be maximized in the Applebaum array is

$$\text{SINR} = \frac{P_d}{P_u} = \frac{\tfrac{1}{2}E\{|a|^2\}|\mathbf{W}^T\mathbf{U}_d|^2}{\tfrac{1}{2}\mathbf{W}^\dagger\mathbf{\Phi}_u\mathbf{W}} = E\{|a|^2\}\frac{|\mathbf{W}^T\mathbf{U}_d|^2}{\mathbf{W}^\dagger\mathbf{\Phi}_u\mathbf{W}}. \tag{2.221}$$

The Optimal Weight Vector

The first step in Applebaum's development is to show that the weight vector $\mathbf{W}$ that maximizes the ratio in Eq. (2.221) is

$$\mathbf{W} = \mu\mathbf{\Phi}_u^{-1}\mathbf{U}_d^*, \tag{2.222}$$

where μ is an arbitrary scalar constant. [Note that this result looks similar to Eq. (2.87) for the LMS array, because we found in Eqs. (2.119) and (2.187) that $\mathbf{S} = A_d R\mathbf{U}_d^*$. However, the $\mathbf{\Phi}$ in Eq. (2.87) is the total covariance matrix, whereas $\mathbf{\Phi}_u$ in Eq. (2.222) is only the undesired part.] We start by making a rotation of coordinates in the weight vector. Let

$$\mathbf{W} = \mathbf{AV}, \tag{2.223}$$

where $\mathbf{A}$ is an $N \times N$ matrix and $\mathbf{V}$ is an $N \times 1$ column vector with elements v_i. Substituting Eq. (2.223) into Eq. (2.220) yields

$$P_u = \tfrac{1}{2}\mathbf{V}^\dagger\mathbf{A}^\dagger\mathbf{\Phi}_u\mathbf{AV}. \tag{2.224}$$

Now $\mathbf{A}$ may be chosen so that

$$\mathbf{A}^\dagger\mathbf{\Phi}_u\mathbf{A} = \mathbf{I}. \tag{2.225}$$

To see how, note that since $\mathbf{\Phi}_u$ is hermitian, a unitary matrix $\mathbf{R}$ exists such that

$$\mathbf{R}^\dagger\mathbf{\Phi}_u\mathbf{R} = \mathbf{\Lambda} = \text{diag}(\lambda_1, \lambda_2, \ldots, \lambda_N), \tag{2.226}$$

where the λ_i are the eigenvalues of $\mathbf{\Phi}_u$. The columns of $\mathbf{R}$ are the eigenvectors of $\mathbf{\Phi}_u$, that is,

$$R = [\mathbf{e}_1, \mathbf{e}_2, \ldots], \tag{2.227}$$

where

$$\mathbf{e}_i = i\text{th eigenvector of } \mathbf{\Phi}_u. \tag{2.228}$$

Moreover, we assume $\mathbf{\Phi}_u$ is positive definite, so $\lambda_i > 0$ for all i. ($\mathbf{\Phi}_u$ will be positive definite as long as the element signals contain thermal noise. This property was seen in Examples 1 and 2 of the last section and will be discussed further in Chapter 4.) Therefore, if **A** is defined to be

$$\mathbf{A} = \left[\frac{1}{\sqrt{\lambda_1}} \mathbf{e}_1, \frac{1}{\sqrt{\lambda_2}} \mathbf{e}_2, \ldots \right], \tag{2.229}$$

then Eq. (2.225) results.

Note also that if Eq. (2.225) is multiplied on the right by $\mathbf{A}^{-1}$ and on the left by $(\mathbf{A}^\dagger)^{-1}$, we obtain

$$\mathbf{\Phi}_u = (\mathbf{A}\mathbf{A}^\dagger)^{-1}, \tag{2.230}$$

a relation that will be useful later.

Next, note that substituting $\mathbf{\Phi}_u$ into Eq. (2.224) gives

$$\begin{aligned} P_u &= \tfrac{1}{2} \mathbf{V}^\dagger \mathbf{A}^\dagger E \left[(\mathbf{X}_i + \mathbf{X}_n)^* (\mathbf{X}_i + \mathbf{X}_n)^T \right] \mathbf{A} \mathbf{V} \\ &= \tfrac{1}{2} E \left\{ \left[\mathbf{V}^T \mathbf{A}^T (\mathbf{X}_i + \mathbf{X}_n) \right]^* \left[\mathbf{V}^T \mathbf{A}^T (\mathbf{X}_i + \mathbf{X}_n) \right]^T \right\} \\ &= \tfrac{1}{2} E \left\{ \left[\mathbf{V}^T (\mathbf{Y}_i + \mathbf{Y}_n) \right]^* \left[\mathbf{V}^T (\mathbf{Y}_i + \mathbf{Y}_n) \right]^T \right\}, \end{aligned} \tag{2.231}$$

where

$$\mathbf{Y}_i = \mathbf{A}^T \mathbf{X}_i \tag{2.232}$$

and

$$\mathbf{Y}_n = \mathbf{A}^T \mathbf{X}_n. \tag{2.233}$$

Hence the transformation $\mathbf{A}^T$ may be interpreted as transforming the actual received signals $\mathbf{X}_i$ and $\mathbf{X}_n$ into new signals $\mathbf{Y}_i$ and $\mathbf{Y}_n$, as shown in Fig. 2.27. The output signal from the array is then obtained by weighting $\mathbf{Y}_i$ and $\mathbf{Y}_n$ with the vector $\mathbf{V}$. The transformation $\mathbf{A}^T$ combined with weight vector $\mathbf{V}$ is equiv-

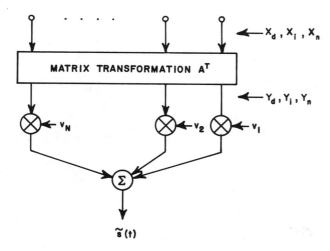

Figure 2.27   The transformation A^T.

alent to the original weight vector $\mathbf{W}$ in Eq. (2.223). Moreover, since

$$\mathbf{A}^{\dagger}\mathbf{\Phi}_u\mathbf{A} = E\left[(\mathbf{Y}_i + \mathbf{Y}_n)^*(\mathbf{Y}_i + \mathbf{Y}_n)^T\right] = \mathbf{I}, \qquad (2.234)$$

the transformation $\mathbf{A}^T$ makes the components of the total undesired signal vector $\mathbf{Y}_i + \mathbf{Y}_n$ uncorrelated with each other.

The desired signal vector after the same transformation will be

$$\mathbf{Y}_d = \mathbf{A}^T\mathbf{X}_d = a\mathbf{A}^T\mathbf{U}_d = a\mathbf{Z}_d, \qquad (2.235)$$

where

$$\mathbf{Z}_d = \mathbf{A}^T\mathbf{U}_d. \qquad (2.236)$$

The array output desired signal is then

$$\tilde{s}_d(t) = \mathbf{V}^T\mathbf{Y}_d = a\mathbf{V}^T\mathbf{Z}_d, \qquad (2.237)$$

and the output desired signal power is

$$P_d = \tfrac{1}{2}E\left\{|\tilde{s}_d(t)|^2\right\} = \tfrac{1}{2}E\left[|a|^2\right]|\mathbf{V}^T\mathbf{Z}_d|^2 \qquad (2.238)$$

Thus, inserting Eqs. (2.224), (2.225), and (2.238) in Eq. (2.221), we have

$$\text{SINR} = \frac{P_d}{P_u} = E\left[|a|^2\right]\frac{|\mathbf{V}^T\mathbf{Z}_d|^2}{\mathbf{V}^{\dagger}\mathbf{V}} \qquad (2.239)$$

Now we show that the ratio in Eq. (2.239) is maximized by choosing

$$\mathbf{V} = \mathbf{V}_{\text{opt}} = \mu\mathbf{Z}_d^*, \qquad (2.240)$$

where μ is an arbitrary constant. To do this, we use the Schwarz inequality [15]:

$$|\mathbf{V}^T\mathbf{Z}_d|^2 = \left|\sum_{i=1}^{N} v_i z_{di}\right|^2 \leqslant \sum_{i=1}^{N}|v_i|^2 \sum_{i=1}^{N}|z_{di}|^2 = \mathbf{V}^{\dagger}\mathbf{V}\mathbf{Z}_d^{\dagger}\mathbf{Z}_d, \qquad (2.241)$$

where v_i and z_{di} are the components of $\mathbf{V}$ and $\mathbf{Z}_d$, respectively. Substituting this inequality into Eq. (2.239) yields

$$\text{SINR} = \frac{P_d}{P_u} \leqslant E\left[|a|^2\right]\frac{\mathbf{V}^{\dagger}\mathbf{V}\mathbf{Z}_d^{\dagger}\mathbf{Z}_d}{\mathbf{V}^{\dagger}\mathbf{V}} = E\left[|a|^2\right]\mathbf{Z}_d^{\dagger}\mathbf{Z}_d. \qquad (2.242)$$

However, if $\mathbf{V} = \mu\mathbf{Z}_d^*$ one finds from Eq. (2.239) that

$$\text{SINR} = \frac{P_d}{P_u} = E\left[|a|^2\right]\frac{\mu^2\left(\mathbf{Z}_d^{\dagger}\mathbf{Z}_d\right)^2}{\mu^2\left(\mathbf{Z}_d^T\mathbf{Z}_d^*\right)} = E\left[|a|^2\right]\mathbf{Z}_d^{\dagger}\mathbf{Z}_d. \qquad (2.243)$$

Thus, the SINR achieves its maximum possible value for the $\mathbf{V}$ in Eq. (2.240). However, the weight vector $\mathbf{V}_{\text{opt}}$ applied after the transformation $\mathbf{A}^T$ is equivalent to a weight vector $\mathbf{W}$ given by

$$\mathbf{W} = \mathbf{W}_{\text{opt}} = \mathbf{A}\mathbf{V}_{\text{opt}} = \mu\mathbf{A}\mathbf{Z}_d^*. \qquad (2.244)$$

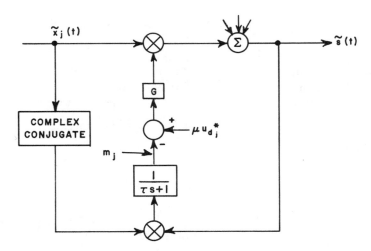

Figure 2.28   The Applebaum loop.

Substituting in Eq. (2.236) for $\mathbf{Z}_d$ and then using Eq. (2.230) yields

$$\mathbf{W}_{\text{opt}} = \mu \mathbf{A}\mathbf{A}^\dagger \mathbf{U}_d^* = \mu \mathbf{\Phi}_u^{-1} \mathbf{U}_d^*, \tag{2.245}$$

which is the result claimed in Eq. (2.222).

The Applebaum Feedback Loop

Having shown that $\mathbf{W}_{\text{opt}}$ in Eq. (2.222) is the optimal weight vector, Applebaum then suggested the feedback loop in Fig. 2.28 as an adaptive loop to produce the weight vector $\mathbf{W}_{\text{opt}}$ in the array [2, 3]. In this figure G is a gain constant, τ is the time constant of the lowpass filter, and s denotes the complex frequency. The variable u_{di}^* is the ith element of $\mathbf{U}_d^*$.

To show that the loop in Fig. 2.28 produces the correct steady-state weights $\mathbf{W}_{\text{opt}}$ in the array, let us determine the differential equation for w_i with this loop. Let the output of the lowpass filter be denoted by m_i as indicated in Fig. 2.28. Then m_i satisfies the equation

$$\tau \frac{dm_i}{dt} + m_i = \tilde{x}_i^*(t)\tilde{s}(t). \tag{2.246}$$

However, w_i is related to m_i by

$$w_i = G[\mu u_{di}^* - m_i]; \tag{2.247}$$

therefore,

$$m_i = \mu u_{di}^* - \frac{1}{G}w_i \tag{2.248}$$

and

$$\frac{dm_i}{dt} = -\frac{1}{G}\frac{dw_i}{dt}. \tag{2.249}$$

Substituting Eqs. (2.248) and (2.249) into Eq. (2.246) gives the differential equation for w_i,

$$\frac{\tau}{G}\frac{dw_i}{dt} + \frac{w_i}{G} = \mu u_{di}^* - \tilde{x}_i^*(t)\tilde{s}(t). \tag{2.250}$$

In vector notation, this becomes

$$\frac{\tau}{G}\frac{d\mathbf{W}}{dt} + \frac{\mathbf{W}}{G} = \mu\mathbf{U}_d^* - \mathbf{X}^*\tilde{s}(t). \tag{2.251}$$

Finally, substituting $\tilde{s}(t) = \mathbf{X}^T\mathbf{W}$ and rearranging gives

$$\frac{\tau}{G}\frac{d\mathbf{W}}{dt} + \left[\frac{1}{G}\mathbf{I} + \mathbf{X}^*\mathbf{X}^T\right]\mathbf{W} = \mu\mathbf{U}_d^*. \tag{2.252}$$

As with the LMS array, we assume the speed of response of the weight vector to be several orders of magnitude less than the speed of the fluctuations in $\mathbf{X}^*\mathbf{X}^T$. We approximate $\mathbf{X}^*\mathbf{X}^T$ in Eq. (2.252) by

$$\mathbf{X}^*\mathbf{X}^T \to E(\mathbf{X}^*\mathbf{X}^T) = \mathbf{\Phi}; \tag{2.253}$$

therefore, the weight differential equation becomes

$$\frac{\tau}{G}\frac{d\mathbf{W}}{dt} + \left[\frac{1}{G}\mathbf{I} + \mathbf{\Phi}\right]\mathbf{W} = \mu\mathbf{U}_d^*. \tag{2.254}$$

Thus, with this loop, the steady-state weight vector will be

$$\mathbf{W} = \left[\frac{1}{G}\mathbf{I} + \mathbf{\Phi}\right]^{-1}\mu\mathbf{U}_d^*. \tag{2.255}$$

If the loop gain G is large, Eq. (2.255) is approximately the same as

$$\mathbf{W} \cong \mu\mathbf{\Phi}^{-1}\mathbf{U}_d^*. \tag{2.256}$$

We note that this weight vector involves $\mathbf{\Phi}^{-1}$, instead of $\mathbf{\Phi}_u^{-1}$ as in Eq. (2.222). However, it turns out that this difference does not matter, for two reasons. First, we shall show below that the weight vector in Eq. (2.256) is equal to that in Eq. (2.222) times a scalar constant, so that both give the same SINR. Second, as a practical matter, much of the interest in the Applebaum array has been for application to pulsed radar systems. In a pulsed radar system, the desired signal is present such a small fraction of the time that its contribution to $\mathbf{\Phi}$ is negligible. For example, if a radar has a duty cycle of 0.001, a desired signal pulse will be present only 0.1% of the time (and then only if there is a target in the field of view of the radar). Usually the signals in the array just consist of the interference and noise. In this case,

$$\mathbf{\Phi} \cong \mathbf{\Phi}_u. \tag{2.257}$$

A Modified Applebaum Loop

Before discussing the relationship between the weights in Eqs. (2.256) and (2.222), we first point out that by making a minor change in the loop configuration of Fig. 2.28, the $1/G$ term in Eq. (2.255) can be eliminated. If, instead of the loop in Fig. 2.28, we consider the loop in Fig. 2.29, we have

$$\frac{dw_i}{dt} = k\left[\mu u_{di}^* - \tilde{x}_i^*(t)\tilde{s}(t)\right], \tag{2.258}$$

or, in vector form,

$$\frac{d\mathbf{W}}{dt} = k\left[\mu \mathbf{U}_d^* - \mathbf{X}^*\tilde{s}(t)\right]. \tag{2.259}$$

Substituting $\tilde{s}(t) = \mathbf{X}^T\mathbf{W}$ and rearranging then yields

$$\frac{d\mathbf{W}}{dt} + k\mathbf{X}^*\mathbf{X}^T\mathbf{W} = k\mu \mathbf{U}_d^* \tag{2.260}$$

or, after making the substitution in Eq. (2.253),

$$\frac{d\mathbf{W}}{dt} + k\mathbf{\Phi}\mathbf{W} = k\mu \mathbf{U}_d^*. \tag{2.261}$$

This loop produces the steady-state weight vector

$$\mathbf{W} = \mu\mathbf{\Phi}^{-1}\mathbf{U}_d^*, \tag{2.262}$$

without any requirement that G be large.

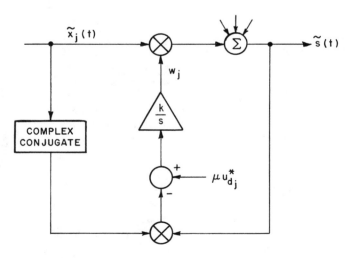

Figure 2.29   Alternative form of the Applebaum loop.

The Equivalence of $\Phi^{-1}U_d^*$ *and* $\Phi_u^{-1}U_d^*$

Now let us show that the weight vectors in Eqs. (2.256) and (2.222) are multiples of one another. We give a proof originally due to Baird and Zahm [16]. Since the desired signal is assumed to be narrowband, Φ may be written [using Eq. (2.207)]

$$\Phi = \Phi_d + \Phi_u = E[|a|^2]U_d^*U_d^T + \Phi_u. \tag{2.263}$$

The inverse of Φ may be calculated with the following matrix inversion lemma [17]:

Lemma. If **B** is a nonsingular $N \times N$ matrix, **Z** is an $N \times 1$ column vector, and β is a scalar, then the inverse of the matrix **Q**,

$$Q = B - \beta Z^*Z^T, \tag{2.264}$$

is given by

$$Q^{-1} = B^{-1} - \tau B^{-1}Z^*Z^TB^{-1}, \tag{2.265}$$

where τ is a scalar related to β by

$$\tau^{-1} + \beta^{-1} = Z^TB^{-1}Z^*. \tag{2.266}$$

Applying this lemma to Φ, we find

$$\Phi^{-1} = \Phi_u^{-1} - \tau\Phi_u^{-1}U_d^*U_d^T\Phi_u^{-1}, \tag{2.267}$$

where

$$\tau = \frac{E[|a|^2]}{1 + E[|a|^2]U_d^T\Phi_u^{-1}U_d^*}. \tag{2.268}$$

Therefore, if Φ^{-1} is a multiplied onto U_d^*, one finds

$$\Phi^{-1}U_d^* = \Phi_u^{-1}U_d^* - \frac{E[|a|^2]\Phi_u^{-1}U_d^*U_d^T\Phi_u^{-1}U_d^*}{1 + E[|a|^2]U_d^T\Phi_u^{-1}U_d^*}. \tag{2.269}$$

Since $U_d^T\Phi_u^{-1}U_d^*$ is a scalar, this equation reduces to

$$\Phi^{-1}U_d^* = \left\{ 1 - \frac{E[|a|^2]U_d^T\Phi_u^{-1}U_d^*}{1 + E[|a|^2]U_d^T\Phi_u^{-1}U_d^*} \right\} \Phi_u^{-1}U_d^*$$

$$\Phi^{-1}U_d^* = \left\{ \frac{1}{1 + E[|a|^2]U_d^T\Phi_u^{-1}U_d^*} \right\} \Phi_u^{-1}U_d^*. \tag{2.270}$$

Thus, $\Phi^{-1}U_d^*$ is just a scalar multiple of $\Phi_u^{-1}U_d^*$. The weights yielded by the loop of Fig. 2.29 are maximum signal-to-noise ratio weights. Moreover, it is clear from this result that the LMS weights in Eq. (2.87) are also maximum signal-to-noise ratio weights.

The Steering Vector

In his paper [2], Applebaum also points out that one does not necessarily have to use the vector $\mathbf{U}_d^*$ in the feedback loop. One may use a vector differing slightly from $\mathbf{U}_d^*$. Suppose a vector $\mathbf{T}^*$ is inserted in the loops shown in Fig. 2.29, instead of $\mathbf{U}_d^*$. Then the weights in the array will satisfy the differential equation

$$\frac{d\mathbf{W}}{dt} + k\mathbf{\Phi}\mathbf{W} = k\mu\mathbf{T}^*. \tag{2.271}$$

The steady-state weight vector will then be

$$\mathbf{W} = \mu\mathbf{\Phi}^{-1}\mathbf{T}^*, \tag{2.272}$$

instead of Eq. (2.262).

Suppose there are no signals incident on the array. With only thermal noise present in the signals $\tilde{x}_i(t)$, the covariance matrix in Eq. (2.272) is simply

$$\mathbf{\Phi} = \sigma^2\mathbf{I}. \tag{2.273}$$

In this case the steady-state weight vector in Eq. (2.272) is

$$\mathbf{W} = \frac{\mu}{\sigma^2}\mathbf{T}^*. \tag{2.274}$$

Therefore, in the absence of incoming signals, the weight vector is a scalar multiple of $\mathbf{T}^*$. When no signals are incident on the array, we say the array is in its *quiescent* state. In this case, the array has a pattern determined by $\mathbf{T}^*$, and we call this pattern the *quiescent pattern* of the array. Clearly, $\mathbf{T}^*$ can be chosen to obtain a desired quiescent pattern from the array.

When $\mathbf{T}^*$ is chosen equal to $\mathbf{U}_d^*$, then we know the array will yield maximum signal-to-noise ratio for the desired signal. With equal thermal noise power on every element of the array, this choice will maximize the array pattern gain on the desired signal. However, $\mathbf{T}^*$ can also be chosen to obtain something other than maximum gain. It is common in antenna design, for example, to give up a small amount of main beam gain in order to achieve better sidelobe performance. The vector $\mathbf{T}^*$ could be chosen using antenna synthesis techniques [18] to obtain a main beam in the desired direction and to obtain some desired sidelobe performance.

Because the vector $\mathbf{T}^*$ steers the main beam of the quiescent antenna pattern, it is usually called the *steering vector*. The Applebaum array in Figs. 2.28 and 2.29 is often referred to as a *steering vector array* or a *steered beam array*.

The Relationship Between the LMS and Applebaum Arrays

The relationship between the Applebaum array and the LMS array is very simple. Note that the weights in the Applebaum array satisfy Eq. (2.271):

$$\frac{d\mathbf{W}}{dt} + k\mathbf{\Phi}\mathbf{W} = k\mu\mathbf{T}^*. \tag{2.275}$$

The weights in the LMS array satisfy Eq. (2.86):

$$\frac{d\mathbf{W}}{dt} + k\mathbf{\Phi}\mathbf{W} = k\mathbf{S}. \tag{2.276}$$

It is obvious from these two equations that if $\mu\mathbf{T}^* = \mathbf{S}$, the two arrays will perform identically. Moreover, because of the identity in Eq. (2.270), it is clear that the steady-state weights in the LMS array (which are based on minimum mean-square error signal) also yield maximum SINR. Thus there is little difference between the two arrays from a mathematical standpoint. Rather, the difference between the two is more a matter of *application*. The Applebaum array is useful when one knows the desired signal arrival angle in advance. (Otherwise, one cannot choose $\mathbf{T}^*$.) The Applebaum array has often been applied in radar, where the desired signal direction is dictated by the transmitting antenna pattern. Moreover, in the Applebaum array, one does not have to know the desired signal waveform. The LMS array, on the other hand, is just the opposite. Its use does not require any knowledge of desired signal arrival angle. As long as a reference signal correlated with the desired signal can be obtained, the array pattern will automatically track the desired signal with maximum signal-to-noise ratio. However, to obtain a reference signal, one must know a great deal about the structure of the desired signal waveform. Methods of obtaining a reference signal for the LMS array will be discussed in Chapter 7.

2.3 THE SHOR ARRAY

The Shor array was the first to appear in the literature [4]. It has not been extensively used, however, because it is more complicated than the LMS or Applebaum array. However, it is interesting to consider it, because it illustrates what happens if one attempts to maximize signal-to-noise ratio directly.

The Optimization Criterion

The Shor array is based on a maximum signal-to-noise ratio concept, like the Applebaum array. The optimal weights for the Shor array are the same as the optimal weights for the Applebaum array, given in Eq. (2.222). The Shor array differs from the Applebaum array in that the Shor feedback loops are based on a direct steepest-ascent optimization of signal-to-noise ratio. Note that Applebaum did not give any rationale for the specific form of his feedback loops, other than showing that they produce the correct steady-state weights. (However, comparing the Applebaum and LMS arrays makes it clear that the Applebaum loops could be derived from a steepest-descent minimization of a suitably defined mean-square error signal.) In the Shor algorithm, the feedback is designed to "climb the SINR hill" as quickly as possible.

The Shor Feedback Loop

To introduce Shor's feedback concept, it is helpful to return to the real signal notation used to discuss the LMS array. [See Eq. (2.5) and succeeding equations.] In general, in an N-element array, the inphase and quadrature signals behind the jth element may be written

$$x_{I_j}(t) = d_{I_j}(t) + i_{I_j}(t) + n_{I_j}(t) \tag{2.277}$$

and

$$x_{Q_j}(t) = d_{Q_j}(t) + i_{Q_j}(t) + n_{Q_j}(t), \tag{2.278}$$

where $d_{P_j}(t)$ is the desired signal component, $i_{P_j}(t)$ is the interference component, and $n_{P_j}(t)$ is the thermal noise component (where P denotes I or Q). As usual, $d_{P_j}(t)$, $i_{P_j}(t)$, and $n_{P_j}(t)$ are all assumed uncorrelated with each other. Let us refer to the sum of the interference and thermal noise components as the *undesired* signals $u_{P_j}(t)$:

$$u_{I_j}(t) = i_{I_j}(t) + n_{I_j}(t) \tag{2.279}$$

and

$$u_{Q_j}(t) = i_{Q_j}(t) + n_{Q_j}(t). \tag{2.280}$$

Then Eqs. (2.277) and (2.278) may be written

$$x_{I_j}(t) = d_{I_j}(t) + u_{I_j}(t) \tag{2.281}$$

and

$$x_{Q_j}(t) = d_{Q_j}(t) + u_{Q_j}(t). \tag{2.282}$$

Also, let $s_d(t)$ and $s_u(t)$ be the total desired and undesired signals, respectively, at the array output. Then the desired and undesired signal powers at the array output are given by

$$P_d = E\{s_d^2(t)\} = E\left\{ \left[\sum_{j=1}^{N} w_{I_j} d_{I_j}(t) + w_{Q_j} d_{Q_j}(t) \right]^2 \right\} \tag{2.283}$$

and

$$P_u = E\{s_u^2(t)\} = E\left\{\left[\sum_{j=1}^{N} w_{I_j} u_{I_j}(t) + w_{Q_j} u_{Q_j}(t)\right]^2\right\}. \qquad (2.284)$$

The signal-to-undesired-signal ratio is

$$\text{SINR} = \frac{P_d}{P_u}. \qquad (2.285)$$

The Shor array is based on a direct steepest-ascent optimization of the SINR. Specifically, we let

$$\frac{dw_{P_j}}{dt} = k\nabla_{w_{P_j}}(\text{SINR}) = k\frac{\partial}{\partial w_{P_j}}\left(\frac{P_d}{P_u}\right). \qquad (2.286)$$

To determine the feedback loop corresponding to Eq. (2.286), we evaluate the various derivatives. First,

$$\frac{\partial}{\partial w_{P_j}}\left(\frac{P_d}{P_u}\right) = \frac{P_u\dfrac{\partial P_d}{\partial w_{P_j}} - P_d\dfrac{\partial P_u}{\partial w_{P_j}}}{P_u^2}$$

$$= \frac{P_d}{P_u}\left(\frac{1}{P_d}\frac{\partial P_d}{\partial w_{P_j}} - \frac{1}{P_u}\frac{\partial P_u}{\partial w_{P_j}}\right). \qquad (2.287)$$

Then, from Eq. (2.283), we find

$$\frac{\partial P_d}{\partial w_{I_i}} = 2E\left\{\left[\sum_{j=1}^{N} w_{I_j} d_{I_j}(t) + w_{Q_j} d_{Q_j}(t)\right] d_{I_i}(t)\right\}$$

$$= 2E\{s_d(t)d_{I_i}(t)\}$$

$$= 2E\{s_d(t)x_{I_i}(t)\}, \qquad (2.288)$$

where the last equality follows from Eq. (2.281) and the fact that

$$E\{s_d(t)u_{I_i}(t)\} = 0. \qquad (2.289)$$

In a similar way, we find

$$\frac{\partial P_d}{\partial w_{Q_i}} = 2E\{s_d(t)x_{Q_i}(t)\}, \qquad (2.290)$$

$$\frac{\partial P_u}{\partial w_{I_i}} = 2E\{s_u(t)x_{I_i}(t)\}, \qquad (2.291)$$

and

$$\frac{\partial P_u}{\partial w_{Q_i}} = 2E\{s_u(t)x_{Q_i}(t)\}. \tag{2.292}$$

Since the expected values of these quantities are not available in a real-time feedback loop, we again use each function itself as an estimate of its expected value, as was done with the LMS algorithm. We substitute for the various derivatives,

$$\frac{\partial P_d}{\partial w_{I_i}} \rightarrow 2s_d(t)x_{I_i}(t), \tag{2.293}$$

$$\frac{\partial P_d}{\partial w_{Q_i}} \rightarrow 2s_d(t)x_{Q_i}(t), \tag{2.294}$$

$$\frac{\partial P_u}{\partial w_{I_i}} \rightarrow 2s_u(t)x_{I_i}(t), \tag{2.295}$$

and

$$\frac{\partial P_u}{\partial w_{Q_i}} \rightarrow 2s_u(t)x_{Q_i}(t). \tag{2.296}$$

Thus, from Eq. (2.286), we have

$$\frac{\partial}{\partial w_{I_i}}\left(\frac{P_d}{P_u}\right) = \frac{P_d}{P_u}\left[\frac{1}{P_d}\frac{\partial P_d}{\partial w_{I_i}} - \frac{1}{P_u}\frac{\partial P_u}{\partial w_{I_i}}\right]$$
$$= 2\frac{P_d}{P_u}x_{I_i}(t)\left[\frac{1}{P_d}s_d(t) - \frac{1}{P_u}s_u(t)\right] \tag{2.297}$$

and, similarly,

$$\frac{\partial}{\partial w_{Q_i}}\left(\frac{P_d}{P_u}\right) = 2\frac{P_d}{P_u}x_{Q_i}(t)\left[\frac{1}{P_d}s_d(t) - \frac{1}{P_u}s_u(t)\right]. \tag{2.298}$$

Therefore, the weight control Eq. (2.286) becomes

$$\frac{dw_{I_i}}{dt} = 2k\frac{P_d}{P_u}x_{I_i}(t)\left[\frac{1}{P_d}s_d(t) - \frac{1}{P_u}s_u(t)\right] \tag{2.299}$$

and

$$\frac{dw_{Q_i}}{dt} = 2k\frac{P_d}{P_u}x_{Q_i}(t)\left[\frac{1}{P_d}s_d(t) - \frac{1}{P_u}s_u(t)\right]. \tag{2.300}$$

As with the LMS array, these can be combined into complex notation. Again, we define

$$w_i = w_{I_i} - jw_{Q_i}, \tag{2.301}$$

$$\tilde{x}_i(t) = x_{I_i}(t) + jx_{Q_i}(t), \tag{2.302}$$

$$\tilde{s}_d(t) = s_d(t) + j\hat{s}_d(t), \tag{2.303}$$

and

$$\tilde{s}_u(t) = s_u(t) + j\hat{s}_u(t). \tag{2.304}$$

By making use of the Hilbert transform relations

$$E[x_{Q_i}(t)\hat{s}_d(t)] = E[\hat{x}_{I_i}(t)\hat{s}_d(t)] = E[x_{I_i}(t)s_d(t)] \tag{2.305}$$

and

$$E[x_{I_i}(t)\hat{s}_d(t)] = -E[\hat{x}_{I_i}(t)s_d(t)] = -E[x_{Q_i}(t)s_d(t)], \tag{2.306}$$

we find

$$\begin{aligned}
E[\tilde{x}_i^*(t)\tilde{s}_d(t)] &= E\{[x_{I_i}(t) - jx_{Q_i}(t)][s_d(t) + j\hat{s}_d(t)]\} \\
&= E\{x_{I_i}(t)s_d(t) + x_{Q_i}(t)\hat{s}_d(t) \\
&\quad + j[x_{I_i}(t)\hat{s}_d(t) - x_{Q_i}(t)s_d(t)]\} \\
&= 2E[x_{I_i}(t)s_d(t)] - j2E[x_{Q_i}(t)s_d(t)]. \tag{2.307}
\end{aligned}$$

Similarly,

$$E[\tilde{x}_i^*(t)\tilde{s}_u(t)] = 2E[x_{I_i}(t)s_u(t)] - j2E[x_{Q_i}(t)s_u(t)]. \tag{2.308}$$

Therefore, Eqs. (2.299) and (2.300) are equivalent to

$$\frac{dw_i}{dt} = k\frac{P_d}{P_u}\tilde{x}_i^*(t)\left[\frac{1}{P_d}\tilde{s}_d(t) - \frac{1}{P_u}\tilde{s}_u(t)\right]. \tag{2.309}$$

This equation corresponds to the feedback loop shown in Fig. 2.30.

Note that a major problem with the feedback in Eq. (2.309) is that we must determine $\tilde{s}_d(t)$ and $\tilde{s}_u(t)$. Since these are the desired and undesired components of the array output signal, we have inserted a black box after the array output in Fig. 2.30 labeled "signal separator." The function of this box is to separate $\tilde{s}_d(t)$ and $\tilde{s}_u(t)$. In general, however, it is not clear how such an operation could be performed. We will return to this problem below.

First, however, let us discuss the steady-state weights achieved by the Shor array. In the steady state, Eq. (2.309) requires

$$E\left\{\tilde{x}_i^*(t)\left[\frac{1}{P_d}\tilde{s}_d(t) - \frac{1}{P_u}\tilde{s}_u(t)\right]\right\} = 0. \tag{2.310}$$

But since

$$\tilde{s}_d(t) = \mathbf{X}_d^T\mathbf{W} \tag{2.311}$$

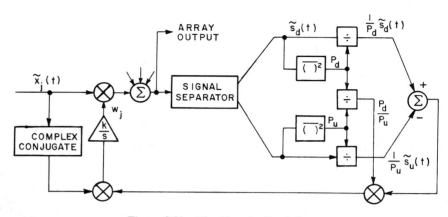

Figure 2.30   The Shor feedback loop.

and

$$\tilde{s}_u(t) = \mathbf{X}_u^T \mathbf{W}, \qquad (2.312)$$

Eq. (2.310) is equivalent to

$$E\left[\mathbf{X}^*\left(\frac{1}{P_d}\mathbf{X}_d^T\mathbf{W} - \frac{1}{P_u}\mathbf{X}_u^T\mathbf{W}\right)\right] = \frac{1}{P_d}\mathbf{\Phi}_d\mathbf{W} - \frac{1}{P_u}\mathbf{\Phi}_u\mathbf{W} = 0, \qquad (2.313)$$

where we have used

$$E\left(\mathbf{X}^*\mathbf{X}_d^T\right) = \mathbf{\Phi}_d \qquad (2.314)$$

and

$$E\left(\mathbf{X}^*\mathbf{X}_u^T\right) = \mathbf{\Phi}_u = \mathbf{\Phi}_i + \mathbf{\Phi}_n. \qquad (2.315)$$

Moreover,

$$P_d = \tfrac{1}{2}E\left\{\left|\mathbf{X}_d^T\mathbf{W}\right|^2\right\} = \tfrac{1}{2}\mathbf{W}^\dagger\mathbf{\Phi}_d\mathbf{W} \qquad (2.316)$$

and

$$P_u = \tfrac{1}{2}E\left\{\left|\mathbf{X}_u^T\mathbf{W}\right|^2\right\} = \tfrac{1}{2}\mathbf{W}^\dagger\mathbf{\Phi}_u\mathbf{W}, \qquad (2.317)$$

so Eq. (2.313) may be written

$$\frac{\mathbf{\Phi}_d\mathbf{W}}{\mathbf{W}^\dagger\mathbf{\Phi}_d\mathbf{W}} = \frac{\mathbf{\Phi}_u\mathbf{W}}{\mathbf{W}^\dagger\mathbf{\Phi}_u\mathbf{W}}. \qquad (2.318)$$

Now let us verify that the maximum SINR solution,

$$\mathbf{W} = \mu\mathbf{\Phi}_u^{-1}\mathbf{U}_d^*, \qquad (2.319)$$

is the solution to Eq. (2.318). Assuming narrowband signals, we have

$$\mathbf{X}_d = a\mathbf{U}_d \tag{2.320}$$

and

$$\boldsymbol{\Phi}_d = E[|a|^2]\mathbf{U}_d^*\mathbf{U}_d^T. \tag{2.321}$$

Substituting Eqs. (2.319) through (2.321) into the left-hand side of Eq. (2.318) gives

$$\frac{\boldsymbol{\Phi}_d\mathbf{W}}{\mathbf{W}^\dagger\boldsymbol{\Phi}_d\mathbf{W}} = \frac{\mu E[|a|^2]\mathbf{U}_d^*\mathbf{U}_d^T\boldsymbol{\Phi}_u^{-1}\mathbf{U}_d^*}{\mu\mathbf{U}_d^T(\boldsymbol{\Phi}_u^{-1})^\dagger E[|a|^2]\mathbf{U}_d^*\mathbf{U}_d^T\boldsymbol{\Phi}_u^{-1}\mathbf{U}_d^*}$$

$$= \frac{\mathbf{U}_d^*}{\mu\mathbf{U}_d^T(\boldsymbol{\Phi}_u^{-1})^\dagger\mathbf{U}_d^*}, \tag{2.322}$$

and substituting them into the right-hand side gives

$$\frac{\boldsymbol{\Phi}_u\mathbf{W}}{\mathbf{W}^\dagger\boldsymbol{\Phi}_u\mathbf{W}} = \frac{\mu\boldsymbol{\Phi}_u\boldsymbol{\Phi}_u^{-1}\mathbf{U}_d^*}{\mu^2\mathbf{U}_d^T(\boldsymbol{\Phi}_u^{-1})^\dagger\boldsymbol{\Phi}_u\boldsymbol{\Phi}_u^{-1}\mathbf{U}_d^*}$$

$$= \frac{\mathbf{U}_d^*}{\mu\mathbf{U}_d^T(\boldsymbol{\Phi}_u^{-1})^\dagger\mathbf{U}_d^*}. \tag{2.323}$$

Thus, Eq. (2.319) is the steady-state solution of Eq. (2.309), and the Shor array will yield maximum SINR, just as the Applebaum array will.

Difficulties with the Shor Array

The Shor array has not received as much attention as the LMS and Applebaum arrays, presumably because it is more complicated than these arrays. The first difficulty faced by a designer is, of course, the "signal separator" in Fig. 2.30. While it may be possible to perform this operation with highly structured signals, such as spread spectrum signals [19, 20], it is certainly not obvious how to proceed with arbitrary signals.[‡] Of course, we must do a similar thing to use the LMS array in a communication system. With the LMS array, we must obtain a reference signal that is correlated with the desired signal and uncorrelated with the interference. Such a signal is usually obtained by performing signal-processing operations on the array output signal. (Methods of obtaining reference signals are discussed in Chapter 7.) However, for the Shor array, the problem is more complicated because we must estimate both the desired and the undesired signal. Moreover, the Shor feedback loop is also more complicated than the LMS or Applebaum loop.

---

‡Bakhru and Torrieri [21] have recently applied a version of the Shor algorithm, which they call the Maximin algorithm, to frequency-hopped signals.

Another difficulty with the Shor array is that its behavior is difficult to analyze mathematically. If Eq. (2.309) is rearranged, using the same substitutions as in Eqs. (2.311) through (2.317), one finds that the weight vector satisfies the differential equation

$$\frac{d\mathbf{W}}{dt} - k\frac{\mathbf{W}^{\dagger}\mathbf{\Phi}_d\mathbf{W}}{\mathbf{W}^{\dagger}\mathbf{\Phi}_u\mathbf{W}}\left[\frac{\mathbf{\Phi}_d\mathbf{W}}{\mathbf{W}^{\dagger}\mathbf{\Phi}_d\mathbf{W}} - \frac{\mathbf{\Phi}_u\mathbf{W}}{\mathbf{W}^{\dagger}\mathbf{\Phi}_u\mathbf{W}}\right] = 0. \qquad (2.324)$$

Because this equation is highly nonlinear, it is not easy to deduce general results about the nature of the transient solutions. However, one point is easily seen. Since Eq. (2.324) is homogeneous, the final value of the weight vector is determined only to within a constant multiplier. [If $\mathbf{W}$ is a steady-state solution of Eq. (2.324), then so is $c\mathbf{W}$, where c is an arbitrary constant.] Consequently, the final weight vector depends on the initial weight vector (in contrast to the LMS and Applebaum arrays, where the final weight vector is determined only by the signals). An undefined steady-state weight vector is a problem in a hardware implementation of the array. In a practical system, the weights have only a finite linear range, and the designer must insure that the weights settle within this linear range.

Now we turn to another subject—the discrete equivalents of the LMS and Applebaum arrays. The three arrays discussed so far, the LMS, Applebaum, and Shor arrays, have all been introduced with continuous control loops. However, any of them can also be implemented in discrete form. (In fact, the LMS and Shor arrays were originally presented in discrete form [4, 5].) In the next section we will discuss the discrete versions of the LMS and Applebaum arrays. (We shall not consider the discrete Shor array.)

2.4 THE DISCRETE LMS ARRAY

The feedback loop for the LMS array is shown in Fig. 2.8 and is described by the equation

$$\frac{dw_i}{dt} = k\tilde{x}_i^*(t)\tilde{\varepsilon}(t). \qquad (2.325)$$

Let us suppose that in Eq. (2.325) all signals are sampled every Δt seconds. Let $w_i(n)$, $\tilde{x}_i(n)$, and $\tilde{\varepsilon}(n)$ denote the values of $w_i(t)$, $\tilde{x}_i(t)$, and $\tilde{\varepsilon}(t)$ at sample times t_n:

$$t_n = n\Delta t. \qquad (2.326)$$

Furthermore, let us approximate the derivative dw_i/dt in Eq. (2.325) by the first difference,

$$\frac{dw_i}{dt} \cong \frac{w_i(n+1) - w_i(n)}{\Delta t}. \qquad (2.327)$$

Then Eq. (2.325) may be rearranged into the form

$$w_i(n+1) = w_i(n) + k\Delta t\, \tilde{x}_i^*(n)\tilde{\varepsilon}(n).$$ (2.328)

It is convenient to absorb Δt into the gain constant by defining

$$\gamma = k\Delta t.$$ (2.329)

Thus the discrete version of the LMS feedback equation is

$$w_i(n+1) = w_i(n) + \gamma\tilde{x}_i^*(n)\tilde{\varepsilon}(n),$$ (2.330)

which is called the *LMS algorithm*. Equation (2.330) is the complex form of the algorithm. It is equivalent to the real form

$$w_{P_i}(n+1) = w_{P_i}(n) + \gamma x_{P_i}(n)\varepsilon(n),$$ (2.331)

where $P = I$ or Q. This is the form introduced by Widrow et al. [5].

The LMS algorithm is a recursive equation that allows the value of each weight w_{P_i} at the $(n+1)$st sample to be calculated from its value at the nth sample, using the signals at the nth sample. The sampled error signal in Eq. (2.331) is obtained from the sampled reference signal and array output,

$$\varepsilon(n) = r(n) - s(n) = r(n) - \sum_{\substack{j=1 \\ P=I,Q}}^{N} w_{P_j}(n)x_{P_j}(n).$$ (2.332)

Stability

An important difference between the LMS algorithm in discrete form and the continuous feedback loop presented earlier is that the sampling can cause instability in the weights. To see this difference, consider first a one-dimensional continuous LMS loop, as shown in Fig. 2.31. (Consider a complex loop.) This loop is described by the differential equation

$$\frac{dw}{dt} = k\tilde{x}^*(t)[\tilde{r}(t) - \tilde{s}(t)],$$ (2.333)

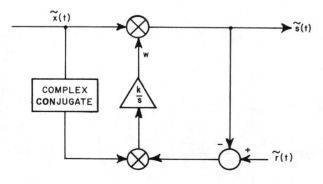

Figure 2.31   A one-dimensional LMS loop.

or after substituting $\tilde{s}(t) = w\tilde{x}(t)$ and rearranging,

$$\frac{dw}{dt} + k|\tilde{x}(t)|^2 w = k\tilde{x}^*(t)\tilde{r}(t). \tag{2.334}$$

Assuming the weights react to the average values of $|\tilde{x}(t)|^2$ and $\tilde{x}^*(t)\tilde{r}(t)$, we define

$$p = E\left[|\tilde{x}(t)|^2\right] \tag{2.335}$$

and

$$q = E\left[|\tilde{x}^*(t)\tilde{r}(t)|\right]. \tag{2.336}$$

Then w satisfies the differential equation

$$\frac{dw}{dt} + kpw = kq. \tag{2.337}$$

We may view w as the output from a linear continuous filter with transfer function

$$H(s) = \frac{k}{s + kp} \tag{2.338}$$

and with input q, as shown in Fig. 2.32(a). (s is complex frequency.) This filter has a single pole on the negative real axis at

$$s = -kp, \tag{2.339}$$

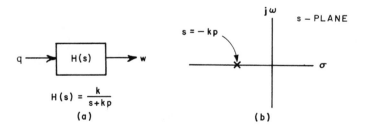

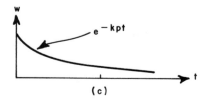

Figure 2.32 Interpretation of continuous LMS loop. (a) Linear continuous filter; (b) single pole in the s-plane; (c) a typical weight transient.

as shown in Fig. 2.32(b). With a given signal power $p = E[|\tilde{x}(t)|^2]$, increasing the loop gain k moves the pole farther to the left. A typical transient response from the filter will be an exponential as shown in Fig. 2.32(c). The important point here is to note that the filter is stable for all loop gains k.

Now consider a one-dimensional discrete LMS equation. The weight $w(n)$ satisfies the difference equation

$$w(n + 1) = w(n) + \gamma \tilde{x}^*(n)[\tilde{r}(n) - \tilde{s}(n)]. \tag{2.340}$$

Substituting again for $\tilde{s}(n)$ and rearranging gives

$$w(n + 1) + \left[\gamma|\tilde{x}(n)|^2 - 1\right]w(n) = \gamma \tilde{x}^*(n)\tilde{r}(n). \tag{2.341}$$

Now replacing $|\tilde{x}(n)|^2$ and $\tilde{x}^*(n)\tilde{r}(n)$ with their average values yields

$$w(n + 1) + [\gamma p - 1]w(n) = \gamma q. \tag{2.342}$$

Let $W(z)$ be the z-transform of $w(n)$:

$$W(z) = \sum_{n=0}^{\infty} w(n)z^{-n}. \tag{2.343}$$

Taking the z-transform of Eq. (2.342) yields

$$[z + (\gamma p - 1)]W(z) = \gamma Q(z), \tag{2.344}$$

where $Q(z)$ is the z-transform of q. Thus, in this case $w(n)$ may be viewed as the output of a linear discrete filter $H(z)$,

$$H(z) = \frac{\gamma}{z + (\gamma p - 1)}, \tag{2.345}$$

as shown in Fig. 2.33(a). This filter has a pole at

$$z = 1 - \gamma p, \tag{2.346}$$

as shown in Fig. 2.33(b). For $\gamma = 0$, this pole is at $z = 1$, and as γ increases, the pole moves to the left. Clearly, if

$$\gamma p > 2, \tag{2.347}$$

the pole moves outside the unit circle, and the algorithm in Eq. (2.342) becomes unstable. Thus, to obtain stability, we must restrict γ to the range

$$0 < \gamma < \frac{2}{p}. \tag{2.348}$$

A typical transient response of Eq. (2.342), with a single pole at $z = 1 - \gamma p$, is of the form

$$w(n) = (1 - \gamma p)^n. \tag{2.349}$$

This response has several forms, depending on $1 - \gamma p$. When $0 < 1 - \gamma p < 1$, the response is a declining geometric series as shown in Fig. 2.33(c). It is similar

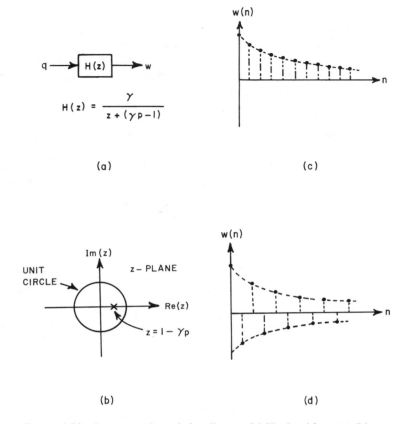

Figure 2.33 Interpretation of the discrete LMS algorithm. (a) Linear discrete filter; (b) pole in the z-plane; (c) $w(n)$ for $0 < 1 - \gamma P < 1$; (d) $w(n)$ for $-1 < 1 - \gamma P < 0$.

to the simple exponential decay in Fig. 2.32(c). For $-1 < 1 - \gamma p < 0$, however, the transient response is a geometric series with alternating signs, as shown in Fig. 2.33(d). Finally, if $1 - \gamma p < -1$, it is an alternating series with a growing value, and the algorithm is unstable.

When the discrete LMS algorithm is used to control the weights in an array, it may not be enough simply to keep the weights stable. A transient response with alternating signs, as in Fig. 2.33(d), is not good. The problem is that such a transient response increases the weight variance over what it would be with the type of response shown in Fig. 2.33(c). For this reason, it is preferable to impose the more stringent requirement

$$0 < \gamma < \frac{1}{p} \tag{2.350}$$

on the loop gain. Equation (2.350) keeps the pole in the right half plane, so that transients as in Fig. 2.33(c) result.

The discrete LMS algorithm is sometimes used to simulate the behavior of the continuous LMS loop. In this case we must also choose γ to satisfy Eq. (2.350). Otherwise, the weight transients computed will not be similar to the exponential response in Fig. 2.32(c).

Now let us consider the stability problem with more than one weight. Suppose first we have a continuous LMS array with several loops. The weight vector in the array will satisfy Eq. (2.86):

$$\frac{d\mathbf{W}}{dt} + k\mathbf{\Phi W} = k\mathbf{S}. \tag{2.351}$$

This has transient solutions of the form

$$\mathbf{S}(t) = \mathbf{C}_1 e^{-k\lambda_1 t} + \mathbf{C}_2 e^{-k\lambda_2 t} + \cdots + \mathbf{\Phi}^{-1}\mathbf{S}, \tag{2.352}$$

where the λ_i are the eigenvalues of the covariance matrix $\mathbf{\Phi}$ [see Eq. (2.94)]. However, since $\mathbf{\Phi}$ is positive definite, we know that

$$\lambda_i > 0 \quad \text{for all } i. \tag{2.353}$$

Therefore, all of the exponentials in Eq. (2.352) are stable, regardless of the loop gain k.

For the discrete array with multiple weights, the weight vector obeys the difference equation

$$\mathbf{W}(n + 1) = \mathbf{W}(n) + \gamma \mathbf{X}^*\big[r(n) - \mathbf{X}^T\mathbf{W}(n)\big]. \tag{2.354}$$

Substituting $\mathbf{\Phi}$ for $\mathbf{X}^*\mathbf{X}^T$ and $\mathbf{S}$ for $\mathbf{X}^*\tilde{r}$ and rearranging gives the vector difference equation

$$\mathbf{W}(n + 1) + \big[\gamma\mathbf{\Phi} - \mathbf{I}\big]\mathbf{W}(n) = \gamma\mathbf{S}. \tag{2.355}$$

By rotating coordinates to diagonalize $\gamma\mathbf{\Phi} - \mathbf{I}$, we can convert this to a set of uncoupled scalar equations similar to Eq. (2.342). Each scalar equation will have a transient solution similar to Eq. (2.349). Rotating coordinates back to $\mathbf{W}$, we find that the solutions to Eq. (2.355) are of the form

$$\mathbf{W}(n) = \sum_{i=1}^{N} \mathbf{C}_i(1 - \gamma\lambda_i)^n + \mathbf{\Phi}^{-1}\mathbf{S}. \tag{2.356}$$

To keep *every* term in the transient response stable, we must choose γ so that

$$-1 < 1 - \gamma\lambda_i < 1, \tag{2.357}$$

for every λ_i. If γ is chosen so that

$$-1 < 1 - \gamma\lambda_{\max} < 1, \tag{2.358}$$

where $\lambda_{\max}$ is the maximum eigenvalue,

$$\lambda_{\max} = \max_i \big[\lambda_i\big], \tag{2.359}$$

then Eq. (2.357) will be satisfied for all λ_i. Equation (2.358) is equivalent to

$$0 < \gamma < \frac{2}{\lambda_{max}}. \qquad (2.360)$$

It is helpful to replace the upper bound for γ with a more simply calculated quantity. To this end, we note that

$$\lambda_{max} \leqslant \sum_{i=1}^{N} \lambda_i = \text{trace } \Phi = \sum_{i=1}^{N} E\left[|\tilde{x}_i(n)|^2\right], \qquad (2.361)$$

since the trace is invariant under an orthogonal coordinate rotation. However, the last sum is just the total power received by the array,

$$P_t = \sum_{i=1}^{N} E\left[|\tilde{x}_i(n)|^2\right]. \qquad (2.362)$$

Hence we can insure stability in the discrete array by choosing

$$0 < \gamma < \frac{2}{P_t}. \qquad (2.363)$$

To obtain a more acceptable weight variance, however, we usually constrain γ to the more restricted range

$$0 < \gamma < \frac{1}{P_t}, \qquad (2.364)$$

which keeps all poles associated with Eq. (2.355) in the right half z-plane.

An Example

Now let us show an example of some weight transients computed with the discrete algorithm. We return to the case considered in Example 1 on page 23. Figure 2.34 shows three sets of transients computed for the same array, a two-element array with half-wavelength element spacing and isotropic element patterns, as shown in Fig. 2.9. The element signals are given by Eqs. (2.95) to (2.98) and the reference signal by Eq. (2.104). The weight transients are computed from Eq. (2.331) starting with the initial values

$$w_{I_1}(0) = w_{Q_1}(0) = w_{I_2}(0) = w_{Q_2}(0) = 1. \qquad (2.365)$$

The other parameter values used are the same as in Example 1 [see Eqs. (2.157) and (2.158)]. Figure 2.34 shows the results for three different values of loop gain γ. Figure 2.34(a) shows $\gamma = 0.1$, Fig. 2.34(b) shows $\gamma = 0.5$, and Fig. 2.34(c) shows $\gamma = 1.5$. The results in Fig. 2.34(a) may be compared with those in Fig. 2.13, which resulted with continuous LMS loops. A loop gain of $\gamma = 0.1$ is low enough that the weight transients are well behaved and look very similar to

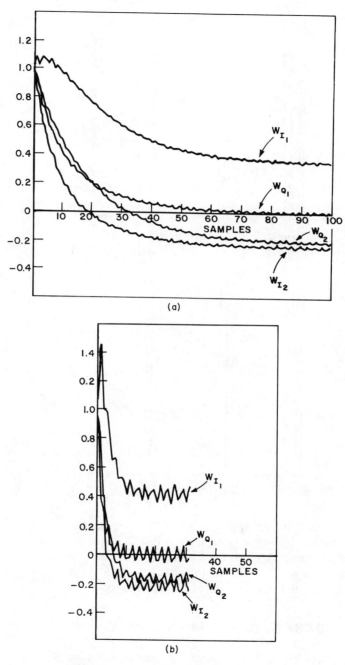

Figure 2.34 Discrete weight
transients for Example 1. (a) $\gamma = 0.1$;
(b) $\gamma = 0.5$.

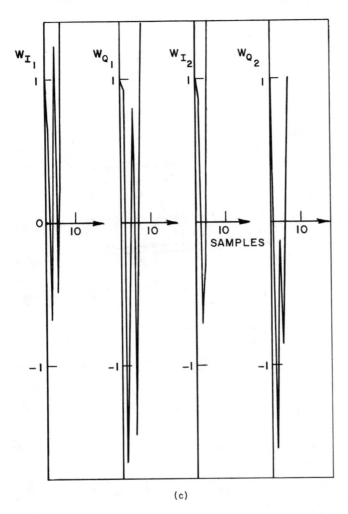

(c)   **Figure 2.34**   (*continued*) (c) $\gamma = 1.5$.

those for the continuous loops. If the loop gain is increased to $\gamma = 0.5$, the loops are still stable, as may be seen in Fig. 2.34(b), but the response time of the array has been reduced and the weight variance has been increased. Finally, when γ is increased to 1.5, the weights have become unstable. Figure 2.34(c) shows the results of the first few iterations for this case.

2.5 THE DISCRETE APPLEBAUM ARRAY

The Applebaum array can be put in discrete form in the same way. The resulting algorithm was first presented by Griffiths [22]. The equations are virtually identical to the LMS algorithm, except that the steering vector μT^*

replaces the vector **S**. The weights in the Applebaum loop of Fig. 2.29 satisfy the equation,

$$\frac{dw_i}{dt} = k\left[\mu t_i^* - \tilde{x}_i^*(t)\tilde{s}(t)\right], \tag{2.366}$$

where **T** is the steering vector with components t_i,

$$\mathbf{T} = \left[t_1, t_2, \ldots\right]^T. \tag{2.367}$$

Replacing dw_i/dt by the first difference in Eq. (2.327) gives

$$w_i(n+1) - w_i(n) = k\Delta t\left[\mu t_i^* - \tilde{x}_i^*(n)\tilde{s}(n)\right], \tag{2.368}$$

or, from Eq. (2.329),

$$w_i(n+1) = w_i(n) + \gamma\mu t_i^* - \gamma\tilde{x}_i^*(n)\tilde{s}(n). \tag{2.369}$$

Equation (3.369) is the complex form of the discrete Applebaum feedback. It is equivalent to the real form

$$w_{P_i}(n+1) = w_{P_i}(n) + \gamma\mu t_{P_i} - \gamma x_{P_i}(n)s(n), \tag{2.370}$$

where $P = I$ or Q. The use of these equations is identical to that of the discrete LMS array.

When Eq. (2.369) is written in vector form, we have

$$\mathbf{W}(n+1) = \mathbf{W}(n) + \gamma\mu\mathbf{T}^* - \gamma\mathbf{X}^*(n)\tilde{s}(n). \tag{2.371}$$

Substituting $\tilde{s} = \mathbf{X}^T\mathbf{W}$ and rearranging gives

$$\mathbf{W}(n+1) + \left[\gamma\mathbf{X}^*\mathbf{X}^T - \mathbf{I}\right]\mathbf{W}(n) = \gamma\mu\mathbf{T}^*, \tag{2.372}$$

or, after replacing $\mathbf{X}^*\mathbf{X}^T$ with $\mathbf{\Phi}$,

$$\mathbf{W}(n+1) + \left[\gamma\mathbf{\Phi} - \mathbf{I}\right]\mathbf{W}(n) = \gamma\mu\mathbf{T}^*. \tag{2.373}$$

If this equation is compared with Eq. (2.355), it is obvious that the range of γ for stable operation is the same,

$$0 < \gamma < \frac{2}{P_t}, \tag{2.374}$$

where P_t is the total received power, defined in Eq. (2.371). In general, the weight transients resulting with this algorithm are similar to those in Fig. 2.34.

We have now discussed the continuous and discrete LMS and Applebaum arrays, and also the continuous Shor array. These array concepts were the original contributions in this field. In Chapter 5, we shall present some additional techniques for weight control in adaptive arrays. First, however, in Chapters 3 and 4 we shall discuss various performance characteristics and limitations of the LMS and Applebaum arrays.

PROBLEMS

2.1. Determine the appropriate form of the complex LMS algorithm, that is,

$$\frac{dw_j}{dt} = ?,$$

if one starts with the definition,

$$w_j = w_{I_j} + jw_{Q_j},$$

instead of Eq. (2.53). Assume $\tilde{x}_j(t)$ is still defined by Eq. (2.52),

$$\tilde{x}_j(t) = x_{I_j}(t) + jx_{Q_j}(t).$$

Draw a block diagram of the resulting complex feedback loop. Determine a differential equation for the weight vector,

$$\mathbf{W} = [w_1, w_2, \ldots, w_N]^T,$$

analogous to Eq. (2.83). Obtain the steady-state solution of this equation in a form similar to Eq. (2.87), and show that this solution leads to the same values of w_{I_j} and w_{Q_j} as Eq. (2.87).

2.2. Show that the inverse of the matrix

$$\mathbf{\Phi} = \mathbf{B} - \beta \mathbf{Z}^* \mathbf{Z}^T,$$

is

$$\mathbf{\Phi}^{-1} = \mathbf{B}^{-1} - \tau \mathbf{B}^{-1} \mathbf{Z}^* \mathbf{Z}^T \mathbf{B}^{-1},$$

where $\mathbf{B}$ is a nonsingular $N \times N$ matrix, $\mathbf{Z}$ is an $N \times 1$ column vector, and β and τ are scalars related by

$$\tau^{-1} + \beta^{-1} = \mathbf{Z}^T \mathbf{B}^{-1} \mathbf{Z}^*. \qquad \tau = \frac{1}{Z^+ B^{-1} Z - \beta^{-1}}$$

2.3. An LMS adaptive array has three isotropic elements spaced along a line a half wavelength apart. A CW desired signal is received from angle θ_d off broadside, as shown in Fig. 2.35. This desired signal produces a received power A_d^2 behind each

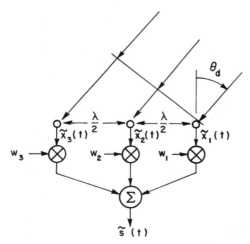

Figure 2.35 A three-element array.

element. Also, statistically independent thermal noise of power σ^2 is present on each signal $\tilde{x}_j(t)$. The reference signal is a CW signal coherent with the desired signal. Using the same notation as in Example 1, page 23, determine the steady-state weight vector, the output desired signal power, the output thermal noise power, and the output SNR. The matrix inversion lemma in Problem 2.2 will be helpful.

2.4. In some adaptive arrays, a quarter-wavelength delay line is used instead of a quadrature hybrid to obtain two signals "in quadrature" from each element, as shown in Fig. 2.36. Discuss the relationship between these two types of processing, and describe any important differences between them. For this purpose, assume the desired signal to be received has envelope and phase modulation, that is,

$$\tilde{d}(t) = a(t)e^{j[\omega_d t + \phi(t) + \psi_d]}.$$

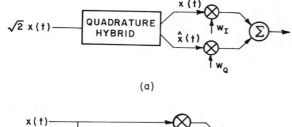

(a)

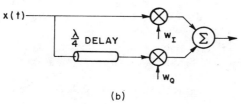

(b)

Figure 2.36 Two types of processing. (a) Quadrature hybrid processing; (b) delay-line processing.

2.5. For the two-element LMS array in Fig. 2.15 of Example 2, compute and draw graphs of P_d/σ^2, P_i/σ^2, P_n/σ^2, and SINR in dB versus θ_i, over the range $-90° \leqslant \theta_i \leqslant 90°$, for the following cases: $\xi_d = 0$ dB, $\theta_d = 0°$, $\xi_i = 40$ dB, and $R^2/2\sigma^2 = 0$ dB. Explain why the curves behave as they do.

2.6. Consider an array of two isotropic elements a half wavelength apart, as in Fig. 2.9. Assume a desired signal arriving from angle $\theta_d = 30°$ produces a signal in element 1 equal to

$$\tilde{x}_1(t) = e^{j\omega_d t}.$$

The reference signal in the array feedback is

$$\tilde{r}(t) = e^{j\omega_d t}.$$

Suppose the element signals $\tilde{x}_1(t)$ and $\tilde{x}_2(t)$ and the reference signal $\tilde{r}(t)$ are sampled every quarter cycle, with sample $n = 0$ corresponding to $t = 0$.

Compute the weight vector $\mathbf{W}(n)$ that results with the discrete LMS algorithm for $1 \leqslant n \leqslant 10$. Assume the loop gain γ is 0.1 and $\mathbf{W}(0) = [0, 0]^T$. Also, assume there is no noise in the array signals.

2.7. This problem shows a simple way to find the steady-state weight vector when the signals received by an array are CW.

(a) Suppose an N-element array receives a CW desired signal, and assume uncorrelated thermal noise is present on each element. Then the covariance matrix and reference correlation vector are given by

$$\mathbf{\Phi} = A_d^2 \mathbf{U}_d^* \, \mathbf{U}_d^T + \sigma^2 \mathbf{I},$$

and

$$\mathbf{S} = A_d R \mathbf{U}_d^*,$$

where

$$\mathbf{U}_d = \left[1, e^{-j\phi_d}, \ldots, e^{-j(N-1)\phi_d}\right]^T.$$

(All notation here is the same as in Chapter 2.) Show that a weight vector $\mathbf{W}$ of the form

$$\mathbf{W} = \alpha \mathbf{U}_d^*,$$

where α is a suitable constant, is a solution of $\mathbf{\Phi W} = \mathbf{S}$. Determine the proper value of α by substituting this $\mathbf{W}$ into $\mathbf{\Phi W} = \mathbf{S}$.

(b) Now suppose the array also receives a CW interference signal as well as the desired signal above. The covariance matrix is now

$$\mathbf{\Phi} = A_d^2 \mathbf{U}_d^* \mathbf{U}_d^T + A_i^2 \mathbf{U}_i^* \mathbf{U}_i^T + \sigma^2 \mathbf{I}.$$

The reference signal is the same as in part (a). Use an approach similar to that in part (a) to find the solution for $\mathbf{W}$ satisfying $\mathbf{\Phi W} = \mathbf{S}$. Determine any unknown constants in $\mathbf{W}$ by substituting $\mathbf{W}$ into $\mathbf{\Phi W} = \mathbf{S}$.

2.8. An array of N isotropic elements receives only a CW desired signal, which arrives from some angle. There is also uncorrelated thermal noise of equal power on each element. The reference signal is a CW signal correlated with the desired signal.

Prove that if the SNR on each element is ξ_d, the output SNR from the array is

$$\text{output SNR} = \frac{P_d}{P_n} = N\xi_d,$$

regardless of the signal arrival angle. (Hint: Use the result in problem 2.7.) Does it make any difference in this proof what the locations of the elements are?

2.9. Consider a four-element adaptive array with isotropic elements spaced a half wavelength apart along a line. Assume that a CW desired signal with amplitude A_d arrives from angle θ_d and that a CW interference signal with amplitude A_i arrives from angle θ_i. Also assume uncorrelated thermal noise of power σ^2 is present on each array element. The reference signal is a CW signal correlated with the desired signal.

Calculate and plot the normalized output powers P_d/σ^2, P_i/σ^2, and P_n/σ^2 and the SINR as functions of θ_d for $-90° \leq \theta_d \leq 90°$, for the following case: $\xi_d = 0$ dB, $\theta_i = 30°$, $\xi_i = 40$ dB, and $R^2/2\sigma^2 = 0$ dB.

Hint: Use the result in problem 2.7 to find the weight vector. Then the powers may be calculated from

$$\frac{P_d}{\sigma^2} = \frac{1}{2\sigma^2} \mathbf{W}^\dagger \left(A_d^2 \mathbf{U}_d^* \mathbf{U}_d^T\right) \mathbf{W} = \frac{\xi_d}{2} \left|\mathbf{U}_d^T \mathbf{W}\right|^2,$$

$$\frac{P_i}{\sigma^2} = \frac{1}{2\sigma^2} \mathbf{W}^\dagger \left(A_i^2 \mathbf{U}_i^* \mathbf{U}_i^T\right) \mathbf{W} = \frac{\xi_i}{2} \left|\mathbf{U}_i^T \mathbf{W}\right|^2,$$

and

$$\frac{P_n}{\sigma^2} = \frac{1}{2\sigma^2} \mathbf{W}^\dagger (\sigma^2 \mathbf{I}) \mathbf{W} = \tfrac{1}{2} |\mathbf{W}|^2.$$

2.10. Figure 2.28 shows the feedback loop originally suggested by Applebaum [2]. Figure 2.29 shows a better loop that yields the weight vector $\mathbf{W} = \mathbf{\Phi}^{-1}\mathbf{S}$ without the need for the loop gain G to be large.

Consider the two additional loops shown in Fig. 2.37(a) and (b). Determine whether either of these could be used instead and what the steady-state weight vector would be in each case.

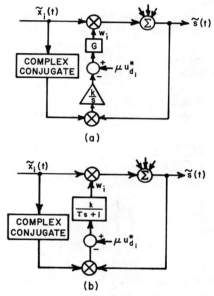

(a)

(b)

Figure 2.37 Modified loops.

2.11. A two-element adaptive array is to be operated with Applebaum feedback loops of the type shown in Fig. 2.29. The elements will be isotropic and a half wavelength apart. A desired signal is expected to arrive from broadside ($\theta_d = 0°$). Hence we use a steering vector

$$\mathbf{T}^* = \begin{bmatrix} 1 \\ 1 \end{bmatrix}$$

in the Applebaum loops, so that the quiescent pattern has a beam maximum at $\theta = 0°$.

Now suppose, however, that the desired signal does not actually arrive from broadside, but from some angle $\theta_d \neq 0°$ near broadside. The purpose of this problem is to determine how sensitive the array performance will be to such a pointing error.

Make the following assumptions:

1. Each element signal contains uncorrelated thermal noise as usual.

2. There is no interference.

3. The desired signal is CW and arrives from angle θ_d with input signal-to-noise ratio per element of ξ_d.
4. The steering vector $\mathbf{T}^* = [1, 1]^T$ is used.

Compute the output signal-to-noise ratio (SNR_{out}) from the array as a function of θ_d and ξ_d. Plot SNR_{out} versus θ_d for two cases: $\xi_d = 0$ dB and $\xi_d = 40$ dB.

Explain why the plots of SNR_{out} you obtain make sense physically. How does the sensitivity of the array to pointing error depend on signal power? If an SNR_{out} no less than 0 dB is required from the array, what pointing error θ_d can be tolerated with $\xi_d = 0$ dB and $\xi_d = 40$ dB?

2.12. Consider an LMS adaptive array with two isotropic elements a half wavelength apart, as in Examples 1 and 2 of Chapter 2. Suppose a CW desired signal arrives from broadside and a CW interference signal arrives from angle θ_i with respect to broadside. Assume there is uncorrelated thermal noise of power σ^2 on each element signal. Also, assume the input signal-to-noise ratio is ξ_d and the input interference-to-noise ratio is ξ_i.

Calculate the time constant spread that will occur in the LMS feedback loops as a function of ξ_d, ξ_i and θ_i. Draw a plot of the time constant spread versus θ_i for $\xi_d = 10$ dB and $\xi_i = 30$ dB.

2.13. Suppose an N-element array receives a single CW desired signal that produces a signal vector

$$\mathbf{X}_d = e^{j\omega_d t} \begin{bmatrix} a_1 \\ a_2 e^{-j\phi_2} \\ \vdots \\ a_N e^{-j\phi_N} \end{bmatrix}.$$

Because of element pattern effects, the a_i are all different coefficients. In addition, suppose each element output contains uncorrelated thermal noise. Suppose the noise power behind element i is σ_i^2, that is,

$$E\left[\tilde{n}_i^*(t)\tilde{n}_j(t)\right] = \sigma_i^2 \delta_{ij},$$

where the σ_i^2 are not necessarily equal.

Determine the array weights that will yield maximum output signal-to-noise ratio from the array. These weights are known as *maximal ratio combiner* weights.

2.14. (a) Determine the discrete form of the complex Shor algorithm.

(b) Consider a one-dimensional form of the discrete algorithm obtained in part (a). Suppose the signal $\tilde{x}(t)$ has a desired part and an undesired part:

$$\tilde{x}(t) = \tilde{d}(t) + \tilde{u}(t).$$

Show that on the average the weight in a one-dimensional discrete Shor algorithm will remain constant. Give a physical explanation of why this result occurs.

REFERENCES

1. P. W. Howells, "Explorations in Fixed and Adaptive Resolution at GE and SURC," *IEEE Transactions on Antennas and Propagation*, AP–24, no. 5 (September 1976): 575.

2. S. P. Applebaum, "Adaptive Arrays," *IEEE Transactions on Antennas and Propagation*, AP–24, no. 5 (September 1976): 585.

3. S. P. Applebaum, "Adaptive Arrays," Syracuse University Research Corporation Report SPL TR 66–1, August 1966.

4. S. W. W. Shor, "Adaptive Technique to Discriminate against Coherent Noise in a Narrow-Band System," *Journal of the Acoustical Society of America*, 39, no. 1 (January 1966): 74.

5. B. Widrow, P. E. Mantey, L. J. Griffiths, and B. B. Goode, "Adaptive Antenna Systems," *Proceedings of the IEEE*, 55, no. 12 (December 1967): 2143.

6. N. Abramson, *Information Theory and Coding*, McGraw-Hill, New York, 1963.

7. F. B. Hildebrand, *Advanced Calculus for Engineers*, Prentice-Hall, 1956, sect. 1.4.

8. F. B. Hildebrand, *Introduction to Numerical Analysis*, McGraw-Hill, New York, 1974, pp. 285ff.

9. E. A. Guillemin, *The Mathematics of Circuit Analysis*, Wiley, New York, 1951, chap. 6, art. 22.

10. B. Widrow, J. McCool, and M. Ball, "The Complex LMS Algorithm," *Proceedings of the IEEE*, 63, no. 4 (April 1975): 719.

11. T. G. Kincaid, "The Complex Representation of Signals," Report No. R67EMHS, October 1966, General Electric Company, HMED Technical Publications, Box 1122 (LeMeyne Avenue), Syracuse, N.Y. 13201.

12. A. S. Al-Ruwais and R. T. Compton, Jr., "Adaptive Array Behavior with Sinusoidal Envelope Modulated Interference," *IEEE Transactions on Aerospace and Electronic Systems*, AES–19, no. 5 (September 1983): 677.

13. R. L. Riegler and R. T. Compton, Jr., "An Adaptive Array for Interference Rejection," *Proceedings of the IEEE*, 61, no. 6 (June 1973): 748. Copyright © 1973 IEEE.

14. R. T. Compton, Jr., "An Experimental Four-Element Adaptive Array," *IEEE Transactions on Antennas and Propagation*, AP–24, no. 5 (September 1976): 697.

15. W. Kaplan, *Advanced Calculus*, Addison-Wesley, Reading, Mass., 1952, p. 162.

16. C. A. Baird, Jr., and C. L. Zahm, "Performance Criteria for Narrowband Array Processing," *IEEE Conference on Decision and Control*, Miami Beach, Fla., December 15–17, 1971.

17. A. S. Householder, *The Theory of Matrices in Numerical Analysis*, Dover, New York, 1964, p. 123.

18. Numerous papers on array synthesis can be found in the Cumulative Index, *IEEE Transactions on Antennas and Propagation*, AP–17, no. 6, part II (1969), under "Arrays." For some typical papers, see A. Ishimaru, "Theory of Unequally-Spaced Arrays," *IEEE Transactions on Antennas and Propagation*, AP–10, no. 6 (November 1962): 691; M. T. Ma, "An Application of the Inverse z-Transform to the Synthesis of Linear Antenna Arrays," *IEEE Transactions on Antennas and Propagation*, AP–12, no. 6 (November

1964): 798; or M. T. Ma, *Theory and Application of Antenna Arrays*, Wiley, New York, 1974.

19. R. C. Dixon, *Spread Spectrum Systems*, Wiley, New York, 1976.

20. R. C. Dixon, ed., *Spread Spectrum Techniques*, IEEE Press, Institute of Electrical and Electronics Engineers, Inc., New York, 1976.

21. K. Bakhru and D. J. Torrieri, "The Maximin Algorithm for Adaptive Arrays and Frequency-Hopping Communications," *IEEE Transactions on Antennas and Propagation*, AP–32, no. 9 (September 1984): 919.

22. L. J. Griffiths, "A Simple Adaptive Algorithm for Real-Time Processing in Antenna Arrays," *Proceedings of the IEEE*, 57, no. 10 (October 1969): 1696.

3

Adaptive Array Performance Capabilities and Limitations

In Chapter 2 we have discussed several methods for weight control in an adaptive array. Our purpose there was simply to present the basic concepts. In this chapter, we shall discuss three factors that affect the performance obtainable with an adaptive array: degrees of freedom, bandwidth, and element patterns. These are basic limitations that affect any adaptive array. That is, they do not depend on the particular weight control technique used. In Chapter 4, we shall consider a number of additional practical limitations that occur when LMS or Applebaum feedback loops are used.

3.1 DEGREES OF FREEDOM

The first limitation a designer must be aware of is that an N-element array has only $N - 1$ degrees of freedom in its pattern. Thus there is a limit to the number of things an array pattern can do at one time.

Consider an N-element array as shown in Fig. 3.1. Assume a unit amplitude signal at frequency ω arrives from angle θ with respect to broadside. This signal produces the following signal vector in the array:

$$\mathbf{X} = e^{j\omega t}\begin{bmatrix} 1 & e^{-j\phi_2} & \cdots & e^{-j\phi_N} \end{bmatrix}^T. \tag{3.1}$$

Here we arbitrarily assume the signal on element 1 has zero phase. The variable ϕ_j is the phase shift between element 1 and element j,

$$\phi_j = \frac{2\pi L_j}{\lambda}\sin\theta, \tag{3.2}$$

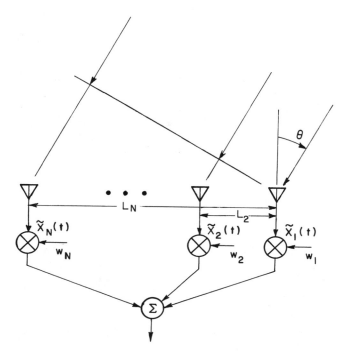

Figure 3.1 An N-element adaptive array.

where L_j is the separation between element 1 and element j, and λ is the wavelength at frequency ω. The signal from each element is multiplied by a complex weight w_j and summed to give the array output signal $\tilde{s}(t)$:

$$\tilde{s}(t) = \left[w_1 + w_2 e^{-j\phi_2} + \cdots + w_N e^{-j\phi_N} \right] e^{j\omega t}. \tag{3.3}$$

Let us define $f(\theta)$ to be the quantity in brackets,

$$f(\theta) = w_1 + w_2 e^{-j\phi_2} + \cdots + w_N e^{-j\phi_N}. \tag{3.4}$$

The function $f(\theta)$ is the voltage pattern of the array for any given set of w_j.

We observe first that we can factor one of the weights out of the expression for $f(\theta)$. For example, if we factor out w_1, we have

$$f(\theta) = w_1 \left[1 + \frac{w_2}{w_1} e^{-j\phi_2} + \cdots + \frac{w_N}{w_1} e^{-j\phi_N} \right]. \tag{3.5}$$

In this form, the dependence of $f(\theta)$ on θ is contained in the bracketed term. The factor w_1 has no effect on the *shape* of the pattern (i.e., its relative strength at different angles). It merely controls the overall amplitude and phase of the entire pattern. Since there are $N - 1$ coefficients $(w_2/w_1, w_3/w_1, \ldots, w_N/w_1)$ in the bracketed term, we see that there are $N - 1$ degrees of freedom in $f(\theta)$.

Let us consider this same idea from a different viewpoint. Suppose we want to have a pattern null at a particular angle θ_1. Then the weights w_j must be chosen so that

$$f(\theta_1) = w_1 + w_2 e^{-j\phi_2(\theta_1)} + \cdots + w_N e^{-j\phi_N(\theta_1)} = 0. \qquad (3.6)$$

This is a linear constraint relation between the weights w_j. Since this is only one equation in N unknowns, we can find nonzero solutions for the w_j (infinitely many of them) that satisfy Eq. (3.6).

Now suppose we want a second null at $\theta = \theta_2$, in addition to the one at $\theta = \theta_1$. Then we must choose the weights to satisfy

$$f(\theta_2) = w_1 + w_2 e^{-j\phi_2(\theta_2)} + \cdots + w_N e^{-j\theta_N(\theta_2)} = 0, \qquad (3.7)$$

as well as Eq. (3.6). For both nulls to occur simultaneously, the weights must satisfy both linear constraint equations. As long as $N \geqslant 3$, there will be nonzero solutions for the w_j satisfying both Eqs. (3.6) and (3.7).

Suppose that, instead of a null, we want a beam maximum at $\theta = \theta_2$. Let us express the array pattern $f(\theta)$ in Eq. (3.4) in terms of an amplitude pattern $a(\theta)$ and a phase pattern $\eta(\theta)$

$$f(\theta) = a(\theta) e^{j\eta(\theta)}. \qquad (3.8)$$

Then, since

$$\frac{df}{d\theta} = \left[\frac{da(\theta)}{d\theta} + ja(\theta) \frac{d\eta(\theta)}{d\theta} \right] e^{j\eta(\theta)}, \qquad (3.9)$$

we find that the condition

$$\left. \frac{df}{d\theta} \right|_{\theta=\theta_2} = 0 \qquad (3.10)$$

implies

$$\left[\frac{da(\theta)}{d\theta} + ja(\theta) \frac{d\eta(\theta)}{d\theta} \right]_{\theta=\theta_2} = 0, \qquad (3.11)$$

and hence [since both the real and imaginary parts of Eq. (3.11) must be zero],

$$\left. \frac{da(\theta)}{d\theta} \right|_{\theta=\theta_2} = 0. \qquad (3.12)$$

Therefore, the condition

$$\left. \frac{df}{d\theta} \right|_{\theta=\theta_2} = -j\phi_2'(\theta_2) w_2 e^{-j\phi_2(\theta_2)} \cdots -j\phi_N'(\theta_2) w_N e^{-j\phi_N(\theta_2)} = 0 \qquad (3.13)$$

will cause $a(\theta)$ to be maximum (or minimum) at $\theta = \theta_2$. Note that this is again a linear constraint relation between the w_j. Requiring a beam maximum at a given angle will "use up" one degree of freedom, the same as requiring a null.

Clearly, each null or beam maximum we want in the pattern $f(\theta)$ will yield an additional linear constraint equation between the w_j. Up to $N - 1$ such

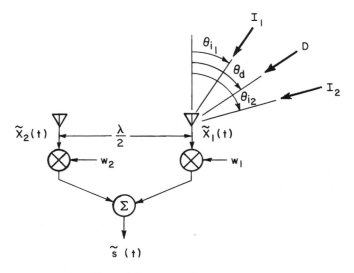

Figure 3.2   A two-element array.

equations can be satisfied with nonzero weights. If we try to impose N or more constraints, however, the only solution for the weights is $w_j = 0$ for all j, because the constraint equations are homogeneous. Thus, with N elements, we can have only $N - 1$ nulls or beam maxima and still have nonzero weights in the array.

Example

The preceding arguments explain why the number of degrees of freedom in an array are limited. However, they do not tell us what actually happens when the number of signals incident on an array exceeds the number of degrees of freedom. Moreover, Example 2 of Chapter 2 showed that when the array nulls an interference signal, the null depth is not infinitely deep as implied by Eq. (3.6) but in fact depends on interference power. Thus it is instructive to consider what actually happens when the number of degrees of freedom in an array is exceeded.

To this end, let us add an additional interference signal to Example 2 in Chapter 2. Consider the two-element array shown in Fig. 3.2. Assume the elements are isotropic and a half wavelength apart at the signal frequency. Suppose three CW signals are incident on the array, one desired and two interference. Also, assume uncorrelated thermal noise is present on each element signal. Thus the signal vector is

$$\mathbf{X} = \mathbf{X}_d + \mathbf{X}_{i1} + \mathbf{X}_{i2} + \mathbf{X}_n, \tag{3.14}$$

where

$$\mathbf{X}_d = A_d e^{j(\omega_d t + \psi_d)} \mathbf{U}_d, \tag{3.15}$$

$$\mathbf{X}_{i1} = A_{i1} e^{j(\omega_d t + \psi_{i1})} \mathbf{U}_{i1}, \tag{3.16}$$

$$\mathbf{X}_{i2} = A_{i2} e^{j(\omega_d t + \psi_{i2})} \mathbf{U}_{i2}, \tag{3.17}$$

and

$$\mathbf{X}_n = \begin{bmatrix} \tilde{n}_1(t) & \tilde{n}_2(t) \end{bmatrix}^T, \tag{3.18}$$

where

$$\mathbf{U}_d = \begin{bmatrix} 1 \\ e^{-j\phi_d} \end{bmatrix}, \tag{3.19}$$

$$\mathbf{U}_{i1} = \begin{bmatrix} 1 \\ e^{-j\phi_{i1}} \end{bmatrix}, \tag{3.20}$$

and

$$\mathbf{U}_{i2} = \begin{bmatrix} 1 \\ e^{-j\phi_{i2}} \end{bmatrix}, \tag{3.21}$$

and where ϕ_d, ϕ_{i1}, and ϕ_{i2} are the interelement phase shifts, related to the arrival angles θ_d, θ_{i1}, and θ_{i2} in the same way as in Eqs. (2.100) and (2.169). We assume $\mathbf{X}_d$, $\mathbf{X}_{i1}$, and $\mathbf{X}_{i2}$, and $\mathbf{X}_n$ are all statistically independent of each other. The covariance matrix $\mathbf{\Phi}$ is then

$$\mathbf{\Phi} = E(\mathbf{X}^*\mathbf{X}^T) = \sigma^2\mathbf{I} + A_d^2\mathbf{U}_d^*\mathbf{U}_d^T + A_{i1}^2\mathbf{U}_{i1}^*\mathbf{U}_{i1}^T + A_{i2}^2\mathbf{U}_{i2}^*\mathbf{U}_{i2}^T$$

$$= \begin{bmatrix} \sigma^2 + A_d^2 + A_{i1}^2 + A_{i2}^2 & A_d^2 e^{-j\phi_d} + A_{i1}^2 e^{-j\phi_{i1}} + A_{i2}^2 e^{-j\phi_{i2}} \\ A_d^2 e^{j\phi_d} + A_{i1}^2 e^{j\phi_{i1}} + A_{i2}^2 e^{j\phi_{i2}} & \sigma^2 + A_d^2 + A_{i1}^2 + A_{i2}^2 \end{bmatrix}. \tag{3.22}$$

As in Example 2 of Chapter 2, we assume the reference signal is correlated with the desired signal,

$$\tilde{r}(t) = \mathrm{Re}^{j(\omega_d t + \psi_d)}. \tag{3.23}$$

The reference correlation vector is then

$$\mathbf{S} = E[\mathbf{X}^*\tilde{r}(t)] = A_d R \mathbf{U}_d^*, \tag{3.24}$$

and the optimal weight vector in the array is given by

$$\mathbf{W} = \mathbf{\Phi}^{-1}\mathbf{S}. \tag{3.25}$$

The inverse of $\mathbf{\Phi}$ is found to be

$$\mathbf{\Phi}^{-1} = \frac{1}{D} \begin{bmatrix} \sigma^2 + A_d^2 + A_{i1}^2 + A_{i2}^2 & -A_d^2 e^{-j\phi_d} - A_{i1}^2 e^{-j\phi_{i1}} - A_{i2}^2 e^{-j\phi_{i2}} \\ -A_d^2 e^{j\phi_d} - A_{i1}^2 e^{j\phi_{i1}} - A_{i2}^2 e^{j\phi_{i2}} & \sigma^2 + A_d^2 + A_{i1}^2 + A_{i2}^2 \end{bmatrix}, \tag{3.26}$$

where D is the determinant of $\mathbf{\Phi}$,

$$D = \left(\sigma^2 + A_d^2 + A_{i1}^2 + A_{i2}^2\right)^2 - |A_d^2 e^{j\phi_d} + A_{i1}^2 e^{j\phi_{i1}} + A_{i2}^2 e^{j\phi_{i2}}|^2. \tag{3.27}$$

Solving for the weight vector in Eq. (3.25), we find

$$\mathbf{W} = \frac{A_d R}{D} \begin{bmatrix} \sigma^2 + A_{i1}^2\left[1 - e^{j(\phi_d - \phi_{i1})}\right] + A_{i2}^2\left[1 - e^{j(\phi_d - \phi_{i2})}\right] \\ -A_{i1}^2 e^{j\phi_{i1}} - A_{i2}^2 e^{j\phi_{i2}} + \left(\sigma^2 + A_{i1}^2 + A_{i2}^2\right)e^{j\phi_d} \end{bmatrix} \tag{3.28}$$

or, after dividing by σ^4,

$$\mathbf{W} = \frac{\sqrt{\xi_d}\,(R/\sigma)}{D/\sigma^4} \begin{bmatrix} 1 + \xi_{i1}\left[1 - e^{j(\phi_d - \phi_{i1})}\right] + \xi_{i2}\left[1 - e^{j(\phi_d - \phi_{i2})}\right] \\ -\xi_{i1} e^{j\phi_{i1}} - \xi_{i2} e^{j\phi_{i2}} + \left(1 + \xi_{i1} + \xi_{i2}\right)e^{j\phi_d} \end{bmatrix}. \tag{3.29}$$

where ξ_{i1} and ξ_{i2} are INRs similar to that in Eq. (2.172): $\xi_{i1} = A_{i1}^2/\sigma^2$, $\xi_{i2} = A_{i2}^2/\sigma^2$.

From $\mathbf{W}$, the array pattern and the output powers of the various signals may be computed. To calculate the pattern, we assume a unit amplitude test signal propagating into the array from angle θ. This signal produces an output signal

$$\tilde{s}(t) = \mathbf{W}^T \mathbf{X} = e^{j(\omega_d t + \psi_d)} \mathbf{W}^T \begin{bmatrix} 1 \\ e^{-j\phi} \end{bmatrix} = e^{j(\omega_d t + \psi_d)}\left[w_1 + w_2 e^{-j\phi}\right]. \tag{3.30}$$

where $\phi = \pi \sin\theta$. The voltage pattern is then given by $|\tilde{s}(t)|$ as a function of θ. The output powers are calculated as follows. The output desired signal is

$$\tilde{s}_d(t) = \mathbf{W}^T \mathbf{X}_d = A_d e^{j(\omega_d t + \psi_d)}\left[w_1 + w_2 e^{-j\phi_d}\right], \tag{3.31}$$

and therefore the output desired signal power is

$$P_d = \tfrac{1}{2} E\left[|\tilde{s}_d(t)|^2\right] = \frac{A_d^2}{2}|w_1 + w_2 e^{-j\phi_d}|^2. \tag{3.32}$$

Similarly, the output interference powers are

$$P_{i1} = \frac{A_{i1}^2}{2}|w_1 + w_2 e^{-j\phi_{i1}}|^2,$$

$$\tag{3.33}$$

$$P_{i2} = \frac{A_{i2}^2}{2}|w_1 + w_2 e^{-j\phi_{i2}}|^2.$$

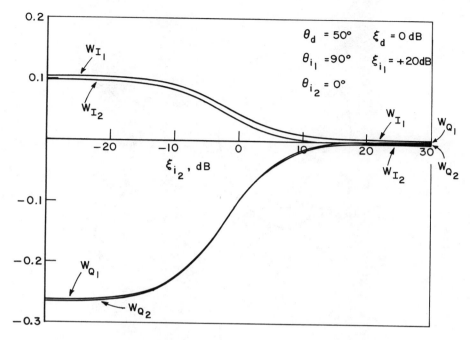

Figure 3.3 Weight dependence on ξ_{i2}.

Finally, the output thermal noise power is

$$P_n = \frac{\sigma^2}{2}\left[|w_1|^2 + |w_2|^2\right], \tag{3.34}$$

and the SINR is

$$\text{SINR} = \frac{P_d}{P_{i1} + P_{i2} + P_n}. \tag{3.35}$$

Using these equations, we may determine what happens to the array. Figures 3.3 through 3.5 show the array weights, the array patterns, and the output signal powers for the following assumed parameters:

$$\begin{aligned}
\theta_d &= 50°, \\
\theta_{i1} &= 90°, \\
\theta_{i2} &= 0°, \\
\xi_d &= 0 \text{ dB},
\end{aligned} \tag{3.36}$$

and

$$\xi_{i1} = +20 \text{ dB}.$$

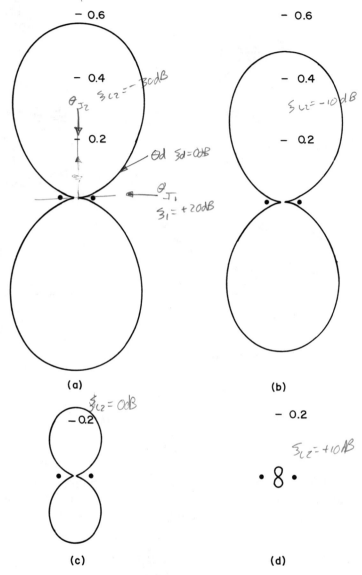

Figure 3.4 Voltage patterns for several ξ_{i2}: $\theta_d = 50°$, $\theta_{i1} = 90°$, $\theta_{i2} = 0°$, $\xi_d = 0$ dB, $\xi_{i1} = 20$ dB. (a) $\xi_{i2} = -30$ dB; (b) $\xi_{i2} = -10$ dB; (c) $\xi_{i2} = 0$ dB; (d) $\xi_{i2} = +10$ dB.

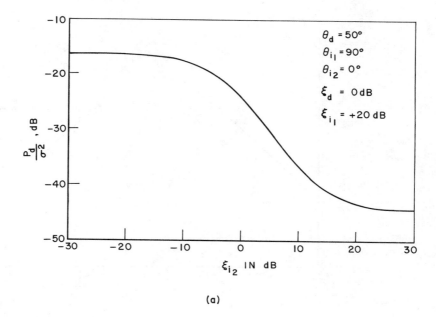

(a)

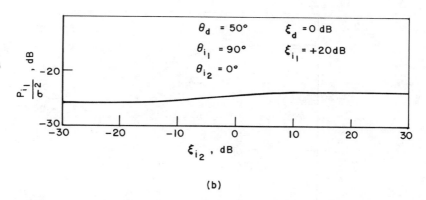

(b)

Figure 3.5   The effect of ξ_{i_2}. (a) P_d/σ^2 versus ξ_{i_2}; (b) P_{i1}/σ^2 versus ξ_{i_2}.

These values are the same as those in Example 2 of Chapter 2. The results in Figs. 3.3 to 3.5 are all plotted versus ξ_{i2}. Note that when ξ_{i2} is very small, the second interference signal has little effect, so the results are the same as those obtained in Example 2 of Chapter 2.

Figure 3.3 shows the array weights as a function of ξ_{i2}. With $\xi_{i2} = -30$ dB, the second interference signal is so weak that it is virtually not present. Hence, the weights on the left side of Fig. 3.3 are essentially the same as in Example 2, for the case where $\xi_{i1} = 100 = 20$ dB. (The INR ξ_i in Example 2

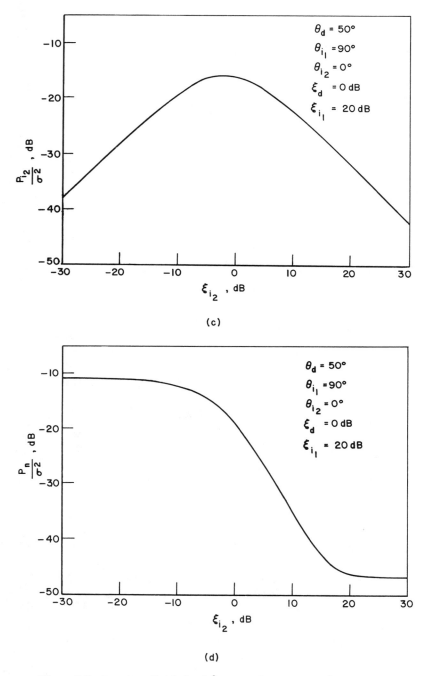

Figure 3.5 (*continued*) (c) P_{i2}/σ^2 versus ξ_{i2}; (d) P_n/σ^2 versus ξ_{i2}.

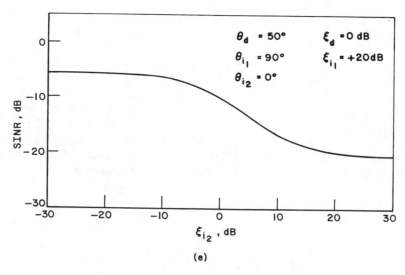

Figure 3.5   (*continued*) (e) SINR versus ξ_{i2}.

corresponds to ξ_{i1} here.) Figure 3.4 shows the absolute voltage pattern, plotted to the same scale in each figure, for $\xi_{i2} = -30$ dB, -10 dB, 0 dB, and $+10$ dB. Figure 3.4(a) for $\xi_{i2} = -30$ dB is essentially the same pattern as in Fig. 2.16(e). [The pattern in Fig. 2.16(e) is the pattern that would result if $\xi_{i2} = 0 = -\infty$ dB.] Finally, Fig. 3.5 shows how the array output powers from the various signals, and the SINR, depend on ξ_{i2}.

We see from Fig. 3.3 that as ξ_{i2} increases, the weights drop to very small values. Moreover, Fig. 3.4 shows the corresponding drop in the pattern response as ξ_{i2} increases. Thus, in the presence of two interfering signals, the array simply turns itself off. (Actually, although it cannot be seen in Fig. 3.4, the array weights and pattern do not continue to drop for $\xi_{i2} > 20$ dB. When $\xi_{i2} < \xi_{i1} = 20$ dB, the array pattern has a null on the first interference signal. When $\xi_{i2} > 20$ dB, the second interference signal is stronger than the first, and the array moves its null over to the second interference signal. As ξ_{i2} is further increased, the null depth on the second interference signal becomes deeper, but the pattern response on the first interference signal and the desired signal remain constant.)

Since the array weights drop as ξ_{i2} increases, both P_d and P_n drop with ξ_{i2}, as may be seen in Figs. 3.5(a) and 3.5(d). Output power P_{i2}, shown in Fig. 3.5(c), has the same type of dependence on ξ_{i2} as did the interference power in Example 2. When ξ_{i2} is small, the second interference signal has little effect on the array weights, because it is too weak. Therefore, P_{i2} increases with ξ_{i2}. However, when ξ_{i2} becomes strong enough to affect the array weights, the array reacts against this signal and P_{i2} drops with ξ_{i2}. At the same time, P_{i1}, shown in Fig. 3.5(b), has relatively little dependence on ξ_{i2}. The reason is that when ξ_{i2} is small, the pattern null is at θ_1, on the first interference signal. As ξ_{i2} grows, the pattern null moves over to θ_2, the second interference signal direction. However, it turns out that the pattern in the θ_1 direction is nearly constant during this change. Because P_d drops as ξ_{i2} is increased, but P_{i1} does not, the SINR drops as ξ_{i2} increases, as seen in Fig. 3.5(e).

From this example, we see what happens when the number of signals incident on an array approaches or exceeds the number of degrees of freedom. Using a two-element array as an example, we first found in Example 1 of Chapter 2 that when the desired signal is the only signal incident on the array, the array yields an output SINR of 3 dB, regardless of the arrival angle of the signal. In this case the array uses its single degree of freedom to form a beam maximum on the desired signal, so the full gain of the array is available to the desired signal. Next, in Example 2 of Chapter 2, we added an interference signal to the problem. This change caused the output SINR to drop from $+3$ dB to -5.8 dB (for $\theta_i = 90°$) as the interference power was increased. With one interference signal the array uses its single degree of freedom to null the interference signal. Because the array does not have two degrees of freedom, it cannot also achieve maximum gain on the desired signal. Thus the desired signal is not received on the peak of the pattern as in Fig. 2.10. Hence the output power of the desired signal drops below its value with no interference signal. However, with only one interference signal, the SINR does not drop below -5.8 dB, regardless of the interference power, because with only one interference signal there is no reason for the array weights to go to zero. Finally, when two interfering signals are present, there are too many conditions for the array to meet. As ξ_{i2} increases, the only way for the array to reduce the error signal is to turn off the weights. In this case the result is a further sharp drop in SINR.

Adaptive arrays often operate with more interfering signals incident on them than they have degrees of freedom. However, if some of these signals are weak, the situation is not necessarily disastrous. How well the array performs depends on the power of the interfering signals, their arrival angles, and the array element configuration. In the preceding example, for instance, we found that the second interference signal had little effect if its interference-to-noise ratio was less than -10 dB. In general one must simply calculate what will happen in a given case.

In two commonly occurring situations, the array needs, strictly speaking, an infinite number of degrees of freedom. These situations occur: (1) when the array receives interference from an extended source, such as the sun, and (2) when the array receives interference with nonzero bandwidth.

Thermal radiation from an extended source such as the sun is equivalent to an infinite number of uncorrelated noise signals arriving from a continuum of angles over some sector. To null such interference completely would require, in principle, infinitely many degrees of freedom. However, adaptive arrays can usually operate satisfactorily in the presence of the sun as long as the solar radiation is weak compared to the other signals to be received.

The problem of interference with nonzero bandwidth is similar to the extended source problem. Nonzero bandwidth creates a problem because the interelement phase shift in an array is a function of frequency. If two elements are separated a distance L, the interelement phase shift for a signal arriving at angle θ from broadside is

$$\phi = \frac{2\pi L}{\lambda} \sin \theta. \qquad (3.37)$$

But since

$$\frac{1}{\lambda} = \frac{\omega}{2\pi c}, \qquad (3.38)$$

where ω is radian frequency and c is the velocity of propagation, ϕ may also be written

$$\phi = \frac{\omega L}{c} \sin \theta. \qquad (3.39)$$

Thus the interelement phase shift depends on frequency. An interference signal occupying nonzero bandwidth is electrically equivalent to infinitely many signals arriving with different values of θ, just like the extended source problem. We shall not study the problem of an extended source further, but in the next section we shall examine the effect of bandwidth on array performance.

3.2 SIGNAL BANDWIDTH

Power Calculations with Analytic Signals

To treat bandwidth, it will be helpful if we first define the autocorrelation function and the power spectral density for an analytic signal. Suppose that $n(t)$ is a real, stationary, stochastic process. Let $S_n(\omega)$ be the power spectral

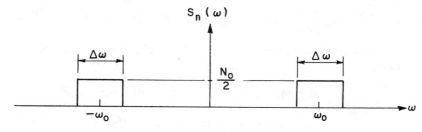

Figure 3.6 The power spectral density $S_n(\omega)$.

density of $n(t)$. To be specific, we shall assume $n(t)$ has a flat, bandlimited power spectral density, with bandwidth $\Delta\omega$ and height $N_0/2$, as shown in Fig. 3.6. The autocorrelation function of $n(t)$, $R_n(\tau)$, is the inverse Fourier transform of $S_n(\omega)$,

$$R_n(\tau) = E\{n(t)n(t+\tau)\}$$

$$= \frac{1}{2\pi}\int_{-\infty}^{\infty} S_n(\omega)e^{j\omega\tau}\,d\omega$$

$$= \frac{N_0\,\Delta\omega}{2\pi}\,\frac{\sin\left(\dfrac{\Delta\omega\,\tau}{2}\right)}{\left(\dfrac{\Delta\omega\,\tau}{2}\right)}\cos\omega_0\tau. \tag{3.40}$$

The average power in $n(t)$ can be calculated from

$$E\{n^2(t)\} = R_n(0) = \frac{N_0\,\Delta\omega}{2\pi}, \tag{3.41}$$

or from

$$E\{n^2(t)\} = \frac{1}{2\pi}\int_{-\infty}^{\infty} S_n(\omega)\,d\omega = \frac{N_0\,\Delta\omega}{2\pi}. \tag{3.42}$$

Now consider the analytic signal $\tilde{n}(t)$ associated with $n(t)$,

$$\tilde{n}(t) = n(t) + j\hat{n}(t). \tag{3.43}$$

For example, $n(t)$ and $\hat{n}(t)$ may be the thermal noise signals on the inphase and quadrature channels, respectively, of a quadrature hybrid. Let us define the autocorrelation function of $\tilde{n}(t)$ to be

$$R_{\tilde{n}}(\tau) = E\{\tilde{n}^*(t)\tilde{n}(t+\tau)\}. \tag{3.44}$$

The function $R_{\tilde{n}}(\tau)$ is related to $R_n(\tau)$ as follows. Multiplying Eq. (3.44) out gives

$$R_{\tilde{n}}(\tau) = E\{[n(t) - j\hat{n}(t)][n(t+\tau) + j\hat{n}(t+\tau)]\}$$

$$= E\{n(t)n(t+\tau)\} + E\{\hat{n}(t)\hat{n}(t+\tau)\}$$

$$+ jE\{n(t)\hat{n}(t+\tau)\} - jE\{\hat{n}(t)n(t+\tau)\}. \tag{3.45}$$

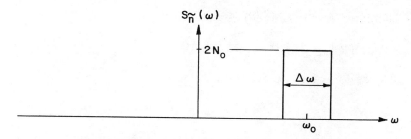

Figure 3.7   The power spectral density $S_{\tilde{n}}(\omega)$.

Using the Hilbert transform relations in Eqs. (2.72) and (2.73), we find

$$R_{\tilde{n}}(\tau) = 2E\{n(t)n(t + \tau)\} + j2E\{n(t)\hat{n}(t + \tau)\}. \qquad (3.46)$$

Finally, using the additional Hilbert transform relation,

$$E\{n(t)\hat{n}(t + \tau)\} = \hat{R}_n(\tau), \qquad (3.47)$$

we have

$$R_{\tilde{n}}(\tau) = 2[R_n(\tau) + j\hat{R}_n(\tau)], \qquad (3.48)$$

where $R_n(\tau)$ is defined in Eq. (3.40) and $\hat{R}_n(\tau)$ denotes the Hilbert transform of $R_n(\tau)$.[‡]

Next, we define the power spectral density associated with $\tilde{n}(t)$ to be

$$S_{\tilde{n}}(\omega) = \int_{-\infty}^{\infty} R_{\tilde{n}}(\tau)e^{-j\omega\tau}\, d\tau. \qquad (3.49)$$

$S_{\tilde{n}}(\omega)$ is related to $S_n(\omega)$ by

$$S_{\tilde{n}}(\omega) = \begin{cases} 4S_n(\omega), & \omega \geqslant 0, \\ 0, & \omega < 0. \end{cases} \qquad (3.50)$$

[Note that a factor 4 occurs in Eq. (3.50), instead of 2, because of the extra factor of 2 in Eq. (3.48).] Thus the real signal $n(t)$ with power spectral density $S_n(\omega)$ shown in Fig. 3.6 has associated with it an analytic signal $\tilde{n}(t)$ with spectral density $S_{\tilde{n}}(\omega)$ shown in Fig. 3.7. Note also that since

$$R_{\tilde{n}}(\tau) = \frac{1}{2\pi} \int_{-\infty}^{\infty} S_{\tilde{n}}(\omega)e^{j\omega\tau}\, d\omega, \qquad (3.51)$$

we have

$$R_{\tilde{n}}(0) = \frac{1}{2\pi} \int_{-\infty}^{\infty} S_{\tilde{n}}(\omega)\, d\omega. \qquad (3.52)$$

[‡]It is common to define $\tilde{R}_n(\tau) = R_n(\tau) + j\hat{R}_n(\tau) = \frac{1}{2}R_{\tilde{n}}(\tau) = \frac{1}{2}E[\tilde{n}^*(t)\tilde{n}(t + \tau)]$. However, we prefer to work with $R_{\tilde{n}}(\tau)$ in this analysis, because the total power in each element signal of the array is $R_{\tilde{n}}(0)$, as will be seen in Eq. (3.55).

Therefore, from Eq. (3.48), the power in $n(t)$ is

$$E\{n^2(t)\} = R_n(0) = \tfrac{1}{2}\operatorname{Re}\{R_{\tilde{n}}(0)\} = \tfrac{1}{2}\operatorname{Re}\left\{\frac{1}{2\pi}\int_{-\infty}^{\infty} S_{\tilde{n}}(\omega)\, d\omega\right\}. \qquad (3.53)$$

But $S_{\tilde{n}}(\omega)$ is real, so this is the same as

$$E\{n^2(t)\} = \frac{1}{2}\frac{1}{2\pi}\int_{-\infty}^{\infty} S_{\tilde{n}}(\omega)\, d\omega = \tfrac{1}{2}R_{\tilde{n}}(0). \qquad (3.54)$$

Finally, we note that if $n(t)$ is the inphase channel voltage out of the quadrature hybrid in Fig. 2.7, the input voltage to the quadrature hybrid will be $\sqrt{2}\,n(t)$. Hence the total input noise power to the hybrid will be twice as much as in Eq. (3.54),

$$\text{total element power} = \frac{1}{2\pi}\int_{-\infty}^{\infty} S_{\tilde{n}}(\omega)\, d\omega = R_{\tilde{n}}(0). \qquad (3.55)$$

Array Analysis with Nonzero Bandwidth Signals

Now, with this notation defined, let us consider what happens when an adaptive array receives signals with nonzero bandwidth. We shall find that nonzero bandwidth degrades the performance of the array. In particular, we shall show that although desired signal bandwidth has only a slight effect on performance, interference bandwidth has a very large effect. There are two separate reasons why bandwidth affects performance. First, when the array receives a signal with nonzero bandwidth, the signals produced in different array elements are not perfectly correlated, because of the interelement propagation time. Second, in practice it can be difficult to match the frequency responses behind different elements perfectly over the signal bandwidth. Any channel mismatch further decorrelates the element signals. We shall consider these two problems separately, starting with the interelement propagation delay.

Suppose we have a two-element array as in Fig. 2.15. Assume that a desired signal is incident from angle θ_d and that an interference signal is incident from angle θ_i. Also, assume uncorrelated thermal noise is present on each element, as usual. To treat this problem, we proceed as follows.

Consider first the desired signal. Suppose the incoming signal produces signals $\tilde{d}_1(t)$ on element 1 and $\tilde{d}_2(t)$ on element 2. The desired signal vector is

$$\mathbf{X}_d = \begin{bmatrix} \tilde{d}_1(t) \\ \tilde{d}_2(t) \end{bmatrix}. \qquad (3.56)$$

Since $\tilde{d}_1(t)$ and $\tilde{d}_2(t)$ are both produced by the same incident signal, the only difference between them is a time delay, which depends on the arrival angle of the signal. Let us denote the desired signal waveform on element 1 by $\tilde{d}(t)$,

$$\tilde{d}_1(t) = \tilde{d}(t). \qquad (3.57)$$

Then the desired signal in element 2 will just be

$$\tilde{d}_2(t) = \tilde{d}(t - T_d), \tag{3.58}$$

where T_d is the propagation time delay between elements. Since the desired signal arrives from angle θ_d, T_d is just

$$T_d = \frac{L}{c}\sin\theta_d. \tag{3.59}$$

Thus, the desired signal vector is

$$\mathbf{X}_d = \begin{bmatrix} \tilde{d}(t) \\ \tilde{d}(t - T_d) \end{bmatrix}. \tag{3.60}$$

The desired signal part of the covariance matrix $\boldsymbol{\Phi}_d$ is then

$$\boldsymbol{\Phi}_d = E\left(\mathbf{X}_d^* \mathbf{X}_d^T\right) = E\begin{bmatrix} \tilde{d}^*(t)\tilde{d}(t) & \tilde{d}^*(t)\tilde{d}(t - T_d) \\ \tilde{d}^*(t - T_d)\tilde{d}(t) & \tilde{d}^*(t - T_d)\tilde{d}(t - T_d) \end{bmatrix}. \tag{3.61}$$

We assume $\tilde{d}(t)$ is a stationary random process and define $R_{\tilde{d}}(\tau)$ to be its autocorrelation function,

$$R_{\tilde{d}}(\tau) = E\left[\tilde{d}^*(t)\tilde{d}(t + \tau)\right]. \tag{3.62}$$

Then $\boldsymbol{\Phi}_d$ is

$$\boldsymbol{\Phi}_d = \begin{bmatrix} R_{\tilde{d}}(0) & R_{\tilde{d}}(-T_d) \\ R_{\tilde{d}}(T_d) & R_{\tilde{d}}(0) \end{bmatrix}. \tag{3.63}$$

{Since $\tilde{d}(t)$ is stationary, $E[\tilde{d}^*(t - T_d)\tilde{d}(t)] = E[\tilde{d}^*(t)\tilde{d}(t + T_d)]$.}

Now let us assume the desired signal has a flat, bandlimited power spectral density, as shown in Fig. 3.8. Within the band $\Delta\omega_d$, let the desired signal have power density $2\pi p_d/\Delta\omega_d$, as shown. Then, since

$$R_{\tilde{d}}(\tau) = \frac{1}{2\pi}\int_{-\infty}^{\infty} S_{\tilde{d}}(\omega)e^{j\omega\tau}\,d\omega$$

$$= p_d \frac{\sin\left(\dfrac{\Delta\omega_d\,\tau}{2}\right)}{\left(\dfrac{\Delta\omega_d\,\tau}{2}\right)}e^{j\omega_d\tau}, \tag{3.64}$$

we have

$$R_{\tilde{d}}(0) = p_d. \tag{3.65}$$

Hence p_d is the total desired signal power per element, according to Eq. (3.55).

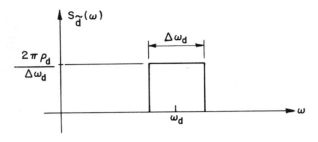

Figure 3.8 The desired signal spectrum.

Also, substituting $\tau = \pm T_d$ into Eq. (3.64) gives

$$R_{\tilde{d}}(\pm T_d) = p_d \frac{\sin\left(\dfrac{\Delta\omega_d T_d}{2}\right)}{\left(\dfrac{\Delta\omega_d T_d}{2}\right)} e^{\pm j\omega_d T_d}. \tag{3.66}$$

Equations (3.65) and (3.66) may be used to evaluate Φ_d in Eq. (3.63). Before evaluating Φ_d, it is helpful to write these equations in normalized form. First, we note that $\omega_d T_d$ is just the interelement phase shift at the carrier frequency, previously denoted by ϕ_d,

$$\omega_d T_d = \phi_d. \tag{3.67}$$

Then, in Eq. (3.66), we may write

$$\frac{\Delta\omega_d T_d}{2} = \frac{1}{2}\left(\frac{\Delta\omega_d}{\omega_d}\right)(\omega_d T_d) = \tfrac{1}{2} B_d \phi_d, \tag{3.68}$$

where B_d is the fractional bandwidth,

$$B_d = \frac{\Delta\omega_d}{\omega_d}. \tag{3.69}$$

Substituting these equations into Eq. (3.63) gives

$$\Phi_d = p_d \begin{bmatrix} 1 & \operatorname{sinc}\left(\tfrac{1}{2}B_d\phi_d\right)e^{-j\phi_d} \\ \operatorname{sinc}\left(\tfrac{1}{2}B_d\phi_d\right)e^{+j\phi_d} & 1 \end{bmatrix}, \tag{3.70}$$

where $\operatorname{sinc} x$ denotes $(\sin x)/x$.

Note that if $B_d = 0$, this result becomes

$$\Phi_d = p_d \begin{bmatrix} 1 & e^{-j\phi_d} \\ e^{j\phi_d} & 1 \end{bmatrix} = p_d \mathbf{U}_d^* \mathbf{U}_d^T, \tag{3.71}$$

where

$$\mathbf{U}_d = \begin{bmatrix} 1 \\ e^{-j\phi_d} \end{bmatrix}. \tag{3.72}$$

This is the same form we found in Eq. (2.116), when the desired signal was assumed to be CW, and where

$$p_d = A_d^2. \tag{3.73}$$

Furthermore, in discussing the Applebaum feedback concept in section 2.2, we assumed the signals were "narrowband." We can now see from the above results that the necessary requirement for signals to be considered narrowband is that $\Delta\omega_d T_d$ or $B_d\phi_d$ is small enough that

$$\text{sinc}\left(\frac{\Delta\omega_d T_d}{2}\right) = \text{sinc}\left(\tfrac{1}{2}B_d\phi_d\right) \simeq 1. \tag{3.74}$$

We shall present examples below that show how close $\text{sinc}\left(\tfrac{1}{2}\Delta\omega_d T_d\right)$ must be to unity to obtain a given performance. [The result in Eq. (3.74) is correct only for a two-element array. For an N-element linear array with half-wavelength element spacing, Eq. (3.74) is replaced by the condition $\text{sinc}\left[\tfrac{1}{2}(N-1)\Delta\omega_d T_d\right]$ ~N-element~ $\simeq 1$ for the signals to be considered narrowband. In general, to treat a signal as narrowband, the bandwidth must be small enough that there is essentially no decorrelation between the signals received on opposite ends of the array.]

Now let us consider the reference correlation vector. Suppose a replica of the desired signal $\tilde{d}(t)$ is available for use as the reference signal. One must decide, however, what timing to use for $\tilde{r}(t)$. Since the desired signal output from element 1 of the array is $w_1\tilde{d}(t)$ and that from element 2 is $w_2\tilde{d}(t - T_d)$, the desired signal contribution to the array output from each element has a different timing. Because it is unclear what timing will be best for the reference signal, let us assume

$$\tilde{r}(t) = \frac{R}{\sqrt{p_d}}\tilde{d}(t - \eta T_d), \tag{3.75}$$

~timing parameter~

where η is a parameter that can be varied over the range $0 \leqslant \eta \leqslant 1$. We will evaluate the performance of the array below for several values of η. In Eq. (3.75), the factor $\sqrt{p_d}$ is included in the denominator to make the amplitude of $\tilde{r}(t)$ independent of the amplitude of $\tilde{d}(t)$.

With the reference signal given in Eq. (3.75), the reference correlation vector is

$$\mathbf{S} = E\{\mathbf{X}_d^*\tilde{r}(t)\}$$

$$= \frac{R}{\sqrt{p_d}}E\left(\begin{bmatrix} \tilde{d}^*(t) \\ \tilde{d}^*(t - T_d) \end{bmatrix}\tilde{d}(t - \eta T_d)\right)$$

$$= \frac{R}{\sqrt{p_d}}\begin{bmatrix} R_{\tilde{d}}[-\eta T_d] \\ R_{\tilde{d}}[(1 - \eta)T_d] \end{bmatrix}. \tag{3.76}$$

Substituting Eq. (3.64) for $R_{\tilde{d}}(\tau)$, and using the definitions in Eqs. (3.67) and

(3.68), we obtain

$$\underline{P}_{xr} \subset S = R\sqrt{p_d} \left[\begin{array}{c} \text{sinc} \left[\frac{1}{2}\eta B_d \phi_d \right] e^{-jn\phi_d} \\ \text{sinc} \left[\frac{1}{2}(1-\eta) B_d \phi_d \right] e^{-j(1-\eta)\phi_d} \end{array} \right]. \tag{3.77}$$

Next consider the interference signal. The interference signal vector is

$$\mathbf{X}_i = \left[\begin{array}{c} \tilde{i}_1(t) \\ \tilde{i}_2(t) \end{array} \right]. \tag{3.78}$$

Let $\tilde{i}(t)$ be the interference signal on element 1. Then the interference signal on element 2 is

$$\tilde{i}_2(t) = \tilde{i}(t - T_i), \tag{3.79}$$

where T_i is the interelement time delay for the interference,

$$T_i = \frac{L}{c} \sin \theta_i. \tag{3.80}$$

The interference contribution to the covariance matrix is therefore

$$\Phi_i = E\left(\mathbf{X}_i^* \mathbf{X}_i^T \right) = E \left[\begin{array}{cc} \tilde{i}^*(t)\tilde{i}(t) & \tilde{i}^*(t)\tilde{i}(t - T_i) \\ \tilde{i}^*(t - T_i)\tilde{i}(t) & \tilde{i}^*(t - T_i)\tilde{i}(t - T_i) \end{array} \right]. \tag{3.81}$$

We define $R_{\tilde{i}}(\tau)$ to be the autocorrelation function of $\tilde{i}(t)$,

$$R_{\tilde{i}}(\tau) = E\left\{ \tilde{i}^*(t)\tilde{i}(t + \tau) \right\}. \tag{3.82}$$

Then Φ_i may be written

$$\Phi_i = \left[\begin{array}{cc} R_{\tilde{i}}(0) & R_{\tilde{i}}(-T_i) \\ R_{\tilde{i}}(T_i) & R_{\tilde{i}}(0) \end{array} \right]. \tag{3.83}$$

Let us assume the interference also has a flat bandlimited power spectral density, as shown in Fig. 3.9, with power density $2\pi p_i / \Delta\omega_i$ over the bandwidth $\Delta\omega_i$. (We assume the center frequency for the interference is the same as for the

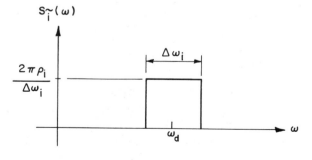

Figure 3.9 The interference spectrum.

desired signal, ω_d.) The autocorrelation function of $\tilde{i}(t)$ is then given by

$$R_{\tilde{i}}(\tau) = p_i \frac{\sin\left(\dfrac{\Delta\omega_i \tau}{2}\right)}{\left(\dfrac{\Delta\omega_i \tau}{2}\right)} e^{j\omega_d \tau}. \tag{3.84}$$

To evaluate the autocorrelation functions in Eq. (3.83), we note that $\omega_d T_i$ is the interelement phase shift at the carrier frequency of the interference, previously denoted by ϕ_i,

$$\omega_d T_i = \phi_i, \quad = 2\pi \times \sin\theta_i \tag{3.85}$$

and we define the interference fractional bandwidth B_i,

$$B_i = \frac{\Delta\omega_i}{\omega_d}. \tag{3.86}$$

The autocorrelation functions in Eq. (3.81) then may be written

$$R_{\tilde{i}}(0) = p_i \tag{3.87}$$

and

$$R_{\tilde{i}}(\pm T_i) = p_i \operatorname{sinc}\left(\tfrac{1}{2}B_i\phi_i\right) e^{\pm j\phi_i}; \tag{3.88}$$

therefore, $\mathbf{\Phi}_i$ is

$$\mathbf{\Phi}_i = p_i \begin{bmatrix} 1 & \operatorname{sinc}\left(\tfrac{1}{2}B_i\phi_i\right) e^{-j\phi_i} \\ \operatorname{sinc}\left(\tfrac{1}{2}B_i\phi_i\right) e^{j\phi_i} & 1 \end{bmatrix}. \tag{3.89}$$

Again, we remark that as B_i goes to zero, $\mathbf{\Phi}_i$ approaches the matrix

$$\mathbf{\Phi}_i = p_i \begin{bmatrix} 1 & e^{-j\phi_i} \\ e^{j\phi_i} & 1 \end{bmatrix} = p_i \mathbf{U}_i^* \mathbf{U}_i^T, \tag{3.90}$$

where

$$\mathbf{U}_i = \begin{bmatrix} 1 \\ e^{-j\phi_i} \end{bmatrix}. \tag{3.91}$$

This equation corresponds to our previous result for CW signals, with $p_i = A_i^2$.

Finally, we also assume there is uncorrelated thermal noise present on each of the element signals. The noise vector is

$$\mathbf{X}_n = \begin{bmatrix} \tilde{n}_1(t) \\ \tilde{n}_2(t) \end{bmatrix}, \tag{3.92}$$

which contributes a term $\mathbf{\Phi}_n$ to the covariance matrix,

$$\mathbf{\Phi}_n = \sigma^2 \mathbf{I}. \tag{3.93}$$

Combining the results in Eqs. (3.70), (3.89), and (3.93), we find that the total covariance matrix is

$$\Phi = \Phi_d + \Phi_i + \Phi_n$$

$$= \begin{bmatrix} \sigma^2 + p_d + p_i & p_d \, \text{sinc} \left(\tfrac{1}{2} B_d \phi_d \right) e^{-j\phi_d} + p_i \, \text{sinc} \left(\tfrac{1}{2} B_i \phi_i \right) e^{-j\phi_i} \\ p_d \, \text{sinc} \left(\tfrac{1}{2} B_d \phi_d \right) e^{j\phi_d} + p_i \, \text{sinc} \left(\tfrac{1}{2} B_i \phi_i \right) e^{j\phi_i} & \sigma^2 + p_d + p_i \end{bmatrix}. \quad (3.94)$$

It is helpful to normalize Φ by dividing by σ^2. We have

$$\frac{1}{\sigma^2} \Phi = \begin{bmatrix} 1 + \xi_d + \xi_i & \xi_d \, \text{sinc} \left(\dfrac{B_d \phi_d}{2} \right) e^{-j\phi_d} + \xi_i \, \text{sinc} \left(\dfrac{B_i \phi_i}{2} \right) e^{-j\phi_i} \\ \xi_d \, \text{sinc} \left(\dfrac{B_d \phi_d}{2} \right) e^{j\phi_d} + \xi_i \, \text{sinc} \left(\dfrac{B_i \phi_i}{2} \right) e^{j\phi_i} & 1 + \xi_d + \xi_i \end{bmatrix}. \quad (3.95)$$

Similarly, we also normalize the reference correlation vector **S** in Eq. (3.77) to σ^2,

$$\frac{1}{\sigma^2} \mathbf{S} = \sqrt{\xi_d} \, \frac{R}{\sigma} \begin{bmatrix} \text{sinc} \left(\dfrac{\eta B_d \phi_d}{2} \right) e^{-j\eta\phi_d} \\ \text{sinc} \left[\dfrac{(1 - \eta) \boldsymbol{B}_d \phi_d}{2} \right] e^{j(1-\eta)\phi_d} \end{bmatrix}. \quad (3.96)$$

The weight vector may then be computed from

$$\mathbf{W} = \left[\frac{1}{\sigma^2} \Phi \right]^{-1} \left[\frac{1}{\sigma^2} \mathbf{S} \right]. \quad (3.97)$$

After the weights are found, the output signal powers may be calculated as follows. First, the desired signal component of the array output is

$$\tilde{s}_d(t) = X_d^T W = w_1 \tilde{d}(t) + w_2 \tilde{d}(t - T_d). \quad (3.98)$$

The output desired signal power is therefore

$$P_d = \tfrac{1}{2} E \left\{ |\tilde{s}_d(t)|^2 \right\} = \tfrac{1}{2} \mathbf{W}^\dagger E \left[\mathbf{X}_d^* \mathbf{X}_d^T \right] \mathbf{W} = \tfrac{1}{2} \mathbf{W}^\dagger \Phi_d \mathbf{W}$$

$$= \tfrac{1}{2} E \left\{ \left[w_1^* \tilde{d}^*(t) + w_2^* \tilde{d}^*(t - T_d) \right] \left[w_1 \tilde{d}(t) + w_2 \tilde{d}(t - T_d) \right] \right\}$$

$$= \tfrac{1}{2} \left[|w_1|^2 R_{\tilde{d}}(0) + w_1^* w_2 R_{\tilde{d}}(-T_d) + w_2^* w_1 R_{\tilde{d}}(T_d) + |w_2|^2 R_{\tilde{d}}(0) \right], \quad (3.99)$$

or, from Eqs. (3.65) and (3.66),

$$P_d = \frac{p_d}{2} \left[|w_1|^2 + |w_2|^2 + 2\text{Re} \left\{ w_1 w_2^* \, \text{sinc} \frac{B_d \phi_d}{2} e^{j\phi_d} \right\} \right]. \quad (3.100)$$

Normalizing this equation to σ^2 gives

$$\frac{P_d}{\sigma^2} = \frac{\xi_d}{2} \left[|w_1|^2 + |w_2|^2 + 2\text{Re} \left\{ w_1 w_2^* \, \text{sinc} \left(\frac{B_d \phi_d}{2} \right) e^{j\phi_d} \right\} \right]. \quad (3.101)$$

$$= \frac{1}{\sigma_n^2} W^\dagger \Phi_d W$$

In a similar way, we obtain for the normalized output interference power,

$$\frac{P_i}{\sigma^2} = \frac{1}{2\sigma^2} \mathbf{W}^\dagger \mathbf{\Phi}_i \mathbf{W}$$

$$= \frac{\xi_i}{2}\left[|w_1|^2 + |w_2|^2 + 2\mathrm{Re}\left\{w_1 w_2^* \,\mathrm{sinc}\left(\frac{B_i \phi_i}{2}\right) e^{j\phi_i}\right\}\right]. \qquad (3.102)$$

The normalized output thermal power is given by the usual formula,

$$\frac{P_n}{\sigma^2} = \frac{1}{2\sigma^2} \mathbf{W}^\dagger (\sigma^2 \mathbf{I}) \mathbf{W} = \tfrac{1}{2}\mathbf{W}^\dagger \mathbf{W} = \tfrac{1}{2}\left[|w_1|^2 + |w_2|^2\right]. \qquad (3.103)$$

Finally, the output SINR is

$$\mathrm{SINR} = \frac{P_d/\sigma^2}{P_i/\sigma^2 + P_n/\sigma^2}. \qquad (3.104)$$

Using these formulas, we may compute a number of interesting results that show the effects of signal bandwidth on array performance.

Bandwidth Degradation Due to Spatial Delay

Consider first the case where there is no interference. Assuming only desired signal and thermal noise are present, let us first investigate the effect of desired signal bandwidth and reference signal timing η on the output SINR. Since the bandwidth B_d always appears in the product $B_d \phi_d$, B_d will have the most effect when ϕ_d is as large as possible. The largest value of ϕ_d will occur when $\theta_d = 90°$. If the array elements are a half wavelength apart, then $\phi_d = \pi$. With this assumption, Fig. 3.10 shows the output SINR plotted versus ξ_d, the input signal-to-noise ratio, for two extreme cases, $B_d = 0$ and $B_d = 0.5$. The SINR for $B_d = 0.5$ is plotted for several values of the timing parameter η. We see that for $\xi_d < 0$ dB, the SINR for $B_d = 0.5$ is identical to that for $B_d = 0$. For $\xi_d > 0$ dB, the SINR for $B_d = 0.5$ drops below that for $B_d = 0$. The amount of the drop depends on η. However, the loss in SINR when $B_d = 0.5$ is at most 3 dB, when $\eta = 0$ and $\eta = 1$, and is only a fraction of a dB when $\eta = 0.5$. Moreover, we note that the performance degradation due to bandwidth occurs only at high values of ξ_d and SINR, where a small loss in SINR is of little significance.

Thus we find that desired signal bandwidth has almost no effect on the performance of a two-element array with half-wavelength spacing. The value of $B_d = 0.5$ used in Fig. 3.10 is so high that practical communication and radar systems would rarely operate with this much bandwidth. We could, of course, increase the performance degradation due to bandwidth by spacing the elements more than a half wavelength apart. However, we will see below that the array is much more sensitive to interference bandwidth than to desired signal bandwidth.

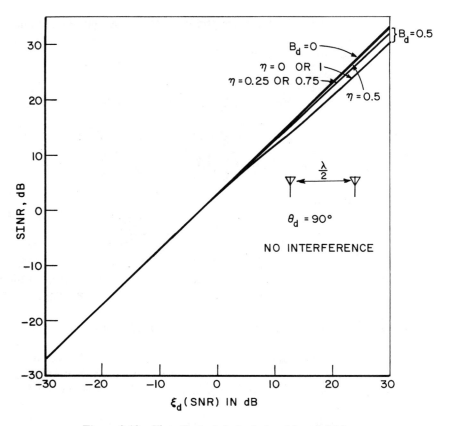

Figure 3.10 The effect of desired signal bandwidth.

Even with only a half-wavelength spacing, the performance deteriorates very quickly with interference bandwidth. For this reason, we do not consider a wider spacing.

Now let us examine the effect of interference bandwidth. Figure 3.11 shows a series of curves plotted for a typical case, where $\theta_d = 0°$, $B_d = 0$, $\eta = 0$, $\theta_i = 50°$, and $\xi_i = 40$ dB. Figure 3.11(a) shows the output SINR versus ξ_d for several values of interference bandwidth B_i. It is immediately clear from this figure that the array is much more sensitive to interference bandwidth than to desired signal bandwidth. For example, when $B_i = 0.02$, the SINR has already dropped 3 dB. With $B_i = 0.05$, the performance is down 8.5 dB from the result for $B_i = 0$.

The behavior of the SINR in Fig. 3.11(a) can be understood by examining Figs. 3.11(b), (c), and (d), which show how output desired signal, interference, and thermal noise powers individually depend on ξ_d for the same conditions.

The most important curve to notice is Fig. 3.11(c), which shows how drastically the output interference power increases with interference bandwidth. Just a small change in interference bandwidth causes several orders of magnitude change in the output interference power. Note also in Figs. 3.11(b) and 3.11(d) that for small ξ_d both P_d and P_n drop as B_i increases. The reason for this behavior is that the output interference power increases so much that it forces the array feedback to turn down the weights in order to keep the mean-square error signal small. Reducing the weights causes P_d and P_n to drop. For higher values of ξ_d, B_i has less effect because the weights are small anyway. That is, since the reference signal amplitude is fixed, the larger the input desired signal, the smaller the weights required to match the output desired signal to the reference signal. The smaller the weights, the less interference power in the error signal.

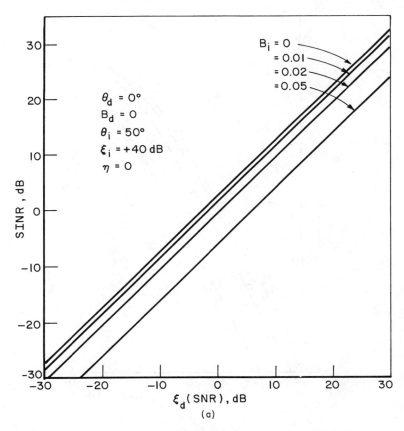

Figure 3.11   The effect of interference bandwidth. (a) SINR versus ξ_d.

It is also important to note that the amount of interference bandwidth the system can tolerate depends strongly on the interference power. The stronger the interference, the more serious the degradation with bandwidth. Figure 3.12 shows another plot of SINR versus ξ_d, under the same conditions as in Fig. 3.11(a), except that now ξ_i is 70 dB instead of 40 dB. As may be seen, the array is much more sensitive to interference bandwidth with $\xi_i = 70$ dB than it was with $\xi_i = 40$ dB.

The Reason for Bandwidth Degradation

Why is the array so much more sensitive to interference bandwidth than to desired signal bandwidth? The reason is that the array sums the desired signal at the array output but nulls the interference. When interference signals from two

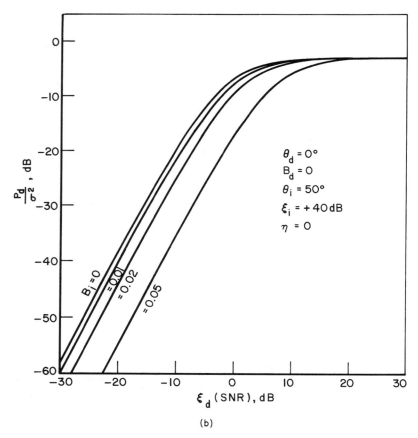

(b)

Figure 3.11   (*continued*) (b) P_d/σ^2 versus ξ_d.

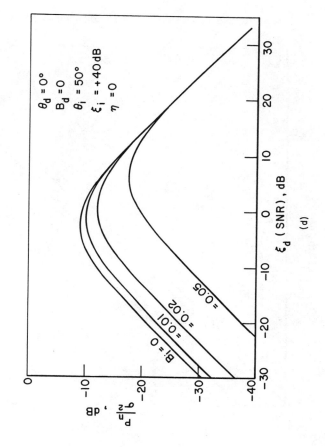

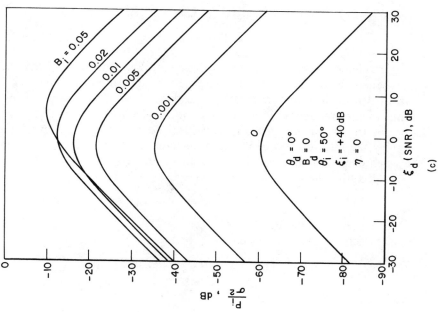

Figure 3.11 (*continued*) (c) P_i/σ^2 versus ξ_d; (d) P_n/σ^2 versus ξ_d.

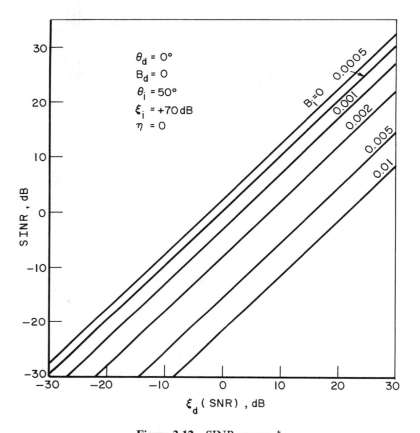

Figure 3.12   SINR versus ξ_d.

or more elements are subtracted from one another, the amount of cancellation is very sensitive to any difference between the interference signals. The effect of bandwidth on interference nulling can be understood by considering the array either in the frequency domain or in the time domain.

In the frequency domain, consider the transfer function of the array as seen by the interference. Since the interference signal undergoes a time delay T_i between elements, the array looks to the interference like the filter shown in Fig. 3.13. This filter has transfer function

$$H(\omega) = w_1 + w_2 e^{-j\omega T_i}. \tag{3.105}$$

To null the interference, suppose the weights w_1 and w_2 are chosen so that $H(\omega)$ is zero at the center frequency of the interference,

$$H(\omega_d) = 0. \tag{3.106}$$

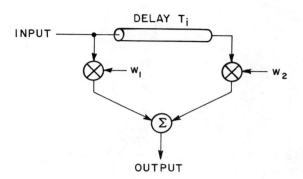

DELAY T_i

INPUT

w_1

w_2

Σ

OUTPUT

Figure 3.13   Filter seen by the interference.

Then w_1 and w_2 satisfy

$$w_1 = -w_2 e^{-j\omega_d T_i}, \tag{3.107}$$

and $H(\omega)$ is

$$H(\omega) = w_2 \left[e^{-j\omega T_i} - e^{-j\omega_d T_i} \right]; \tag{3.108}$$

therefore,

$$\left| \frac{H(\omega)}{w_2} \right| = |e^{-j\omega T_i} - e^{-j\omega_d T_i}|. \tag{3.109}$$

A typical curve of $|H(\omega)/w_2|$ is plotted in Fig. 3.14 for $\omega_d T_i = \pi$ (correspond-

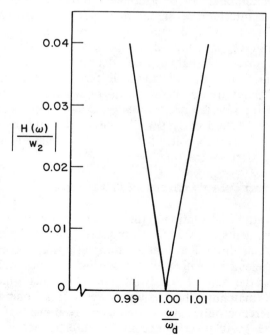

Figure 3.14 $|H(\omega)/w_2|$ versus ω/ω_d.

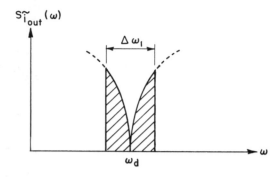

Figure 3.15 Output interference spectrum.

ing to $\lambda/2$ element spacing and $\theta_i = 90°$). It is seen that this transfer function is zero at frequency ω_d, but it rises quickly away from zero at other frequencies. Thus when the interference has a nonzero bandwidth as in Fig. 3.9, the interference spectrum at the array output is $|H(\omega)|^2 S_i(\omega)$, as shown in Fig. 3.15, and the output interference power from the array is

$$P_i = \frac{1}{2\pi} \int_{-\infty}^{\infty} |H(\omega)|^2 S_i(\omega)\, d\omega. \tag{3.110}$$

Because of the steep rise in $|H(\omega)|$ for $\omega \neq \omega_d$, P_i increases very quickly as the interference bandwidth increases.

In the time domain, the effect of interference bandwidth may be understood by noting that an interference signal arrives at two different array elements at slightly different times, because of the propagation time delay between elements. This interelement time delay causes the interference signals on the elements to be decorrelated slightly. Such decorrelation manifests itself mathematically in the fact that the off-diagonal terms in the interference covariance matrix in Eq. (3.89) are less than the diagonal terms. Physically, this decorrelation means that the interference signals on different elements are not identical and cannot be subtracted perfectly. The larger the interference bandwidth, the more two element signals differ for a given interelement time delay and the larger the residue after subtraction.

Bandwidth Degradation Due to Channel Mismatch

In the preceding bandwidth calculations, the decorrelation of interference signals on two different elements was due to the interelement propagation delay. However, it is clear from this discussion that anything else that decorrelates the interference on different elements will also degrade interference nulling. This observation brings us to the second bandwidth problem mentioned earlier, namely, the difficulty of matching the frequency responses behind different array elements. Any difference between the frequency responses of two array channels will reduce the correlation between the interference on the two channels and will limit our ability to subtract one signal from the other. In practice it is difficult to match two array channels exactly. Slight differences in channel characteristics due to seemingly minor variations in coaxial cable lengths, impedance mismatches at coaxial cable connectors, stray capacitances, variations in amplifier passband characteristics, and the like often limit the bandwidth of the array.

To estimate the seriousness of this problem, let us consider the following simple model. Suppose we have a two-element array as shown in Fig. 3.16, with transfer function $H_1(\omega)$ after element 1 and $H_2(\omega)$ after element 2. Let $\tilde{x}_j(t)$ be the received signal on element j and $\tilde{y}_j(t)$ the signal after filter $H_j(\omega)$. Assume noise $\tilde{n}_j(t)$ is added to each $\tilde{y}_j(t)$ to produce $\tilde{z}_j(t)$,[‡]

$$\tilde{z}_j(t) = \tilde{y}_j(t) + \tilde{n}_j(t). \tag{3.111}$$

As before, let each $\tilde{n}_j(t)$ have power σ^2 and assume the $\tilde{n}_j(t)$ are mutually independent. Let the signals $\tilde{z}_j(t)$ be the signals presented to the adaptive processor.

With signals $\tilde{z}_j(t)$ in the processor, the steady-state weight vector will be

$$\mathbf{W} = \mathbf{\Phi}_z^{-1}\mathbf{S}_z, \tag{3.112}$$

where

$$\mathbf{\Phi}_z = E(\mathbf{Z}^*\mathbf{Z}^T), \tag{3.113}$$

$$\mathbf{S}_z = E[\mathbf{Z}^*\tilde{r}(t)], \tag{3.114}$$

and where $\mathbf{Z}$ is the signal vector seen by the processor,

$$\mathbf{Z} = [z_1(t), \tilde{z}_2(t)]^T. \tag{3.115}$$

The array output signal powers and SINR can be computed from $\mathbf{W}$.

With the filters $H_j(\omega)$ in the signal paths, $\mathbf{\Phi}_z$ and S_z may be computed as follows. First, we define

$$R_{\tilde{x}_i\tilde{x}_j}(\tau) = E[\tilde{x}_i^*(t)\tilde{x}_j(t+\tau)]. \tag{3.116}$$

For $i = j$, $R_{\tilde{x}_i\tilde{x}_j}(\tau)$ is the autocorrelation function of $\tilde{x}_i(t)$. For $i \neq j$, $R_{\tilde{x}_i\tilde{x}_j}(\tau)$ is the cross-correlation function of $\tilde{x}_i(t)$ and $\tilde{x}_j(t)$. Then, we define $S_{\tilde{x}_i\tilde{x}_j}(\omega)$ to be the Fourier transform of $R_{\tilde{x}_i\tilde{x}_j}(\tau)$,

$$S_{\tilde{x}_i\tilde{x}_j}(\omega) = \int_{-\infty}^{\infty} R_{\tilde{x}_i\tilde{x}_j}(\tau)e^{-j\omega\tau}\,d\tau. \tag{3.117}$$

[‡]Where the thermal noise should be added in Fig. 3.16 depends on what noise sources we wish to model. In an actual array, thermal noise will be added to the signals in several ways. Some will be collected by the antenna elements from sky noise. More will be added by the losses in the RF cabling behind the antennas. Still more will be added by preamplifiers, mixers, and so on, in the signal paths. In the analysis here, we assume the most important source of noise is the noise added by mixers after the filters $H_j(\omega)$. This assumption simplifies the analysis, because we do not need to take into account modification of the noise power spectral densities by the $H_j(\omega)$.

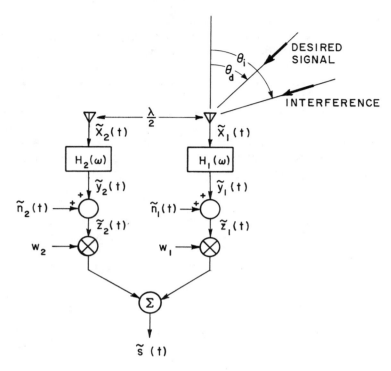

Figure 3.16 Two-element array with channel mismatch filters.

The transform $S_{\tilde{x}_i \tilde{x}_j}(\omega)$ is the power spectral density of $\tilde{x}_i(t)$ for $i = j$ and the cross-spectral density of $\tilde{x}_i(t)$ and $\tilde{x}_j(t)$ for $i \neq j$. In terms of these $S_{\tilde{x}_i \tilde{x}_j}(\omega)$, the auto- and cross-correlations of the $\tilde{y}_j(t)$ are given by

$$E\left[\tilde{y}_i^*(t)\tilde{y}_j(t)\right] = \frac{1}{2\pi} \int_{-\infty}^{\infty} H_i^*(\omega) H_j(\omega) S_{\tilde{x}_i \tilde{x}_j}(\omega)\, d\omega. \qquad (3.118)$$

Adding the noise to the $\tilde{y}_j(t)$, we find that the ijth element of Φ_z is

$$E\left[\tilde{z}_i^*(t)\tilde{z}_j(t)\right] = E\left[\tilde{y}_i^*(t)\tilde{y}_j(t)\right] + \sigma^2 \delta_{ij}. \qquad (3.119)$$

Let us assume a desired signal and an interference signal are received by the array, the same as before. The signal vector $\mathbf{Z}$ can be written as a sum of a desired, an interference, and a noise component,

$$\mathbf{Z} = \mathbf{Z}_d + \mathbf{Z}_i + \mathbf{Z}_n. \qquad (3.120)$$

Let the desired signal and interference power spectral densities be those shown in Figs. 3.8 and 3.9. For the filters $H_j(\omega)$, note that only the difference between $H_1(\omega)$ and $H_2(\omega)$ affects the interference nulling capability of the array. If $H_1(\omega)$ and $H_2(\omega)$ were identical, the interference signals in $\tilde{x}_1(t)$ and $\tilde{x}_2(t)$ would each be modified in an identical way, so $\tilde{y}_1(t)$ and $\tilde{y}_2(t)$ would be

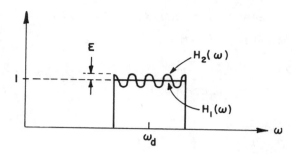

Figure 3.17 Channel mismatch transfer functions.

identical and could be cancelled perfectly. Any degradation in nulling capability is due to the difference between $H_1(\omega)$ and $H_2(\omega)$. Hence, to have the simplest model, let us assume

$$H_1(\omega) = 1, \qquad (3.121)$$

and

$$H_2(\omega) = 1 + \Delta(\omega). \qquad (3.122)$$

The function $\Delta(\omega)$ is the difference between the $H_j(\omega)$.

In general, $\Delta(\omega)$ will consist of frequency-dependent amplitude and phase mismatches across the signal bandwidth. Here we shall consider the case where there is only an amplitude mismatch. Specifically, suppose

$$\Delta(\omega) = E \cos(\omega - \omega_d) T_e. \qquad (3.123)$$

Thus $|H_1(\omega)|$ and $|H_2(\omega)|$ are as shown in Fig. 3.17. With these assumptions, we calculate $\mathbf{\Phi}_z$ and $\mathbf{S}_z$ as follows.

Let $R^d_{\tilde{x}_i \tilde{x}_j}(\tau)$ and $R^i_{\tilde{x}_i \tilde{x}_j}(\tau)$ be the desired and interference signal contributions to $R_{\tilde{x}_i \tilde{x}_j}(\tau)$, respectively,

$$R_{\tilde{x}_i \tilde{x}_j}(\tau) = R^d_{\tilde{x}_i \tilde{x}_j}(\tau) + R^i_{\tilde{x}_i \tilde{x}_j}(\tau). \qquad (3.124)$$

[Since the thermal noise is added after the filters, there is no thermal noise in the $\tilde{x}_j(t)$.] From the desired signal terms in Eqs. (3.56) through (3.58), we find

$$R^d_{\tilde{x}_1 \tilde{x}_1}(\tau) = E[\tilde{d}^*(t)\tilde{d}(t + \tau)] = R_{\tilde{d}}(\tau), \qquad (3.125)$$

$$R^d_{\tilde{x}_1 \tilde{x}_2}(\tau) = E[\tilde{d}^*(t)\tilde{d}(t - T_d + \tau)] = R_{\tilde{d}}(\tau - T_d), \qquad (3.126)$$

$$R^d_{\tilde{x}_2 \tilde{x}_1}(\tau) = E[\tilde{d}^*(t - T_d)\tilde{d}(t + \tau)] = R_{\tilde{d}}(\tau + T_d), \qquad (3.127)$$

and

$$R^d_{\tilde{x}_2 \tilde{x}_2}(\tau) = E[\tilde{d}^*(t - T_d)\tilde{d}(t - T_d + \tau)] = R_{\tilde{d}}(\tau), \qquad (3.128)$$

where $R_{\tilde{d}}(\tau)$ is the autocorrelation function of $\tilde{d}(t)$ in Eq. (3.62). The $R^i_{\tilde{x}_i \tilde{x}_j}(\tau)$ are similar to Eqs. (3.125) through (3.128) with all desired signal quantities replaced with interference quantities. The total $R_{\tilde{x}_i\tilde{x}_j}(\tau)$ are then

$$R_{\tilde{x}_1\tilde{x}_1}(\tau) = R_{\tilde{d}}(\tau) + R_{\tilde{i}}(\tau), \tag{3.129}$$

$$R_{\tilde{x}_1\tilde{x}_2}(\tau) = R_{\tilde{d}}(\tau - T_d) + R_{\tilde{i}}(\tau - T_i), \tag{3.130}$$

$$R_{\tilde{x}_2\tilde{x}_1}(\tau) = R_{\tilde{d}}(\tau + T_d) + R_{\tilde{i}}(\tau + T_i), \tag{3.131}$$

and

$$R_{\tilde{x}_2\tilde{x}_2}(\tau) = R_{\tilde{d}}(\tau) + R_{\tilde{i}}(\tau). \tag{3.132}$$

From Eq. (3.117), we find

$$S_{\tilde{x}_1\tilde{x}_1}(\omega) = S_{\tilde{d}}(\omega) + S_{\tilde{i}}(\omega), \tag{3.133}$$

$$S_{\tilde{x}_1\tilde{x}_2}(\omega) = S_{\tilde{d}}(\omega)e^{-j\omega T_d} + S_{\tilde{i}}(\omega)e^{-j\omega T_i}, \tag{3.134}$$

$$S_{\tilde{x}_2\tilde{x}_1}(\omega) = S_{\tilde{d}}(\omega)e^{+j\omega T_d} + S_{\tilde{i}}(\omega)e^{+j\omega T_i}, \tag{3.135}$$

and

$$S_{\tilde{x}_2\tilde{x}_2}(\omega) = S_{\tilde{d}}(\omega) + S_{\tilde{i}}(\omega). \tag{3.136}$$

Inserting the $H_j(\omega)$ of Eqs. (3.121) and (3.122) in Eq. (3.118), we find

$$E\left[\tilde{y}_1^*(t)\tilde{y}_1(t)\right] = \frac{1}{2\pi}\int_{-\infty}^{\infty}\left[S_{\tilde{d}}(\omega) + S_{\tilde{i}}(\omega)\right]d\omega, \tag{3.137}$$

$$E\left[\tilde{y}_1^*(t)\tilde{y}_2(t)\right] = \frac{1}{2\pi}\int_{-\infty}^{\infty}\left[1 + \Delta(\omega)\right]\left[S_{\tilde{d}}(\omega)e^{-j\omega T_d} + S_{\tilde{i}}(\omega)e^{-j\omega T_i}\right]d\omega, \tag{3.138}$$

and

$$E\left[\tilde{y}_2^*(t)\tilde{y}_2(t)\right]$$

$$= \frac{1}{2\pi}\int_{-\infty}^{\infty}\left[1 + \Delta(\omega) + \Delta^*(\omega) + |\Delta(\omega)|^2\right]\left[S_{\tilde{d}}(\omega) + S_{\tilde{i}}(\omega)\right]d\omega. \tag{3.139}$$

Also, $E[\tilde{y}_2^*(t)\tilde{y}_1(t)]$ is just the conjugate of $E[\tilde{y}_1^*(t)\tilde{y}_2(t)]$. Note that $E[\tilde{y}_1^*(t)\tilde{y}_1(t)]$ does not involve $\Delta(\omega)$, and Eq. (3.137) immediately yields,

$$E\left[\tilde{y}_1^*(t)\tilde{y}_1(t)\right] = R_{\tilde{d}}(0) + R_{\tilde{i}}(0) = p_d + p_i. \tag{3.140}$$

Thus

$$E\left[\tilde{z}_1^*(t)\tilde{z}_1(t)\right] = p_d + p_i + \sigma^2. \tag{3.141}$$

To evaluate Eqs. (3.138) and (3.139), we substitute for $S_{\tilde{d}}(\omega)$, $S_{\tilde{i}}(\omega)$, and $\Delta(\omega)$.

After some algebra, we find

$$E\left[\tilde{z}_1^*(t)\tilde{z}_2(t)\right]$$

$$= p_d e^{-j\phi_d}\left[\operatorname{sinc}\frac{B_d\phi_d}{2} + \frac{E}{2}\operatorname{sinc}\frac{B_d(\phi_d - \phi_e)}{2} + \frac{E}{2}\operatorname{sinc}\frac{B_d(\phi_d + \phi_e)}{2}\right]$$

$$+ p_i e^{-j\phi_i}\left[\operatorname{sinc}\frac{B_i\phi_i}{2} + \frac{E}{2}\operatorname{sinc}\frac{B_i(\phi_i - \phi_e)}{2} + \frac{E}{2}\operatorname{sinc}\frac{B_i(\phi_i + \phi_e)}{2}\right],$$

$$(3.142)$$

and

$$E\left[\tilde{z}_2^*(t)\tilde{z}_2(t)\right]$$

$$= p_d\left[1 + \frac{E^2}{2} + 2E\operatorname{sinc}\frac{B_d\phi_e}{2} + \frac{E^2}{2}\operatorname{sinc}B_d\phi_e\right]$$

$$+ p_i\left[1 + \frac{E^2}{2} + 2E\operatorname{sinc}\frac{B_i\phi_e}{2} + \frac{E^2}{2}\operatorname{sinc}B_i\phi_e\right] + \sigma^2, \quad (3.143)$$

where

$$\phi_e = \omega_d T_e. \tag{3.144}$$

All other quantities in Eqs. (3.142) and (3.143) have been defined previously.

For convenience, we shall normalize Φ_z with respect to σ^2. Also, we note that $(1/\sigma^2)\Phi_z$ can be written as a sum of desired, interference, and noise terms,

$$\frac{1}{\sigma^2}\Phi_z = \frac{1}{\sigma^2}\Phi_{zd} + \frac{1}{\sigma^2}\Phi_{zi} + \frac{1}{\sigma^2}\Phi_{zn}. \tag{3.145}$$

The normalized desired and interference covariance matrices can be written

$$\frac{1}{\sigma^2}\Phi_{zp} = \begin{bmatrix} \phi_{11p} & \phi_{12p} \\ \phi_{21p} & \phi_{22p} \end{bmatrix}, \tag{3.146}$$

where

$$\phi_{11p} = \xi_p, \tag{3.147}$$

$$\phi_{12p} = \xi_p e^{-j\phi_p}\left[\operatorname{sinc}\frac{B_p\phi_p}{2} + \frac{E}{2}\operatorname{sinc}\frac{B_p(\phi_p - \phi_e)}{2} + \frac{E}{2}\operatorname{sinc}\frac{B_p(\phi_p + \phi_e)}{2}\right],$$

$$(3.148)$$

$$\phi_{21p} = \phi_{12p}^*, \tag{3.149}$$

and

$$\phi_{22p} = \xi_p\left[1 + \frac{E^2}{2} + 2E\operatorname{sinc}\frac{B_p\phi_e}{2} + \frac{E^2}{2}\operatorname{sinc}B_p\phi_e\right]. \tag{3.150}$$

and where the subscript p is either d or i. The normalized noise matrix is simply

$$\frac{1}{\sigma^2}\Phi_{zn} = \mathbf{I}. \qquad (3.151)$$

Before continuing, let us discuss ϕ_e in Eq. (3.144). To choose ϕ_e, it will be helpful to relate T_e to the number of cycles of amplitude ripple in a given bandwidth. With $\Delta(\omega)$ defined in Eq. (3.123), and for a given T_e, a frequency change of

$$\Delta\omega = \frac{2\pi}{T_e} \qquad (3.152)$$

is required to produce one cycle of amplitude ripple. Hence, the number of cycles of ripple in a bandwidth $\Delta\omega_d$ is

$$K = \frac{\Delta\omega_d}{\Delta\omega} = \frac{\Delta\omega_d T_e}{2\pi}. \qquad (3.153)$$

To obtain K cycles in bandwidth $\Delta\omega_d$, T_e should be chosen to be

$$T_e = \frac{2\pi K}{\Delta\omega_d}. \qquad (3.154)$$

Therefore,

$$\phi_e = \omega_d T_e = \frac{2\pi K}{B_d}. \qquad (3.155)$$

We can determine the proper value of ϕ_e by choosing the number of cycles of ripple K for a given bandwidth B_d.

Next let us compute the reference correlation vector with the filters $H_j(\omega)$ in the signal paths. For the reference signal, we assume

$$\tilde{r}(t) = \frac{R}{\sqrt{p_d}}\tilde{d}(t), \qquad (3.156)$$

as in Eq. (3.75) with $\eta = 0$. Since only the desired signal component of $\tilde{z}_j(t)$ correlates with $\tilde{r}(t)$, we have

$$E[\tilde{z}_1^*(t)\tilde{r}(t)] = E\left[\tilde{d}^*(t)\frac{R}{\sqrt{p_d}}\tilde{d}(t)\right] = \frac{R}{\sqrt{p_d}}R_d(0) = R\sqrt{p_d}. \qquad (3.157)$$

To obtain $E[\tilde{z}_2^*(t)\tilde{r}(t)]$, we note that since $H_1(\omega) = 1$, the desired signal component of $\tilde{z}_1(t)$ is just $\tilde{d}(t)$. Hence $E[\tilde{z}_2^*(t)\tilde{r}(t)]$ is just $R/\sqrt{p_d}$ times the desired signal part of $E[\tilde{z}_2^*(t)\tilde{z}_1(t)]$,

$$E\left[\tilde{z}_2^*(t)\tilde{r}(t)\right] = R\sqrt{p_d}\,e^{j\phi_d}\left[\operatorname{sinc}\frac{B_d\phi_d}{2} + \frac{E}{2}\operatorname{sinc}\frac{B_d(\phi_d - \phi_e)}{2}\right.$$
$$\left. + \frac{E}{2}\operatorname{sinc}\frac{B_d(\phi_d + \phi_e)}{2}\right]. \qquad (3.158)$$

Hence the normalized reference correlation vector is

$$\frac{1}{\sigma^2}\mathbf{S}_z = \frac{R}{\sigma}\sqrt{\xi_d}\left[e^{j\phi_d}\left\{\operatorname{sinc}\frac{B_d\phi_d}{2} + \frac{E}{2}\operatorname{sinc}\frac{B_d(\phi_d - \phi_e)}{2}\right.\right.$$
$$\left.\left. + \frac{E}{2}\operatorname{sinc}\frac{B_d(\phi_d + \phi_e)}{2}\right\}\right]. \qquad (3.159)$$

The weight vector can now be computed from Eq. (3.112).

From the weight vector, the output desired signal may be found. It is

$$\tilde{s}_d(t) = \mathbf{W}^T\mathbf{Z}_d. \qquad (3.160)$$

The output desired signal power, normalized to σ^2, is

$$\frac{1}{\sigma^2}P_d = \frac{1}{2\sigma^2}E\left[|\tilde{s}_d(t)|^2\right] = \frac{1}{2\sigma^2}E\left[|\mathbf{W}^T\mathbf{Z}_d|^2\right]$$
$$= \frac{1}{2\sigma^2}\mathbf{W}^\dagger E\left[\mathbf{Z}_d^*\mathbf{Z}_d^T\right]\mathbf{W} = \tfrac{1}{2}\mathbf{W}^\dagger\left[\frac{1}{\sigma^2}\Phi_{zd}\right]\mathbf{W}. \qquad (3.161)$$

Similarly, the normalized output interference power is

$$\frac{1}{\sigma^2}P_i = \tfrac{1}{2}\mathbf{W}^\dagger\left[\frac{1}{\sigma^2}\Phi_{zi}\right]\mathbf{W}, \qquad (3.162)$$

and the normalized output noise power is

$$\frac{1}{\sigma^2}P_n = \tfrac{1}{2}\mathbf{W}^\dagger\left[\frac{1}{\sigma^2}\Phi_{zn}\right]\mathbf{W} = \tfrac{1}{2}\mathbf{W}^\dagger\mathbf{W}, \qquad (3.163)$$

according to Eq. (3.151). The output SINR is then

$$\mathrm{SINR} = \frac{P_d/\sigma^2}{P_i/\sigma^2 + P_n/\sigma^2} = \frac{\mathbf{W}^\dagger\left[\dfrac{1}{\sigma^2}\Phi_{zd}\right]\mathbf{W}}{\mathbf{W}^\dagger\left[\dfrac{1}{\sigma^2}\Phi_{zi} + \mathbf{I}\right]\mathbf{W}}. \qquad (3.164)$$

Figure 3.18 shows a typical set of calculations obtained from these equations for the case where $\xi_i = 40$ dB, $B_d = 0$, $B_i = 0.01$, $\theta_d = 50°$, $\theta_i = 0°$, and $\phi_e =$

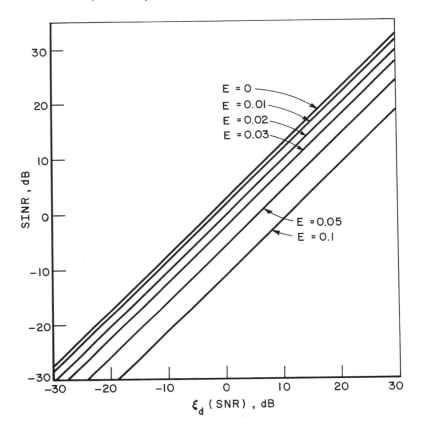

Figure 3.18 SINR versus ξ_d for several E: $\theta_d = 50°$, $\theta_i = 0°$, $B_d = 0$, $B_i = 0.01$, $K = 10$, $\xi_i = 40$ dB.

$2,000\pi$. (This value of ϕ_e yields 10 cycles of ripple in bandwidth 0.01.) We have chosen $\theta_i = 0°$ for these calculations so there is no interference decorrelation between channels due to interelement propagation delay. The SINR degradation in Fig. 3.18 is due entirely to filter mismatch between the channels.

Figure 3.18 shows the SINR versus the input SNR, ξ_d, for $E = 0.01, 0.02, 0.03, 0.05$, and 0.1. It may be seen how the SINR drops as E increases. To get a feeling for the allowable mismatch, suppose we wish to keep the SINR from being degraded more than 1 dB below its ideal value. To do so, Fig. 3.18 shows that E must not exceed 0.01. Thus the passband ripple must be held to $\pm 1\%$, or equivalently, the channels must match to within 0.086 dB.

Moreover, things are even worse if the array must handle higher interference power. Figure 3.19 shows another plot of SINR versus ξ_d for the same conditions as in Fig. 3.18 except that the input INR is 70 dB. In this case,

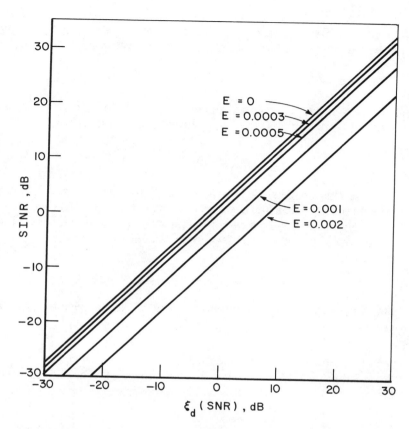

Figure 3.19 SINR versus ξ_d for several E: $\theta_d = 50°$, $\theta_i = 0°$, $B_d = 0$, $B_i = 0.01$, K = 10, $\xi_i = 70$ dB.

holding the SINR degradation to 1 dB will require $E \leqslant 0.0003$ or, equivalently, will require the amplitudes of the channel transfer functions to match to within 0.0026 dB! Obviously, this is a severe requirement. Nulling high power interference with nonzero bandwidth requires extremely careful channel matching in an adaptive array.

Thus, to summarize, interference bandwidth can be a problem in an adaptive array for two reasons. First, an interference signal with nonzero bandwidth becomes decorrelated between elements when there is an interelement propagation delay. Second, any mismatch in channel characteristics can also reduce the interference correlation between elements. It is clear from the above discussion that the nulling performance of an adaptive array may be unsatisfactory even for modest bandwidths.

How then can we operate an adaptive array if the interference will have significant bandwidth? One possible answer is to use tapped delay lines behind the elements instead of quadrature hybrids. We consider this option below.

The Use of Tapped Delay Lines

First, let us see why tapped delay lines are helpful. For an interference signal arriving from angle θ_i, the interelement phase shift is

$$\phi_i = \frac{\omega L}{c} \sin \theta_i. \quad = \quad 2\pi \left(\frac{d}{\lambda}\right) \sin \theta_i \atop \leftarrow K \qquad (3.165)$$

Because this phase shift is a function of frequency, its value varies across the interference bandwidth. If we wish to cancel the interference signal perfectly in the array output, the processing behind the elements must be able to provide a phase shift that also varies with frequency. To create a perfect null on the interference would require

$$w_2 = -w_1 e^{-j\phi_i} = -w_1 e^{-j(\omega L/c)\sin \theta_i}. \qquad (3.166)$$

However, the transfer function of a single complex weight w_i is simply

$$H(\omega) = w_i = w_{I_i} - jw_{Q_i}, \qquad (3.167)$$

which is constant with frequency.

Suppose a tapped delay line as shown in Fig. 3.20 is used behind each element of the array. Such a tapped delay line has transfer function,

$$H(\omega) = w_1 + w_2 e^{-j\omega T} + w_3 e^{-j2\omega T} + \cdots + w_K e^{-j(K-1)\omega T}, \qquad (3.168)$$

which is a function of frequency. (It is, in fact, a finite Fourier series.) If the weights are properly chosen, this transfer function can compensate (approximately) for the variation in ϕ_i over the bandwidth.

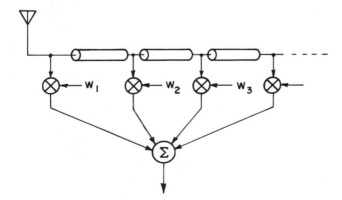

Figure 3.20 Tapped delay-line processing.

Viewed in the time domain, a tapped delay line allows the array to insert a variable amount of delay behind each element. This delay can be used by the adaptive processor to compensate for interelement propagation delays between elements. If the delay-line sections are very short and there are many taps, then the processor can approximate almost any delay by turning on the weight at the appropriate tap and turning off the other weights. However, such a delay line would probably have too many taps to be practical. A more practical tapped delay line with longer delays between taps and just a few weights can match only certain amounts of delay exactly. For other amounts of delay, it forms an approximate match. But even this approximate match yields better array bandwidth than quadrature hybrid processing.

Analysis of Tapped Delay-Line Arrays[‡]

Let us first see how to analyze an array with tapped delay lines. To illustrate the method, we shall consider a two-element array as shown in Fig. 3.21. Assume the elements are isotropic and a half wavelength apart at the signal frequency ω_d. Also, assume each element is followed by a tapped delay line with K taps and a delay of T_0 seconds between taps, as shown. Let $\tilde{x}_{mk}(t)$ denote the analytic signal from element m at tap k. The output of the first tap behind each element is the element signal itself, with no delay. Thus, $\tilde{x}_{11}(t)$ is the signal received on element 1, $\tilde{x}_{21}(t)$ is the signal on element 2, $\tilde{x}_{12}(t) = \tilde{x}_{11}(t - T_0)$, $\tilde{x}_{1k}(t) = \tilde{x}_{11}(t - [k - 1]T_0)$, and so forth.

The tap signals are combined by an adaptive processor, which multiplies each $\tilde{x}_{mk}(t)$ by a complex weight w_{mk} and then sums the signals to produce the array output $\tilde{s}(t)$, as shown in Fig. 3.21. We assume the adaptive processor sets the weights equal to the optimal LMS weights. To find the optimal weights, we proceed as follows: Let $\mathbf{X}_m$ and $\mathbf{W}_m$ be column vectors containing the signals and weights at the K taps behind element m,

$$\mathbf{X}_m = \left[\tilde{x}_{m1}(t), \tilde{x}_{m2}(t), \dots, \tilde{x}_{mK}(t) \right]^T \tag{3.169}$$

and

$$\mathbf{W}_m = \left[w_{m1}, w_{m2}, \dots, w_{mK} \right]^T. \tag{3.170}$$

We shall refer to $\mathbf{X}_m$ as the *element* signal vector and $\mathbf{W}_m$ as the *element* weight vector. Next, let $\mathbf{X}$ and $\mathbf{W}$ be the *total* signal and weight vectors for the entire array,

$$\mathbf{X} = \left[\frac{\mathbf{X}_1}{\mathbf{X}_2} \right], \tag{3.171}$$

and

$$\mathbf{W} = \left[\frac{\mathbf{W}_1}{\mathbf{W}_2} \right], \tag{3.172}$$

---

‡Portions of this section have been reprinted from the author's paper [18] with permission of IEEE.

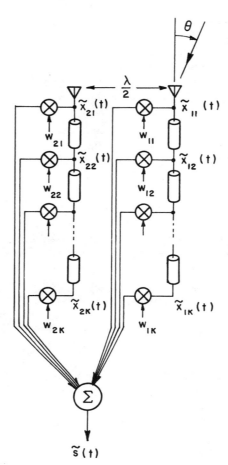

Figure 3.21 A two-element adaptive array with tapped delay lines.

where $\mathbf{X}$ and $\mathbf{W}$ are written in partitioned form. The optimal weight vector is

$$\mathbf{W} = \boldsymbol{\Phi}^{-1}\mathbf{S}, \qquad (3.173)$$

where, as usual,

$$\boldsymbol{\Phi} = E[\mathbf{X}^*\mathbf{X}^T], \qquad (3.174)$$

and

$$\mathbf{S} = E[\mathbf{X}^*\tilde{r}(t)], \qquad (3.175)$$

with $\tilde{r}(t)$ the reference signal.

Assume the array receives a desired signal and an interference signal. Also, assume each element signal contains uncorrelated thermal noise. The signal $\tilde{x}_{mk}(t)$ may be written

$$\tilde{x}_{mk}(t) = \tilde{d}_{mk}(t) + \tilde{i}_{mk}(t) + \tilde{n}_{mk}(t), \qquad (3.176)$$

where $\tilde{d}_{mk}(t)$, $\tilde{i}_{mk}(t)$, and $\tilde{n}_{mk}(t)$ are the desired, interference, and noise components, respectively. The element signal vectors $\mathbf{X}_m$ and the total signal vector $\mathbf{X}$ may then be split in a similar way,

$$\mathbf{X}_m = \mathbf{X}_{dm} + \mathbf{X}_{im} + \mathbf{X}_{nm} \qquad (3.177)$$

and

$$\mathbf{X} = \mathbf{X}_d + \mathbf{X}_i + \mathbf{X}_n. \qquad (3.178)$$

The signals $\tilde{d}_{mk}(t)$, $\tilde{i}_{mk}(t)$, and $\tilde{n}_{mk}(t)$ may be found as follows.

First, suppose the desired signal arrives from angle θ_d. If $\tilde{d}(t)$ is the desired signal waveform on element 1, the desired signal at an arbitrary tap is

$$\tilde{d}_{mk}(t) = \tilde{d}(t - [k-1]T_0 - [m-1]T_d), \qquad (3.179)$$

where T_d is the desired signal spatial propagation delay between elements,

$$T_d = \frac{\lambda}{2c} \sin \theta_d. \qquad (3.180)$$

(λ is the wavelength.) Next, let the interference signal arrive from angle θ_i and produce waveform $\tilde{i}(t)$ on element 1. The interference signal at an arbitrary tap is then

$$\tilde{i}_{mk}(t) = \tilde{i}(t - [k-1]T_0 - [m-1]T_i), \qquad (3.181)$$

with

$$T_i = \frac{\lambda}{2c} \sin \theta_i. \qquad (3.182)$$

Finally, let the signal from element m contain a thermal noise voltage $\tilde{n}_{m1}(t)$ of power σ^2, independent between elements, so

$$E\left[\tilde{n}_{j1}^*(t)\tilde{n}_{m1}(t)\right] = \sigma^2\delta_{jm}, \; 1 \leqslant j, m \leqslant 2, \qquad (3.183)$$

where δ_{jm} is the Kronecker delta. The noise voltage at tap k is just a delayed version of $\tilde{n}_{m1}(t)$,

$$\tilde{n}_{mk}(t) = \tilde{n}_{m1}(t - [k-1]T_0). \qquad (3.184)$$

We assume the $\tilde{n}_{m1}(t)$ are independent of $\tilde{d}(t)$ and $\tilde{i}(t)$, as usual.

From the signals, Φ and $\mathbf{S}$ in Eqs. (3.174) and (3.175) may be calculated. Because $\tilde{d}(t)$, $\tilde{i}(t)$, and the $\tilde{n}_{m1}(t)$ are all independent, Φ is a sum of desired, interference, and thermal noise terms,

$$\Phi = \Phi_d + \Phi_i + \Phi_n. \qquad (3.185)$$

Consider Φ_d first. In partitioned form, Φ_d is

$$\Phi_d = \left[\begin{array}{c|c} \Phi_{d_{11}} & \Phi_{d_{12}} \\ \hline \Phi_{d_{21}} & \Phi_{d_{22}} \end{array} \right], \qquad (3.186)$$

where each submatrix $\Phi_{d_{mn}}$ is a $K \times K$ covariance matrix associated with a pair of element signal vectors $\mathbf{X}_{dm}$ and $\mathbf{X}_{dn}$,

$$\Phi_{d_{mn}} = E\left[\mathbf{X}_{dm}^* \mathbf{X}_{dn}^T\right]. \tag{3.187}$$

The matrix $\Phi_{d_{mn}}$ may be found by substituting $\tilde{d}_{mk}(t)$ of Eq. (3.179) into Eq. (3.187). The jkth term of $\Phi_{d_{mn}}$ (i.e., the element in the jth row and kth column of $\Phi_{d_{mn}}$) is

$$\left[\Phi_{d_{mn}}\right]_{jk} = R_{\tilde{d}}\left[(j-k)T_0 + (m-n)T_d\right], \tag{3.188}$$

where $R_{\tilde{d}}(\tau)$ is the autocorrelation function of $\tilde{d}(t)$ in Eq. (3.62). We shall again assume $\tilde{d}(t)$ has a flat, bandlimited power spectral density $S_{\tilde{d}}(\omega)$ equal to $2\pi p_d/\Delta\omega_d$ over a bandwidth $\Delta\omega_d$ centered at frequency ω_d, as shown in Fig. 3.8. $R_{\tilde{d}}(\tau)$ is then given in Eq. (3.64).

For a specific arrival angle θ_d and tap delay T_0, the matrix Φ_d in Eq. (3.186) can be found by substituting Eq. (3.64) into Eq. (3.188). First, however, we write the autocorrelation function in normalized form. From Eq. (3.64), we have

$$R_d\left[(j-k)T_0 + (m-n)T_d\right]$$

$$= p_d \,\text{sinc}\left\{\frac{\Delta\omega_d}{2}\left[(j-k)T_0 + (m-n)T_d\right]\right\} e^{j\omega_d[(j-k)T_0 + (m-n)T_d]}. \tag{3.189}$$

For $\omega_d T_d$ we substitute $B_d\phi_d$ as in Eq. (3.68). In addition, we shall arbitrarily normalize T_0 to a quarter-wavelength delay. Note that the time delay required to produce a 90° phase shift at frequency ω_d is

$$T_{90°} = \frac{\pi}{2\omega_d}. \tag{3.190}$$

Therefore, we write T_0 in the form

$$T_0 = rT_{90°} = \frac{\pi r}{2\omega_d}, \tag{3.191}$$

where r is the number of quarter-wave delays in T_0 at frequency ω_d. Then also

$$\Delta\omega_d T_0 = \Delta\omega_d \frac{\pi r}{2\omega_d} = \frac{\pi}{2} r B_d. \tag{3.192}$$

Using the normalized parameters B_d, ϕ_d, and r, we write the jkth element of $\Phi_{d_{mn}}$ as

$$\left[\Phi_{d_{mn}}\right]_{jk} = p_d \,\text{sinc}\left\{\frac{B_d}{2}\left[\frac{\pi}{2}(j-k)r + (m-n)\phi_d\right]\right\}$$

$$e^{j[(\pi/2)(j-k)r + (m-n)\phi_d]}. \tag{3.193}$$

The interference matrix $\mathbf{\Phi}_i$ in Eq. (3.185) is found in the same way. We have

$$\mathbf{\Phi} = \left[\begin{array}{c|c} \mathbf{\Phi}_{i_{11}} & \mathbf{\Phi}_{i_{12}} \\ \hline \mathbf{\Phi}_{i_{21}} & \mathbf{\Phi}_{i_{22}} \end{array}\right], \tag{3.194}$$

where each submatrix $\mathbf{\Phi}_{i_{mn}}$ is a $K \times K$ covariance matrix of the element signal vectors $\mathbf{X}_{im}$ and $\mathbf{X}_{in}$,

$$\mathbf{\Phi}_{imn} = E\left[\mathbf{X}_{im}^* \mathbf{X}_{in}^T\right]. \tag{3.195}$$

The jkth element of $\mathbf{\Phi}_{i_{mn}}$ is

$$\left[\mathbf{\Phi}_{i_{mn}}\right]_{jk} = R_{\tilde{i}}[(j-k)T_0 + (m-n)T_i], \tag{3.196}$$

where $R_{\tilde{i}}(\tau)$ is the autocorrelation function of the interference, given in Eq. (3.84). Assuming the interference has the spectral density shown in Fig. 3.9 and using the normalized quantities in Eqs. (3.85), (3.86), (3.191), and (3.192), we find

$$\left[\mathbf{\Phi}_{i_{mn}}\right]_{jk} = p_i \, \text{sinc}\left\{\frac{B_i}{2}\left[\frac{\pi}{2}(j-k)r + (m-n)\phi_i\right]\right\}$$

$$e^{j[(\pi/2)(j-k)r+(m-n)\phi_i]}. \tag{3.197}$$

The noise covariance matrix is slightly different because the noise is independent between elements. As a result, the noise cross products are all zero except those associated with the same element. We find

$$\mathbf{\Phi}_i = \left[\begin{array}{c|c} \mathbf{\Phi}_{n_{11}} & 0 \\ \hline 0 & \mathbf{\Phi}_{n_{22}} \end{array}\right]. \tag{3.198}$$

Note that when the array includes tapped delay lines, we must specify not only the noise power as in Eq. (3.93), but also its spectral density. We shall assume the noise has a flat bandlimited spectral density $S_{\tilde{n}}(\omega)$, equal to $2\pi\sigma^2/\Delta\omega_n$ over a bandwidth $\Delta\omega_n$, as shown in Fig. 3.22. The jkth element of $\mathbf{\Phi}_{n_{mn}}$ is then

$$\left[\mathbf{\Phi}_{n_{mn}}\right]_{jk} = \sigma^2 \, \text{sinc}\left[\frac{B_n}{4}(j-k)r\pi\right] e^{j(\pi/2)(j-k)r}, \tag{3.199}$$

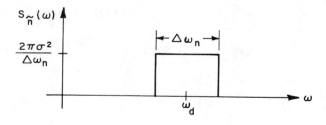

Figure 3.22 The noise power spectral density.

where B_n is the relative noise bandwidth,

$$B_n = \frac{\Delta\omega_n}{\omega_d}. \tag{3.200}$$

We have now obtained all terms in the matrix $\mathbf{\Phi}$ of Eq. (3.174).

Next, consider the reference correlation vector $\mathbf{S}$. Since the interference and noise vectors $\mathbf{X}_i$ and $\mathbf{X}_n$ are independent of $\tilde{d}(t)$, only $\mathbf{X}_d$ contributes to $\mathbf{S}$,

$$\mathbf{S} = E[\mathbf{X}^*\tilde{r}(t)] = E[\mathbf{X}_d^*\tilde{r}(t)]. \tag{3.201}$$

We assume the reference signal is a normalized version of $\tilde{d}(t)$,

$$\tilde{r}(t) = \frac{1}{\sqrt{p_d}}\tilde{d}(t). \tag{3.202}$$

[The factor $1/\sqrt{p_d}$ makes $\tilde{r}(t)$ have a fixed voltage, independent of the desired signal power p_d.] Substituting Eqs. (3.179) and (3.202) into Eq. (3.201) and using the autocorrelation function in Eq. (3.189), we find

$$\mathbf{S} = \begin{bmatrix} s_{11} \\ s_{12} \\ \vdots \\ s_{1K} \\ s_{21} \\ s_{22} \\ \vdots \\ s_{2K} \end{bmatrix} \tag{3.203}$$

where

$$s_{mk} = \sqrt{p_d}\,\text{sinc}\left\{\frac{B_d}{2}\left[\frac{\pi}{2}(j-1)r + (m-1)\phi_d\right]\right\}e^{j[(\pi/2)(j-1)r+(m-1)\phi_d]}. \tag{3.204}$$

From $\mathbf{\Phi}$ and $\mathbf{S}$, the optimal array weight vector may be found by solving Eq. (3.173) numerically. Before doing so, we also divide $\mathbf{\Phi}$ and $\mathbf{S}$ by σ^2, so that the solution for $\mathbf{W}$ will depend only on the desired signal-to-noise ratio per element ξ_d and the interference-to-noise ratio per element ξ_i.

From the optimal weight vector $\mathbf{W}$, the output SINR may be computed in the usual way. The output desired signal power P_d is

$$P_d = \tfrac{1}{2}E\left[|\tilde{s}_d(t)|^2\right] = \tfrac{1}{2}\mathbf{W}^\dagger\mathbf{\Phi}_d\mathbf{W}, \tag{3.205}$$

and the output interference and thermal noise powers are

$$P_i = \tfrac{1}{2}\mathbf{W}^\dagger\mathbf{\Phi}_i\mathbf{W} \tag{3.206}$$

and

$$P_n = \tfrac{1}{2}\mathbf{W}^\dagger\mathbf{\Phi}_n\mathbf{W}. \qquad (3.207)$$

From these formulas, we can calculate the output SINR in Eq. (3.104).

Array Performance with Tapped Delay Lines

Now let us examine how tapped delay lines affect the bandwidth performance of this two-element array. We begin by comparing its performance with and without tapped delay lines, and then we determine how the number of taps and the amount of delay between taps affect the results.

First, consider the performance of the array without tapped delay lines. Figure 3.23 shows the SINR of the two-element array with a single complex weight and no delay behind each element. It is assumed that the desired signal arrives from broadside ($\theta_d = 0°$) and the interference from an arbitrary angle θ_i. The SINR is shown as a function of θ_i. The desired interference and noise signals each have the same bandwidth B, and Fig. 3.23 shows the SINR for $B = 0$, 0.0, 0.02, 0.05, and 0.2. The SNR per element is $\xi_d = 0$ dB, and the INR per element is $\xi_i = 40$ dB for all curves.

As may be seen in Fig. 3.23, when $B = 0.02$ the output SINR has dropped about 3 dB below its value for $B = 0$. Larger bandwidths reduce the SINR even more. For $B = 0.2$, the degradation is as much as 22 dB for some θ_i. Array performance is unacceptable for such large bandwidths.

Now suppose we add a quarter-wavelength delay and one extra tap behind each element. (In the preceding equations we let $K = 2$ and $r = 1$.) Figure 3.24 shows the output SINR for this case with $B = 0.2$ and with all other parameters the same as in Fig. 3.23. Note that the array performance is now just as good as for the simple array in Fig. 3.23 with $B = 0$. Thus, adding a quarter-wavelength delay and one extra weight to each element completely eliminates the bandwidth degradation.

Figures 3.23 and 3.24 are computed for $\theta_d = 0°$. However, similar results are obtained for other values of θ_d. Regardless of θ_d, when the array has a single

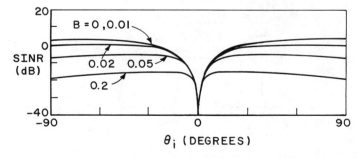

Figure 3.23   SINR versus θ_i: $K = 1$, $\theta_d = 0°$, $\xi_d = 0$ dB, $\xi_i = 40$ dB (reprinted from [18] with permission, © 1988 IEEE).

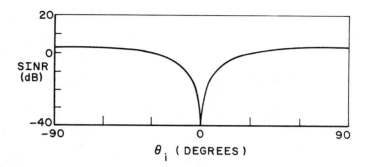

Figure 3.24 SINR versus θ_i: $r = 1$, $K = 2$, $B = 0.2$, $\theta_d = 0°$, $\xi_d = 0$ dB, $\xi_i = 40$ dB (reprinted from [18] with permission, © 1988 IEEE).

weight behind each element, the SINR for $B = 0.2$ is much poorer than for $B = 0$. But if a quarter-wave delay and one extra tap are added to each element, the performance is fully restored.

Now let us consider how the amount of delay between taps affects these results. To obtain Fig. 3.24, we assumed $r = 1$, that is, a quarter wavelength between taps. However, this is just an arbitrary choice. If other values of r are used, one finds an interesting result: the value of r hardly affects the SINR! Starting from $r = 1$, we find that reducing r, even to an arbitrarily small value, has no effect on the SINR. A plot of SINR versus θ_i for $r = 10^{-4}$, for example, looks identical to Fig. 3.24. On the other hand, if we increase r above 1, we also find very little change in SINR, until r exceeds about 5. To illustrate this behavior, Fig. 3.25 shows the SINR versus θ_i for $r = 5, 10, 15, 20,$ and 25, with all other parameters the same as in Fig. 3.24. Note that when $r = 5$ the SINR is still as good as the optimal value in Fig. 3.24. When $r = 10$ (i.e., for 2.5 wavelengths between taps), the SINR has dropped about 1 dB below optimal. For $r = 15$ and above, the degradation is more serious, particularly for θ_i near $\pm 90°$.

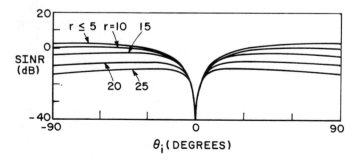

Figure 3.25 SINR versus θ_i: $K = 2$, $B = 0.2$, $\theta_d = 0°$, $\xi_d = 0$ dB, $\xi_i = 40$ dB (reprinted from [18] with permission, © 1988 IEEE).

Thus the array performance is not very sensitive to r. All values of r in the range $0 < r < 5$ yield essentially the same SINR. The reader may find this result puzzling, especially the fact that the SINR is unaffected when r approaches zero. At first glance, it seems intuitively that a tapped delay line should become equivalent to a single weight when the delay goes to zero. However, this is not the case, as we shall see.

To understand why r affects the performance the way it does, consider the transfer function of the array as seen by the interference. First, let $H_m(\omega)$ be the transfer function of the delay line behind element m in Fig. 3.21. In general, with K taps and $K-1$ delays behind element m, $H_m(\omega)$ is

$$H_m(\omega) = w_{m1} + w_{m2}e^{-j\omega T_0} + \cdots + w_{mK}e^{-j\omega(K-1)T_0}. \qquad (3.208)$$

Then let $H_i(\omega)$ be the transfer function of the entire array as seen by the interference:

$$H_i(\omega) = H_1(\omega) + H_2(\omega)e^{-j\omega T_i}, \qquad (3.209)$$

with T_i given in Eq. (3.182). To null an interference signal completely, $H_i(\omega)$ must be zero over the interference bandwidth; that is $H_1(\omega)$ and $H_2(\omega)$ must be related by

Always required $$H_1(\omega) = -H_2(\omega)e^{-j\omega T_i}. \quad \text{for nulling } \theta_i. \qquad (3.210)$$

The reason for Eq. (3.210) is easy to see. An interference signal from angle θ_i arrives at element 2 at a time T_i later than at element 1. If the interference has nonzero bandwidth, this delay decorrelates the signals on the two elements and makes it difficult to null the interference by subtracting one element signal from another. But when $H_1(\omega)$ and $H_2(\omega)$ satisfy Eq. (3.210), the factor $e^{-j\omega T_i}$ will delay the interference an additional time T_i in element 1 and restore its correlation with the interference on element 2. The minus sign will then make the interference cancel at the array output.

Before we consider the effect of varying r, let us see how well Eq. (3.210) is satisfied by the arrays studied in Figs. 3.23 and 3.24. Note that Eq. (3.210) requires $H_1(\omega)$ and $H_2(\omega)$ to have identical amplitudes,

$$|H_1(\omega)| = |H_2(\omega)|, \qquad (3.211)$$

and to have phases related by

$$\angle H_1(\omega) = \angle H_2(\omega) - \pi - \omega T_i, \qquad (3.212)$$

over the signal bandwidth. For the curves in Fig. 3.23, we assumed one weight (with no delays) behind each element. For this case $H_m(\omega)$ is simply

$$H_m(\omega) = w_{m1}, \qquad (3.213)$$

which is a constant independent of frequency. With such an $H_m(\omega)$, Eq. (3.210) can be satisfied at only one frequency, not over a band of frequencies. For the array in Fig. 3.24, however, we used two weights and one delay behind each

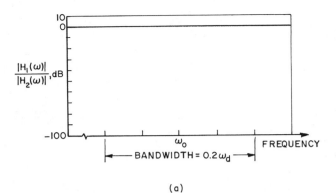

(a)

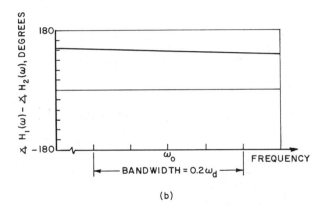

(b)

Figure 3.26 The transfer functions $H_1(\omega)$ and $H_2(\omega)$: $r = 1$, $K = 2$, $B = 0.2$, $\theta_d = 0°$, $\theta_i = 20°$, $\xi_d = 0$ dB, $\xi_i = 40$ dB. (a) $|H_1(\omega)/H_2(\omega)|$ versus ω; (b) $\angle H_1(\omega) - \angle H_2(\omega)$ versus ω (reprinted from [18] with permission, © 1988 IEEE).

element. In this case each $H_m(\omega)$ has the form

$$H_m(\omega) = w_{m1} + w_{m2}e^{-j\omega T_0}. \qquad (3.214)$$

Because of the term $e^{-j\omega T_0}$, the $H_m(\omega)$ can now vary with frequency. Hence $H_1(\omega)$ and $H_2(\omega)$ can do a better job of satisfying Eq. (3.210) over the signal bandwidth, so better bandwidth performance results, as Fig. 3.24 shows.

If we compute the $H_1(\omega)$ and $H_2(\omega)$ that actually result with two weights and one delay behind each element, we find that the processor does attempt to satisfy Eq. (3.210). For example, Fig. 3.26 shows $|H_1(\omega)/H_2(\omega)|$ and $\angle H_1(\omega) - \angle H_2(\omega)$ versus ω for the same parameters as in Fig. 3.24: $\theta_d = 0°$, $\xi_d = 0$ dB, $\xi_i = 40$ dB, $r = 1$, $B = 0.2$, and $\theta_i = 20°$. Note how $|H_1(\omega)/H_2(\omega)|$ is unity (0 dB) and $\angle H_1(\omega) - \angle H_2(\omega)$ varies linearly with frequency over the signal bandwidth. The slope of $\angle H_1(\omega) - \angle H_2(\omega)$ has the proper value to satisfy Eq. (3.210).

Now consider how r affects the performance. First, suppose we let r approach zero. For very small r (small delay between taps), $H_m(\omega)$ in Eq.

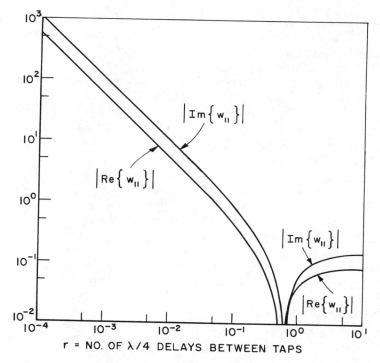

Figure 3.27 w_{11} versus r: $\theta_d = 0°$, $\theta_i = 20°$, $\xi_d = 0$ dB, $\xi_i = 40$ dB, $B = 0.2$ (reprinted from [18] with permission, © 1988 IEEE).

(3.214) becomes

$$H_m(\omega) = w_{m1} + w_{m2}\cos \omega T_0 - jw_{m2}\sin \omega T_0$$

$$\approx w_{m1} + w_{m2} - jw_{m2}\omega T_0. \qquad (3.215)$$

From this equation we note that no matter how small T_0 (or r) is (as long as $T_0 \neq 0$), the array can always obtain any given linear slope for $\angle H_1(\omega) - \angle H_2(\omega)$ by making the weights sufficiently large. That is what happens. As r is made smaller and smaller, the weights obtained from Eq. (3.173) increase without bound. Figure 3.27 shows an example of this behavior. It shows $\text{Re}(w_{11})$ and $\text{Im}(w_{11})$ as functions of r for $\theta_d = 0°$, $\theta_i = 20°$, $\xi_d = 0$ dB, $\xi_i = 40$ dB, and $B = 0.2$, the same parameters as in Fig. 3.26.[‡] The other weights have a similar behavior as $r \to 0$.

Thus, because the weights increase without bound, the array can satisfy Eq. (3.210) regardless of how small r becomes (as long as $r \neq 0$). This behavior is the reason an array with two weights and one delay behind each element does

‡$\text{Re}(x)$ and $\text{Im}(x)$ denote the real and imaginary parts of x, respectively.

not become equivalent to an array with a single weight behind each element as $r \to 0$. With two weights and one delay, the SINR obtained versus θ_i does not change significantly from that in Fig. 3.24 as $r \to 0$.

The unlimited weight increase as $r \to 0$ may also be understood by noting that the covariance matrix in Eq. (3.174) becomes singular when r goes to zero. As $r \to 0$, the signal $\tilde{x}_{m2}(t)$ at the second tap becomes equal to $\tilde{x}_{m1}(t)$, the signal at the first tap. In the limit, when two tap signals are equal, the covariance matrix in Eq. (3.174) has two identical columns (or rows) and hence is singular. Thus it is not surprising that the weight vector $\mathbf{W}$ satisfying Eq. (3.173) exhibits unusual behavior as $r \to 0$.

In a hardware array, there will be some limit to how large the weights can actually become, of course. With analog weights, the feedback circuits always saturate eventually. With digital weights, the maximum attainable weight values are limited by finite register lengths. Because the weights cannot increase indefinitely in a real array, below some minimum r the array will not be able to maintain the SINR.

Now consider what happens if we increase r. Figure 3.25 showed that when r is increased, the array performance is unaffected at first. But finally, for large values of r, the performance begins to drop. This behavior may again be understood from the $H_m(\omega)$.

Regardless of r, the transfer functions $H_1(\omega)$ and $H_2(\omega)$ in a two-element array must satisfy Eq. (3.210) over the interference bandwidth to null the interference. Note, however, that each $H_m(\omega)$ in Eq. (3.208) is a periodic function of frequency. (It is a finite Fourier series.) The value of $H_m(\omega)$ repeats every Ω_0 along the frequency axis, where

$$\text{period of } H_m(\omega) \quad \Omega_0 = \frac{2\pi}{T_0} = \frac{4\omega_d}{r}. \tag{3.216}$$

For small r, this period is much larger than the signal bandwidth. But as r is increased, the period drops. The period Ω_0 will equal the signal bandwidth when

$$r = \frac{4}{B}. \tag{3.217}$$

When r is small and the period is much larger than the bandwidth, $\angle H_1(\omega) - \angle H_2(\omega)$ can easily approximate a linear function of frequency over the signal bandwidth (as seen in Fig. 3.25 for example). But as r is made large, the period Ω_0 becomes comparable to the signal bandwidth. Because the $H_m(\omega)$ are periodic, it then becomes difficult for the $H_m(\omega)$ to satisfy Eq. (3.210) over the whole bandwidth. In particular, if $r > 4/B$, $\angle H_1(\omega) - \angle H_2(\omega)$ cannot vary linearly over the entire bandwidth, since its value must repeat periodically within the bandwidth. It is for this reason that array performance degrades when r becomes too large.

Figure 3.25, computed for $B = 0.2$, illustrates this point. For $B = 0.2$, the period Ω_0 will equal the signal bandwidth when $r = 20$. One finds that there is no drop in SINR for r up to about 5 (i.e., $1/B$). Beyond 5, the SINR drops as r approaches and then passes 20. We find the same general result for all values of B (up to $B = 0.5$): *With two weights and one delay behind each element, the SINR is unaffected by r as long as r is in the range $0 < r < 1/B$.*

The reason the performance degrades for large r may also be understood from a time domain point of view. Signals with nonzero bandwidth remain correlated with themselves for time shifts up to approximately the reciprocal of the bandwidth. Hence, we would expect that adding an extra delay and tap to each element will be effective only if the delays are short compared with the reciprocal of the bandwidth. When the delays are too large, the signals on different taps become decorrelated, and the interference cannot be nulled by subtracting one tap signal from another.

In Figs. 3.24 and 3.25, we assumed two weights and one delay behind each element. Let us now consider what happens if we add extra taps behind each element.

We note first that adding extra taps can help the performance only for certain values of r. On one hand, if $r < 1/B$, the array is already capable of nulling a wideband interference signal. Hence for $r < 1/B$ there is no point in adding extra taps. On the other hand, if $r > 4/B$, the period Ω_0 of the $H_m(\omega)$ is less than the signal bandwidth. In this case it is impossible for the $H_m(\omega)$ to satisfy Eq. (3.210) over the whole bandwidth, regardless of how many taps are used, because $\angle H_1(\omega) - \angle H_2(\omega)$ must repeat periodically within this bandwidth. Hence extra taps can help only when r is in the range $1/B < r < 4/B$. In this range, the period of $H_m(\omega)$ is somewhat larger than the bandwidth, but not large enough that $\angle H_1(\omega) - \angle H_2(\omega)$ can vary linearly with frequency over the bandwidth (with only two weights and one delay). Hence, in this range, adding more Fourier terms in Eq. (3.208) will allow $\angle H_1(\omega) - \angle H_2(\omega)$ to approximate a linear behavior more accurately.

Let us illustrate these remarks for $B = 0.2$. First, for $r < (1/B) = 5$, no extra taps are needed. An array with one delay and two weights already has optimal performance, as may be seen in Fig. 3.24. Next, for $5 < r < 20$, we find that with only two weights and one delay, the SINR is reduced from that in Fig. 3.24. Figure 3.25 showed this behavior. However, for this range of r, the performance will improve if we increase the number of taps. Figure 3.28 shows the SINR versus θ_i for $r = 15$ and for $K = 2, 4, 8,$ and 16 taps. As may be seen, for this r the performance improves with K. The reason for this improvement is seen in Fig. 3.29, which shows $\angle H_1(\omega) - \angle H_2(\omega)$ versus ω for the same cases. Note how $\angle H_1(\omega) - \angle H_2(\omega)$ becomes more nearly linear with ω over the signal bandwidth as K increases. (For this case, $|H_1(\omega)/H_2(\omega)|$ turns out to be unity over the bandwidth for all four values of K.)

Finally, when $r > (4/B) = 20$, we expect poor nulling performance no matter how many extra taps are added, because the period of $\angle H_1(\omega) - \angle H_2(\omega)$

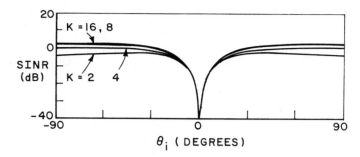

Figure 3.28 SINR versus θ_i: $r = 15$, $B = 0.2$, $\theta_d = 0°$, $\xi_d = 0$ dB, $\xi_i = 40$ dB (reprinted from [18] with permission, © 1988 IEEE).

is smaller than the bandwidth. Figure 3.30 shows such a case. It shows the SINR versus θ_i for $r = 22$ (with $B = 0.2$, $\theta_d = 0°$, $\xi_d = 0$ dB, $\xi_i = 40$ dB) and for $K = 2$, 4, 8, and 16. As may be seen, the SINR improves somewhat with K but never achieves the value in Fig. 3.24. Figure 3.31 shows $|H_1(\omega)/H_2(\omega)|$ and $\angle H_1(\omega) - \angle H_2(\omega)$ for these same cases. Note how $|H_1(\omega)/H_2(\omega)|$ and $\angle H_1(\omega) - \angle H_2(\omega)$ repeat periodically within the signal bandwidth. The ratio $|H_1(\omega)/H_2(\omega)|$ differs from unity at some frequencies within the bandwidth, and $\angle H_1(\omega) - \angle H_2(\omega)$ does not vary linearly across the bandwidth, regardless of how many Fourier series terms are used in the $H_m(\omega)$.

Whether an adaptive array should be operated with r in the range $1/B < r < 4/B$ and with a large value of K depends on how the array is to be implemented. For an array with analog control loops, there is no reason to use such a large value of r. For one thing, it is difficult to implement long analog time delays between taps. For another, each weight in an adaptive processor

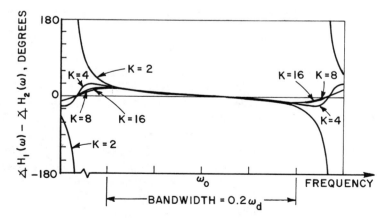

Figure 3.29 $\angle H_1(\omega) - \angle H_2(\omega)$ versus ω: $r = 15$, $B = 0.2$, $\theta_d = 0°$, $\xi_d = 0$ dB, $\xi_i = 40$ dB (reprinted from [18] with permission, © 1988 IEEE).

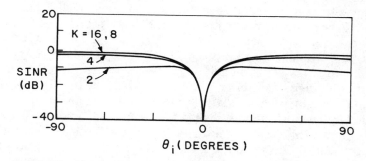

Figure 3.30 SINR versus θ_i: $r = 22$, $B = 0.2$, $\theta_d = 0°$, $\xi_d = 0$ dB, $\xi_i = 40$ dB (reprinted from [18] with permission, © 1988 IEEE).

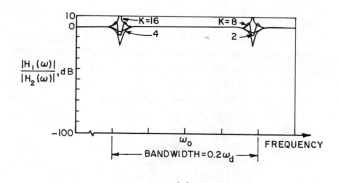

(a)

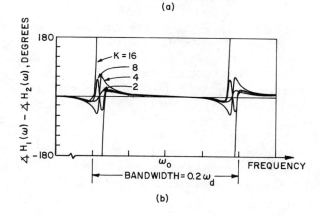

(b)

Figure 3.31 The transfer functions $H_1(\omega)$ and $H_2(\omega)$: $r = 22$, $B = 0.2$, $\theta_d = 0°$, $\xi_d = 0$ dB, $\xi_i = 40$ dB. (a) $|H_1(\omega)/H_2(\omega)|$ versus ω; (b) $\angle H_1(\omega) - \angle H_2(\omega)$ versus ω (reprinted from [18] with permission, © 1988 IEEE).

adds complexity and cost to the processor. To obtain good bandwidth performance from the array, it is simpler just to use a small value of r, such as $r = 1$, and to use only two weights and one delay per element. (We would also not choose $r < 1$, because doing so will result in larger weight values and will increase dynamic range problems in the weight control loops.)

An array with digital weight control, on the other hand, will use an analog-to-digital converter behind each element. In this case, a large value of r may be useful, because a large r corresponds to a low sampling rate. However, if r is large enough, more weights will be needed, as discussed above. Increasing the number of weights in a digital array may be easier than in an analog array, but it will still decrease the speed of the weight control algorithm.[‡]

An additional problem that must be considered when r is large is the effect of the array on the desired signal. The two-element array presents a transfer function

$$H_d(\omega) = \sum_{m=1}^{2} H_m(\omega) e^{-j\omega(m-1)T_d} \tag{3.218}$$

to the desired signal, where T_d is given in Eq. (3.180) and $H_m(\omega)$ in Eq. (3.208). If $H_d(\omega)$ has anything other than a constant amplitude and a linear phase slope over the desired signal bandwidth, the desired signal waveform will be distorted in passing through the array. Whether this distortion is a problem or not depends on the desired signal waveform and the application. However, in communication systems, it is usually difficult to accommodate a desired signal whose waveform changes as the array adapts.

Because the array weights depend on the incoming signals, $H_d(\omega)$ varies in general with all the signal parameters: the power and arrival angle of the desired signal and the power and arrival angle of the interference. For the two-element array considered above, one finds that when r is small ($r < 1/B$), $|H_d(\omega)|$ is constant and $\angle H_d(\omega)$ varies linearly with frequency. But when $r > 1/B$, $H_d(\omega)$ can vary substantially over the desired signal bandwidth. When r is in the range $1/B < r < 4/B$, it turns out that $|H_d(\omega)|$ becomes more nearly constant and $\angle H_d(\omega)$ becomes more nearly linear with frequency as the number of weights K is increased. Figure 3.32 shows a typical case. It shows $|H_d(\omega)|$ and $\angle H_d(\omega)$ over the signal bandwidth for $r = 15$ and $K = 2, 4, 8,$ and 16, with all other parameters the same as in Figs. 3.28 and 3.29. Note how the behavior of $H_d(\omega)$ improves as K increases. On the other hand, for $4/B < r$, it is impossible for $H_d(\omega)$ to have the required behavior over the signal bandwidth, because its period is less than the signal bandwidth. With $r > 4/B$, some desired signal distortion always occurs, no matter how large K is.

[‡]For the discrete LMS algorithm, the computational burden increases linearly with the number of weights. For the sample matrix inverse method, which will be discussed in Section 5.4, it increases with the cube of the number of weights.

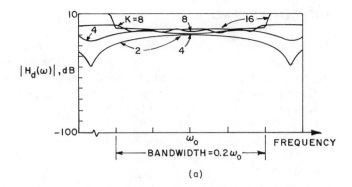

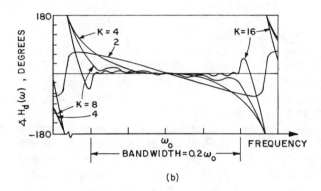

Figure 3.32 The transfer function $H_d(\omega)$: $r = 15$, $B = 0.2$, $\theta_d = 0°$, $\xi_d = 0$ dB, $\xi_i = 40$ dB. (a) $|H_d(\omega)|$ versus ω; $\angle H_d(\omega)$ versus ω (reprinted from [18] with permission, © 1988 IEEE).

These results show how the bandwidth performance of an adaptive array can be improved by using tapped delay lines behind the elements. We found that for a two-element array, two weights and one delay behind each element yield optimal performance (i.e., equal to that obtained with CW interference) for any r in the range $0 < r < 1/B$. If r is reduced below 1, the SINR remains optimal but the array weights become very large. For $r > 1/B$ the SINR is suboptimal with only one delay and two weights behind each element. For r in the range $1/B < r < 4/B$, the performance will improve as more taps are added to each element. But for $r > 4/B$, the performance is suboptimal no matter how many taps are used.

This concludes our discussion of bandwidth effects in adaptive arrays. Our purpose in this section has been to describe why bandwidth is a problem, to show how bandwidth performance may be calculated, to present some typical results, and to show that tapped delay lines can be used to improve bandwidth performance. Additional results on bandwidth may be found in Rodgers and Compton [1, 2]; Mayhan [3]; Mayhan, Simmons, and Cummings [4]; and White [5].

3.3 ELEMENT PATTERNS AND LOCATIONS‡

Until now we have assumed the elements in an adaptive array to be isotropic and have usually assumed half-wavelength spacing between elements. However, real antenna elements do not have isotropic patterns, of course, and it may not be possible or desirable to space the elements a half wavelength apart. Hence, it is important to be able to calculate the effects of element patterns and locations on array performance.

To include nonisotropic elements in the analysis, we shall proceed as follows. First, we present a method for calculating the response of a single antenna to a signal arriving from an arbitrary direction with arbitrary polarization. (When we take element patterns into account, we must necessarily consider signal polarization as well.) We begin by discussing how the polarization of a received signal may be characterized. Then we describe the method we shall use to calculate the output voltage from an antenna when it receives an arbitrarily polarized signal from an arbitrary direction. Using this result, we shall be able to calculate the signal vector when a signal strikes an array in which each element has a different pattern. Then, assuming a given set of signals incident on the array, we can calculate the covariance matrix, the reference correlation vector, the weight vector, and the output SINR.

As an aid in this last step, we also present in this section the general solution for output SINR when a CW desired signal and one CW interference signal are incident on the array. This solution can be derived only for CW signals. (It could not have been used in the previous section on bandwidth.) However, since antenna patterns are defined for CW signals anyway, and since we will study pattern effects with CW signals, this section is an appropriate place to introduce this solution. The result we shall prove is helpful because it allows us to calculate output SINR directly from the signal vectors. It bypasses the need to calculate the covariance matrix and solve for the weights.

After presenting these general methods, we shall then consider some simple problems that illustrate how element patterns and spacings, and also signal polarization, affect adaptive array performance.

Signal Polarization

We begin by considering the polarization of an incoming signal. We shall use the Poincaré sphere of Deschamps [6] to characterize signal polarization. Suppose we have an antenna at the origin of a spherical coordinate system, as shown in Fig. 3.33. Assume a CW signal propagates into this antenna from angles θ, ϕ. Let this signal be a transverse electromagnetic (TEM) wave, and consider the polarization ellipse produced by the electric field in a fixed

‡Portions of this section are reprinted from the author's papers [10, 13, 16] with permission of the IEEE.

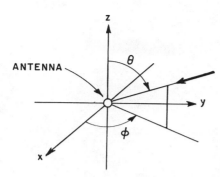

Figure 3.33 An incoming signal in three dimensions.

transverse plane (as we view the incoming wave from the coordinate origin). Note that unit vectors $\hat{\phi}$, $\hat{\theta}$, and $-\hat{r}$, in that order, form a right-handed coordinate system for an incoming wave. Suppose the electric field has transverse components

$$\mathbf{E} = E_\phi \hat{\phi} + E_\theta \hat{\theta}. \tag{3.219}$$

(We shall call E_ϕ the horizontal component and E_θ the vertical component of the field.) In general, for a given state of polarization, E_ϕ and E_θ may be written

$$E_\phi = A \cos \gamma e^{j(\omega t + \psi)} \tag{3.220}$$

and

$$E_\theta = A \sin \gamma e^{j\eta} e^{j(\omega t + \psi)} , \tag{3.221}$$

where A is the signal amplitude, γ and η are two angles that describe the state of polarization, and ψ is the carrier phase angle. As time progresses, the real parts of E_ϕ and E_θ will describe a polarization ellipse as shown in Fig. 3.34. Given this ellipse, we define β to be the orientation angle of the major axis of the ellipse with respect to E_ϕ, as shown in Fig. 3.34. To eliminate ambiguities, we define β to be in the range $0 \leqslant \beta < \pi$. We also define the ellipticity angle α

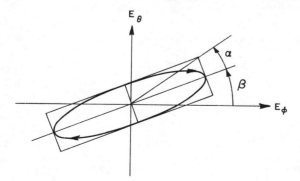

Figure 3.34 The polarization ellipse (reprinted from [13, 16] with permission, © 1981 IEEE).

to be an angle with magnitude

$$\alpha = \tan^{-1} r, \tag{3.222}$$

where r is the axial ratio

$$r = \frac{\text{minor axis}}{\text{major axis}}. \tag{3.223}$$

In addition, the sign of α is defined positive when the electric vector rotates clockwise and negative when it rotates counterclockwise (when the incoming wave is viewed from the coordinate origin, as in Fig. 3.34). The angle α is always in the range $-\pi/4 \leqslant \alpha \leqslant \pi/4$. Figure 3.34 depicts a situation in which α is positive. The angles γ and η in Eqs. (3.220) and (3.221) are related to the angles α and β defined above by the relations [6]

$$\cos 2\gamma = \cos 2\alpha \cos 2\beta \tag{3.224}$$

and

$$\tan \eta = \tan 2\alpha \csc 2\beta. \tag{3.225}$$

The relationship between the four angular variables α, β, γ, and η is most easily visualized by making use of the Poincaré sphere concept [6]. This technique represents the state of polarization by a point on a sphere, such as point P in Fig. 3.35. For a given P, 2β, 2α, and 2γ form the sides of a right spherical triangle, as shown. The angle 2γ is the side of the triangle between P and a point labeled H in the figure; H is the point representing horizontal linear polarization. Side 2β extends along the equator, and side 2α is vertical, that is, perpendicular to side 2β. The angle η in Eqs. (3.221) and (3.225) is the angle between sides 2γ and 2β. (These relationships are all derived in reference [6].) The special case when $\alpha = 0$ in Eq. (3.222) and Fig. 3.34 corresponds to linear polarization; in this case the point P lies on the equator. If in addition $\beta = 0$, only E_ϕ is nonzero and the wave is horizontally polarized. This case defines point H in Fig. 3.35. If, instead, $\beta = \pi/2$, only E_θ is nonzero and the wave is vertically polarized. Point P then lies on the equator diametrically behind H. The poles of the sphere correspond to circular polarization ($\alpha = \pm 45°$), with clockwise circular polarization ($\alpha = +45°$) at the upper pole.

Thus an arbitrary plane wave coming into the array may be characterized by four angular parameters and an amplitude. For example, the desired signal

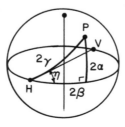

Figure 3.35 The Poincaré sphere (reprinted from [13, 16] with permission, © 1981 IEEE).

will be characterized by its arrival angles (θ_d, ϕ_d), its polarization ellipticity angle α_d and orientation angle β_d, and its amplitude A_d. [That is, A_d is the value of A in Eqs. (3.220) and (3.221) for the desired signal.] We shall say the desired signal is defined by $(\theta_d, \phi_d, \alpha_d, \beta_d, A_d)$. Similarly, the interference is defined by $(\theta_i, \phi_i, \alpha_i, \beta_i, A_i)$.

In the sequel, it will be helpful to express the electric field of an incoming signal in terms of its x-, y- and z-components. The signal in Eq. (3.219), with arbitrary electric field components E_ϕ and E_θ, has x-, y- and z-components:

$$E = E_\phi \hat{\phi} + E_\theta \hat{\theta} = (E_\theta \cos\theta \cos\phi - E_\phi \sin\phi)\hat{x}$$
$$+ (E_\theta \cos\theta \sin\phi + E_\phi \cos\phi)\hat{y}$$
$$- (E_\theta \sin\theta)\hat{z}. \tag{3.226}$$

When E_ϕ and E_θ are expressed in terms of A, γ, and η as in Eqs. (3.220) and (3.221), the electric field components become

$$E = A\big[(\sin\gamma \cos\theta \cos\phi e^{j\eta} - \cos\gamma \sin\phi)\hat{x}$$
$$+ (\sin\gamma \cos\theta \sin\phi e^{j\eta} + \cos\gamma \cos\phi)\hat{y}$$
$$- (\sin\gamma \sin\theta e^{j\eta})\hat{z}\big] e^{j(\omega t + \psi)}. \tag{3.227}$$

This is the electric field that exists at the coordinate origin in Fig. 3.33 due to an arbitrarily polarized signal arriving from an arbitrary direction.

The Element Response to a Polarized Signal

Now let us consider the response of an antenna located at the coordinate origin in Fig. 3.33 to this incoming signal. The antenna will have its own polarization properties, of course. There are several methods for describing the polarization characteristics of an antenna and for calculating the response of the antenna to an arbitrarily polarized signal [7, 8, 9]. We shall use the following method:

We shall characterize the antenna in terms of its response to linearly polarized signals in the x-, y- and z-directions. Let V_x be the complex voltage induced at the antenna output terminals by an incoming electromagnetic signal with a unit electric field polarized entirely in the x-direction. Similarly, let V_y and V_z be the output voltages induced by signals with unit electric fields polarized in the y- and z-directions, respectively. In general, the coefficients V_x, V_y, and V_z are complex numbers with different amplitudes and phase angles. These three numbers characterize the polarization properties of the antenna. The total output voltage from this antenna in response to the electromagnetic signal in Eq. (3.227) is then

$$V = A\big[V_x(\sin\gamma \cos\theta \cos\phi e^{j\eta} - \cos\gamma \sin\phi)$$
$$+ V_y(\sin\gamma \cos\theta \sin\phi e^{j\eta} + \cos\gamma \cos\phi)$$
$$- V_z(\sin\gamma \sin\theta e^{j\eta})\big] e^{j(\omega t + \psi)}. \tag{3.228}$$

We define the antenna pattern of the antenna to be

$$f(\theta, \phi, P) = V_x\left(\sin\gamma\cos\theta\cos\phi e^{j\eta} - \cos\gamma\sin\phi\right)$$
$$+ V_y\left(\sin\gamma\cos\theta\sin\phi e^{j\eta} + \cos\gamma\cos\phi\right)$$
$$- V_z\left(\sin\gamma\sin\theta e^{j\eta}\right). \tag{3.229}$$

Then

$$V = Af(\theta, \phi, P)e^{j(\omega t + \psi)}. \tag{3.230}$$

The pattern $f(\theta, \phi, P)$ is the complex voltage produced at the output terminals by a unit amplitude signal. We denote the pattern by $f(\theta, \phi, P)$ to indicate its dependence on both the arrival direction θ, ϕ and the state of polarization P of the received signal.

Now suppose we have an array with N elements, each at a different location. Let $\mathbf{r}_j$ be the vector position of the phase center of element j with respect to the coordinate origin. In general, each element in the array may have different polarization characteristics. The output voltage of element j due to the incoming signal in Eq. (3.227) will be

$$V_j = Af_j(\theta, \phi, P)e^{j(\omega t - \mathbf{k}\cdot\mathbf{r}_j + \psi)}, \tag{3.231}$$

where

$$f_j(\theta, \phi, P) = V_{xj}\left(\sin\gamma\cos\theta\cos\phi e^{j\eta} - \cos\gamma\sin\phi\right)$$
$$+ V_{yj}\left(\sin\gamma\cos\theta\sin\phi e^{j\eta} + \cos\gamma\cos\phi\right)$$
$$- V_{zj}\left(\sin\gamma\sin\theta e^{j\eta}\right), \tag{3.232}$$

and where V_{xj}, V_{yj}, and V_{zj} are the voltage responses of element j to unit signals polarized in the x-, y- and z-directions, respectively; $\mathbf{k}$ is the propagation vector,

$$\mathbf{k} = \frac{2\pi}{\lambda}\hat{\mathbf{p}}; \tag{3.233}$$

and $\hat{\mathbf{p}}$ is a unit vector in the direction of signal propagation. The term $e^{-j\mathbf{k}\cdot\mathbf{r}_j}$ in Eq. (3.231) is the phase of the signal on element j relative to the phase of the signal at the coordinate origin. The signal vector produced in the entire N-element array by this signal is then

$$\mathbf{X} = Ae^{j(\omega t + \psi)}\begin{bmatrix} f_1(\theta, \phi, P)e^{-j\mathbf{k}\cdot\mathbf{r}_1} \\ f_2(\theta, \phi, P)e^{-j\mathbf{k}\cdot\mathbf{r}_2} \\ \vdots \\ f_N(\theta, \phi, P)e^{-j\mathbf{k}\cdot\mathbf{r}_N} \end{bmatrix}. \tag{3.234}$$

From the signal vector, the covariance matrix contribution from this signal may be calculated in the usual way. An array with arbitrarily polarized elements may be handled in this way.

Before we do a specific example using this approach, we also develop a general formula for the output SINR from an N-element array when it receives CW signals. This formula will be very useful for interpreting the effects of element patterns on array performance.

A General Formula for SINR

Suppose a desired signal is incident on the array from direction θ_d, ϕ_d with polarization P_d. This signal produces a signal vector

$$\mathbf{X}_d = A_d e^{j(\omega_d t + \psi_d)} \mathbf{U}_d \qquad \text{\textit{NB assumption}} \tag{3.235}$$

with

$$\mathbf{U}_d = \begin{bmatrix} f_1(\theta_d, \phi_d, P_d) e^{-j\phi_{d1}} \\ f_2(\theta_d, \phi_d, P_d) e^{-j\phi_{d2}} \\ \vdots \\ f_N(\theta_d, \phi_d, P_d) e^{-j\phi_{dN}} \end{bmatrix} \tag{3.236}$$

where ϕ_{dj} is the interelement phase shift between element j and the coordinate origin,

$$\phi_{dj} = \mathbf{k}_d \cdot \mathbf{r}_j, \tag{3.237}$$

and $\mathbf{k}_d$ is the propagation vector for the desired signal. Suppose in addition a CW interference signal arrives from direction θ_i, ϕ_i with polarization P_i. This signal contributes a signal vector

$$\mathbf{X}_i = A_i e^{j(\omega_d t + \psi_i)} \mathbf{U}_i, \tag{3.238}$$

with

$$\mathbf{U}_i = \begin{bmatrix} f_1(\theta_i, \phi_i, P_i) e^{-j\phi_{i1}} \\ f_2(\theta_i, \phi_i, P_i) e^{-j\phi_{i2}} \\ \vdots \\ f_N(\theta_i, \phi_i, P_i) e^{-j\phi_{iN}} \end{bmatrix} \tag{3.239}$$

where

$$\phi_{ij} = \mathbf{k}_i \cdot \mathbf{r}_j, \tag{3.240}$$

and $\mathbf{k}_i$ is the propagation vector for the interference. Finally, assume uncorrelated thermal noise of power σ^2 is present on each element signal, as usual.

Then the covariance matrix is given by

$$\mathbf{\Phi} = \sigma^2 \mathbf{I} + A_d^2 \mathbf{U}_d^* \mathbf{U}_d^T + A_i^2 \mathbf{U}_i^* \mathbf{U}_i^T. \tag{3.241}$$

Also, we suppose a reference signal coherent with the desired signal is available,

$$\tilde{r}(t) = \text{Re}^{j(\omega_d t + \psi_d)}. \tag{3.242}$$

The reference correlation vector is then

$$\mathbf{S} = A_d R \mathbf{U}_d^*. \tag{3.243}$$

From $\mathbf{\Phi}$ and $\mathbf{S}$, the weight vector may be computed in the usual manner,

$$\mathbf{W} = \mathbf{\Phi}^{-1} \mathbf{S}. \tag{3.244}$$

From the weight vector, the desired, interference, and thermal noise powers are given by

$$P_d = \tfrac{1}{2} E\{|\mathbf{W}^T \mathbf{X}_d|^2\} = \frac{A_d^2}{2} |\mathbf{W}^T \mathbf{U}_d|^2, \tag{3.245}$$

$$P_i = \tfrac{1}{2} E\{|\mathbf{W}^T \mathbf{U}_i|^2\} = \frac{A_i^2}{2} |\mathbf{W}^T \mathbf{U}_i|^2, \tag{3.246}$$

and

$$P_n = \tfrac{1}{2} E\{|\mathbf{W}^T \mathbf{X}_n|^2\} = \frac{\sigma^2}{2} \mathbf{W}^\dagger \mathbf{W}. \tag{3.247}$$

(The vector $\mathbf{X}_n$ is the thermal noise vector.) The SINR is given by

$$\text{SINR} = \frac{P_d}{P_i + P_n} \tag{3.248}$$

We now show that the SINR in Eq. (3.248) can be reduced to the simple form [10]

$$\text{SINR} = \xi_d \left[\mathbf{U}_d^T \mathbf{U}_d^* - \frac{|\mathbf{U}_d^T \mathbf{U}_i^*|^2}{\xi_i^{-1} + \mathbf{U}_i^T \mathbf{U}_i^*} \right], \tag{3.249}$$

where, as usual, ξ_d is the input desired signal-to-noise ratio,

$$\xi_d = \frac{A_d^2}{\sigma^2}, \tag{3.250}$$

and ξ_i is the input interference-to-noise ratio,

$$\xi_i = \frac{A_i^2}{\sigma^2}. \tag{3.251}$$

This result is extremely useful in studying pattern effects, because it allows one to calculate the SINR directly from $\mathbf{U}_d$ and $\mathbf{U}_i$ in Eqs. (3.236) and (3.239), without the need to find the weight vector or the individual signal powers in Eqs. (3.245) through (3.247).

To prove the result in Eq. (3.249), the first step is to determine the weight vector in Eq. (3.244). To find $\mathbf{\Phi}^{-1}$, we make use of the matrix inversion lemma [11],

$$\left[\mathbf{B} - \beta\mathbf{Z}^*\mathbf{Z}^T\right]^{-1} = \mathbf{B}^{-1} - \tau\mathbf{B}^{-1}\mathbf{Z}^*\mathbf{Z}^T\mathbf{B}^{-1}, \tag{3.252}$$

where $\mathbf{B}$ is a nonsingular $N \times N$ matrix, $\mathbf{Z}$ is an $N \times 1$ column vector, and β and τ are scalars related by

$$\tau^{-1} + \beta^{-1} = \mathbf{Z}^T\mathbf{B}^{-1}\mathbf{Z}^*. \tag{3.253}$$

We start by using this lemma on the matrix $\sigma^2\mathbf{I} + A_i^2\mathbf{U}_i^*\mathbf{U}_i^T$. We find

$$\left[\sigma^2\mathbf{I} + A_i^2\mathbf{U}_i^*\mathbf{U}_i^T\right]^{-1} = \frac{1}{\sigma^2}\left[\mathbf{I} - \frac{\mathbf{U}_i^*\mathbf{U}_i^T}{\xi_i^{-1} + \mathbf{U}_i^T\mathbf{U}_i^*}\right]. \tag{3.254}$$

Then we let $\mathbf{B} = \sigma^2\mathbf{I} + A_i^2\mathbf{U}_i^*\mathbf{U}_i^T$, $\mathbf{Z} = \mathbf{U}_d$, and $\beta = -A_d^2$ and use the lemma again to find

$$\mathbf{\Phi}^{-1} = \frac{1}{\sigma^2}\mathbf{I} - \frac{\tau}{\sigma^4}\mathbf{U}_d^*\mathbf{U}_d^T$$

$$- \frac{1}{\xi_i^{-1} + \mathbf{U}_i^T\mathbf{U}_i^*}\left[\frac{1}{\sigma^2} + \frac{\tau}{\sigma^4}\frac{(\mathbf{U}_i^T\mathbf{U}_d^*)(\mathbf{U}_d^T\mathbf{U}_i^*)}{\xi_i^{-1} + \mathbf{U}_i^T\mathbf{U}_i^*}\right]\mathbf{U}_i^*\mathbf{U}_i^T$$

$$+ \frac{\tau}{\sigma^4}\frac{(\mathbf{U}_d^T\mathbf{U}_i^*)}{\xi_i^{-1} + \mathbf{U}_i^T\mathbf{U}_i^*}\mathbf{U}_d^*\mathbf{U}_i^T + \frac{\tau}{\sigma^4}\frac{(\mathbf{U}_i^T\mathbf{U}_d^*)}{\xi_i^{-1} + \mathbf{U}_i^T\mathbf{U}_i^*}\mathbf{U}_i^*\mathbf{U}_d^T, \tag{3.255}$$

where

$$\tau^{-1} = \frac{1}{A_d^2} + \frac{1}{\sigma^2}\mathbf{U}_d^T\mathbf{U}_d^* - \frac{1}{\sigma^2}\left[\frac{(\mathbf{U}_d^T\mathbf{U}_i^*)(\mathbf{U}_i^T\mathbf{U}_d^*)}{\xi_i^{-1} + \mathbf{U}_i^T\mathbf{U}_i^*}\right]. \tag{3.256}$$

It is helpful to define the quantity

$$\gamma = A_d^2\left[\mathbf{U}_d^T\mathbf{U}_d^* - \frac{(\mathbf{U}_i^T\mathbf{U}_d^*)(\mathbf{U}_d^T\mathbf{U}_i^*)}{\xi_i^{-1} + \mathbf{U}_i^T\mathbf{U}_i^*}\right], \tag{3.257}$$

and then Eq. (3.256) may be written

$$\tau = A_d^2\left(1 + \frac{\gamma}{\sigma^2}\right)^{-1}. \tag{3.258}$$

Now multiplying $\mathbf{\Phi}^{-1}$ in Eq. (3.255) onto $\mathbf{S}$ in Eq. (3.243), we have

$$\mathbf{W} = \mathbf{\Phi}^{-1}A_d R\mathbf{U}_d^*, \tag{3.259}$$

which simplifies to

$$\mathbf{W} = \frac{A_d R}{\sigma^2}\left(1 - \frac{\tau}{\sigma^2}\frac{\gamma}{A_d^2}\right)\left[\mathbf{U}_d^* - \frac{(\mathbf{U}_i^T \mathbf{U}_d^*)}{\xi_i^{-1} + \mathbf{U}_i^T \mathbf{U}_i^*}\mathbf{U}_i^*\right]. \tag{3.260}$$

Next we find

$$\mathbf{W}^T \mathbf{U}_d = \frac{A_d R}{\sigma^2}\left(1 - \frac{\tau}{\sigma^2}\frac{\gamma}{A_d^2}\right)\frac{\gamma}{A_d^2}, \tag{3.261}$$

or, after substituting Eq. (3.258) for τ,

$$\mathbf{W}^T \mathbf{U}_d = \frac{R}{A_d}\left(\frac{\gamma}{\sigma^2 + \gamma}\right). \tag{3.262}$$

Therefore, from Eq. (3.245), the output desired signal power is

$$P_d = \frac{A_d^2}{2}|\mathbf{W}^T \mathbf{U}_d|^2 = \frac{R^2}{2}\left(\frac{\gamma}{\sigma^2 + \gamma}\right)^2. \tag{3.263}$$

Similarly, we find

$$\mathbf{W}^T \mathbf{U}_i = \frac{A_d R}{\sigma^2}\left(1 - \frac{\tau}{\sigma^2}\frac{\gamma}{A_d^2}\right)\mathbf{U}_i^T \mathbf{U}_d^*\left(\frac{\xi_i^{-1}}{\xi_i^{-1} + \mathbf{U}_i^T \mathbf{U}_i^*}\right); \tag{3.264}$$

therefore, from Eq. (3.246),

$$\begin{aligned}
P_i &= \frac{A_i^2}{2}|\mathbf{W}^T \mathbf{U}_i|^2 \\
&= \frac{A_d^2 R^2 A_i^2}{2}\left(\frac{1}{\sigma^2 + \gamma}\right)^2\left(\frac{\xi_i^{-1}}{\xi_i^{-1} + \mathbf{U}_i^T \mathbf{U}_i^*}\right)^2|\mathbf{U}_i^T \mathbf{U}_d^*|^2. \tag{3.265}
\end{aligned}$$

Finally, from Eq. (3.260), we have

$$\mathbf{W}^\dagger \mathbf{W} = A_d^2 R^2\left(\frac{1}{\sigma^2 + \gamma}\right)^2\left[\frac{\gamma}{A_d^2} - |\mathbf{U}_i^T \mathbf{U}_d^*|^2\frac{\xi_i^{-1}}{(\xi_i^{-1} + \mathbf{U}_i^T \mathbf{U}_i^*)^2}\right]; \tag{3.266}$$

therefore, from Eq. (3.247),

$$P_n = \frac{A_d^2 R^2 A_i^2}{2}\left(\frac{1}{\sigma^2 + \gamma}\right)^2\left\{\frac{\gamma\xi_i^{-1}}{A_d^2} - |\mathbf{U}_i^T \mathbf{U}_d^*|^2\left(\frac{\xi_i^{-1}}{\xi_i^{-1} + \mathbf{U}_i^T \mathbf{U}_i^*}\right)^2\right\}. \tag{3.267}$$

Combining Eqs. (3.265) and (3.267) gives

$$P_i + P_n = \frac{A_i^2 R^2}{2}\left(\frac{1}{\sigma^2 + \gamma}\right)^2\gamma\xi_i^{-1}. \tag{3.268}$$

Then, using Eq. (3.263) for P_d, we find that the SINR reduces to the form

$$\text{SINR} = \frac{P_d}{P_i + P_n} = \frac{\gamma}{\sigma^2}. \qquad (3.269)$$

From the definition of γ in Eq. (3.257), we see that this result is the same as Eq. (3.249).

It should be noted that the result in Eq. (3.249) is only valid when the signals incident on the array are CW. The CW assumption allows the signal vectors $\mathbf{X}_d$ and $\mathbf{X}_i$ to be written as in Eqs. (3.235) and (3.238) and gives a covariance matrix of the form in Eq. (3.241). The covariance matrix must have this form in order to invoke the matrix inversion lemma to calculate Φ^{-1}. If the signal bandwidth is nonzero, Φ cannot be written in the form of Eq. (3.241), as we found in section 3.2 [e.g., see Eq. (3.94)].

Grating Nulls

Now let us use these techniques to see what element patterns and spacings do to array performance. The first problem we shall consider is grating nulls [10]. To discuss this subject, it will suffice to consider the pattern behavior for an array in only one angle. Suppose we have the N-element array in Fig. 3.36. Let us assume that all signals to be received by the array have the same polarization and that the response of element j to a signal with this polarization from angle θ is $f_j(\theta)$. Let element j be spaced a distance L_j from element 1. Suppose a desired signal and an interference signal are incident on the array from angles θ_d and θ_i, respectively. The signal vectors are

$$\mathbf{X}_d = A_d e^{j(\omega_d t + \psi_d)} \begin{bmatrix} f_1(\theta_d) \\ f_2(\theta_d) e^{-j\phi_{d2}} \\ \vdots \\ f_N(\theta_d) e^{-j\phi_{dN}} \end{bmatrix} \qquad (3.270)$$

and

$$\mathbf{X}_i = A_i e^{j(\omega_d t + \psi_i)} \begin{bmatrix} f_1(\theta_i) \\ f_2(\theta_i) e^{-j\phi_{i2}} \\ \vdots \\ f_N(\theta_i) e^{-j\phi_{iN}} \end{bmatrix} \qquad (3.271)$$

where

$$\phi_{dj} = \frac{2\pi L_j}{\lambda} \sin \theta_d \quad = \quad 2\pi \alpha_j \sin\theta d \qquad (3.272)$$

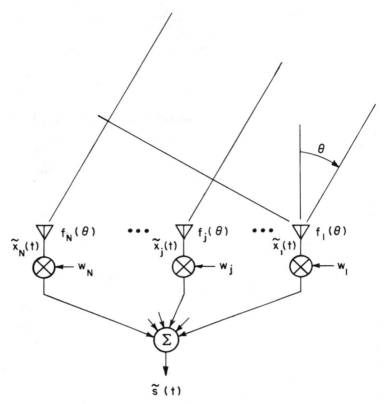

Figure 3.36   An N-element array with patterns $f_j(\theta)$.

and

$$\phi_{ij} = \frac{2\pi L_j}{\lambda} \sin \theta_i. \quad = 2\pi \alpha_j \sin \theta_i \quad (3.273)$$

As a basis for comparison, let us begin by assuming the elements are isotropic and examine the effect of element spacing. With isotropic elements, we have

$$f_j(\theta) = 1 \quad (3.274)$$

for all j, and hence

$$U_d^T U_d^* = U_i^T U_i^* = N. \quad (3.275)$$

Therefore, the SINR in Eq. (3.249) is simply

$$\text{SINR} = \xi_d \left[N - \frac{|U_d^T U_i^*|^2}{\xi_i^{-1} + N} \right]. \quad (3.276)$$

From Eqs. (3.270) through (3.273), $\mathbf{U}_d^T \mathbf{U}_i^*$ is given by

$$\mathbf{U}_d^T \mathbf{U}_i^* = 1 + e^{j(\phi_{i2} - \phi_{d2})} + e^{j(\phi_{i3} - \phi_{d3})} + \cdots. \tag{3.277}$$

Suppose, for example, that there are two elements in the array. Then

$$\mathbf{U}_d^T \mathbf{U}_i^* = 1 + e^{j(\phi_{i2} - \phi_{d2})} = 1 + e^{j(\phi_i - \phi_d)} \tag{3.278}$$

(with only two elements we omit the subscript 2), so

$$|\mathbf{U}_d^T \mathbf{U}_i^*|^2 = 4 \cos^2\left(\frac{\phi_i - \phi_d}{2}\right). \tag{3.279}$$

Thus,

$$\text{SINR} = \xi_d \left[2 - \frac{4 \cos^2\left(\dfrac{\phi_i - \phi_d}{2}\right)}{\xi_i^{-1} + 2} \right]$$

$$= 2\xi_d \left[\frac{\xi_i^{-1} + 2 \sin^2\left(\dfrac{\phi_i - \phi_d}{2}\right)}{\xi_i^{-1} + 2} \right]. \tag{3.280}$$

This result may be used to examine how the SINR behaves for different element spacings $L\ (= L_2)$. To be specific, let $\theta_d = 0°$, $\xi_d = 0$ dB, and $\xi_i = +40$ dB. Figure 3.37 shows plots of the SINR versus θ_i, computed from Eq. (3.280) for $L = 0.5\lambda$, 0.75λ, λ, 1.5λ, and 3λ. It is seen that for $L \leqslant 0.75\lambda$, the SINR is well-behaved for all θ_i except near $\theta_d\ (= 0°)$. However, as L is increased, more and more angles occur for $\theta_i \neq \theta_d$ where the SINR drops to a low value.

The drop in SINR when $\theta_i \simeq \theta_d$ occurs simply because the array forms a null on the interference, and when $\theta_i \simeq \theta_d$ the desired signal falls in this null. Nothing can be done about this drop in SINR for $\theta_i \simeq \theta_d$, as long as the elements are isotropic. (However, we will see that when cross-polarized elements are used in the array, the array can null an interference signal without nulling the desired signal, when both are from the same direction, as long as the two signals have different polarizations.)

The drop in SINR seen in Fig. 3.37(c) through (e) for $\theta_i \neq \theta_d$ is due to the problem of grating nulls. Grating nulls in an adaptive array are analogous to grating lobes in an ordinary array. The problem occurs because interference nulled by the array at one angle causes additional nulls (grating nulls) to appear at other angles. If the desired signal falls in a grating null, a low SINR results. In Fig. 3.37(c), for example, an interference signal at $\theta_i = 90°$ produces a grating null at $\theta = 0°$. Since $\theta_d = 0°$, a low SINR results when $\theta_i = 90°$.

In general, a grating null problem will occur whenever the signal vectors for the desired and interference signals are parallel, that is, whenever

$$\mathbf{U}_d = K\mathbf{U}_i, \tag{3.281}$$

where K is any constant. If $\mathbf{U}_d$ and $\mathbf{U}_i$ are parallel, a weight vector chosen to

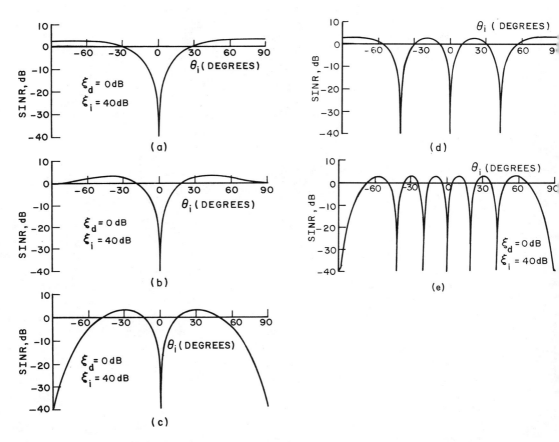

Figure 3.37 Two isotropic elements: SINR versus θ_i. (a) $L/\lambda = 0.5$; (b) $L/\lambda = 0.75$; (c) $L/\lambda = 1.0$; (d) $L/\lambda = 1.5$; (e) $L/\lambda = 3$.

null the interference,

$$\mathbf{W}^T\mathbf{X}_i = A_i e^{j(\omega_d t + \psi_i)}\mathbf{W}^T\mathbf{U}_i = 0, \tag{3.282}$$

will also null the desired signal,

$$\mathbf{W}^T\mathbf{X}_d = A_d e^{j(\omega_d t + \psi_d)}\mathbf{W}^T\mathbf{U}_d = KA_d e^{j(\omega_d t + \psi_d)}\mathbf{W}^T\mathbf{U}_i = 0. \tag{3.283}$$

Consider for example, the two-element array discussed in connection with Fig. 3.37. With two isotropic elements, $\mathbf{U}_d$ and $\mathbf{U}_i$ are

$$\mathbf{U}_d = \begin{bmatrix} 1 \\ e^{-j(2\pi L/\lambda)\sin\theta_d} \end{bmatrix} \tag{3.284}$$

and

$$\mathbf{U}_i = \begin{bmatrix} 1 \\ e^{-j(2\pi L/\lambda)\sin\theta_i} \end{bmatrix}. \tag{3.285}$$

In this case $\mathbf{U}_d$ and $\mathbf{U}_i$ will be parallel whenever

$$\frac{2\pi L}{\lambda}\sin\theta_d = \frac{2\pi L}{\lambda}\sin\theta_i - 2\pi n, \tag{3.286}$$

where n is any integer. When $\theta_d = 0°$, as in Fig. 3.37, Eq. (3.286) reduces to

$$\frac{L}{\lambda}\sin\theta_i = n. \tag{3.287}$$

For $n = 0$, the solutions to this are $\theta_i = 0°$ and $\theta_i = 180°$. These solutions correspond to the case when the interference arrives from broadside, the same as the desired signal. There is always a solution for $n = 0$, regardless of the value of L/λ. However, solutions for $n = \pm 1, \pm 2, \ldots$ will exist only if L/λ is large enough. These solutions, for $n \neq 0$, are the grating null solutions. The larger L/λ is, the more of these solutions will exist. For example, Eq. (3.287) can be solved for $n = \pm 1$ only if $L/\lambda \geqslant 1$. When $L/\lambda = 1$, Eq. (3.287) is satisfied at $\theta_i = 90°$. Figure 3.37(c) shows the drop in SINR when $L/\lambda = 1$ and $\theta_i = 90°$. If $L/\lambda \geqslant 2$, then solutions will exist for $n = \pm 2$, and so forth.

Grating null problems occur because interference and desired signal from two different spatial directions produce element signals with the same amplitude ratios and interelement phase shifts. Thus the two signals are electrically indistinguishable. To avoid grating null problems, we must choose element patterns and spacings so that this situation cannot occur for any possible pair of arrival directions. In general, grating null problems are reduced by increasing the number of elements in the array, by using elements with different patterns, and by making the element spacings unequal.

Let us illustrate the effect of using unequal element patterns in an array. Consider a three-element array with elements one wavelength apart, as shown in Fig. 3.38. First, assume the elements are isotropic [see Fig. 3.38(a)]. Then Eq. (3.277) becomes

$$\mathbf{U}_d^T\mathbf{U}_i^* = 1 + e^{j(\phi_{i2} - \phi_{d2})} + e^{j2(\phi_{i2} - \phi_{d2})}, \tag{3.288}$$

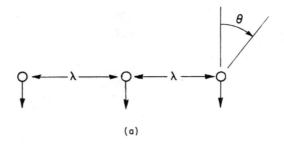

(a)

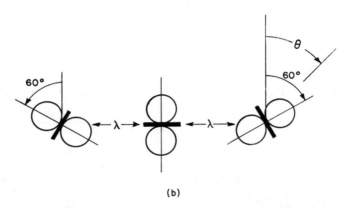

(b)

Figure 3.38   Three-element arrays. (a) Isotropic elements; (b) dipole elements.

where

$$\phi_{i2} = 2\pi \sin \theta_i \tag{3.289}$$

and

$$\phi_{d2} = 2\pi \sin \theta_d, \tag{2.290}$$

and Eq. (3.276) yields

$$\text{SINR} = \xi_d \left[3 - \frac{|\mathbf{U}_d^T \mathbf{U}_i^*|^2}{\xi_i^{-1} + 3} \right]. \tag{3.291}$$

This result is plotted in Fig. 3.39 for $\theta_d = 0°$, $30°$, and $60°$. It is clear that this

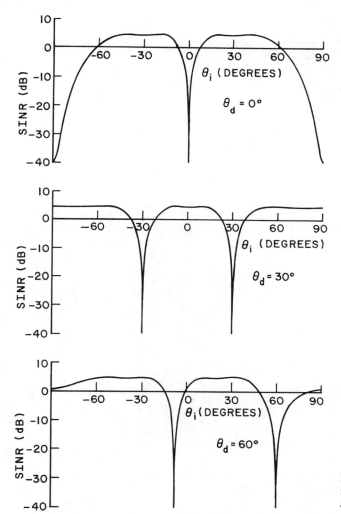

Figure 3.39   Three isotropic elements: SINR versus θ_i: $\xi_d = 0$ dB, $\xi_i = 40$ dB.

array has grating null problems. For instance, when $\theta_d = 60°$, the SINR drops not only when $\theta_i = 60°$ but also when $\theta_i = -8°$.

Now suppose each element in this array has a dipole pattern. Let the jth element pattern be

$$f_j(\theta) = \cos(\theta - \alpha_j),\qquad(3.292)$$

where

$$\alpha_1 = 60°,\ \alpha_2 = 0,\ \alpha_3 = -60°.\qquad(3.293)$$

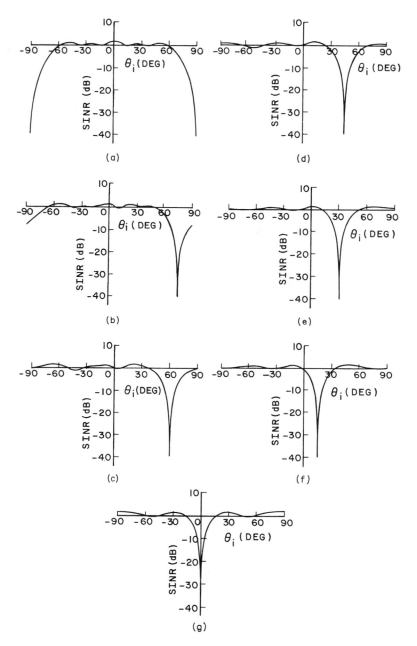

Figure 3.40 Three-dipole array: SINR versus θ_i: $L_2 = \lambda$, $L_3 = 2\lambda$, $\alpha_1 = 60°$, $\alpha_2 = 0°$, $\alpha_3 = -60°$, $\xi_d = 0$ dB, $\xi_i = 40$ dB; (a) $\theta_d = 90°$; (b) $\theta_d = 75°$; (c) $\theta_d = 60°$; (d) $\theta_d = 45°$; (e) $\theta_d = 30°$; (f) $\theta_d = 15°$; (g) $\theta_d = 0°$ (reprinted from [10] with permission, © 1980 IEEE).

In this case the element patterns are oriented as shown in Fig. 3.38(b). Also

$$
\mathbf{U}_d = \begin{bmatrix} \cos\left(\theta_d - \dfrac{\pi}{3}\right) \\[2ex] \cos\left(\theta_d\right)e^{-j\phi_{d2}} \\[2ex] \cos\left(\theta_d + \dfrac{\pi}{3}\right)e^{-j2\phi_{d2}} \end{bmatrix} \tag{3.294}
$$

and

$$
\mathbf{U}_i = \begin{bmatrix} \cos\left(\theta_i - \dfrac{\pi}{3}\right) \\[2ex] \cos\left(\theta_i\right)e^{-j\phi_{i2}} \\[2ex] \cos\left(\theta_i + \dfrac{\pi}{3}\right)e^{-j2\phi_{i2}} \end{bmatrix}. \tag{3.295}
$$

The SINR can be calculated by substituting these into Eq. (3.249). Figure 3.40 shows typical results for $\theta_d = 0°$, $15°$, $30°$, $45°$, $60°$, $75°$, and $90°$ [10]. It is seen that these curves are an improvement over the results in Fig. 3.39 for isotropic elements because the grating nulls have been eliminated.

These results illustrate how using different element patterns in the array can reduce or eliminate grating nulls. The pointing directions chosen in Eq. (3.293) for the dipole patterns were found by trial and error to have good performance [10]. Not all choices for the $f_j(\theta)$ work equally well, of course. For a given set of patterns, one must evaluate the SINR for arbitrary signal directions over a volume of space. If angles are found where the performance is bad, the element patterns or locations must then be changed to try to eliminate the bad angles.

The example we have considered was a rather idealized situation. We assumed the signal direction to be specified by a single angle, and we did not consider the effect of signal polarization. However, in a more realistic problem where signal directions vary over both spatial angles θ and ϕ and where signal polarization must be taken into account, a grating null problem will occur for any combination of desired signal direction and polarization (θ_d, ϕ_d, P_d) and interference direction and polarization (θ_i, ϕ_i, P_i) for which Eq. (3.281) holds. The only difference in this more general case is that one must use Eqs. (3.236) and (3.239) for $\mathbf{U}_d$ and $\mathbf{U}_i$. In a design problem, the usual procedure is to start with an initial set of elements, chosen by some means, and compute the SINR using Eqs. (3.236), (3.239), and (3.249) over the range of arrival directions and polarizations of interest. If angles and polarizations are found where the SINR is inadequate, one makes some change in the elements to improve performance. One method is to augment the array by adding additional elements until the SINR is suitable. Reference [12] describes this method.

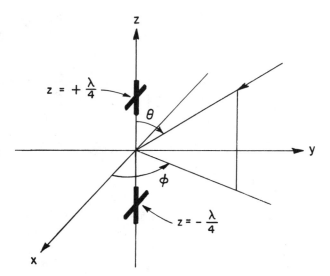

Figure 3.41 Two pairs of crossed dipoles.

Next, to illustrate the use of these general methods of analysis, we shall consider the performance of two different dipole arrays. We shall compute the SINR performance of these arrays when signals arrive from any direction with any polarization. Besides illustrating the method of analysis, these examples will also demonstrate the performance advantage of arrays that adapt to polarization as well as angle of arrival.

A Four-Dipole Array

For the first example, suppose we have a four-element array consisting of two pairs of crossed dipoles, as shown in Fig. 3.41 [13]. The signal from each dipole is to be processed separately in the array. The upper and lower dipole pairs have their centers at $z = +\lambda/4$ and $z = -\lambda/4$, respectively. Let $\tilde{x}_1(t)$ and $\tilde{x}_3(t)$ be the complex signals received from the upper and lower vertical dipoles and $\tilde{x}_2(t)$ and $\tilde{x}_4(t)$ the signals received from the upper and lower horizontal dipoles, respectively. The signal vector produced in this array by an incoming signal characterized by the parameters $(\theta, \phi, \alpha, \beta, A)$ may be found from Eq. (3.234). Let us assume the dipoles in Fig. 3.41 are short dipoles, each of which produces an output voltage proportional to the electric field parallel to the dipole. Because of the way the dipoles are oriented, the coefficients $V_{pj}(p = x,$ $y,$ or $z)$ in Eq. (3.232) are

$$V_{x1} = 0, \ V_{y1} = 0, \ V_{z1} = 1, \tag{3.296}$$

$$V_{x2} = 1, \ V_{y2} = 0, \ V_{z2} = 0, \tag{3.297}$$

$$V_{x3} = 0, \ V_{y3} = 0, \ V_{z3} = 1, \tag{3.298}$$

and

$$V_{x4} = 1, \ V_{y4} = 0, \ V_{z4} = 0. \tag{3.299}$$

Using these in Eq. (3.232) gives the element patterns,

$$f_1(\theta, \phi, P) = f_3(\theta, \phi, P) = -\sin \gamma \sin \theta \, e^{j\eta}, \tag{3.300}$$

$$f_2(\theta, \phi, P) = f_4(\theta, \phi, P) = \sin \gamma \cos \theta \cos \phi \, e^{j\eta} - \cos \gamma \sin \phi. \tag{3.301}$$

Substituting these into Eq. (3.234) yields the signal vector

$$\mathbf{X} = A e^{j(\omega t + \psi)} \mathbf{U}, \tag{3.302}$$

where $\mathbf{U}$ is

$$\mathbf{U} = \begin{bmatrix} \left(-\sin \gamma \sin \theta \, e^{j\eta} \right) e^{jp} \\ \left(\sin \gamma \cos \theta \cos \phi \, e^{j\eta} - \cos \gamma \sin \phi \right) e^{jp} \\ \left(-\sin \gamma \sin \theta \, e^{j\eta} \right) e^{-jp} \\ \left(\sin \gamma \cos \theta \cos \phi \, e^{j\eta} - \cos \gamma \sin \phi \right) e^{-jp} \end{bmatrix}. \tag{3.303}$$

Here p is the phase shift of the signals at the dipoles due to spatial delay,

$$p = \frac{\pi}{2} \cos \theta. \tag{3.304}$$

Let us assume that a desired signal with parameters $(\theta_d, \phi_d, \alpha_d, \beta_d, A_d)$ and an interference signal with parameters $(\theta_i, \phi_i, \alpha_i, \beta_i, A_i)$ are incident on the array. Under these conditions, the total signal vector is given by

$$\mathbf{X} = \mathbf{X}_d + \mathbf{X}_i + \mathbf{X}_n = A_d e^{j(\omega_d t + \phi_d)} \mathbf{U}_d + A_i e^{j(\omega_d t + \phi_i)} \mathbf{U}_i + \mathbf{X}_n, \tag{3.305}$$

where $\mathbf{U}_d$ and $\mathbf{U}_i$ are each given by Eq. (3.303) with appropriate subscripts d or i added to each angular quantity. $\mathbf{X}_n$ is the noise vector. From $\mathbf{U}_d$ and $\mathbf{U}_i$, the output SINR from the array can be calculated using Eq. (3.249), where ξ_d and ξ_i are the signal-to-noise ratios in Eqs. (3.250) and (3.251).

Because of the way the signals are defined in Eqs. (3.220) and (3.221), we note that ξ_d and ξ_i are the signal-to-noise ratios that will exist in a given array element if the incoming signal arrives broadside to that element and is linearly polarized parallel to that element. For example, if $\alpha_d = 0°$ and $\beta_d = 0°$, the desired signal is polarized entirely in the E_ϕ direction. Then if the signal arrives from $\phi_d = 90°$, the SNR on elements 2 and 4 will be ξ_d. (In this case, the SNR on elements 1 and 3 will be zero.) In general, with an arbitrary state of polarization ($\alpha_d \neq 0°$ or $\beta_d \neq 0°$), if the signal arrives from $\theta_d = 90°$, $\phi_d = 90°$ (broadside to both elements 1 and 2), the SNR on elements 1 and 2 will each be less than ξ_d. However, if the signals from elements 1 and 2 are combined with optimal weights (i.e., maximal ratio combiner weights [14]), the total output SNR from elements 1 and 2 combined will be ξ_d. The value ξ_d thus represents the maximum available SNR out of each *pair* of crossed dipoles when the signal arrives broadside to both dipoles.

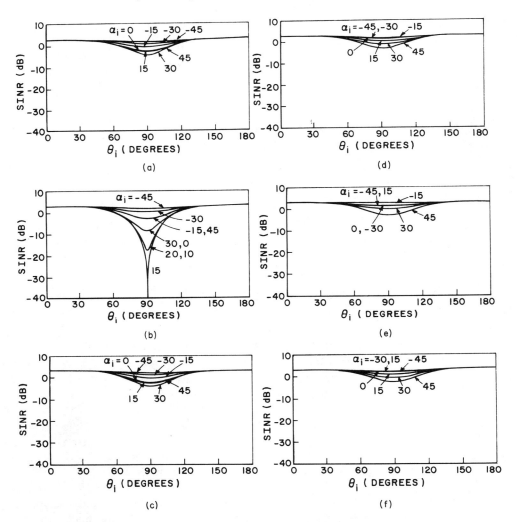

Figure 3.42 SINR versus θ_i: $\theta_d = 90°$, $\phi_d = 90°$, $\alpha_d = 15°$, $\beta_d = 30°$, $\xi_d = 0$ dB, $\phi_i = 90°$, $\xi_i = 40$ dB; (a) $\beta_i = 0°$; (b) $\beta_i = 30°$; (c) $\beta_i = 60°$; (d) $\beta_i = 90°$; (e) $\beta_i = 120°$; (f) $\beta_i = 150°$ (reprinted from [13] with permission, © 1981 IEEE).

Now let us show some SINR results based on Eq. (3.249). Because of the large number of parameters required to specify both the desired and interference signals, many types of curves can be plotted. Unfortunately we cannot show an exhaustive set of curves. However, we will show a number of typical curves, including those illustrating the worst performance.

Figures 3.42 and 3.43 show curves of output SINR when the desired signal arrives from broadside ($\theta_d = \phi_d = 90°$). The desired signal has been chosen to

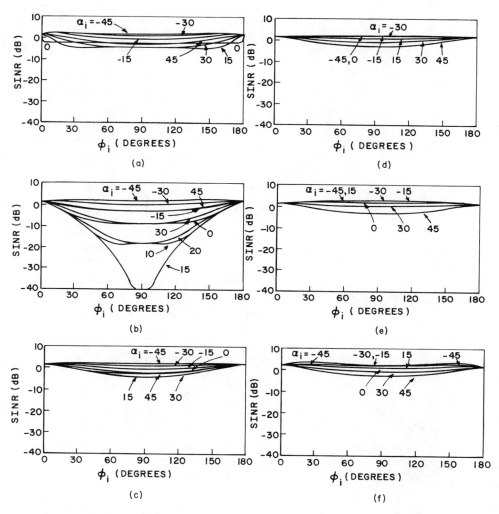

Figure 3.43 SINR versus ϕ_i: $\theta_d = 90°$, $\phi_d = 90°$, $\alpha_d = 15°$, $\beta_d = 30°$, $\xi_d = 0$ dB, $\theta_i = 90°$, $\xi_i = 40$ dB; (a) $\beta_i = 0°$; (b) $\beta_i = 30°$; (c) $\beta_i = 60°$; (d) $\beta_i = 90°$; (e) $\beta_i = 120°$; (f) $\beta_i = 150°$ (reprinted from [13] with permission, © 1981 IEEE).

have an arbitrary elliptical polarization: $\alpha_d = 15°$ and $\beta_d = 30°$. The SNR (ξ_d) is 0 dB, and the INR (ξ_i) is 40 dB. As stated previously, the element pairs are assumed to be a half wavelength apart. Figure 3.42 shows the output SINR as a function of the interference polar angle θ_i, with $\phi_i = 90°$, for various interference polarizations. Specifically, Fig. 3.42(a) shows the SINR for $\beta_i = 0°$, Fig. 3.42(b) for $\beta_i = 30°$, and so forth, up to Fig. 3.42(f) for $\beta_i = 150°$. Each figure shows the results for $\alpha_i = -45°$, $-30°$, $-15°$, $0°$, $15°$, $30°$, and $45°$. Figure

3.43 shows similar results as a function of the interference aximuthal angle ϕ_i, with $\theta_i = 90°$.

Examination of these curves shows that the worst output SINR is obtained when the interference arrives from the same direction as the desired signal (broadside) and has the same polarization as the desired signal. This result is not surprising, of course, because in this case when the array nulls the interference it also nulls the desired signal. However, the interesting thing about this case is how little difference in polarization between the signals is required to allow the array to provide substantial protection. For example, it may be seen in Fig. 3.42(b) or 3.43(b) (for $\beta_i = \beta_d = 30°$) that when $\theta_i = 90°$ and $\phi_i = 90°$, if either $\alpha_i = 0°$ or $\alpha_i = 30°$ (i.e., if α_i differs from $\alpha_d = 15°$ by $\pm 15°$) the SINR out of the array is higher than -9 dB. Thus, with this small difference in polarization, the array can provide more than 31 dB of protection against the interference.

For the special case where both signals arrive from broadside, the output SINR from the array can be simply related to the polarization of two signals. If

$$\theta_d = \phi_d = \theta_i = \phi_i = 90°, \tag{3.306}$$

Eq. (3.303) yields

$$\mathbf{U}_d^T \mathbf{U}_d^* = \mathbf{U}_i^T \mathbf{U}_i^* = 2, \tag{3.307}$$

and also

$$\left| \mathbf{U}_d^T \mathbf{U}_i^* \right|^2 = 4 |\cos \gamma_d \cos \gamma_i + \sin \gamma_d \sin \gamma_i \, e^{j(\eta_d - \eta_i)}|^2$$

$$= 2 \left[1 + \cos 2\gamma_d \cos 2\gamma_i + \sin 2\gamma_d \sin 2\gamma_i \cos (\eta_d - \eta_i) \right]. \tag{3.308}$$

Let P_d and P_i be the points on the Poincaré sphere representing the polarizations of the desired and interference signals, respectively. Then, in Eq. (3.308), $2\gamma_d$, $2\gamma_i$, and the arc $P_d P_i$ form the sides of a spherical triangle, as shown in Fig. 3.44. The angle $\eta_d - \eta_i$ is the angle opposite side $P_d P_i$. Using a well-known spherical trigonometric identity [15], we have

$$\cos 2\gamma_d \cos 2\gamma_i + \sin 2\gamma_d \sin 2\gamma_i \cos (\eta_d - \eta_i) = \cos (P_d P_i), \tag{3.309}$$

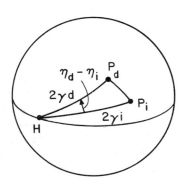

Figure 3.44 The points P_d and P_i (reprinted from [13] with permission, © 1981 IEEE).

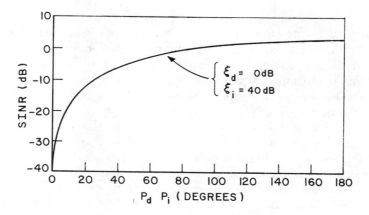

Figure 3.45   SINR versus Poincaré sphere separation: $\theta_d = \phi_d = \theta_i = \phi_i$ = 90° (reprinted from [13] with permission, © 1981 IEEE).

so Eq. (3.308) can be written

$$\left| U_d^T U_i^* \right|^2 = 2\left[1 + \cos\left(P_d P_i\right)\right] = 4\cos^2\left(\frac{P_d P_i}{2}\right), \tag{3.310}$$

and Eq. (3.249) becomes

$$\text{SINR} = \xi_d \left[2 - \frac{4\cos^2\left(\dfrac{P_d P_i}{2}\right)}{\xi_i^{-1} + 2}\right]. \tag{3.311}$$

If $\xi_i^{-1} \ll 2$, this result may be approximated by

$$\text{SINR} = \frac{\xi_d}{\xi_i}\left[1 + 2\xi_i \sin^2\left(\frac{P_d P_i}{2}\right)\right]. \tag{3.312}$$

These formulas show that the SINR obtained from the array when both signals are at broadside depends only on the separation between the two points P_d and P_i on the Poincaré sphere.

A plot of the SINR versus the spherical distance $P_d P_i$ in angular measure, as obtained from Eq. (3.311), is shown in Fig. 3.45 for $\xi_d = 0$ dB and $\xi_i = 40$ dB. It is seen, for example, that a separation of $P_d P_i = 26°$ on the Poincaré sphere results in SINR $= -10$ dB, an improvement of 30 dB over what it would be without the array.[‡] This result holds regardless of the specific polarizations of the signals, so long as they are separated by 26° on the Poincaré sphere.

[‡]To reconcile the curve in Fig. 3.45 with the results in Figs. 3.42(b) and 3.43(b), one must note that point P in Fig. 3.35 lies above the equator by an angle 2α. Thus, for example, a separation of $P_d P_i = 26°$ corresponds to a difference of only $|\alpha_d - \alpha_i| = 13°$, if $\beta_i = \beta_d$.

In general, when the desired signal arrives from some direction other than broadside, the curves of SINR versus interference arrival angle are similar to those in Figs. 3.42 and 3.43. The worst performance always occurs when the interference arrives from the same direction as the desired signal and has the same polarization. When both signals arrive from the same direction off broadside, however, it is found that the SINR cannot be related to the polarization difference so simply as in Eq. (3.311). In this case, the SINR depends on the angle of arrival as well as the polarizations. The reason is that the electric field component in the y-direction is not received by the array, because the array contains only x- and z-oriented dipoles. When the arrival angle and polarization of a signal are such that there is a y-component of electric field, the SINR is affected by the loss of power in this component to the receiving system. The amount of electric field in the y-direction depends on the angle of arrival as well as the polarization.

The curves in Figs. 3.42 and 3.43 show typical performance from the array for an arbitrarily polarized desired signal. However, it must be noted that with this array certain desired signal polarizations allow the system to be jammed over a wide range of interference angles. Namely, if the desired signal excites only two of the four dipoles, then when the interference excites only the same two dipoles, the array has no ability to discriminate between signals in the azimuthal coordinate ϕ. This situation leaves the array vulnerable to interference from a wide range of angles.

Specifically, there are two cases where poor performance occurs: when the desired signal is either vertically or horizontally polarized. For example, suppose the desired signal is vertically polarized ($\alpha_d = 0°$, $\beta_d = 90°$) and arrives from an arbitrary direction θ_d, ϕ_d. Then a vertically polarized interference signal ($\alpha_i = 0°$, $\beta_i = 90°$) will produce a poor SINR as long as it arrives from the same polar angle, that is, if $\theta_i = \theta_d$, regardless of ϕ_i. It is clear from the arrangement of elements in Fig. 3.41 why this is so. For vertically polarized signals, the array has no ability to discriminate in the azimuthal coordinate ϕ.

A particularly bad case occurs when $\theta_d = 90°$ (and ϕ_d has any value). In this case, *any* interference signal with a nonzero vertical component (i.e., *all* polarizations *except* the case where both $\alpha_i = 0°$ and $\beta_i = 0°$) arriving from the particular direction $\theta_i = 90°$, $\phi_i = 0°$ or $180°$ will cause a poor SINR. The reason is that the horizontal component of a signal from $\theta_i = 90°$, $\phi_i = 0°$ is not received by the array, so it cannot be used to cancel interference received by the vertical elements.

Figure 3.46 shows calculations illustrating this situation. In these curves, the desired signal arrives from broadside and is linearly polarized in the vertical direction. The interference arrives from $\theta_i = 90°$ and is also linearly polarized ($\alpha_i = 0°$). The curves show the output SINR versus ϕ_i for various interference orientation angles β_i. Two special cases should be noted. First, when $\beta_i = 90°$, the interference is vertically polarized, and the output SINR is -40 dB

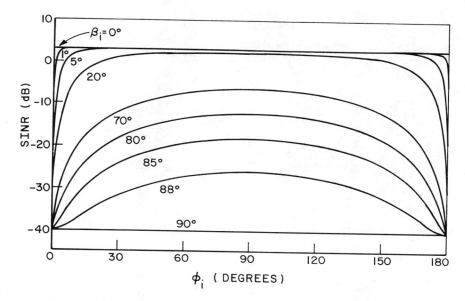

Figure 3.46   SINR versus ϕ_i: $\theta_d = 90°$, $\phi_d = 90°$, $\alpha_d = 0°$, $\beta_d = 90°$, $\xi_d = 0$ dB, $\theta_i = 90°$, $\alpha_i = 0°$, $\xi_i = 40$ dB (reprinted from [13] with permission, © 1981 IEEE).

regardless of ϕ_i. (The reason is obvious from the array geometry in Fig. 3.38.) Second, when $\beta_i = 0°$, the interference is horizontally polarized, and it has no effect on the SINR for any ϕ_i. The SINR is always 3 dB in this case. (The interference is eliminated by the array by turning off the horizontal dipoles.) Between these two limiting cases, one obtains a wide variation in SINR, depending on ϕ_i and β_i. The important point here is to note how little the interference polarization has to differ from horizontal to jam the array quite effectively at the particular angle $\phi_i = 0°$ or 180°. For example, if β_i is only 5°, the SINR is already down to -18.8 dB. To reiterate, a vertically polarized desired signal at $\theta_d = 90°$ (and any ϕ_d) is particularly vulnerable to interference from the angle $\theta_i = 90°$, $\phi_i = 0°$ or 180°.

The second case where the array performance is poor is when the desired signal has horizontal linear polarization. A horizontally polarized desired signal ($\alpha_d = 0°$, $\beta_d = 0°$) at any θ_d, ϕ_d will be interfered with by a horizontally polarized interference signal with the same polar angle, $\theta_i = \theta_d$, and any ϕ_i. The only exception occurs when the interference is near $\phi_i = 0°$ or $\phi_i = 180°$, where a horizontally polarized signal is not received.

Figure 3.47 illustrates this situation. Here the desired signal is again at broadside ($\theta_d = 90°$, $\phi_d = 90°$) with horizontal linear polarization ($\alpha_d = \beta_d = 0°$). The curves show SINR versus ϕ_i for an interfering signal at $\theta_i = 90°$ with

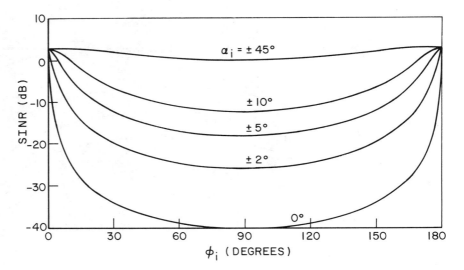

Figure 3.47   SINR versus ϕ_i: $\theta_d = 90°$, $\phi_d = 90°$, $\alpha_d = 0°$, $\beta_d = 0°$, $\xi_d = 0$ dB, $\theta_i = 90°$, $\beta_i = 0°$, $\xi_i = 40$ dB (reprinted from [13] with permission, © 1981 IEEE).

$\beta_i = 0°$. The different curves are for different α_i between $-45°$ and $+45°$. In the case $\alpha_i = 0°$, the interference has horizontal linear polarization, and it produces a poor SINR over a very wide range of ϕ_i. Only for ϕ_i near $0°$ or $180°$ does the SINR rise, because for these angles the interference is not received by the array.

Figures 3.46 and 3.47 illustrate the vulnerability of the system to jamming when both the desired signal and the interference have either vertical linear or horizontal linear polarization. This problem occurs because in these cases the signals excite only two of the four elements and also because the dipoles in Fig. 3.43 are all located at $x = 0$. That is, there is no displacement of the dipoles along the x-axis, and hence the array has poor ability to provide spatial discrimination in the ϕ-coordinate. If we wish to discriminate well against interference that arrives with $\theta_i = \theta_d$ but with arbitrary ϕ_i, we must do one of two things: either avoid using a vertical or horizontal linearly polarized desired signal, or add more elements that can provide azimuthal discrimination, such as another dipole pair at $x = \lambda/2$, $y = z = 0$.

If the desired signal polarization is chosen to be something besides vertical or horizontal linear polarization, so the problems above are avoided, then the crossed dipole array is quite effective in rejecting interference. If used in a communication system, for example, this array will be rather difficult to jam with a single interference signal. Not only must the jammer arrive from the same direction as the desired signal, it must have the same polarization.

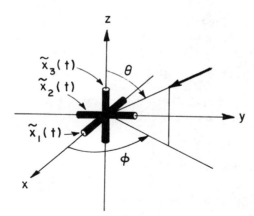

Figure 3.48 The "tripole" antenna (reprinted from [16] with permission, © 1981 IEEE).

A Tripole Array

For our second example of a dipole array, we shall examine the performance of an even simpler adaptive array—one consisting of three mutually perpendicular dipoles all with their centers at the same location, as shown in Fig. 3.48 [16]. Such an array is interesting for several reasons. First, it discriminates between signals on the basis of polarization alone. (With all elements centered at the same location, there is no interelement phase shift due to angle of arrival, as in the last example.) Second, we shall see that such an array protects a desired signal rather well from interference. Finally, such an array could itself be used as a building block in larger arrays that adapt to polarization as well as angle of arrival. Because this array has three dipoles, we shall call it a "tripole" antenna.

In Fig. 3.48, let $\tilde{x}_1(t)$, $\tilde{x}_2(t)$, and $\tilde{x}_3(t)$ be the signals received from the x-, y-, and z-oriented dipoles, respectively. As before, assume that two CW signals are incident on the array, one desired and the other interference, each having arbitrary direction and polarization. The desired signal has parameters (θ_d, ϕ_d, α_d, β_d, A_d) and the interference has parameters (θ_i, ϕ_i, α_i, β_i, A_i). Again, we assume each dipole in the array is a short dipole, so its output voltage is proportional to the electric field component along that dipole. From Eqs. (3.231) through (3.234), we find that an incoming signal with parameters (θ, ϕ, α, β, A) will produce a signal vector

$$\mathbf{X} = Ae^{j(\omega t + \psi)}\mathbf{U}, \tag{3.313}$$

where $\mathbf{U}$ is

$$\mathbf{U} = \begin{bmatrix} \sin\gamma\cos\theta\cos\phi\,e^{j\eta} - \cos\gamma\sin\phi \\ \sin\gamma\cos\theta\sin\phi\,e^{j\eta} + \cos\gamma\cos\phi \\ -\sin\gamma\sin\theta\,e^{j\eta} \end{bmatrix}. \tag{3.314}$$

With a desired signal specified by (θ_d, ϕ_d, α_d, β_d, A_d) and an interference signal specified by (θ_i, ϕ_i, α_i, β_i, A_i) incident on the array, and with the usual thermal noise voltage present on each element signal, the signal vector is

$$\mathbf{X} = A_d e^{j(\omega_d t + \psi_d)}\mathbf{U}_d + A_i e^{j(\omega_d t + \psi_i)}\mathbf{U}_i + \mathbf{X}_n, \qquad (3.315)$$

where $\mathbf{U}_d$ and $\mathbf{U}_i$ are given by Eq. (3.314) with a subscript d or i added to each angular quantity. For these $\mathbf{U}_d$ and $\mathbf{U}_i$, we find

$$\mathbf{U}_d^T \mathbf{U}_d^* = \mathbf{U}_i^T \mathbf{U}_i^* = 1. \qquad (3.316)$$

Hence Eq. (3.249) yields the simple result,

$$\text{SINR} = \xi_d \left[1 - \frac{|\mathbf{U}_d^T \mathbf{U}_i^*|^2}{\xi_i^{-1} + 1} \right]. \qquad (3.317)$$

Before discussing the SINR, we note again that ξ_d and ξ_i defined in Eqs. (3.250) and (3.251) are the signal-to-noise ratios computed from the total power in the incoming signals. Thus, ξ_d and ξ_i are the signal-to-noise ratios that will exist in a given array element if the incoming signal arrives broadside to that element and is linearly polarized in the direction of that element. For example, if $\alpha_d = 0°$ and $\beta_d = 0°$, the desired signal is polarized entirely in the E_ϕ-direction. Then if the signal arrives from $\phi_d = 90°$, the SNR on element 1 will be ξ_d. (In this case, the SNR on elements 2 and 3 will be zero.) In general, with an arbitrary state of polarization ($\alpha_d \neq 0°$ or $\beta_d \neq 0°$) and an arbitrary arrival angle θ_d, ϕ_d, the SNR on every element will be less than ξ_d. However, if the signals from all elements are combined with optimal weights (maximal ratio combiner weights [14]), the total output SNR from all elements combined will be ξ_d. The value of ξ_d thus represents the maximum available SNR out of all three dipoles.

Now let us show some typical curves of SINR computed from Eq. (3.317). First, we show curves representing typical performance for an arbitrarily polarized desired signal arriving from an arbitrary direction. We assume $\theta_d = \phi_d = 45°$, $\alpha_d = 15°$, $\beta_d = 30°$, and $\xi_d = 0$ dB. Also, we assume $\xi_i = 40$ dB. Figures 3.49 and 3.50 show the array output SINR as a function of the interference arrival angle for various interference polarizations. Figure 3.49 shows SINR versus θ_i, for $\phi_i = 45°$, and Fig. 3.50 shows SINR versus ϕ_i, for $\theta_i = 45°$. Figures 3.49(a) and 3.50(a) show $\beta_i = 0°$, Figs. 3.49(b) and 3.50(b) show $\beta_i = 30°$, and so forth, up to Figs. 3.49(f) and 3.50(f) for $\beta_i = 150°$. Each graph shows the SINR for $\alpha_i = -45°, -30°, -15°, 0°, 15°, 30°$, and $45°$.

Study of these curves shows that this simple antenna system, which responds only to polarization, has a remarkable ability to protect a desired signal from interference. To cause a poor SINR, an interference signal must not only arrive from the same direction as the desired signal, it must also have the same polarization. (The relationship between SINR and polarization when both signals arrive from the same direction will be discussed below under Special

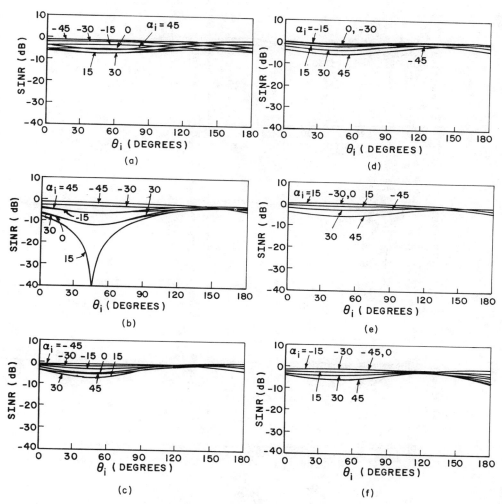

Figure 3.49   SINR versus θ_i: $\theta_d = 45°$, $\phi_d = 45°$, $\alpha_d = 15°$, $\beta_d = 30°$, $\xi_d = 0$ dB, $\phi_i = 45°$, $\xi_i = 40$ dB; (a) $\beta_i = 0°$; (b) $\beta_i = 30°$; (c) $\beta_i = 60°$; (d) $\beta_i = 90°$; (e) $\beta_i = 120°$; (f) $\beta_i = 150°$ (reprinted from [16] with permission, © 1981 IEEE).

Case 1.) Figure 3.49 shows that for all θ_i not near θ_d the output SINR is above -8 dB for all α_i, β_i, and Fig. 3.50 shows that for all ϕ_i not near ϕ_d the output SINR is above -12 dB for all α_i, β_i. Thus, with interference from these arrival angles, the array provides at least 28 dB of protection in all cases except when the conditions $\theta_i \approx \theta_d$, $\phi_i \approx \phi_d$, $\alpha_i \approx \alpha_d$, and $\beta_i \approx \beta_d$ are all simultaneously fulfilled.

When the SINR is computed for this desired signal and for other values of θ_i, ϕ_i, the results are generally similar to those in Figs. 3.49 and 3.50. However,

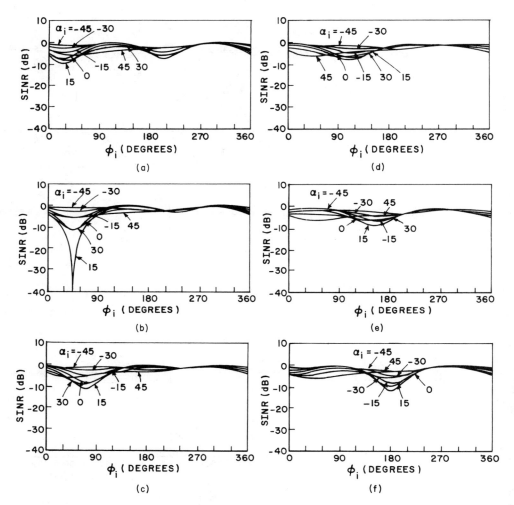

Figure 3.50 SINR versus ϕ_i: $\theta_d = 45°$, $\phi_d = 45°$, $\alpha_d = 15°$, $\beta_d = 30°$, $\xi_d = 0$ dB, $\theta_i = 45°$, $\xi_i = 40$ dB; (a) $\beta_i = 0°$; (b) $\beta_i = 30°$; (c) $\beta_i = 60°$; (d) $\beta_i = 90°$; (e) $\beta_i = 120°$; (f) $\beta_i = 150°$ (reprinted from [16] with permission, © 1981 IEEE).

there is one exception. When the interference arrives from the opposite direction from the desired signal, an SINR of -40 dB can result for one particular polarization (which we call the "conjugate" polarization). This case will be examined in detail below under Special Case 2.

When the performance of this array is examined for other desired signal arrival angles and polarizations, the results are again generally similar to those in Figs. 3.49 and 3.50. There is, however, one type of situation where the performance is not good. If the desired signal is linearly polarized, the array is vulnerable to linearly polarized interference from a wide range of angles. This situation will be examined in detail under Special Case 3.

Thus there are three situations where this array does not protect well against interference: (1) when both signals arrive from the same direction with the same polarization, (2) when the signals arrive from opposite directions with "conjugate" polarizations, and (3) when the desired signal has linear polarization. Let us consider these cases in detail.

Special Case 1. Both Signals Arrive from the Same Direction.

When both signals arrive from the same direction, it turns out that the output SINR is simply related to the separation of the two signal polarizations on the Poincaré sphere. Specifically, if $\theta_d = \theta_i$ and $\phi_d = \phi_i$, then Eq. (3.314) yields

$$\mathbf{U}_d^T \mathbf{U}_i^* = \sin \gamma_d \sin \gamma_i \, e^{j(\eta_d - \eta_i)} + \cos \gamma_d \cos \gamma_i. \tag{3.318}$$

From this, using trigonometric identities, one finds that

$$\left| \mathbf{U}_d^T \mathbf{U}_i^* \right|^2 = \tfrac{1}{2} \left[1 + \cos 2\gamma_d \cos 2\gamma_i + \sin 2\gamma_d \sin 2\gamma_i \cos (\eta_d - \eta_i) \right]. \tag{3.319}$$

Let P_d and P_i be points on the Poincaré sphere representing the polarizations of the desired and interference signals, as before. Then in Eq. (3.319), $2\gamma_d$ and $2\gamma_i$ are sides of a spherical triangle with arc $P_d P_i$ as the third side, as shown in Fig. 3.44. The angle $\eta_d - \eta_i$ is the angle opposite side $P_d P_i$. Using the identity in Eq. (3.309), we have

$$\left| \mathbf{U}_d^T \mathbf{U}_i^* \right|^2 = \tfrac{1}{2} \left[1 + \cos (P_d P_i) \right] = \cos^2 \left(\frac{P_d P_i}{2} \right). \tag{3.320}$$

Then, from Eq. (3.317), we have

$$\text{SINR} = \xi_d \left[\frac{1 + \xi_i \sin^2 \left(\dfrac{P_d P_i}{2} \right)}{1 + \xi_i} \right]. \tag{3.321}$$

This result shows that when both signals arrive from the same angle, the SINR obtained depends only on the separation $P_d P_i$ on the Poincaré sphere. The specific polarizations do not matter, only the separation.[‡]

Figure 3.51 shows a plot of SINR versus the spherical distance $P_d P_i$, in angular measure, for $\xi_d = 0$ dB and $\xi_i = 40$ dB. We see that a separation of $P_d P_i = 37°$ is required to have SINR $= -10$ dB, that is, for 30 dB of interference protection. Thus, for example, if $\beta_i = \beta_d$, we need $\alpha_d - \alpha_i = 18.5°$ for 30 dB of protection. (The point P on the Poincaré sphere is above the equator by 2α.)

[‡] Note that this result holds regardless of the angle from which both signals arrive. Thus this result is more general than the analogous result in Eq. (3.311) for the two pairs of crossed dipoles, since Eq. (3.311) is valid only when both signals arrive from broadside.

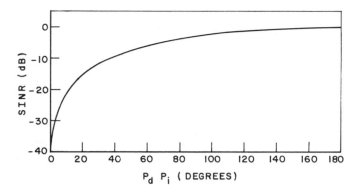

Figure 3.51 SINR versus $P_d P_i$ for $\theta_i = \theta_d$, $\phi_i = \phi_d$: $\xi_d = 0$ dB, $\xi_i = 40$ dB (reprinted from [16] with permission, © 1981 IEEE).

Special Case 2. Signals Arrive from Opposite Directions.

A poor SINR will also occur if the interference arrives from the opposite direction from the desired signal and if the interference polarization is conjugate to that of the desired signal. (We define "conjugate" below.)

First let us illustrate this situation. Figure 3.52 shows a set of SINR calculations similar to those in Fig. 3.50. The desired signal is again at $\theta_d = \phi_d = 45°$ with $\alpha_d = 15°$, $\beta_d = 30°$, $\xi_d = 0$ dB, and $\xi_i = 40$ dB. The curves show SINR versus ϕ_i, but now with $\theta_i = 135°$, instead of $45°$ as in Fig. 3.50. In Fig. 3.52(f), for $\beta_i = 150°$, we see that the SINR drops to -40 dB when $\phi_i = 225°$ and $\alpha_i = -15°$. Note that the angle of arrival $\theta_i = 135°$, $\phi_i = 225°$ is exactly in the opposite direction from the desired signal, with $\theta_d = \phi_d = 45°$. Moreover, as will be explained below, the polarization $\alpha_i = -15°$, $\beta_i = 150°$ is conjugate to that of the desired signal with $\alpha_d = 15°$ and $\beta_d = 30°$.

Consider the general case. When the interference arrives from the direction opposite to the desired signal, we have

$$\theta_i = 180° - \theta_d, \tag{3.322}$$

and

$$\phi_i = \phi_d + 180°. \tag{3.323}$$

For these values of θ_i and ϕ_i, one finds from Eq. (3.314) that

$$\mathbf{U}_d^T \mathbf{U}_i^* = \sin \gamma_d \sin \gamma_i \, e^{j(\eta_d - \eta_i)} - \cos \gamma_d \cos \gamma_i. \tag{3.324}$$

This equation differs from Eq. (3.318), when both signals arrive from the same direction, only in the minus sign preceding $\cos \gamma_d \cos \gamma_i$.

Given a desired signal polarization γ_d, η_d, let us define a new polarization with parameters γ_d^*, η_d^* given by

$$\gamma_d^* = \gamma_d \tag{3.325}$$

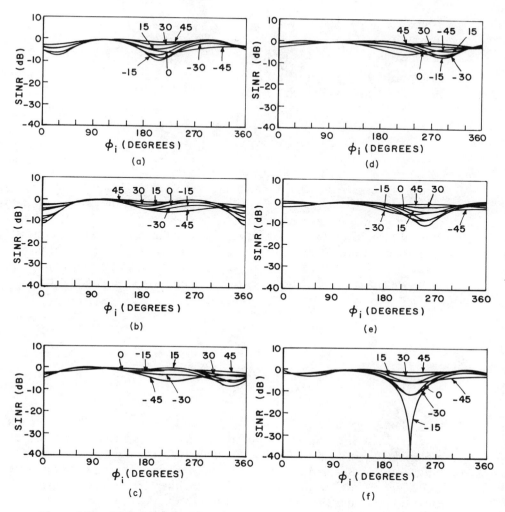

Figure 3.52   SINR versus ϕ_i: $\theta_d = 45°$, $\phi_d = 45°$, $\alpha_d = 15°$, $\beta_d = 30°$, $\xi_d = 0$ dB, $\theta_i = 135°$, $\xi_i = 40$ dB; (a) $\beta_i = 0°$; (b) $\beta_i = 30°$; (c) $\beta_i = 60°$; (d) $\beta_i = 90°$; (e) $\beta_i = 120°$; (f) $\beta_i = 150°$ (reprinted from [16] with permission, © 1981 IEEE).

and

$$\eta_d^* = \eta_d \pm 180°, \qquad (3.326)$$

where we choose the sign to keep η_d^* in the range $-180° \leqslant \eta_d^* \leqslant 180°$. In terms of γ_d^* and η_d^*, $\mathbf{U}_d^T \mathbf{U}_i^*$ in Eq. (3.324) may be written

$$\mathbf{U}_d^T \mathbf{U}_i^* = -\sin \gamma_d^* \sin \gamma_i \, e^{j(\eta_d^* - \eta_i)} - \cos \gamma_d^* \cos \gamma_i. \qquad (3.327)$$

Therefore, $|U_d^T U_i^*|^2$ is

$$\left| U_d^T U_i^* \right|^2 = |\sin \gamma_d^* \sin \gamma_i \, e^{j(\eta_d^* - \eta_i)} + \cos \gamma_d^* \cos \gamma_i|^2. \tag{3.328}$$

Comparing Eq. (3.327) with Eq. (3.318) and considering the steps leading up to Eq. (3.321), we see that the SINR may now be written

$$\text{SINR} = \xi_d \left[\frac{1 + \xi_i \sin^2 \left(\dfrac{P_d^* P_i}{2} \right)}{1 + \xi_i} \right], \tag{3.329}$$

where P_d^* is the point on the Poincaré sphere defined by γ_d^*, η_d^*. Thus, for this interference arrival angle, the SINR depends only on the separation between P_i and P_d^* on the Poincaré sphere.

We shall say that polarization P_d^* is conjugate to polarization P_d. These two polarizations differ only in that the angle η_d^* is 180° away from η_d, as seen in Eq. (3.326). By examining Eqs. (3.224) and (3.225), we find that the polarization inverse to α_d, β_d will have ellipticity and orientation given by

$$\alpha_d^* = -\alpha_d \tag{3.330}$$

and

$$\beta_d^* = 180° - \beta_d. \tag{3.331}$$

Thus, in Fig. 3.52(f), where $\alpha_d = 15°$ and $\beta_d = 30°$, the conjugate polarization is $\alpha_d^* = -15°$ and $\beta_d^* = 150°$, and the SINR is poor when $\alpha_i \approx \alpha_d^*$ and $\beta_i \approx \beta_d^*$.

The physical explanation for this result is simple. When the interference arrives from the direction opposite to the desired signal and has conjugate polarization, it produces element signals with exactly the same relative amplitudes and phases as the desired signal produces. Thus this situation is electrically equivalent to the case where the interference arrives from the same direction and has the same polarization as the desired signal.

Special Case 3. Linear Desired Signal Polarization.   The case where the desired signal is linearly polarized is the worst situation for this array. In this case, the array is vulnerable to similarly polarized interference from a wide range of angles. Moreover, it does not matter what direction the desired signal arrives from, or in what direction its (linear) polarization is oriented. The more closely the desired signal polarization approaches linear, the wider is the range of angles from which an interference signal can effectively reduce the SINR.

Let us first illustrate this with a simple example. Suppose $\theta_d = \phi_d = 90°$ and $\theta_i = 90°$. Also, suppose that both signals are linearly polarized, $\alpha_d = \alpha_i = 0°$, and the orientation angles of both signals are the same. $\beta_d = \beta_i$. Under these conditions, Fig. 3.53 shows the SINR versus ϕ_i for several values of β_d ($= \beta_i$)

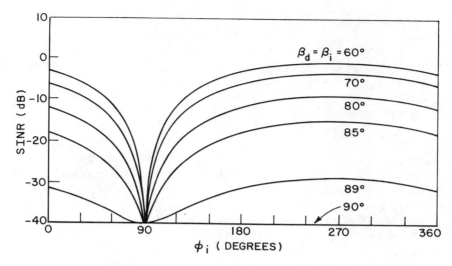

Figure 3.53   SINR versus ϕ_i for $\beta_d = \beta_i$: $\theta_d = 90°$, $\phi_d = 90°$, $\alpha_d = 0°$, $\xi_d = 0$ dB, $\theta_i = 90°$, $\alpha_i = 0°$, $\xi_i = 40$ dB (reprinted from [16] with permission, © 1981 IEEE).

approaching 90° (polarization parallel to the z-oriented dipole), for $\xi_d = 0$ dB and $\xi_i = 40$ dB. As may be seen in the figure, the closer β_d approaches 90°, the wider an angular separation $(\phi_i - \phi_d)$ is required between the two signals to achieve a given SINR.

If the desired signal is linearly polarized but the interference arrives from an arbitrary direction with arbitrary polarization, then the SINR depends on the interference parameters in a simple way. Suppose, for example, $\theta_d = 90°$, $\alpha_d = 0°$, and $\beta_d = 90°$. (In this case, the desired signal excites only the z-axis dipole.) Then, from Eqs. (3.224) and (3.225), we have $\gamma_d = 90°$, and Eq. (3.314) yields

$$\left| \mathbf{U}_d^T \mathbf{U}_i^* \right|^2 = \sin^2 \theta_i \sin^2 \gamma_i; \tag{3.332}$$

therefore, the SINR in Eq. (3.317) becomes

$$\mathrm{SINR} = \xi_d \left[1 - \frac{\sin^2 \theta_i \sin^2 \gamma_i}{\xi_i^{-1} + 1} \right]. \tag{3.333}$$

Note that this result holds regardless of ϕ_i or η_i.

Equation (3.333) shows that, for a given θ_i, a constant SINR will be obtained for all polarizations P_i with the same γ_i on the Poincaré sphere. As may be seen from Fig. 3.35, a locus of constant γ_i is a circle on the sphere. For $\gamma_i = 45°$, for example, it is a great circle passing through the equator at $\alpha_i = 0°$, $\beta_i = 45°$ and 135°, and through the top and bottom poles corresponding to circular polarization. For $\gamma_i = 0°$ or $\gamma_i = 90°$, the circle reduces to a point, corresponding to horizontal or vertical polarization, respectively. For any given γ_i, associated values of α_i and β_i can be found from Eq. (3.224).

The physical reason the SINR in Eq. (3.333) is invariant with η_i is as follows. For a given θ_i, varying the polarization parameters α_i, β_i in such a way that γ_i remains constant holds the amplitudes of the vertical and horizontal components of the incident field constant. Only the relative phase between E_θ and E_ϕ changes. For example, if $\gamma_i = 45°$, the polarization ellipse stays inside of and tangent to a square, as shown in Fig. 3.54. The vertical component E_θ appears in $\tilde{x}_3(t)$, and the horizontal component E_ϕ appears in the combined outputs from $\tilde{x}_1(t)$ and $\tilde{x}_2(t)$. It can be shown that, with no desired signal component in $\tilde{x}_1(t)$ or $\tilde{x}_2(t)$, the array combines $\tilde{x}_1(t)$ and $\tilde{x}_2(t)$ with maximal ratio combiner weights [14, sec. 2, para. 3, p. 108] to yield the E_ϕ-component of the interference at maximum interference-to-noise ratio, regardless of ϕ_i. This combined output from $\tilde{x}_1(t)$ and $\tilde{x}_3(t)$ is adjusted to the proper phase by the weights and then subtracted from $\tilde{x}_3(t)$ to null the interference. Since the *amplitudes* of the vertical and horizontal components are fixed as η_i varies, the output SINR is also fixed.

Since the SINR in Eq. (3.333) does not depend on ϕ_i, the array will be equally vulnerable to interference from any ϕ_i; separating the two signals in ϕ does not help. The worst case occurs if $\theta_i = 90°$, $\alpha_i = 0°$, and $\beta_i = 90°$ (so $\gamma_i = 90°$), when Eq. (3.333) gives

$$\text{SINR} = \frac{\xi_d}{\xi_i + 1} \qquad (3.334)$$

which is essentially -40 dB if SNR = 0 dB and INR = 40 dB, again regardless of ϕ_i.

In Eq. (3.333), we assumed that $\theta_d = 90°$, $\alpha_d = 0°$, and $\beta_d = 90°$ but that the interference parameters were arbitrary. Alternatively, we may assume the interference is linearly polarized, say $\theta_i = 90°$, $\alpha_i = 0°$, and $\beta_i = 90°$, and the desired signal is arbitrary. In this case, $\gamma_i = 90°$ and Eq. (3.314) yields

$$\left| \mathbf{U}_d^T \mathbf{U}_i^* \right|^2 = \sin^2 \theta_d \sin^2 \gamma_d, \qquad (3.335)$$

so that

$$\text{SINR} = \xi_d \left[1 - \frac{\sin^2 \theta_d \sin^2 \gamma_d}{\xi_i^{-1} + 1} \right] \qquad (3.336)$$

regardless of ϕ_d or η_d. This result is analogous to Eq. (3.333). With the interference linearly polarized parallel to the z-oriented dipole, it tells us how close $\sin \theta_d \sin \gamma_d$ can approach unity if a given SINR must be obtained. For example, if an SINR of -3 dB is necessary (with $\xi_d = 0$ dB and $\xi_i = 40$ dB), either θ_d must be less than $45°$ if vertical linear polarization ($\gamma_d = 90°$) is used, or, if the polarization is circular ($\gamma_d = 45°$), the signal may arrive from $\theta_d = 90°$.

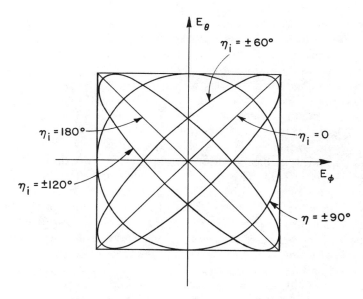

Figure 3.54   Polarization ellipses with $\gamma_i = 45°$ (reprinted from [16] with permission, © 1981 IEEE).

In this example it is easy to see the reason for the poor performance of the array. When $\theta_d = 90°$, $\alpha_d = 0°$, and $\beta_d = 90°$ (and ϕ_d has any value), the desired signal excites only the z-axis dipole. Clearly, an interference signal from $\theta_i = 90°$ with the same polarization ($\alpha_i = 0°$, $\beta_i = 90°$) will also produce a signal only in this dipole, regardless of ϕ_i. The array will then have no ability to null one signal and not the other, whether $\phi_i = \phi_d$ or not.

However, it turns out the poor performance of the array with a linearly polarized desired signal does not depend on having the electric field aligned with one of the dipoles. A similar result occurs whenever the desired signal is linearly polarized, regardless of its arrival angles θ_d, ϕ_d or orientation angle β_d.[‡] In general, with a linearly polarized desired signal, the array will be vulnerable to any linearly polarized interference signal whose electric field is parallel to that of the desired signal. More specifically, suppose the desired signal arrives from a given direction with a given linear polarization. Imagine a plane passing through the center of the tripole and oriented perpendicular to the desired signal electric field. Then a linearly polarized interference signal incident on the tripole from any direction *in this plane*, with its electric field *perpendicular to this plane*, will produce a low SINR from the array. The physical reason is that such an interference signal produces the same element voltages in the array as the

---

[‡]The author is grateful to Andrew Zeger of Zeger and Abrams, Inc., who first pointed this property out to him.

desired signal (except for a scale constant). Hence, a set of array weights that nulls the interference also nulls the desired signal.

Simple SINR formulas for the general case of a linearly polarized desired signal may be obtained by defining a new coordinate system whose axes are chosen to align with the desired signal. We shall not carry out the details here, which are tedious and appear to give little additional insight into the problem, but shall merely describe the procedure.

Assume the desired signal arrival direction θ_d, ϕ_d and orientation angle β_d are given. We define a new $x'y'z'$ coordinate system oriented such that the x'-axis points in the direction θ_d, ϕ_d and the z'-axis is parallel to the desired signal electric field. This coordinate system may be obtained by a sequence of three orthogonal coordinate rotations of the original xyz coordinate system in Fig. 3.48 about each of its axes. (The three angles of rotation are frequently called Eulerian angles [17].) Using the $x'y'z'$ axes, we define polar coordinates r', θ', ϕ' in the usual way, with θ' measured from the z'-axis and ϕ' from the x'-axis. In this coordinate system, the desired signal arrives from $\theta'_d = 90°$, $\phi'_d = 0°$ and has orientation angle $\beta'_d = 90°$. The interference parameters θ'_i, ϕ'_i, γ'_i, and η'_i in the primed frame may be derived from the corresponding parameters in the unprimed frame by means of the Eulerian angle rotations. (Note that angle α_i, which describes the ellipticity of the interference, is the same in either frame.) To evaluate the SINR in Eq. (3.317), we note that $\mathbf{U}_d$ and $\mathbf{U}_i$ are vectors, which may be represented in terms of either their xyz components or their $x'y'z'$ components. Since the $x'y'z'$ system is obtained from the xyz system by an orthogonal transformation, $|\mathbf{U}_d^T \mathbf{U}_i^*|^2$ is invariant under this transformation and may be computed in either system with the same result. In the primed system, however, since $\theta'_d = 90°$, $\alpha'_d = 0°$, and $\beta'_d = 90°$, the steps required to evaluate $|\mathbf{U}_d^T \mathbf{U}_i^*|^2$ are identical to those used to obtain Eq. (3.332) except that all quantities are now primed. Thus we find

$$\left| \mathbf{U}_d^T \mathbf{U}_i^* \right|^2 = \sin^2 \theta'_i \sin^2 \gamma'_i \tag{3.337}$$

and

$$\text{SINR} = \xi_d \left[1 - \frac{\sin^2 \theta'_i \sin^2 \gamma'_i}{\xi_i^{-1} + 1} \right], \tag{3.338}$$

where θ'_i is the polar angle and γ'_i the polarization parameter of the interference, both as seen in the primed system. Since $\theta_i = 90°$ is the plane perpendicular to the desired signal electric field, we see from Eq. (3.338) that any linearly polarized interference signal arriving in this plane and polarized perpendicular to the plane (so $\beta'_i = 90°$ and hence $\gamma'_i = 90°$) will produce a low SINR from the array, as discussed previously.

Thus, in conclusion, Special Cases 1, 2, and 3 describe the situations in which this array will not yield good performance. Other than in these cases, however, performance such as that shown in Figs. 3.49, 3.50, and 3.52 is typical of what is obtained. In general, this array has quite a good ability to protect a desired signal from interference.

As a final remark, we note that the tripole antenna may itself be used as a building block in a larger adaptive array. For example, the poor performance of the tripole with linearly polarized signals can be eliminated by arraying two or more tripoles. Such an array will not have the difficulties described in Special Cases 2 and 3. (However, it will still have the behavior described in Special Case 1.)

In this chapter, we have discussed three things that greatly influence the performance of adaptive arrays: the number of degrees of freedom in the array, the signal bandwidths, and the element patterns. These limitations affect all adaptive arrays, regardless of which weight control technique is used. For example, the bandwidth degradations discussed in section 3.2 were computed under the assumption that the array weight vector $\mathbf{W}$ has the optimal value, $\mathbf{\Phi}^{-1}\mathbf{S}$. It makes no difference to the bandwidth performance what technique we use to make $\mathbf{W}$ equal $\mathbf{\Phi}^{-1}\mathbf{S}$.

In the next chapter, we shall discuss some additional performance limitations that are associated with LMS and Applebaum feedback loops.

PROBLEMS

3.1. In section 3.1 we discussed the fact that an N-element array has $N - 1$ degrees of freedom. It is interesting to ask how these degrees of freedom are "distributed in space."

(a) Consider a four-element array with isotropic elements spaced one wavelength apart long the z-axis, as shown in Fig. 3.55(a). Let a CW signal arrive from angles θ, ϕ as shown and produce a signal vector

$$\mathbf{X} = Ae^{j\omega t}\mathbf{U},$$

where

$$\mathbf{U} = \begin{bmatrix} 1 \\ e^{-j2\pi \sin \theta} \\ e^{-j4\pi \sin \theta} \\ e^{-j6\pi \sin \theta} \end{bmatrix}.$$

Suppose we want the array to have a null at $\theta = 30°$, $\phi = 90°$. We require a weight vector $\mathbf{W}$ satisfying

$$\mathbf{W}^T\mathbf{U} = 0$$

for this signal direction. However, this weight vector will also produce nulls in other spatial directions besides $\theta = 30°$, $\phi = 90°$.

For this element configuration, choose a weight vector $\mathbf{W}$ satisfying $\mathbf{W}^T\mathbf{U} = 0$ (note that $\mathbf{W}$ is not unique), and for this $\mathbf{W}$ determine all angles in space where the array has a null.

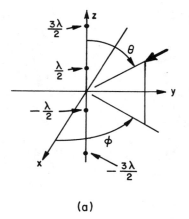

(a)

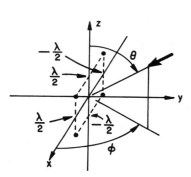

(b)

Figure 3.55 Element locations. (a) Elements on a line; (b) elements on a square.

(b) Now suppose the four elements are located at the corners of a square one wavelength on a side, as shown in Fig. 3.55(b). Assume we again choose a weight vector **W** so the array has a null at $\theta = 30°$, $\phi = 90°$. Now for this element configuration, determine all directions where the array has nulls. Discuss the advantage and disadvantage of each choice of element locations.

3.2. Consider an adaptive array with two isotropic elements. Assume this array receives a desired signal and an interference signal with nonzero bandwidth, as described in Eqs. (3.56) through (3.104). Let the elements be a half wavelength apart at the center frequency of the signals. Assume there is no channel mismatch problem, so bandwidth degradation is due entirely to spatial decorrelation. Suppose the desired signal arrives from broadside ($\theta_d = 0°$).

(a) Consider the question of how interference arrival angle affects bandwidth degradation. On the one hand, interference bandwidth should have the most effect when the interference arrives from endfire, because at this angle the interelement propagation delay is maximum. On the other hand, for a desired signal at broadside, the optimal weights form a pattern with a maximum at broadside and a null at endfire, even without interference. Hence, an interference signal at endfire arrives in this null, so it seems that its bandwidth should not matter. Which of these two points of view seems more correct? Should the degradation due to bandwidth be larger or smaller for $\theta_i = 90°$ than for $\theta_i = 50°$, the case shown in Fig. 3.11(a)? Will the SINR be maximum for some θ_i between $0°$ and $90°$, or will it be maximum at $\theta_i = 90°$?

(b) Now use the results in Eqs. (3.95) through (3.97) and (3.101) through (3.104) to compute the SINR versus θ_i for the case $\xi_d = 0$ dB, $\xi_i = 40$ dB, $B_d = 0$, $\eta = 0$ and for interference bandwidths $B_i = 0.01$ and 0.05. How do these results compare with your intuitive answer in part (a)?

3.3. Repeat the analysis of Eqs. (3.56) through (3.104) for a three-element array.

(a) Assume there are three isotropic elements spaced a half wavelength apart along a line. Assume that a desired signal with bandwidth B_d and SNR per element ξ_d arrives from θ_d and an interference signal with bandwidth B_i and INR ξ_i arrives from θ_i. Assume the reference signal is $\tilde{r}(t) = (R/\sqrt{p_d})\tilde{d}(t)$, where $\tilde{d}(t)$ is the desired signal received on element 1. Determine the normalized covariance matrix and the normalized reference correlation vector for this situation. Obtain formulas for the output desired signal, interference, and thermal noise powers normalized to σ^2.

(b) Use the results in (a) to plot the output SINR in dB versus ξ_d in dB of $\theta_d = 0$, $B_d = 0$, $\xi_i = 40$ dB, $\theta_i = 50°$ and for $B_i = 0$, 0.01, 0.02, and 0.05.

(c) Does the three-element array have more or less bandwidth degradation than the two-element array discussed in the text? Take into consideration that with no interference a three-element array yields SINR $= 3\xi_d$ (or a gain of 4.77 dB), whereas a two-element array yields only SINR $= 2\xi_d$ (a gain of 3 dB).

3.4. Verify the results in Eqs. (3.142) and (3.143).

3.5. Using the model of channel mismatch error given in Fig. 3.16 and Eqs. (3.121) through (3.123), we calculated the curves in Figs. 3.18 and 3.19. These figures show how the SINR drops as E, the maximum channel mismatch, increases. Both figures were calculated for a fixed bandwidth, $B_i = 0.01$.

It is also interesting to fix the value of E and calculate curves of SINR versus ξ_d for different values of bandwidth B_i. Figure 3.56 shows a typical result for such a calculation. It shows the SINR as a function of the input SNR (ξ_d) for $\xi_i = 40$ dB, $\theta_d = 50°$, $\theta_i = 0°$, $B_d = 0$, $E = 0.05$, $K = 5$ and for several values of B_i.

If we examine these curves carefully, we see that the SINR begins to drop below its ideal value when B_i is about 0.003. As B_i is increased above 0.003, the SINR is reduced further. However, when B_i reaches 0.01, the drop in SINR below its ideal value does not continue. Increasing B_i above 0.01 causes no further reduction in SINR.

Explain why this result makes sense physically.

3.6. This problem derives a classical result known as the maximal ratio combiner, which was originally discussed in connection with diversity communications [14]. This problem also generalizes the result in problem 2.8.

Consider an adaptive array with N elements. Let the pattern of element j be $f_j(\theta, \phi)$. Suppose a CW desired signal propagates into the array from the direction θ_d, ϕ_d. This signal produces a signal vector

$$\mathbf{X}_d = A_d e^{j(\omega_d t + \psi_d)} \mathbf{U}_d,$$

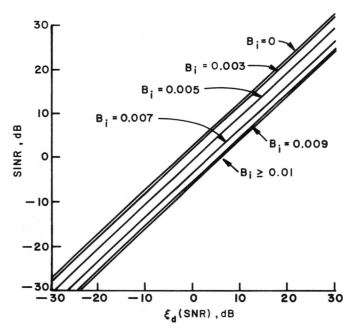

Figure 3.56 SINR versus ξ_d for fixed E: $\xi_i = 40$ dB, $\theta_d = 50°$, $\theta_i = 0°$, $B_d = 0$, $E = .05$, $K = 5$.

where

$$
U_d = \begin{bmatrix} f_1(\theta_d, \phi_d) \\ f_2(\theta_d, \phi_d)\, e^{-j\phi_{d2}} \\ \vdots \\ f_N(\theta_d, \phi_d)\, e^{-j\phi_{dN}} \end{bmatrix}
$$

and where ϕ_{dj} is the electrical phase shift of the signal between element j and element 1. (ϕ_{dj} depends on θ_d, ϕ_d and on the element locations.)

Assume the array also has independent thermal noise on each element. Suppose the noise power on different elements may be different. Let the noise power on element j be σ_j^2.

Finally, let the reference signal be

$$
\tilde{r}(t) = \mathrm{Re}^{\,j(\omega_d t + \psi_d)}.
$$

Now do the following:

(a) Define ξ_j to be the signal-to-noise ratio on element j. Show that

$$
\xi_j = \frac{A_d^2 |f_j(\theta_d, \phi_d)|^2}{\sigma_j^2}.
$$

(b) Find the weight vector $\mathbf{W}_{opt}$ that maximizes the array output SNR, defined as follows. Let $\mathbf{\Phi}_n$ be the noise covariance matrix,

$$\mathbf{\Phi}_n = \begin{bmatrix} \sigma_1^2 & 0 & \cdots & 0 \\ 0 & \sigma_2^2 & \cdots & 0 \\ \vdots & \vdots & \ddots & \vdots \\ 0 & 0 & \cdots & \sigma_N^2 \end{bmatrix}.$$

$\mathbf{W}_{opt}$ is then the solution to

$$\left[\mathbf{\Phi}_n + A_d^2 \mathbf{U}_d^* \mathbf{U}_d^T \right] \mathbf{W}_{opt} = A_d R \mathbf{U}_d^*.$$

Use the matrix inversion lemma of problem 2.2 to show that

$$\mathbf{W}_{opt} = \kappa \mathbf{\Phi}_n^{-1} \mathbf{U}_d^*,$$

where κ is a scalar constant. Determine the value of κ.

(c) For this weight vector, show that the array output desired signal power is

$$P_d = \frac{\kappa^2 A_d^2}{2} \left[\mathbf{U}_d^T \mathbf{\Phi}_n^{-1} \mathbf{U}_d^* \right]^2,$$

and the array output thermal noise power is

$$P_n = \frac{\kappa^2}{2} \left[\mathbf{U}_d^T \mathbf{\Phi}_n^{-1} \mathbf{U}_d^* \right].$$

(d) Show from the results of part (c) that the output signal-to-noise ratio is

$$\mathrm{SNR}_{out} = \sum_{j=1}^{N} \xi_j,$$

that is, the sum of the signal-to-noise ratios on each element.

(e) Show that when all the elements have the same noise power and the elements are isotropic, the weight vector in part (b) reduces to that found in problem 2.7(a) and the output SNR in part (d) reduces to that found in problem 2.8.

Comment: Note from part (b) that the optimal weight on each element is proportional to the conjugate of the signal voltage on that element divided by the noise power on that element. A "combiner" that uses these weights is known as a *maximal ratio combiner*. (The "ratio" referred to is P_d/P_n!)

3.7. Assume the element pattern (voltage response) for a short dipole is

$$f(\theta) = \cos \theta,$$

where θ is the signal arrival angle measured with respect to the dipole, as shown in Fig. 3.57(a).

Now consider an adaptive array using three such short dipoles. The three dipoles are centered $\lambda/2$ apart and have their axes aligned as shown in Fig. 3.57(b). (All three dipoles lie in the plane of the paper.) The signals from the three dipoles are to be combined with an Applebaum adaptive array processor. If the desired signal will arrive from the direction shown (30° from vertical), find the appropriate steering vector $\mathbf{T}^*$ to be used in the Applebaum feedback loops. The thermal noise power is assumed equal on each element.

(a) A Short Dipole

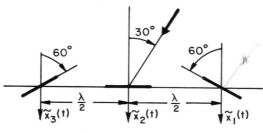

(b) A 3-Element Array

Figure 3.57   An array with element patterns. (a) A short dipole; (b) a three-element array.

3.8.   An adaptive array consists of two short dipoles. The first dipole has its center at $x = 0$, $y = 0$, $z = \lambda/4$ (where λ is the wavelength) and is parallel to the x-axis. The second dipole has its center at $x = 0$, $y = 0$, and $z = -\lambda/4$ and is parallel to the z-axis.

Assume the array receives a CW desired signal with parameters $(\theta_d, \phi_d, \alpha_d, \beta_d, A_d)$ and a CW interference signal with parameters $(\theta_i, \phi_i, \alpha_i, \beta_i, A_i)$. Each element signal also contains independent thermal noise of power σ^2, and the reference signal is a CW signal correlated with the desired signal, as usual.

Do the following:
(a) Find the signal vectors $\mathbf{U}_d$ and $\mathbf{U}_i$ for this array and these signals.
(b) Using Eq. (3.219), obtain a formula for the array output SINR in terms of the signal parameters.
(c) Evaluate the SINR numerically for the following case. Let $\theta_d = \phi_d = 90°$ (the desired signal arrives broadside to both dipoles) and $\alpha_d = 0°$, $\beta_d = 45°$ (the desired signal is linearly polarized with its E-field at 45° with respect to the x- and z-axes). Assume $\xi_d = 0$ dB and $\xi_i = 40$ dB. Then let $\theta_i = 90°$ and plot the SINR as a function of ϕ_i for $0 \leqslant \phi_i \leqslant 180°$ and for the following interference parameters:

1. $\alpha_i = 45°$, $\beta_i = 0°$.
2. $\alpha_i = 0°$, $\beta_i = 45°$.
3. $\alpha_i = 0°$, $\beta_i = 90°$.

(d) Explain why your results make sense physically.

3.9.   This problem derives a formula for output SINR that is very useful for studying the performance of adaptive arrays with multiple interfering signals. This result is originally due to I. J. Gupta.

Consider an adaptive array having N elements with arbitrary patterns. Suppose a CW desired signal of amplitude A_d is incident on the array and produces a signal vector $\mathbf{U}_d$. Suppose that M mutually independent CW interference signals are also incident on the array. Assume interference signal j has amplitude A_j and produces signal vector $\mathbf{U}_j$. Finally, assume as usual that thermal noise of power σ^2 is present on each element signal.

Applebaum has shown that the weight vector

$$\mathbf{W} = \mu \Phi_u^{-1} \mathbf{U}_d^*$$

will produce maximum array output SINR, where Φ_u is the part of the covariance matrix due to the undesired signals, and μ is an arbitrary (nonzero) constant. Do the following:

(a) Show that when the Applebaum weight vector is used, the array output SINR will be

$$\text{SINR} = \frac{A_d^2 |\mathbf{U}_d^T \Phi_u^{-1} \mathbf{U}_d^*|^2}{\sum_{j=1}^{M} A_j^2 |\mathbf{U}_j^T \Phi_u^{-1} \mathbf{U}_d^*|^2 + \sigma^2 |\Phi_u^{-1} \mathbf{U}_d^*|^2}.$$

(b) Show that the denominator in part (a) can be rearranged into the form

$$\text{denominator} = \mathbf{U}_d^T \Phi_u^{-1} \mathbf{U}_d^*.$$

(c) Using the result in part (b), show that the SINR may be written

$$\text{SINR} = A_d^2 \mathbf{U}_d^T \Phi_u^{-1} \mathbf{U}_d^*.$$

(d) Will this result still be correct if the LMS weight vector, $\mathbf{W} = \Phi^{-1} \mathbf{U}_d^*$, is used instead of the Applebaum weight vector? (Φ is the total covariance matrix, including the desired signal terms.)

3.10. An adaptive array consists of N isotropic elements equally spaced with separation L along a straight line. The arrival angle θ is measured from broadside to the array.

A CW desired signal and a CW interference signal are incident on the array from angles θ_d and θ_i, respectively. Both signals are on frequency ω_d but are uncorrelated. As usual, uncorrelated thermal noise of power σ^2 is present on each element signal, and the reference signal is a CW signal coherent with the desired signal.

(a) Show that the output SINR from the array is

$$\text{SINR} = \xi_d \left[\frac{N\left(N + \xi_i^{-1}\right) \sin^2\left(\dfrac{\eta}{2}\right) - \sin^2\left(\dfrac{N\eta}{2}\right)}{\left(N + \xi_i^{-1}\right) \sin^2\left(\dfrac{\eta}{2}\right)} \right],$$

where

$$\eta = \frac{2\pi L}{\lambda} \left[\sin(\theta_i) - \sin(\theta_d) \right].$$

(b) Now assume every element in the array has the same voltage pattern $f(\theta)$. (The pattern $f(\theta)$ may be complex.) Derive the corresponding formula for the SINR.

REFERENCES

1. W. E. Rodgers and R. T. Compton, Jr., "Adaptive Array Bandwidth with Tapped Delay-Line Processing," *IEEE Transactions on Aerospace and Electronic Systems*, AES–15, no. 1 (January 1979): 21.

2. W. E. Rodgers and R. T. Compton, Jr., "Adaptive Array Bandwidth with Tapped Delay-Line Processing," Report 3832–3, May 1975, Ohio State University ElectroScience Laboratory, Columbus; prepared under Contract N00019–74–C–0141 for Naval Air Systems Command.

3. J. T. Mayhan, "Some Techniques for Evaluating the Bandwidth Characteristics of Adaptive Nulling Systems," *IEEE Transactions on Antennas and Propagation*, AP–27, no. 3 (May 1979): 363.

4. J. T. Mayhan, A. J. Simmons, and W. C. Cummings, "Wideband Adaptive Antenna Nulling Using Tapped Delay Lines," Report 1979–45, 26 June 1979, M.I.T. Lincoln Laboratory, Lexington, Mass.; prepared under Contract F19628–78–C–0002 for the Department of the Air Force and the Defense Communications Agency.

5. W. D. White, "Wideband Interference Cancellation in Adaptive Sidelobe Cancellers," *IEEE Transactions on Aerospace and Electronic Systems*, AES–19, no. 6 (November 1983): 915.

6. G. A. Deschamps, "Geometrical Representation of the Polarization of a Plane Electromagnetic Wave," *Proceedings of the IRE*, 39, no. 5 (May 1951): 540.

7. V. H. Rumsey, G. A. Deschamps, M. L. Kales, and J. I. Bohnert, "Techniques for Handling Elliptically Polarized Waves with Special Reference to Antennas," *Proceedings of the IRE*, 39, no. 5 (May 1951): 533.

8. G. Sinclair, "The Transmission and Reception of Elliptically Polarized Waves, *Proceedings of the IRE*, 38, no. 2 (February 1950): 148.

9. C. T. Tai, "On the Definition of the Effective Aperture of Antennas," *IRE Transaction on Antennas and Propagation*, AP–9, no. 2 (March 1961): 224.

10. A. Ishide and R. T. Compton, Jr., "On Grating Nulls in Adaptive Arrays," *IEEE Transactions on Antennas and Propagation*, AP–28, no. 4 (July 1980): 467. Copyright © 1980 IEEE.

11. A. S. Householder, *The Theory of Matrices in Numerical Analysis*, Dover, New York, 1964, pp. 3, 123.

12. R. T. Compton, Jr., "A Method of Choosing Element Patterns in an Adaptive Array," *IEEE Transactions on Antennas and Propagation*, AP–30, no. 3 (May 1982): 489.

13. R. T. Compton, Jr., "On the Performance of a Polarization Sensitive Adaptive Array," *IEEE Transactions on Antennas and Propagation*, AP–29, no. 5 (September 1981): 718. Copyright © 1981 IEEE.

14. D. G. Brennan, "Linear Diversity Combining Techniques," *Proceedings of the IRE*, 47, no. 6 (June 1959): 1075.

15. K. L. Nielson and J. H. Vanlonkhuyzen, *Plane and Spherical Trigonometry*, Barnes & Noble, New York, 1954, pp. 110–119.

16. R. T. Compton, Jr., "The Tripole Antenna: An Adaptive Array with Full Polarization Flexibility," *IEEE Transactions on Antennas and Propagation*, AP–29, no. 6 (November 1981): 944. Copyright © 1981 IEEE.

17. H. Goldstein, *Classical Mechanics*, Addison-Wesley, Reading, Mass., 1959, chap. 4.

18. R. T. Compton, Jr., "The Bandwidth Performance of a Two-Element Adaptive Array with Tapped Delay-Line Processing," *IEEE Transactions on Antennas and Propagation*, AP-36, no. 1 (January 1988).

4

Performance Characteristics of LMS and Applebaum Loops

In this chapter, we shall discuss certain performance characteristics and limitations that occur with adaptive arrays using LMS or Applebaum loops. In Chapter 3, we described the effect of the number of degrees of freedom, the signal bandwidths, and the element patterns. These limitations affect all adaptive arrays, regardless of the type of weight control used. The only assumption is that the weight vector is set equal to $\Phi^{-1}S$. In this chapter, we describe some additional limitations that are associated with LMS and Applebaum loops. We begin with a discussion of feedback loop bandwidth.

4.1 LOOP BANDWIDTH

The LMS array has a feedback loop bandwidth that depends on signal power. The effect of this bandwidth on weight behavior must be understood when designing an array for use with communication signals.

Consider a one-dimensional complex LMS loop as shown in Fig. 4.1. With input signal $\tilde{x}(t)$ and reference signal $\tilde{r}(t)$, the weight in this loop satisfies the differential equation

$$\frac{dw}{dt} + k|\tilde{x}(t)|^2 w = k\tilde{x}^*(t)\tilde{r}(t). \tag{4.1}$$

Suppose $\tilde{x}(t)$ is a CW signal,

$$\tilde{x}(t) = Ae^{j\omega t}. \tag{4.2}$$

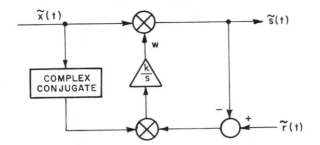

Figure 4.1   A single LMS loop.

Then Eq. (4.1) becomes

$$\frac{dw}{dt} + kA^2w = kf(t),$$ (4.3)

where

$$f(t) = Ae^{-j\omega t}\tilde{r}(t).$$ (4.4)

We observe that w may be interpreted as the output of a linear filter with transfer function $H(s)$:

$$H(s) = \frac{k}{s + kA^2},$$ (4.5)

and with input $f(t)$, as shown in Fig. 4.2. The transfer function $H(s)$ is also identical to that of a simple feedback loop with an integrator in the forward path, as shown in Fig. 4.3. For this reason, the LMS loop is sometimes said to be equivalent to a Type I feedback loop [1]. Note that the gain in the feedback path in Fig. 4.3 depends on the received signal power A^2. The higher the signal power, the larger the feedback gain and the faster the response of the loop.

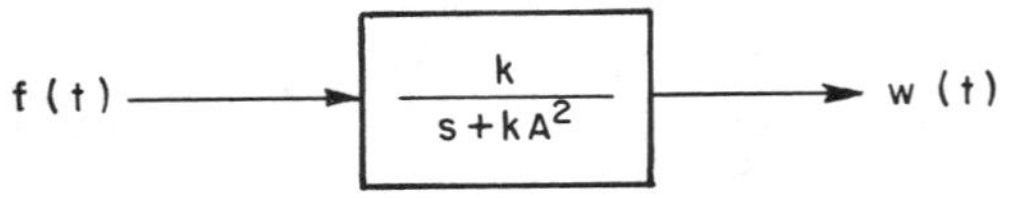

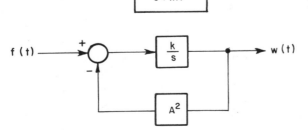

Figure 4.2   A linear filter.

Figure 4.3   An equivalent feedback loop.

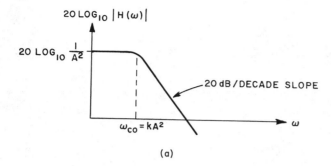

(a)

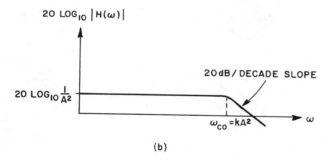

(b)

Figure 4.4   Filter transfer functions. (a) Small A^2; (b) large A^2.

The frequency response of the filter in Fig. 4.2 is obtained by substituting $j\omega$ for s:

$$H(j\omega) = \frac{k}{j\omega + kA^2}. \tag{4.6}$$

The loop is a simple lowpass filter with DC gain

$$H(0) = \frac{1}{A^2} \tag{4.7}$$

and cutoff frequency

$$\omega_{co} = kA^2. \tag{4.8}$$

Figure 4.4 shows a typical $|H(j\omega)|$ versus ω for small A^2 and for large A^2. We see that the higher the signal power, the wider the bandwidth of the loop and the smaller the DC gain. We also note (for later use) that the homogeneous response of Eq. (4.3) is $e^{-kA^2 t}$, so the time constant of the loop transient may be written

$$\tau = \frac{1}{kA^2} = \frac{1}{\omega_{co}}. \tag{4.9}$$

To illustrate the effect of the loop bandwidth on the performance of the array, let us consider the response of this loop when the reference signal is a CW signal similar to $\tilde{x}(t)$, but not necessarily on the same frequency. Let the reference signal be given by

$$\tilde{r}(t) = \text{Re}^{j\omega_r t}. \tag{4.10}$$

Then

$$f(t) = A\text{Re}^{j(\omega_r - \omega)t} = A\text{Re}^{j\Delta\omega t}, \tag{4.11}$$

where

$$\Delta\omega = \omega_r - \omega. \tag{4.12}$$

Equation (4.3) becomes

$$\frac{dw}{dt} + kA^2w = kA\text{Re}^{j\Delta\omega t} \tag{4.13}$$

If $\Delta\omega = 0$, so that the reference signal is on the same frequency as the received signal, then this equation reduces to

$$\frac{dw}{dt} + kA^2w = kAR, \tag{4.14}$$

whose solution is

$$w(t) = \left[w(0) - \frac{R}{A} \right] e^{-kA^2t} + \frac{R}{A}. \tag{4.15}$$

This is the standard weight transient we have seen many times previously. However, now suppose $\Delta\omega \neq 0$. If the reference signal is on a different frequency from the received signal, Eq. (4.13) will have the solution

$$w(t) = \left[w(0) - \frac{kAR}{j\Delta\omega + kA^2} \right] e^{-kA^2t} + \frac{kAR}{j\Delta\omega + kA^2} e^{j\Delta\omega t}. \tag{4.16}$$

This result contains two terms. The first is the homogeneous response, which is an exponential transient that dies out with time. The second term is a time-harmonic steady-state term. After the transient has died out, only this term remains, and the weight is given by

$$W_{ss}(t) = w(t) = \frac{kAR}{j\Delta\omega + kA^2} e^{j\Delta\omega t}. \tag{4.17}$$

Since the complex weight w is equal to $w_I - jw_Q$ where w_I and w_Q are the

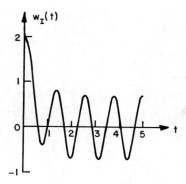

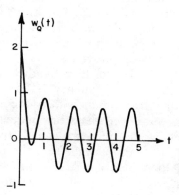

Figure 4.5 Typical weight response with $\omega_r \neq \omega$.

associated inphase and quadrature weights, we find that w_I and w_Q vary sinusoidally in time quadrature:

$$w_I(t) = \frac{kAR}{\sqrt{\Delta\omega^2 + k^2 A^4}} \cos\left(\Delta\omega\, t - \eta\right) \tag{4.18}$$

and

$$w_Q(t) = \frac{kAR}{\sqrt{\Delta\omega^2 + k^2 A^4}} \sin\left(\Delta\omega\, t - \eta\right), \tag{4.19}$$

where

$$\eta = \tan^{-1}\left(\frac{\Delta\omega}{kA^2}\right). \;\; = \; tan^{-1}\left(\frac{\Delta\omega}{W_{co}}\right) \tag{4.20}$$

Thus a typical weight response will be as shown in Fig. 4.5.

Let us compute the output signal $\tilde{s}(t)$ when the weight w is given by Eq. (4.17). Multiplying $w(t)$ in Eq. (4.17) by $\tilde{x}(t)$ in Eq. (4.2), we have

$$\tilde{s}(t) = w(t)\tilde{x}(t) = \frac{kA^2R}{j\Delta\omega + kA^2} e^{j\omega t}e^{j\Delta\omega t} = \frac{kA^2R}{j\Delta\omega + kA^2} e^{j\omega_r t}. \qquad (4.21)$$

Thus we find that the array weight *frequency modulates* the input signal! The LMS loop makes the output signal frequency match the frequency of the reference signal. If $\Delta\omega$ is very small, so

$$\Delta\omega \ll \omega_{co} = kA^2 \qquad (4.22)$$

then

$$s(t) \simeq Re^{j\omega_r t}, \qquad (4.23)$$

and $\tilde{s}(t)$ matches the reference signal exactly, both in amplitude and phase. As $\Delta\omega$ is increased, however, the amplitude of $\tilde{s}(t)$ drops below R and $\tilde{s}(t)$ begins to lag $\tilde{r}(t)$ in phase. [However, it always stays on the same frequency as $\tilde{r}(t)$!] For very large $\Delta\omega$, w and $\tilde{s}(t)$ both approach zero—that is, the array turns off the weight and makes the array output zero.

This result illustrates the effect of loop bandwidth on the performance of the array. If the reference signal frequency is close to the received signal frequency (within the feedback loop bandwidth), the array retains the received signal in the array output. Moreover, the array frequency modulates the signal so that its frequency matches the reference signal frequency. However, if the reference signal frequency is too far away from the received signal frequency (farther than the feedback loop bandwidth), the array nulls it. Thus, to receive a desired signal, the reference signal frequency must not differ from the desired signal frequency by more than the feedback loop bandwidth. However, the loop bandwidth is a function of the signal power. When the array must operate with signals whose power varies over a certain dynamic range, the permissible frequency offset will usually be dictated by the weakest signals of interest.

4.2 FEEDBACK LOOP TIME DELAYS‡

When the LMS feedback loop is implemented with practical hardware, the designer must be careful about time delays around the loop [2]. Consider the LMS loop shown in Fig. 4.6. Ideally, the signals in this loop should undergo no time delays in the RF signal paths around the loop. In an ideal loop, with no time delays, the error signal would be given by

$$\tilde{\varepsilon}(t) = \tilde{r}(t) - \tilde{s}(t) = \tilde{r}(t) - \sum_{n=1}^{N} w_n\tilde{x}_n(t), \qquad (4.24)$$

‡Portions of this section are reprinted from the author's paper [2] with permission, © 1981 IEEE.

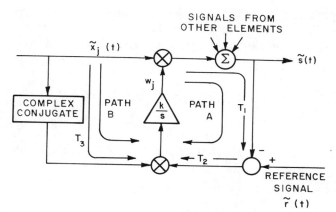

Figure 4.6 The LMS loop (reprinted from [2] with permission, © 1981 IEEE).

and the input to the integrator would be

$$\frac{1}{k}\frac{dw_j}{dt} = \tilde{x}_j^*(t)\left[\tilde{r}(t) - \sum_{n=1}^{N} w_n\tilde{x}_n(t)\right]. \tag{4.25}$$

Rearranging this equation yields the differential equation for the weight vector in an ideal array,

$$\frac{d\mathbf{W}(t)}{dt} + k\mathbf{X}^*(t)\mathbf{X}^T(t)\mathbf{W}(t) = k\mathbf{X}^*(t)\tilde{r}(t). \tag{4.26}$$

If we assume the loop gain is low enough that the weights do not track the instantaneous fluctuations in $\mathbf{X}^*(t)\mathbf{X}^T(t)$ or $\mathbf{X}^*(t)\tilde{r}(t)$, Eq. (4.26) may be approximated by

$$\frac{d\mathbf{W}(t)}{dt} + k\boldsymbol{\Phi}\mathbf{W}(t) = k\mathbf{S}, \qquad\text{infrequent update assumption} \tag{4.27}$$

where

$$\boldsymbol{\Phi} = E\left[\mathbf{X}^*(t)\mathbf{X}^T(t)\right] \tag{4.28}$$

and

$$\mathbf{S} = E\left[\mathbf{X}^*(t)\tilde{r}(t)\right]. \tag{4.29}$$

In a hardware implementation of the LMS loop, however, time delays unavoidably occur in the various signal paths of the loop. Usually path A in Fig. 4.6 contains more delay than path B. The reason is that path A includes cabling and passive hybrids (for the summer and the reference signal port), whereas path B is a simple electronic circuit connection. Let us examine the effect of these path delays.

Suppose the signal through path A undergoes a time delay of T_1 seconds between the weight multiplier and the reference signal hybrid, and an additional delay of T_2 seconds between this hybrid and the correlator multiplier. Also, suppose the signal in path B is delayed by T_3 seconds in reaching the correlator multiplier. (These delays are indicated in Fig. 4.6.) Then the input to the integrator will be

$$\frac{1}{k} \frac{dw_j(t)}{dt} = \tilde{x}_j^*(t - T_3)\left[\tilde{r}(t - T_2) - \sum_{n=1}^{N} w_n(t - T_1 - T_2)\tilde{x}_n(t - T_1 - T_2) \right],$$

(4.30)

instead of Eq. (4.25), and the differential equation for the weight vector becomes

$$\frac{d\mathbf{W}(t)}{dt} + k\mathbf{X}^*(t - T_3)\mathbf{X}^T(t - T_1 - T_2)\mathbf{W}(t - T_1 - T_2)$$

$$= k\mathbf{X}^*(t - T_3)\tilde{r}(t - T_2), \qquad (4.31)$$

instead of Eq. (4.26). Assuming again that k is small enough that $\mathbf{W}(t)$ does not follow the instantaneous variations of $\mathbf{X}^*\mathbf{X}^T$ or $\mathbf{X}^*\tilde{r}$, we may approximate this equation by

$$\frac{d\mathbf{W}(t)}{dt} + k\mathbf{\Phi}_1\mathbf{W}(t - T_1 - T_2) = k\mathbf{S}_1, \qquad (4.32)$$

where

$$\mathbf{\Phi}_1 = E\left[\mathbf{X}^*(t - T_3)\mathbf{X}^T(t - T_1 - T_2)\right] \qquad (4.33)$$

and

$$\mathbf{S}_1 = E\left[\mathbf{X}^*(t - T_3)\tilde{r}(t - T_2)\right]. \qquad (4.34)$$

Equation (4.32) for the practical loop differs from Eq. (4.27) for the ideal loop in two ways. First, the covariance matrix $\mathbf{\Phi}$ and the reference correlation vector $\mathbf{S}$ of Eqs. (4.28) and (4.29) are replaced by $\mathbf{\Phi}_1$ and $\mathbf{S}_1$ of Eqs. (4.33) and (4.34). Second, Eq. (4.32) for $\mathbf{W}(t)$ is now a differential-difference equation [3], instead of an ordinary differential equation.[‡] That is, Eq. (4.32) involves $\mathbf{W}$ at time "$t - T_1 - T_2$," but $d\mathbf{W}/dt$ at time "t." The change from a differential to a differential-difference equation occurs because the feedback loop has transport lag.

Of these changes, only the first is of any significance. In practice the values of the time delays T_1, T_2, and T_3 are negligibly short compared to the time constants of the weight transients. In this case it can be shown [3] that the solution to Eq. (4.32) is virtually the same as the solution obtained by replacing $\mathbf{W}(t - T_1 - T_2)$ by $\mathbf{W}(t)$ in Eq. (4.32).

On the other hand, the change from $\mathbf{\Phi}$ and $\mathbf{S}$ of Eqs. (4.28) and (4.29) to $\mathbf{\Phi}_1$ and $\mathbf{S}_1$ of Eqs. (4.33) and (4.34) has important consequences for the

---

[‡]It is a differential-difference equation of retarded type [3, sec. 3.3].

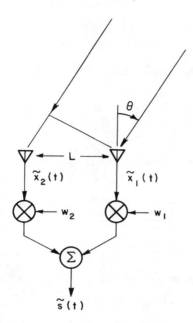

Figure 4.7 A two-element array (reprinted from [2] with permission, © 1981 IEEE).

performance of the array. We now examine the effects of this change to determine how much time delay is acceptable.

To be specific, let us suppose we have a two-element array with isotropic elements, as shown in Fig. 4.7. Assume two signals are incident on the array, one desired and the other interference, from angles θ_d and θ_i, respectively, as shown. As usual, we also assume each element signal $\tilde{x}_j(t)$ contains uncorrelated thermal noise. Then the element signals are

$$\tilde{x}_1(t) = \tilde{d}(t) + \tilde{i}(t) + \tilde{n}_1(t) \tag{4.35}$$

and

$$\tilde{x}_2(t) = \tilde{d}(t - T_d) + \tilde{i}(t - T_i) + \tilde{n}_2(t), \tag{4.36}$$

where T_d and T_i are the interelement propagation time delays,

$$T_d = \frac{L}{c} \sin \theta_d \tag{4.37}$$

and

$$T_i = \frac{L}{c} \sin \theta_i, \tag{4.38}$$

with c the velocity of propagation. The signals $\tilde{d}(t)$, $\tilde{i}(t)$, and $\tilde{n}_j(t)$ are all assumed to be stationary, zero-mean, stochastic signals, each independent of the others. Let us also assume the reference signal $\tilde{r}(t)$ is perfectly correlated with the desired signal from element 1 after delay T_1, that is,

$$\tilde{r}(t) = \tilde{d}(t - T_1).\tag{4.39}$$

With these assumptions, one finds for $\mathbf{\Phi}_1$ and $\mathbf{S}_1$ in Eqs. (4.33) and (4.34),

$$\mathbf{\Phi}_1 = \begin{bmatrix} R_{\tilde{d}}(-T_0) + R_{\tilde{i}}(-T_0) + R_{\tilde{n}}(-T_0) & R_{\tilde{d}}(-T_d - T_0) + R_{\tilde{i}}(-T_i - T_0) \\ R_{\tilde{d}}(T_d - T_0) + R_{\tilde{i}}(T_i - T_0) & R_{\tilde{d}}(-T_0) + R_{\tilde{i}}(-T_0) + R_{\tilde{n}}(-T_0) \end{bmatrix}\tag{4.40}$$

and

$$\mathbf{S}_1 = \begin{bmatrix} R_{\tilde{d}}(-T_0) \\ R_{\tilde{d}}(T_d - T_0) \end{bmatrix}\tag{4.41}$$

where $R_{\tilde{d}}(\tau)$ and $R_{\tilde{i}}(\tau)$ are the autocorrelation functions of $\tilde{d}(t)$ and $\tilde{i}(t)$ as defined in Eqs. (3.62) and (3.82), and $R_{\tilde{n}}(\tau)$ is the autocorrelation function of $\tilde{n}_j(t)$,

$$R_{\tilde{n}}(\tau) = E\left[\tilde{n}_j^*(t)\tilde{n}_j(t + \tau)\right], \qquad j = 1, 2,\tag{4.42}$$

and where T_0 is the differential time delay between paths A and B,

$$T_0 = T_1 + T_2 - T_3.\tag{4.43}$$

(Positive T_0 corresponds to more delay in path A than in path B.) In order to carry out a specific calculation, let us further assume that $\tilde{d}(t)$, $\tilde{i}(t)$, and the $\tilde{n}_j(t)$ each have a flat bandlimited spectral density, with bandwidths $\Delta\omega_d$, $\Delta\omega_i$, and $\Delta\omega_n$ and total powers p_d, p_i, and σ^2, respectively. Then the autocorrelation functions are

$$R_{\tilde{d}}(\tau) = p_d \frac{\sin\left(\dfrac{\Delta\omega_d \tau}{2}\right)}{\left(\dfrac{\Delta\omega_d \tau}{2}\right)} e^{j\omega_d\tau},\tag{4.44}$$

$$R_{\tilde{i}}(\tau) = p_i \frac{\sin\left(\dfrac{\Delta\omega_i \tau}{2}\right)}{\left(\dfrac{\Delta\omega_i \tau}{2}\right)} e^{j\omega_d\tau},\tag{4.45}$$

and

$$R_{\tilde{n}}(\tau) = \sigma^2 \frac{\sin\left(\dfrac{\Delta\omega_n \tau}{2}\right)}{\left(\dfrac{\Delta\omega_n \tau}{2}\right)} e^{j\omega_d\tau}.\tag{4.46}$$

These autocorrelation functions may be substituted into Eqs. (4.40) and (4.41) to yield $\mathbf{\Phi}_1$ and $\mathbf{S}_1$. The adaptive array weight vector will then be given by the solution to

$$\frac{d\mathbf{W}(t)}{dt} + k\mathbf{\Phi}_1\mathbf{W}(t) = k\mathbf{S}_1, \tag{4.47}$$

which in general is of the form

$$\mathbf{W}(t) = \mathbf{C}_1 e^{-k\lambda_1 t} + \mathbf{C}_2 e^{-k\lambda_2 t} + \mathbf{\Phi}_1^{-1}\mathbf{S}_1, \tag{4.48}$$

where $\mathbf{C}_1$ and $\mathbf{C}_2$ are vectors depending on the initial value of $\mathbf{W}(t)$ and λ_1 and λ_2 are the eigenvalues of $\mathbf{\Phi}_1$.

Examination of Eqs. (4.40) and (4.41) shows that the effect of the differential delay is to add a term $-T_0$ to the argument of every term in $\mathbf{\Phi}_1$ and $\mathbf{S}_1$. [The ideal $\mathbf{\Phi}$ and $\mathbf{S}$ of Eqs. (4.28) and (4.29) correspond to $T_0 = 0$.] This change has two effects on the array weights. First, it affects their transient behavior, and second, it affects their steady-state values and hence the array performance. We consider these effects in the next two subsections.

Weight Cycling

First, consider the transient behavior. When Eqs. (4.44) through (4.46) are substituted in for the autocorrelation functions in Eqs. (4.40) and (4.41), we find that every term in both $\mathbf{\Phi}_1$ and $\mathbf{S}_1$ contains the exponential factor $e^{-j\omega_d T_0}$. This factor does not affect the steady-state weight vector, because it cancels off in $\mathbf{\Phi}_1^{-1}\mathbf{S}_1$. However, it does influence the transient behavior of the weights, since it affects the eigenvalues of $\mathbf{\Phi}_1$. To illustrate this point in a simple way, suppose there is no interference ($p_i = 0$), and suppose all bandwidths are very small, so the $(\sin x)/x$ functions in Eqs. (4.44) through (4.46) are unity for the delays involved in Eq. (4.33). Moreover, assume the desired signal arrives from broadside, so $T_d = 0$. Then $\mathbf{\Phi}_1$ is given by

$$\mathbf{\Phi}_1 = \begin{bmatrix} (p_d + \sigma^2)e^{-j\omega_d T_0} & p_d e^{-j\omega_d T_0} \\ p_d e^{-j\omega_d T_0} & (p_d + \sigma^2)e^{-j\omega_d T_0} \end{bmatrix}. \tag{4.49}$$

The eigenvalues of $\mathbf{\Phi}_1$ are

$$\lambda_1 = \sigma^2 e^{-j\omega_d T_0}, \qquad \lambda_2 = (\sigma^2 + 2p_d)e^{-j\omega_d T_0}, \tag{4.50}$$

so the transient weight vector in Eq. (4.48) will have the form

$$\mathbf{W}(t) = \mathbf{C}_1 e^{-k\sigma^2(\cos\omega_d T_0)t} e^{jk\sigma^2(\sin\omega_d T_0)t}$$

$$+ \mathbf{C}_2 e^{-k(\sigma^2 + 2p_d)(\cos\omega_d T_0)t} e^{jk(\sigma^2 + 2p_d)(\sin\omega_d T_0)t} + \mathbf{\Phi}_1^{-1}\mathbf{S}_1, \tag{4.51}$$

where we have separated λ_1 and λ_2 into their real and imaginary parts. The imaginary part of $e^{-j\omega_d T_0}$ will be nonzero unless $\omega_d T_0 \neq 0 \pmod{\pi}$, and as a result the weights have an oscillatory behavior. Moreover, the differential delay

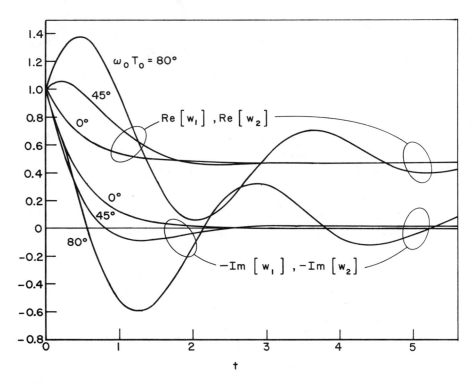

Figure 4.8   Typical weight transients (reprinted from [2] with permission, © 1981 IEEE).

T_0 must be such that $-\frac{1}{2}\pi < \omega_d T_0 < \frac{1}{2}\pi$ (mod 2π) to keep the weights stable. In general, for $-\frac{1}{2}\pi < \omega_d T_0 < \frac{1}{2}\pi$ (mod 2π), $\cos(\omega_d T_0)$ decreases as $\sin(\omega_d T_0)$ increases, so that the time required for the weights to settle into their steady-state values increases.

Figure 4.8 illustrates this behavior. This figure shows the weight transients that result when $p_d = 1$ and $\sigma^2 = 0.1$ in Eq. (4.51), for $\omega_d T_0 = 0°$, $45°$, and $80°$. The initial weights are arbitrarily assumed to be $w_1(0) = w_2(0) = 1 - j$. It may be seen that as $\omega_d T_0$ increases, the weights oscillate at a higher frequency and are less damped, so it takes longer for the weights to settle into their steady-state values.

The physical reason for this weight cycling is not difficult to see. For an adaptive array with inphase and quadrature feedback loops, the time delay T_0 (or phase shift $\omega_d T_0$) causes the inphase channel output to correlate with the signal in the quadrature channel. Thus an incorrectly set weight in the inphase channel causes an error voltage correction in the quadrature channel, and vice versa.

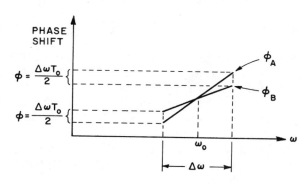

Figure 4.9 Phase shifts ϕ_A and ϕ_B versus frequency (reprinted from [2] with permission, © 1981 IEEE).

In order to avoid the problem of weight cycling, the designer must adjust the total differential phase shift $\omega_d T_0$ to be an integral number of 2π. The phase shift in path A of Fig. 4.6 should be adjusted (by using a phase shifter in the loop, or by trimming cables, for example) so that $\omega_d T_0 = 0 \pmod{2\pi}$. However, there is a problem in setting this phase shift. With $T_0 \neq 0$, the adjustment can be done at only one frequency. Usually it is not possible to keep the phase shifts in paths A and B matched over a band of frequencies. If the phase shift in path A is

$$\phi_A = \omega(T_1 + T_2), \tag{4.52}$$

and that in path B is

$$\phi_B = \omega T_3, \tag{4.53}$$

then ϕ_A and ϕ_B will depend on frequency as shown in Fig. 4.9. The phase shift ϕ_A can be set equal to $\phi_B \pmod{2\pi}$ at one frequency ω_d, but they will not be matched at other frequencies. If signals must be accommodated whose frequencies vary, because of doppler shift or oscillator inaccuracies, the differential phase shift may not be zero at the actual signal frequency. The result will be weight cycling and an increase in the array response time, as illustrated in Fig. 4.8.

To determine how much differential phase shift is acceptable, suppose the signal frequency varies over a bandwidth $\Delta\omega$ centered at ω_d. Then if the phases are matched at ω_d, the maximum differential phase shift at the band edge is $\Delta\omega\, T_0/2$. It is clear from Eq. (4.50) that when $\Delta\omega\, T_0/2$ is 45°, the array time constant will be increased by a factor 2 over its value with no phase shift. Also, it may be seen from Fig. 4.8 that the weight transients with a 45° phase shift are still reasonably well behaved. Based on this somewhat arbitrary criterion, we arrive at the following rule-of-thumb:

If frequency uncertainty of $\Delta\omega$ must be accommodated in the array, the band edge differential phase shift between paths A and B should be held to no more than $\Delta\omega\, T_0/2 = 45°$.

Performance Degradation

The second effect of the differential time delay in Fig. 4.6 is to decorrelate the signals in the error-by-signal multiplier when the signals have nonzero bandwidth. This effect occurs even if the center frequency of the received signal is at ω_d. Since the differential delay affects the values of the matrices $\mathbf{\Phi}_1$ and $\mathbf{S}_1$, it makes the weights differ from their optimum values and thus affects the performance of the system.

To study this effect, let us now assume the signals have nonzero bandwidth. Their autocorrelation functions are as given in Eqs. (4.44) through (4.46). For notational convenience, let us define

$$\rho_l(\tau) = \frac{\sin\left(\dfrac{\Delta\omega_l\,\tau}{2}\right)}{\left(\dfrac{\Delta\omega_l\,\tau}{2}\right)}e^{j\omega_d\tau} = \frac{\sin\frac{1}{2}B_l\omega_d\tau}{\frac{1}{2}B_l\omega_d\tau}e^{j\omega_d\tau}, \tag{4.54}$$

where l stands for d, i, or n, and where

$$B_l = \frac{\Delta\omega_l}{\omega_d} \tag{4.55}$$

is the fractional bandwidth for signal l. Also, it is convenient to normalize both $\mathbf{\Phi}_1$ and $\mathbf{S}_1$ to σ^2, the noise power. Thus, the steady-state weight vector is the solution to

$$\frac{1}{\sigma^2}\mathbf{\Phi}_1\mathbf{W} = \frac{1}{\sigma^2}\mathbf{S}_1, \tag{4.56}$$

where

$$\frac{1}{\sigma^2}\mathbf{\Phi}_1 = \begin{bmatrix} \xi_d\rho_d(-T_0) + \xi_i\rho_i(-T_0) + \rho_n(-T_0) & \xi_d\rho_d(-T_d - T_0) + \xi_i\rho_i(-T_i - T_0) \\ \xi_d\rho_d(T_d - T_0) + \xi_i\rho_i(T_i - T_0) & \xi_d\rho_d(-T_0) + \xi_i\rho_i(-T_0) + \rho_n(-T_0) \end{bmatrix} \tag{4.57}$$

and

$$\frac{1}{\sigma^2}\mathbf{S}_1 = \begin{bmatrix} \xi_d\rho_d(-T_0) \\ \xi_d\rho_d(T_d - T_0) \end{bmatrix} \tag{4.58}$$

and where

$$\xi_d = \frac{P_d}{\sigma^2} = \text{desired signal-to-noise ratio (SNR) per element, and}$$

$$\xi_i = \frac{P_i}{\sigma^2} = \text{interference-to-noise ratio (INR) per element.} \tag{4.59}$$

Using Eqs. (4.57) and (4.58), Eq. (4.56) may be solved for the steady-state weight vector $\mathbf{W}$. Then, given $\mathbf{W}$, the powers of the desired signals, interference, and thermal noise at the array output may be calculated in the usual manner. The output desired signal power is

$$P_d = \tfrac{1}{2} E\left[\tilde{s}_d^*(t)\tilde{s}_d(t)\right]$$

$$= \frac{p_d}{2}\left[|w_1|^2 + |w_2|^2 + 2\,\text{Re}\left\{w_1 w_2^* \rho_d(T_d)\right\}\right], \tag{4.60}$$

where $\mathbf{W} = (w_1, w_2)^T$. Normalizing this equation to σ^2, we have

$$\frac{P_d}{\sigma^2} = \frac{\xi_d}{2}\left[|w_1|^2 + |w_2|^2 + 2\,\text{Re}\left\{w_1 w_2^* \rho_d(T_d)\right\}\right]. \tag{4.61}$$

Similarly, the normalized output interference power P_i/σ^2 is found to be

$$\frac{P_i}{\sigma^2} = \frac{\xi_i}{2}\left[|w_1|^2 + |w_2|^2 + 2\,\text{Re}\left\{w_1 w_2^* \rho_i(T_i)\right\}\right], \tag{4.62}$$

and the normalized output thermal noise power P_n/σ^2 is

$$\frac{P_n}{\sigma^2} = \tfrac{1}{2}\left[|w_1|^2 + |w_2|^2\right]. \tag{4.63}$$

The output SINR is then

$$\text{SINR} = \frac{P_d}{P_i + P_n} = \frac{P_d/\sigma^2}{P_i/\sigma^2 + P_n/\sigma^2}. \tag{4.64}$$

The effect of differential phase shift between paths A and B on system performance (SINR) can be computed from these equations, for various values of θ_d, θ_i, ξ_d, ξ_i, B_d, B_i, B_n, and T_0. We show here a typical result.

Let us suppose $B_d = B_i = B_n$. Define the differential phase shift at the band edge to be

$$\phi = \frac{\Delta\omega_d T_0}{2}\left(= \frac{\Delta\omega_i T_0}{2} = \frac{\Delta\omega_n T_0}{2}\right), \tag{4.65}$$

as indicated in Fig. 4.9. Figure 4.10 shows a plot of SINR versus ϕ for the case $\theta_d = 0°$, $\theta_i = 50°$, $\xi_d = 10$ dB, and $\xi_i = 40$ dB. Several curves are shown, for fractional bandwidths of 0.001, 0.01, 0.03, and 0.1.

Consider first the case where the bandwidth is 0.001 and $\phi = 0$. The output SINR is 12.4 dB. In this case the array yields essentially ideal performance. That is, the interference is being suppressed and an array gain of 2.4 dB (the maximum available from a two-element array with desired signal at $\theta_d = 0°$ and interference at $\theta_i = 50°$) is added to the input SNR of 10 dB, yielding a 12.4 dB output SINR. Next, note that if we keep $\phi = 0$ but increase the fractional bandwidth, the output SINR drops. At $B_i = 0.1$, for example, the SINR has dropped to about 11.5 dB and at $B_i = 0.3$, SINR = 7.4 dB (all for

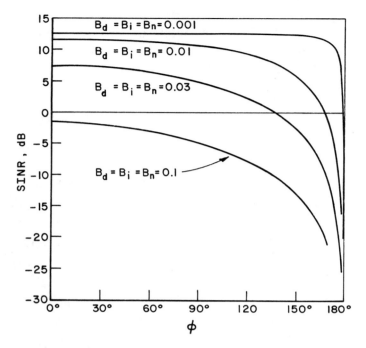

Figure 4.10   SINR versus band edge differential phase shift ϕ (reprinted from [2] with permission, © 1981 IEEE).

$\phi = 0$). This drop is due to the interference bandwidth and to the fact that quadrature hybrid processing is used, as described in Chapter 3. As the interference bandwidth increases, the array is less able to null it (because the signals from the two elements are not completely correlated), so a drop in SINR occurs. This effect has nothing to do with the differential path delay.

Now consider what happens when $\phi \neq 0$. It is seen that for any given bandwidth, increasing ϕ (the band edge differential phase shift) further degrades system performance. For $B_I = 0.01$, for example, the SINR is 1.5 dB when $\phi = 0$ but has dropped 1 dB to 0.5 dB at $\phi = 90°$. For $B_I = 0.03$, the SINR has dropped 1 dB (from 7.4 to 6.4 dB) at $\phi = 55°$. Thus a given ϕ has more effect as the bandwidth increases.

Figure 4.10 illustrates that the band edge differential phase shift ϕ that can be tolerated in a given system design depends on the bandwidth of the signals and on the acceptable performance degradation. Since these quantities depend on the particular system, one cannot give a universal guideline for ϕ. However, if one assumes that the fractional bandwidth of the signals is no more than 0.01 (so the array performance is not already limited by bandwidth effects) and that a performance degradation of 1 dB is acceptable, then ϕ can be as large as 90°.

Thus differential time delay in the LMS feedback loop has two effects on array performance. First, it causes a weight cycling during transients, which increases the adaptation time, and second, it causes a degradation in array output SINR in the steady state. To keep weight transients reasonably well behaved, the band edge differential phase shift should be kept to within about 45°. To keep steady-state performance degradation less than 1 dB for a fractional signal bandwidth of 0.01, the band edge differential phase shift should be less than about 90°. Which of these two requirements is the more stringent depends on the bandwidth of the signals and the carrier frequency uncertainty (resulting from doppler shift or oscillator uncertainty) that must be accommodated.

4.3 MULTIPLIER OFFSET VOLTAGES

Next we consider a very important problem in implementing LMS loops—the problem of DC balance in the error-by-signal multiplier of the LMS loop. Spurious DC output voltages from this multiplier can seriously degrade the performance of the array.

The Cause of Offset Voltages

Consider a single inphase or quadrature loop as shown in Fig. 4.11. Ideally, the output of the error-by-signal multiplier should be

$$\text{multiplier output} = x_{P_j}(t)\varepsilon(t). \tag{4.66}$$

In practice, however, we find that multipliers are subject to leakage effects, nonlinearities, and circuit imbalances. Typically, the actual multiplier output will contain terms such as the following:

$$\text{multiplier output} = \kappa_{P_j} + x_{P_j}(t)\varepsilon(t) + c_1 x_{P_j}^2(t) + c_2\varepsilon(t) + c_3 x_{P_j}^2(t)$$

$$+ c_4\varepsilon^2(t) + c_5 x_{P_j}^2(t)\varepsilon(t) + \cdots . \tag{4.67}$$

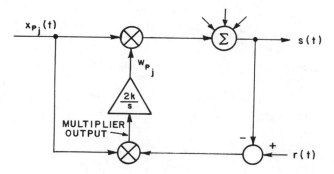

Figure 4.11   A single LMS loop.

The term $x_{P_j}(t)\varepsilon(t)$ is the desired output from the multiplier, and in a well-designed multiplier it is the dominant term. The term κ_{P_j} is a DC voltage unrelated to the signals $x_{P_j}(t)$ or $\varepsilon(t)$. With active circuit multipliers (such as transconductance multipliers [4]), it is usually due to circuit imbalance. The terms $c_1 x_{P_j}(t)$ and $c_2\varepsilon(t)$ represent leakage of the input signals into the multiplier output. The terms $c_3 x_{P_j}^2(t)$, $c_4\varepsilon^2(t)$, $c_5 x_{P_j}(t)\varepsilon(t)$, and similar higher order terms result either from device nonlinearities or from leakage of one input signal into the other input port and reflection back into the multiplier where it multiplies itself.

Since the multiplier output goes directly into an integrator, only those output frequency components centered around DC are important. In adaptive arrays for radar and communications, the signals $x_{P_j}(t)$ and $\varepsilon(t)$ are band-limited signals at a nonzero carrier frequency. Thus their presence in the multiplier output does not matter. Of the nonlinear terms, only the term $c_1 x_{P_j}^2(t)$ is important. The other terms are either at the wrong frequency or have too small an amplitude. For example, although the term $c_2\varepsilon^2(t)$ does have a DC component, its effect is negligible because $\varepsilon(t)$ becomes small in the steady state.

The term $c_1 x_{P_j}^2(t)$, however, is particularly important in connection with multiplier offset voltages. This term is important because it contains a nonzero DC value, and this DC value depends on the input signal power. Hence, although one can adjust the balance of the multiplier so the DC value of $\kappa_{P_j} + c_1 x_{P_j}^2(t)$ is zero for one particular input signal level, the balance is thrown off if the signal power changes.

Analysis of Offset Voltages

For purposes of analysis, we may lump the DC component of $c_1 x_{P_j}^2(t)$ together with κ_{P_j}. Thus we model the error-by-signal multiplier by the equation

$$\text{multiplier output} = x_{P_j}(t)\varepsilon(t) + \delta_{P_j}, \tag{4.68}$$

where

$$\delta_{P_j} = \kappa_{P_j} + \overline{c_1 x_{P_j}^2(t)}, \tag{4.69}$$

and where the overbar denotes the DC value of $x_{P_j}^2(t)$. We will refer to δ_{P_j} as the multiplier offset voltage.

Let us examine the effect of the voltages δ_{P_j} on the performance of the array. With the input to the integrator given by Eq. (4.68), the array weights satisfy

$$\frac{1}{2k}\frac{dw_{P_j}}{dt} = x_{P_j}(t)\varepsilon(t) + \delta_{P_j}, \qquad 1 \leqslant j \leqslant N, \; P = I, Q. \tag{4.70}$$

As usual, we combine the quadrature weights behind each element of the array into a single complex weight as in Eq. (2.53). We define

$$\delta_j = \delta_{I_j} - j\delta_{Q_j},$$ (4.71)

and then Eq. (4.70) is equivalent to

$$\frac{dw_j}{dt} = k\left[\tilde{x}_j^*(t)\tilde{\varepsilon}(t) + \delta_j\right], \qquad 1 \leqslant j \leqslant N.$$ (4.72)

Substituting for $\tilde{\varepsilon}(t)$ as in Eq. (2.81) and rearranging, we find that the weight vector satisfies the differential equation,

$$\frac{d\mathbf{W}}{dt} + k\boldsymbol{\Phi}\mathbf{W} = k(\mathbf{S} + \boldsymbol{\Delta}),$$ (4.73)

where $\boldsymbol{\Delta}$ is the *offset vector*, with components δ_j,

$$\boldsymbol{\Delta} = [\delta_1, \delta_2, \ldots, \delta_N]^T.$$ (4.74)

Thus the effect of the offset voltages is to add an extraneous term $k\boldsymbol{\Delta}$ to the right side of Eq. (4.73). The steady-state weight vector will now be given by

$$\mathbf{W} = \boldsymbol{\Phi}^{-1}(\mathbf{S} + \boldsymbol{\Delta}) = \mathbf{W}_{\text{opt}} + \boldsymbol{\Phi}^{-1}\boldsymbol{\Delta}$$ (4.75)

instead of by $\mathbf{W}_{\text{opt}}$.

Example 1

To illustrate the effects of the term $\boldsymbol{\Phi}^{-1}\boldsymbol{\Delta}$ on the array performance, consider the two-element array shown in Fig. 4.12. Suppose that a CW desired signal is incident on the array from angle θ_d and that thermal noise is present in the element signals. The signal vector is given by

$$\mathbf{X} = \mathbf{X}_d + \mathbf{X}_n,$$ (4.76)

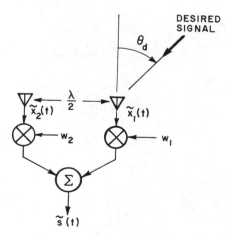

Figure 4.12 A two-element array.

with

$$\mathbf{X}_d = A_d e^{j(\omega_d t + \psi_d)} \mathbf{U}_d, \tag{4.77}$$

$$\mathbf{U}_d = \begin{bmatrix} 1 \\ e^{-j\phi_d} \end{bmatrix}, \tag{4.78}$$

$$\phi_d = \pi \sin \theta_d, \tag{4.79}$$

and

$$\mathbf{X}_n = \begin{bmatrix} \tilde{n}_1(t) \\ \tilde{n}_2(t) \end{bmatrix}. \tag{4.80}$$

The covariance matrix is Eq. (2.118):

$$\mathbf{\Phi} = \sigma^2 \mathbf{I} + A_d^2 \mathbf{U}_d^* \mathbf{U}_d^T. \tag{4.81}$$

Also, assume the reference signal is

$$\tilde{r}(t) = \mathbf{Re}^{j(\omega_d t + \psi_d)}, \tag{4.82}$$

so that the reference correlation vector is given by Eq. (2.119):

$$\mathbf{S} = A_d R \mathbf{U}_d^*. \tag{4.83}$$

Let us normalize all quantities in Eq. (4.75) to σ^2. We write Eq. (4.75) in the form:

$$\mathbf{W} = \left[\frac{1}{\sigma^2} \mathbf{\Phi} \right]^{-1} \left[\frac{1}{\sigma^2} \mathbf{S} + \frac{1}{\sigma^2} \Delta \right], \tag{4.84}$$

where

$$\frac{1}{\sigma^2} \mathbf{\Phi} = \mathbf{I} + \xi_d \mathbf{U}_d^* \mathbf{U}_d^T, \tag{4.85}$$

and

$$\frac{1}{\sigma^2} \mathbf{S} = \frac{A_d R}{\sigma^2} \mathbf{U}_d^* = \sqrt{2 \xi_d \xi_r} \, \mathbf{U}_d^*. \tag{4.86}$$

The SNR ξ_d is defined in Eq. (2.110), and ξ_r is the ratio of the reference signal power to σ^2:

$$\xi_r = \frac{R^2}{2\sigma^2}. \tag{4.87}$$

Also, we define the normalized offset vector to be

$$\frac{1}{\sigma^2} \Delta = \begin{bmatrix} \delta_1/\sigma^2 \\ \delta_2/\sigma^2 \end{bmatrix} = \begin{bmatrix} \delta_1' \\ \delta_2' \end{bmatrix}. \tag{4.88}$$

After $\mathbf{W}$ is obtained from Eq. (4.84), the output desired signal may be found from

$$\tilde{s}_d(t) = A_d e^{j(\omega_d t + \psi_d)} \mathbf{U}_d^T \mathbf{W}, \tag{4.89}$$

and the normalized output desired signal power from

$$\frac{P_d}{\sigma^2} = \frac{1}{2\sigma^2} E\{|\tilde{s}_d(t)|^2\} = \frac{\xi_d}{2} \mathbf{W}^\dagger \mathbf{U}_d^* \mathbf{U}_d^T \mathbf{W}. \tag{4.90}$$

The normalized output thermal noise power is

$$\frac{P_n}{\sigma^2} = \tfrac{1}{2}\left[|w_1|^2 + |w_2|^2\right] = \tfrac{1}{2}\mathbf{W}^\dagger \mathbf{W}, \tag{4.91}$$

and the SINR is

$$\text{SINR} = \frac{P_d/\sigma^2}{P_n/\sigma^2}. \tag{4.92}$$

(Although we have no interference in the array, we still denote the output ratio by "SINR," in order to have a consistent notation.)

Before calculating the output SINR for some offset vector $\mathbf{\Delta}$, we first determine what direction $\mathbf{\Delta}$ should have to produce the largest effect on the SINR (i.e., for a given magnitude $|\mathbf{\Delta}|$). Suppose $\mathbf{\Delta W}$ is the change in $\mathbf{W}$, away from $\mathbf{W}_{\text{opt}}$, due to the offset vector $\mathbf{\Delta}$:

$$\mathbf{\Delta W} = \mathbf{\Phi}^{-1}\mathbf{\Delta}. \tag{4.93}$$

Then, since

$$\mathbf{W} = \mathbf{W}_{\text{opt}} + \mathbf{\Delta W}, \tag{4.94}$$

the SINR is

$$\text{SINR} = \xi_d \frac{\mathbf{W}^\dagger \mathbf{U}_d^* \mathbf{U}_d^T \mathbf{W}}{\mathbf{W}^\dagger \mathbf{W}}$$

$$= \xi_d \frac{\mathbf{W}_{\text{opt}}^\dagger \mathbf{U}_d^* \mathbf{U}_d^T \mathbf{W}_{\text{opt}} + \mathbf{W}_{\text{opt}}^\dagger \mathbf{U}_d^* \mathbf{U}_d^T \mathbf{\Delta W} + \mathbf{\Delta W}^\dagger \mathbf{U}_d^* \mathbf{U}_d^T \mathbf{W}_{\text{opt}} + \mathbf{\Delta W}^\dagger \mathbf{U}_d^* \mathbf{U}_d^T \mathbf{\Delta W}}{\mathbf{W}_{\text{opt}}^\dagger \mathbf{W}_{\text{opt}} + \mathbf{W}_{\text{opt}}^\dagger \mathbf{\Delta W} + \mathbf{\Delta W}^\dagger \mathbf{W}_{\text{opt}} + \mathbf{\Delta W}^\dagger \mathbf{\Delta W}}.$$

$$\tag{4.95}$$

Note that if $\mathbf{\Delta W}$ is in the same direction as $\mathbf{W}_{\text{opt}}$, that is,

$$\mathbf{\Delta W} = \alpha \mathbf{W}_{\text{opt}}, \tag{4.96}$$

where α is a constant, then there will be no change in the SINR from its maximum value, since then

$$\text{SINR} = \xi_d \frac{1 + 2\,\text{Re}\,(\alpha) + |\alpha|^2}{1 + 2\,\text{Re}\,(\alpha) + |\alpha|^2} \frac{\mathbf{W}_{\text{opt}}^\dagger \mathbf{U}_d^* \mathbf{U}_d^T \mathbf{W}_{\text{opt}}}{\mathbf{W}_{\text{opt}}^\dagger \mathbf{W}_{\text{opt}}^\dagger} = \text{SINR}_{\text{opt}}. \tag{4.97}$$

It follows that the drop in SINR will be largest if $\Delta\mathbf{W}$ is perpendicular[‡] to $\mathbf{W}_{opt}$, i.e., if

$$\mathbf{W}_{opt}^{\dagger}\,\Delta\mathbf{W} = 0. \tag{4.98}$$

For the two-element array in Fig. 4.12, $\mathbf{W}_{opt}$ was found previously in Eq. (2.125),

$$\mathbf{W}_{opt} = \left(\frac{1}{\sigma^2}\Phi\right)^{-1}\left(\frac{1}{\sigma^2}\mathbf{S}\right) = \frac{\xi_d\left(\dfrac{R}{A_d}\right)}{1 + 2\xi_d}\mathbf{U}_d^*. \tag{4.99}$$

Therefore, the largest drop in SINR will be obtained for $\Delta\mathbf{W}$ satisfying

$$\mathbf{U}_d^T\,\Delta\mathbf{W} = 0. \tag{4.100}$$

The corresponding direction for Δ is

$$\Delta = \Phi\,\Delta\mathbf{W} = \left[\sigma^2\mathbf{I} + A_d^2\mathbf{U}_d^*\mathbf{U}_d^T\right]\Delta\mathbf{W}. \tag{4.101}$$

However, since $\mathbf{U}_d^T\,\Delta\mathbf{W} = 0$ [from Eq. (4.100)], Eq. (4.101) yields

$$\Delta = \sigma^2\,\Delta\mathbf{W}. \tag{4.102}$$

Thus Δ must be in the same direction as $\Delta\mathbf{W}$. To have the greatest effect on SINR, we choose a Δ satisfying

$$\mathbf{U}_d^T\Delta = 0 \tag{4.103}$$

or

$$\delta_1 + \delta_2 e^{-j\phi_d} = 0. \tag{4.104}$$

Figure 4.13 shows a typical calculation of SINR in the presence of offsets. These curves are for the case $\theta_d = 0°$ and $\xi_r = 0$ dB. The figure shows the SINR as a function of ξ_d for several values of δ_i'. The δ_i' chosen all satisfy Eq. (4.104).

It may be seen how the offset voltages cause the SINR to drop below its optimal value. For a given Δ, we see that the smallest drop in SINR occurs when ξ_d is near 0 dB. When ξ_d is substantially smaller than 0 dB or greater than 0 dB, the degradation is worse. This is a fortunate result, because the region $\xi_d \approx 0$ dB is typically the region where the system is most vulnerable to a drop in performance.

However, even though the drop in SINR is least around $\xi_d = 0$ dB, in practice it can still be difficult to hold $|\Delta|$ to within acceptable limits for some types of multiplier circuits. Figure 4.13 shows that to keep the degradation near

---

[‡]Note that we are considering two-dimensional vectors (we have a two-element array), so the direction perpendicular to $\mathbf{W}_{opt}$ is a uniquely defined direction.

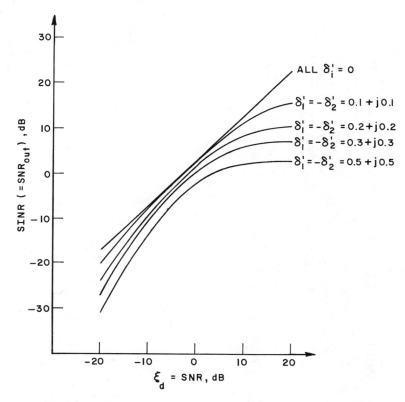

Figure 4.13 The effect of offset voltages on SINR. Two-element array, $\xi_r = 0$ dB, $\theta_d = 0°$, no interference.

$\xi_d = 0$ dB small, one should hold $|\delta_i'| \leqslant 0.1$. Experience with hardware shows that this specification is sometimes difficult to meet.

In addition, we find that the offset voltages that can be tolerated depend on the reference signal level. Figure 4.14 shows another plot of SINR versus ξ_d with $\theta_d = 0°$, the same as in Fig. 4.13, except that now $\xi_r = -6$ dB. Comparison of Figs. 4.13 and 4.14 shows that the array performance becomes more sensitive to Δ as ξ_r decreases.

Example 2

Next let us consider a case when an interference signal is also present. In order to have enough degrees of freedom, assume we have a three-element array with $\lambda/2$ element spacing, as shown in Fig. 4.15. Suppose both a CW desired signal and a CW interference signal are incident from angles θ_d and θ_i, respectively. Assume uncorrelated thermal noise is also present on each element signal. Let the reference signal again be given by Eq. (4.82). In the presence of the

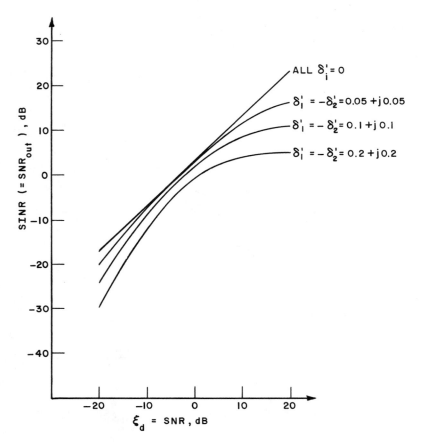

Figure 4.14 The effect of offset voltages on SINR. Two-element array, $\xi_r = -6$ dB, $\theta_d = 0°$, no interference.

normalized offset vector

$$\frac{1}{\sigma^2}\Delta = \begin{bmatrix} \delta_1/\sigma^2 \\ \delta_2/\sigma^2 \\ \delta_3/\sigma^2 \end{bmatrix} = \begin{bmatrix} \delta_1' \\ \delta_2' \\ \delta_3' \end{bmatrix} \tag{4.105}$$

the array weight vector will be

$$\mathbf{W} = \left[\frac{1}{\sigma^2}\Phi\right]^{-1}\left[\frac{1}{\sigma^2}\mathbf{S} + \frac{1}{\sigma^2}\Delta\right], \tag{4.106}$$

where the normalized covariance matrix is

$$\frac{1}{\sigma^2}\Phi = \mathbf{I} + \xi_d\mathbf{U}_d^*\mathbf{U}_d^T + \xi_i\mathbf{U}_i^*\mathbf{U}_i^T \tag{4.107}$$

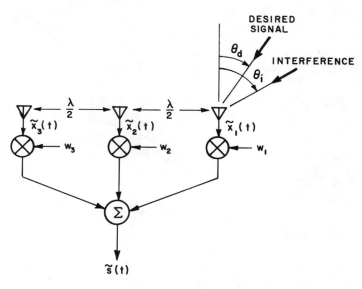

Figure 4.15 A three-element array.

and the normalized reference correlation vector is

$$\frac{1}{\sigma^2}\mathbf{S} = \sqrt{2\xi_d\xi_r}\,\mathbf{U}_d^*. \tag{4.108}$$

Here $\mathbf{U}_d$ and $\mathbf{U}_i$ are now vectors with three components:

$$\mathbf{U}_d = \begin{bmatrix} 1 & e^{-j\phi_d} & e^{-j2\phi_d} \end{bmatrix}^T \tag{4.109}$$

and

$$\mathbf{U}_i = \begin{bmatrix} 1 & e^{-j\phi_i} & e^{-j2\phi_i} \end{bmatrix}^T, \tag{4.110}$$

with

$$\phi_d = \pi \sin\theta_d \tag{4.111}$$

and

$$\phi_i = \pi \sin\theta_i. \tag{4.112}$$

The signal-to-noise ratios ξ_d and ξ_r are defined as before, and ξ_i is the INR defined in Eq. (2.172).

Figures 4.16 through 4.19 show typical calculations of SINR versus ξ_d for the three-element array,[‡] with $\theta_d = 0°$ and $\xi_r = -6$ dB. In Fig. 4.16, there is no interference, and the SINR is shown for three choices of Δ. These curves are

---

[‡]In this example we simply use some representative values for Δ. We have not tried to choose the direction of Δ to maximize the SINR degradation.

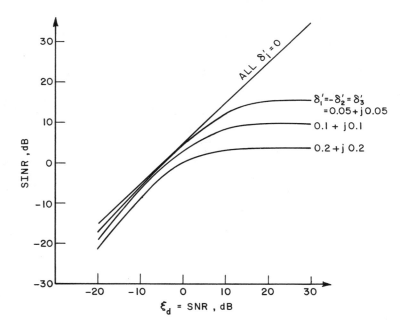

Figure 4.16 The effect of offset voltages on SINR. Three-element array, $\xi_r = -6$ dB, $\theta_d = 0°$, no interference.

similar to those in Figs. 4.13 and 4.14. In Fig. 4.17, interference is added at $\theta_i = 50°$, and the offset vector is fixed at $\delta_1' = -\delta_2' = \delta_3' = 0.1 + j0.1$. Three curves are shown, for three different values of ξ_i. It is seen that as ξ_i increases, the SINR improves. This is a typical result. It occurs because the stronger the interference, the less the weights need to deviate from their optimal values to make the signal products at the multiplier output cancel the offset voltages. (The array is in steady state when all the integrator inputs are zero. To make the integrator input be zero with nonzero offsets requires that the signal component at the multiplier output cancel the offset voltage.)

Finally, Figs. 4.18 and 4.19 illustrate the effect of interference angle of arrival on SINR degradation with offsets. Figure 4.18 shows the output SINR versus ξ_d when $\boldsymbol{\Delta} = \mathbf{0}$ for $\xi_i = 30$ dB, $\theta_d = 0°$, and for several θ_i: $50°$, $30°$, $20°$, $10°$, and $5°$. This figure shows the drop in SINR that occurs with an ideal array when θ_i approaches θ_d. Figure 4.19 shows the same calculations for nonzero offsets, for the particular case

$$\frac{1}{\sigma^2}\boldsymbol{\Delta} = \begin{bmatrix} 0.1 - j0.1 \\ -0.1 + j0.1 \\ 0.1 - j0.1 \end{bmatrix}. \tag{4.113}$$

The additional degradation in SINR due to the offsets may be seen by comparing Fig. 4.19 with Fig. 4.18.

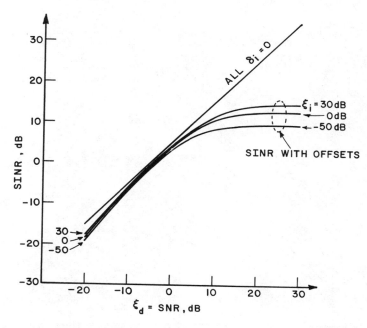

Figure 4.17 The effect of offset voltages on SINR. Three-element array, $\xi_r = -6$ dB, $\theta_d = 0°$, $\theta_i = 50°$, $\delta_1' = -\delta_2' = \delta_3' = 0.1 + j0.1$.

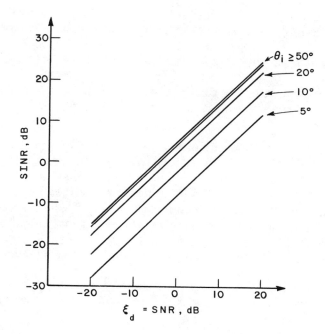

Figure 4.18 The effect of angular separation between interference and desired signal without offset voltages. Three-element array, $\xi_r = -6$ dB, $\xi_i = 30$ dB, all $\delta_i = 0$.

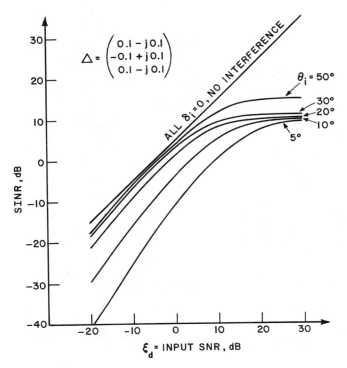

Figure 4.19 The effect of angular separation between interference and desired signal with offset voltages. Three-element array, $\xi_r = -6$ dB; $\xi_i = 30$ dB; $\delta_1' = -\delta_2' = \delta_3' = 0.1 - j0.1$.

These results again illustrate (as did Figs. 4.13 and 4.14) that to keep the SINR degradation small, the offsets must be held to the approximate tolerance,

$$|\delta_i'| = \left| \frac{\delta_i}{\sigma^2} \right| \leqslant 0.1. \tag{4.114}$$

Whether this tolerance can be met or not depends on the particular multiplers used. Typically each multiplier in the array must be balanced to obtain the smallest possible offset voltage.

These examples clearly show how important the problem of multiplier offset voltages is. The performance of an adaptive array deteriorates very rapidly when the offset voltages are not carefully controlled. We shall not show any additional calculations of offset voltage effects here, but we mention that one can also characterize these effects by assuming the offset voltages are random quantities and computing their average effect. (This approach is especially useful when the array has more than two or three elements.) Such an analysis is mathematically identical to the analysis of random steering vector errors in the Applebaum array, a problem that we shall treat in detail in Chapter 6. In particular, the curves presented in Figs. 6.13 through 6.26 for random steering vector errors also describe the effects of random offset voltages (see problem 6.9).

Techniques for Avoiding Offset Voltages

Besides simply attempting to balance the multiplier circuits as well as possible, other approaches can be used to eliminate the problem of offset voltages. We describe two methods here. The first approach is due to Miller, Caldecott, and Huff [5], who implemented an array using the loop shown in Fig. 4.20. In this loop, the error signal $\tilde{\varepsilon}(t)$ is mixed with a local oscillator (LO) signal $\tilde{l}(t)$. With $\tilde{\varepsilon}(t)$ on frequency ω_d and $\tilde{l}(t)$ on frequency ω_1, the product signal $\tilde{\varepsilon}_1(t)$ will be on either the sum or difference frequency, say $\omega_d + \omega_1$. Thus when $\tilde{\varepsilon}_1(t)$ is multiplied by $\tilde{x}_i^*(t)$, the desired output product $\tilde{p}_1(t)$ from multiplier 1 is centered at frequency ω_1, instead of at baseband. The DC offset voltage present in $\tilde{p}_1(t)$ can then be removed by filtering, say with filter $F(\omega)$ in Fig. 4.20. Let $\tilde{p}_2(t)$ be the signal after filtering. The signal $\tilde{p}_2(t)$ is next shifted to baseband, by mixing it again with the same LO signal $\tilde{l}(t)$ in multiplier 2. Although a multiplier offset voltage in multiplier 2 will cause the same performance degradation as discussed previously, it is easier to eliminate the offset voltage in multiplier 2 than it is in multiplier 1, because the LO signal used on one side of multipler 2 has fixed amplitude. Thus the DC balance of multiplier 2 does not depend on received signal amplitude. Also, as pointed out by Miller, Caldecott,

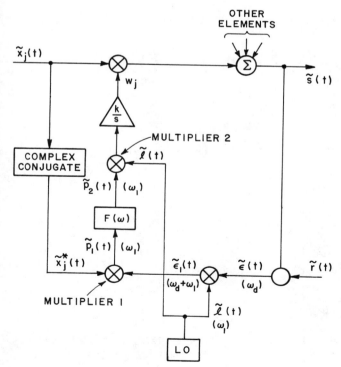

Figure 4.20   A loop that avoids offset voltages.

and Huff [5], multiplier 2 can actually be implemented with a passive mixer, since one of its inputs has fixed amplitude. (A mixer is simpler to implement than a multiplier.)

The IF Loop

Another approach for overcoming offset voltage problems is to avoid baseband weights altogether, by using control loops that operate with IF weights [6]. In this technique, there is only one "weight" per antenna element. The two quadrature weights required in the LMS algorithm are combined into a single "IF weight," that is, a sinusoidal waveform at a nonzero frequency. The required inphase and quadrature weighting for each element is carried in the amplitude and phase of this IF weight. Because the weight is at a nonzero frequency, the output frequency of the array processor is different from its input frequency.

To see how the array can be implemented with IF weights, let us compare the two feedback loops shown in Figs. 4.21 and 4.22. Figure 4.21 shows the standard LMS loop with a baseband weight w_j. Figure 4.22 shows the LMS loop with an IF weight, instead of a baseband weight. To understand Fig. 4.22 suppose that, at a given instant of time, the complex weight in Fig. 4.21 is w_j.

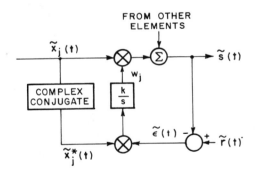

Figure 4.21 The standard LMS loop.

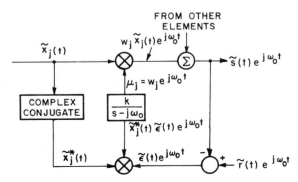

Figure 4.22 The LMS loop with an IF weight.

Then, in Fig. 4.22, assume that at the same instant the weight μ_j is

$$\mu_j = w_j e^{j\omega_0 t}, \tag{4.115}$$

where ω_0 is a suitable nonzero frequency. The input signal to the loops in both Figs. 4.21 and 4.22 is the same, $\tilde{x}_j(t)$. Hence in Fig. 4.22 the output of the signal-by-weight multiplier is

$$\mu_j \tilde{x}_j(t) = w_j \tilde{x}_j(t) e^{j\omega_0 t}, \tag{4.116}$$

and the array output signal is

$$\tilde{s}(t) e^{j\omega_0 t} = \mathbf{W}^T \mathbf{X} e^{j\omega_0 t}. \tag{4.117}$$

These are the same as in Fig. 4.21 except multiplied by $e^{j\omega_0 t}$. Moreover, assume the reference signal in Fig. 4.22 is $\tilde{r}(t) e^{j\omega_0 t}$; then the error signal will be $\tilde{\varepsilon}(t) e^{j\omega_0 t}$ [where $\tilde{r}(t)$ and $\tilde{\varepsilon}(t)$ are the reference and error signals in Fig. 4.21], and the output of the signal-by-error multiplier is $\tilde{x}_j^*(t) \tilde{\varepsilon}(t) e^{j\omega_0 t}$, again the same as the corresponding quantity in Fig. 4.21 except multiplied by $e^{j\omega_0 t}$. Thus all quantities in the feedback path in Fig. 4.22 are the same as those in Fig. 4.21 except for the extra factor $e^{j\omega_0 t}$.

Note that in Fig. 4.21, the weight w_j is the output of an integrator, that is, a filter with a simple pole at the origin of the complex frequency plane. To make the loop in Fig. 4.22 equivalent to that in Fig. 4.21, the integrator pole, which is at zero frequency in Fig. 4.22, must be shifted to frequency ω_0 on the $j\omega$-axis, as shown in Fig. 4.23. It is easily shown that if w_j is the output of a filter with a pole at zero frequency when the input is $\tilde{x}_j^*(t) \tilde{\varepsilon}(t)$, then the output of a filter with pole at $j\omega_0$ will be $w_j e^{j\omega_0 t}$ when the input is $\tilde{x}_j^*(t) \tilde{\varepsilon}(t) e^{j\omega_0 t}$. Thus, if the pole in Fig. 4.22 is at $s = +j\omega_0$, the loops in Figs. 4.21 and 4.22 operate identically except that the weight and all signals on the output side of the loop in Fig. 4.22 are higher in frequency by ω_0 than they are in Fig. 4.21.

In practice, one cannot build a filter with a single complex pole. One must use a filter with conjugate poles at $s = \pm j\omega_0$. Since

$$\frac{k}{s - j\omega_0} + \frac{k}{s + j\omega_0} = \frac{2ks}{s^2 + \omega_0^2}, \tag{4.118}$$

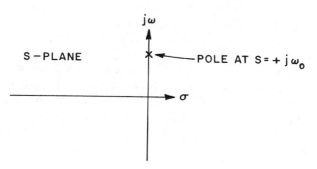

Figure 4.23   Weight filter for IF loop.

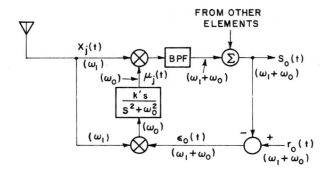

Figure 4.24 Practical implementation of IF weight loop.

the appropriate filter for the IF weight loop has conjugate $j\omega$-axis poles and a zero at the origin. Moreover, the weight in an IF loop will be real-valued, not complex. Hence the output of the signal-by-weight-multiplier will include both sum and difference frequencies. To restrict the feedback signal to one frequency, it will be necessary to introduce a bandpass filter (BPF) at the output of the signal-by-weight multiplier. Thus a practical realization of the IF loop is as shown in Fig. 4.24.

To illustrate the behavior of a loop with an IF weight, Figs. 4.25 and 4.26 show a simulation of the transient response of a single IF loop, shown in Fig. 4.25(a), with input signal

$$x(t) = \cos 7t \tag{4.119}$$

and a weight filter with transfer function

$$H(s) = \frac{ks}{s^2 + 9}. \tag{4.120}$$

The weight frequency with this filter will be $\omega_0 = 3$ rad/sec. The bandpass filter used after the signal-by-weight multiplier is a three-pole Butterworth filter. The Butterworth poles lie on a circle of radius 0.1 rad/sec, centered at 10 rad/sec, as shown in Fig. 4.25(b). The transient behavior of the weight and the array output signal were computed with all variables in the loop initially set to zero. The input signal $x(t)$ and a reference signal

$$r(t) = \cos 10t \tag{4.121}$$

were switched on at $t = 0$. Figure 4.26 shows the results. Figure 4.26(a) shows the input signal $x(t)$, Fig. 4.26(b) the reference signal $r(t)$, Fig. 4.26(c) the IF weight, and Fig. 4.26(d) the array output signal. As may be seen, the weight builds up with an exponential envelope on a carrier frequency of 3 rad/sec. The time constant of the exponential envelope is the same as that for the response of the equivalent baseband quadrature weights. Also, as the IF weight builds up in Fig. 4.26(c), it is seen how the output signal builds up correspondingly. When steady state is reached, the output signal matches the reference signal in amplitude and phase. The weighting normally carried in the two baseband LMS weights is now carried as the amplitude and phase of the IF weight.

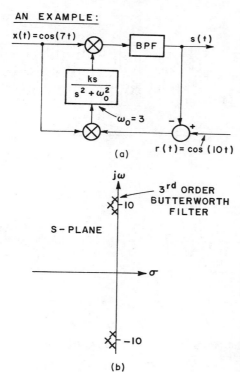

Figure 4.25   A simulated IF weight loop. (a) A single IF weight; (b) the three-pole Butterworth filter.

The use of IF weights has several important practical advantages over baseband weights:

1. Only one loop per element is required (instead of two).
2. There is no multiplier offset voltage problem.
3. No quadrature hybrids are required.
4. Multiplier leakage or stray coupling in the signal-by-weight multiplier is not a problem, since the weighted output is at a different frequency from the input signal and leakage components are easily separated by the bandpass filter.

However, the use of IF weights also has certain disadvantages compared to baseband weights. Essentially, two new problems are introduced when the weights are implemented at IF:

1. To obtain satisfactory performance from the array, the Q required in the weight filter may be unrealistically high. If inadequate Q is used, the performance of the array is degraded.

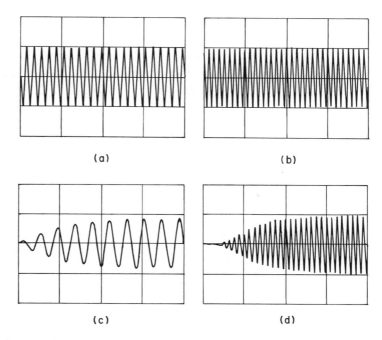

Figure 4.26 Simulation results. (a) Input signal; (b) reference signal; (c) weight; (d) array output signal.

2. Introducing the bandpass filter after the signal-by-weight multiplier (in Fig. 4.24) can cause the loop to be unstable.

We discuss each of these problems below.

Consider first the filter Q. Ideally, the IF loop should have a filter with transfer function

$$F(s) = \frac{ks}{s^2 + \omega_0^2} \tag{4.122}$$

in the weight feedback path. However, such a filter has infinite Q. In practice, the transfer function of a filter with finite Q will be

$$F(s) = \frac{ks}{(s + \alpha)^2 + \omega_0^2}, \tag{4.123}$$

where α is the displacement of the poles to the left of the $j\omega$-axis. This filter has Q

$$Q = \frac{\omega_0}{2\alpha}. \tag{4.124}$$

To determine the effect of nonzero α, we consider the corresponding baseband

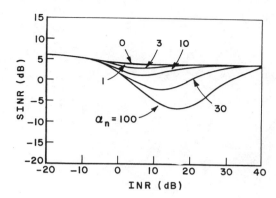

Figure 4.27 SINR versus INR(ξ_i) for several $\alpha_n = \alpha/k\sigma^2$: four-element array, $\lambda/2$ spacing, $\theta_d = 0°$, $\theta_i = 15°$, SNR(ξ_d) = 0 dB.

problem. Moving the $j\omega$-axis pole to the left by α in the IF loop has the same effect as using a transfer function

$$F(s) = \frac{k}{s + \alpha} \tag{4.125}$$

in the baseband loop. Moving the baseband pole to $s = -\alpha$ causes the adaptive array to produce a steady-state weight vector [7]

$$\mathbf{W} = \left[\frac{\alpha}{k}\mathbf{I} + \mathbf{\Phi}\right]^{-1}\mathbf{S}, \tag{4.126}$$

instead of the optimum weight vector,

$$\mathbf{W} = \mathbf{\Phi}^{-1}\mathbf{S}, \tag{4.127}$$

where, as usual, $\mathbf{\Phi}$ is the covariance matrix, $\mathbf{S}$ is the reference correlation vector, $\mathbf{I}$ is the identity matrix, and k is the loop gain. Thus, when $\alpha \neq 0$, the steady-state weights are not equal to their optimum values. The result is a degradation in array performance. It turns out that this degradation is most significant for intermediate values of interference power. Figure 4.27 shows a typical calculation. It shows the output SINR from a four-element linear array of isotropic elements with half-wavelength spacing. The SINR is plotted as a function of the input interference-to-noise ratio ξ_i. These calculations are for the case where the desired signal arrives from broadside with $\xi_d = 0$ dB and the interference arrives from 15° off broadside. Several curves are shown for different values of α. We define normalized α as

$$\alpha_n = \frac{\alpha}{k\sigma^2}. \tag{4.128}$$

where k is the loop gain and σ^2 is the thermal noise power per element. The bottom curve in Fig. 4.27 is for $\alpha_n = 100$ and the top curve for $\alpha_n = 0$. (The case where $\alpha_n = 0$ is a perfect integrator and represents ideal performance from the array.) The intermediate curves are for $\alpha_n = 30, 10, 3,$ and 1. These curves

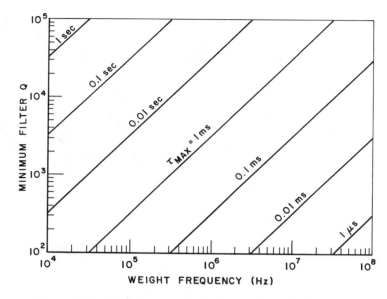

Figure 4.28 Minimum acceptable Q versus weight frequency.

(and similar curves computed for other cases [7]) show that the array performance is essentially equal to its optimum value only if $\alpha_n \leqslant 1$, that is, if

$$\alpha \leqslant k\sigma^2. \tag{4.129}$$

If α exceeds this value, the array output SINR drops below its optimum value for intermediate INRs.

Thus, to obtain full performance from the adaptive array, α must satisfy Eq. (4.129), and then it is seen from Eq. (4.124) that the filter Q in the IF loop must be at least

$$Q \geqslant \frac{\omega_0}{2k\sigma^2} = \frac{\omega_0}{2}\tau_{\max}, \tag{4.130}$$

where

$$\tau_{\max} = \frac{1}{k\sigma^2}. \tag{4.131}$$

The variable $\tau_{\max}$ is the slowest time constant in the array response and is a convenient parameter to use in calculating Q. Figure 4.28 shows the required minimum Q as a function of the weight frequency in Hz and of $\tau_{\max}$ in seconds. It is seen that the required Q can easily become rather high.

To keep the required Q from becoming too high, one must choose a low enough weight frequency. However, a low weight frequency may not allow one to obtain sufficient bandwidth for the received signal. Whether this is a problem or not depends on the application, of course.

A way to circumvent the problem of high Q is to translate the output of the signal-by-error multiplier to baseband, do the required integration at baseband, and then translate the integrator output back to the weight frequency. This approach, which has been used by Abrams, Harris, and Zeger [8], allows one to achieve a suitably small α, regardless of the weight frequency, but reintroduces some of the circuit complexity that would otherwise be avoided with an IF weight.

The second difficulty with IF weights, as mentioned above, is the problem of stability. Filtering the output of the signal-by-weight multiplier to eliminate unwanted spectral products in the loop introduces additional poles in the loop. The transient behavior of the IF weight can be determined by computing the transient behavior of the weight in a baseband loop with all poles of the IF loop translated to baseband. In general, when the equivalent baseband filter has transfer function

$$F_b(s) = \frac{k}{s^n + a_{n-1}s^{n-1} + \cdots + a_1 s + a_0},\qquad(4.132)$$

the adaptive array weight vector will satisfy the differential equation

$$\frac{d^n\mathbf{W}}{dt^n} + a_{n-1}\frac{d^{n-1}\mathbf{W}}{dt^{n-1}} + \cdots + (a_0\mathbf{I} + k\mathbf{\Phi})\mathbf{W} = k\mathbf{S}.\qquad(4.133)$$

Stability then depends on the roots of the polynomial

$$s^n + a_{n-1} + \cdots + a_1 s + (a_0 + k\lambda_i) = 0,\qquad(4.134)$$

where λ_i is the ith eigenvalue of the covariance matrix $\mathbf{\Phi}$.

Consider the loop shown in Fig. 4.25, where the bandpass filter is a three-pole Butterworth filter and the weight filter has a pair of poles near the $j\omega$-axis at $\omega = 3$ rad/sec. To determine the transient behavior of $\mu(t)$, we consider a baseband loop whose filter has three equivalent poles on a circle around the origin and a single pole at $s = 0$. If the roots are calculated for this case, the root locus, as $k\lambda_i$ is varied, is shown in Fig. 4.29. As may be seen, two poles go into the right half plane as $k\lambda_i$ increases. Thus, as signal power (λ_i) or loop gain k is increased, the IF loop will eventually become unstable. Figure 4.30 illustrates the effect of loop gain k on transient response for this example. Figure 4.30(a) shows the weight transient and the array output signal for $k = 0.002$, and Fig. 4.30(b) shows them for $k = 0.004$. In Fig. 4.30(b), two poles are approaching the $j\omega$-axis, and the ringing in the response may be seen. If k is increased still further, the weight becomes unstable.

To avoid problems with stability, one must choose the gain and other parameters so that the loop remains stable for the highest input signal power of interest. If necessary, other steps can be taken to improve stability. For example, extra poles and zeros may be added to the feedback path, using conventional feedback compensation techniques, to improve stability. Or, the bandpass filter in Fig. 4.24 can be eliminated by using a single-sideband mixer for the weight

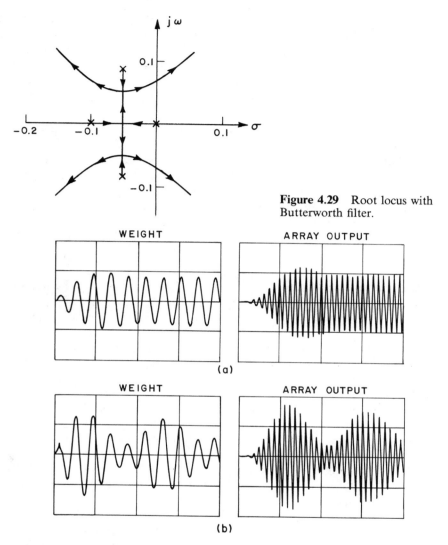

Figure 4.29 Root locus with Butterworth filter.

Figure 4.30 Transient response of IF loop. (a) $k = 0.002$; (b) $k = 0.004$.

multiplier, instead of the conventional mixer-filter as shown. A single-sideband mixer does not generate the unwanted frequency component, but it is more difficult to implement. Also, one other step may be necessary to insure stability. If the frequency of the received signals varies sufficiently, or if the bandwidth of the signals is wide enough, an additional filter with suitable poles may be needed on the signal side of the signal-by-error multiplier to make the phase shifts match on both sides of the loop. Without such compensation the phase shift on one side of the loop may differ from that on the other side sufficiently that the loop becomes unstable.

4.4 WEIGHT SATURATION

In a practical LMS array, the array weights cannot take on completely arbitrary values. Each weight is always limited to a certain finite range of values. If the optimum weight vector $\Phi^{-1}S$ requires one or more weights outside this finite range, the array will not be able to achieve optimal performance. In this section we explore the effect of weight limits on performance and also see how to avoid this problem.

To understand how the problem of weight saturation arises, consider first the behavior of the weight in a single LMS loop. Consider a single quadrature loop, as shown in Fig. 4.31. Assume the signal $x(t)$ is

$$x(t) = A_d \cos\left[\omega_d t + \psi_d\right] + n(t), \tag{4.135}$$

where the noise power is

$$E\{n^2(t)\} = \frac{\sigma^2}{2}, \tag{4.136}$$

and also assume the reference signal is

$$r(t) = R \cos\left[\omega_d t + \psi_d\right]. \tag{4.137}$$

The weight satisfies the differential equation

$$\frac{dw}{dt} + 2kE\left[x^2(t)\right]w = 2kE\left[x(t)r(t)\right] \tag{4.138}$$

or

$$\frac{dw}{dt} + k\left(A_d^2 + \sigma^2\right)w = kA_d R. \tag{4.139}$$

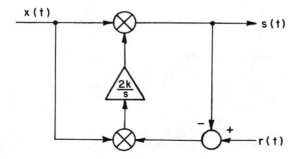

Figure 4.31 A single LMS loop.

The steady-state weight will be

$$w = \frac{A_d R}{A_d^2 + \sigma^2} = \frac{\sqrt{2\xi_d \xi_r}}{1 + \xi_d}, \qquad (4.140)$$

where ξ_r is the reference signal power normalized to σ^2, as defined in Eq. (4.87). The output desired signal in the steady state is

$$s_d(t) = wA_d \cos[\omega_d t + \psi_d] = \frac{\xi_d}{1 + \xi_d} R \cos[\omega_d t + \psi_d], \qquad (4.141)$$

so the output desired signal power is

$$P_d = \left(\frac{\xi_d}{1 + \xi_d}\right)^2 \frac{R^2}{2}. \qquad (4.142)$$

Since the reference signal power is

$$P_r = \frac{R^2}{2}, \qquad (4.143)$$

we have

$$\frac{P_d}{P_r} = \left(\frac{\xi_d}{1 + \xi_d}\right)^2. \qquad (4.144)$$

Figure 4.32 shows a plot of P_d/P_r versus ξ_d. We see that when ξ_d is large, the

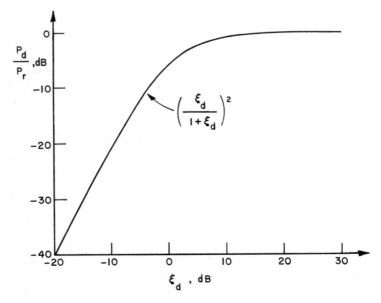

Figure 4.32 P_d/P_r versus ξ_d.

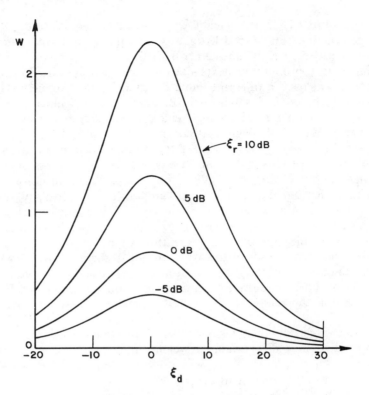

Figure 4.33   The weight w versus ξ_d.

LMS loop matches the output desired signal to the reference signal. However, when ξ_d is small, the desired signal power drops. [We obtained a similar result for a two-element array in Eq. (2.139).]

Now consider what happens to the weight as ξ_d varies. Figure 4.33 shows w versus ξ_d, obtained from Eq. (4.140), for several values of ξ_r. For large ξ_d, the weight drops as ξ_d increases, because the LMS loop matches the output desired signal to the reference signal, which has fixed amplitude. On the other hand, for small ξ_d, the weight again drops toward zero. This behavior occurs because for very small ξ_d the desired signal is a negligible part of the array output. The mean-square error signal is minimized by lowering the weight to reduce the amount of noise in the array output. The mismatch between the desired signal and the reference signal becomes less important at low ξ_d. The largest value of w occurs for intermediate values of ξ_d, in this case at $\xi_d = 0$ dB. Also, the value of w for any given ξ_d is directly proportional to the reference signal amplitude ($\sqrt{\xi_r}$).

Now suppose that for the circuitry used to implement the loop in Fig. 4.31 the weight has a maximum attainable value. For example, suppose w cannot exceed unity. Then the weight will saturate whenever the curve in Fig. 4.33 exceeds unity. If $\xi_r = 5$ dB, for instance, the weight will saturate if ξ_d has a value between -6 dB and $+6$ dB. If ξ_d is in this range, the weight will not achieve its optimum value (the value specified by the LMS algorithm) but instead will have a different value dictated by the circuitry. However, if ξ_r is chosen to be 0 dB, instead of 5 dB, the weight will never saturate for any ξ_d. This behavior is typical for the weights in an adaptive array, even with several elements. We avoid weight saturation by keeping ξ_r small enough.

In general, we might expect the performance of an array to suffer when one or more of its weights saturate. For the simple one-weight "array" above, saturation of w does not affect the output signal-to-noise ratio, of course, because the signal and the noise are both multiplied by the same weight. However, in an array with several elements, we might expect weight saturation to lower the output SINR. In fact, we find that weight saturation usually does not reduce the output SINR greatly. Adaptive arrays seem to be able to maintain a good SINR at the array output in the presence of weight saturation. The major effect of weight saturation appears to be a change in the level of the signals at the array output. Saturation increases the mismatch between the array output and the reference signal, but typically does not reduce the SINR very much.

To illustrate this behavior, we shall first set up the general equations required to find the remaining weights in an array when some weights have become saturated. Then we will use these equations to study the effect of saturation in a two-element array.

Array Analysis with Saturated Weights

The problem of finding the weights in an array when some weights are saturated is simply an optimization problem with constraints. In general, the array feedback attempts to adjust the weights to minimize the mean-square error signal $E\{\varepsilon^2(t)\}$. If the optimum weight vector, which yields minimum $E\{\varepsilon^2(t)\}$, cannot be attained because some of the weights saturate, the array will then minimize $E\{\varepsilon^2(t)\}$ subject to the constraint that the saturated weights have their given values. Figure 4.34 illustrates this situation for the case of two weights. This figure shows a typical quadratic $E\{\varepsilon^2(t)\}$ surface, with elliptical contours of constant $E\{\varepsilon^2(t)\}$. The optimal weight vector $\mathbf{W}_{\text{opt}}$ is at the "bottom of the bowl," as shown. However, suppose w_1 is limited to a maximum value A,

$$w_1 \leqslant A, \tag{4.145}$$

where A is less than the value needed to attain $\mathbf{W}_{\text{opt}}$. Then the weight vector must always stay to the left of the shaded boundary shown in the figure. If the adaptive array feedback loops begin adapting from, say, the origin, the weights will travel along the gradient trajectory labeled T_1 in the figure. However, at

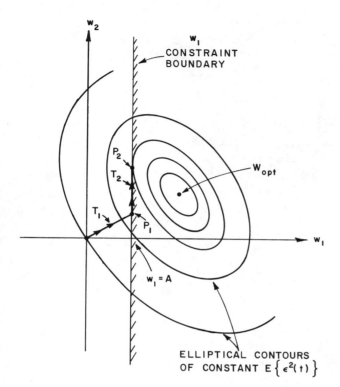

Figure 4.34 The weight trajectory with a saturated weight.

point P_1 this trajectory hits the weight limit $w_1 = A$, and the weight vector can no longer continue in the gradient direction toward $\mathbf{W}_{\text{opt}}$. Instead, the weight vector will travel on trajectory T_2 to the final point P_2. The point P_2 is where $E\{\varepsilon^2(t)\}$ is minimum when w_1 is constrained to have the value A. Clearly $E\{\varepsilon^2(t)\}$ is higher at point P_2 than it would have been at $\mathbf{W}_{\text{opt}}$. Hence the imposition of the weight constraint results in a larger mean-square error signal, that is, a larger difference between the array output and the reference signal. However, as stated previously, we often find only a small change in output SINR from the array between w_{opt} and point P_2.

Suppose one or more weights in an array are saturated. Let us see how to calculate the values of the remaining unsaturated weights. For this purpose it is helpful to return to the real notation used in Eqs. (2.5) through (2.35). The mean-square error is given by Eq. (2.8),

$$E\{\varepsilon^2(t)\} = E\{r^2(t)\} - 2\mathbf{S}_r^T\mathbf{W}_r + \mathbf{W}_r^T\mathbf{\Phi}_r\mathbf{W}_r, \qquad (4.146)$$

where $\mathbf{W}_r$ is the weight vector in Eq. (2.9), $\mathbf{\Phi}_r$ is the covariance matrix in Eq. (2.11), and $\mathbf{S}_r$ is the reference correlation vector in Eq. (2.10). Suppose that in Eq. (4.146) certain weights are fixed. We wish to find the values of the remaining weights that minimize $E\{\varepsilon^2(t)\}$. We do this by differentiating Eq. (4.146) with respect to each of the unconstrained weights and setting these derivatives to zero. Let us illustrate the general procedure with a specific example. Suppose we have a two-element array with four weights. The mean-square error in Eq. (4.146) is

$$E\{\varepsilon^2(t)\} = E\{r^2(t)\} - 2(S_{I_1}S_{Q_1}S_{I_2}S_{Q_2}) \begin{bmatrix} w_{I_1} \\ w_{0_1} \\ w_{I_2} \\ w_{Q_2} \end{bmatrix}$$

$$+ (w_{I_1}w_{Q_1}w_{I_2}w_{Q_2}) \begin{bmatrix} \phi_{I_1I_1} & \phi_{I_1Q_1} & \phi_{I_1I_2} & \phi_{I_1Q_2} \\ \phi_{Q_1I_1} & \phi_{Q_1Q_1} & \phi_{Q_1I_2} & \phi_{Q_1Q_2} \\ \phi_{I_2I_1} & \phi_{I_2Q_1} & \phi_{I_2I_2} & \phi_{I_2Q_2} \\ \phi_{Q_2I_1} & \phi_{Q_2Q_1} & \phi_{Q_2I_2} & \phi_{Q_2Q_2} \end{bmatrix} \begin{bmatrix} w_{I_1} \\ w_{Q_1} \\ w_{I_2} \\ w_{Q_2} \end{bmatrix}. \qquad (4.147)$$

Assume that w_{I_1} and w_{Q_2} are fixed, because of saturation. Then we seek the minimum of $E\{\varepsilon^2(t)\}$ with respect to w_{Q_1} and w_{I_2}. We set

$$\frac{\partial E\{\varepsilon^2(t)\}}{\partial w_{Q_1}} = 0 \qquad (4.148)$$

and

$$\frac{\partial E\{\varepsilon^2(t)\}}{\partial w_{I_2}} = 0. \qquad (4.149)$$

Differentiating Eq. (4.147) with respect to w_{Q_1} gives

$$(0 \quad 1 \quad 0 \quad 0)\Phi_r\mathbf{W}_r = \phi_{Q_1I_1}w_{I_1} + \phi_{Q_1Q_1}w_{Q_1} + \phi_{Q_1I_2}w_{I_2}$$

$$+ \phi_{Q_1Q_2}w_{Q_2} = S_{Q_1}. \qquad (4.150)$$

We recognize that this is the same equation as the one we would obtain even if w_{I_1} and w_{Q_2} were not saturated. That is, Eq. (4.150) is just the second row of the system of equations

$$\Phi_r\mathbf{W}_r = \mathbf{S}_r. \qquad (4.151)$$

The difference now is only that w_{I_1} and w_{Q_2} are known. Therefore, the terms involving w_{I_1} and w_{Q_2} can be taken to the other side of the equation, leaving one equation in the two unknowns w_{Q_1} and w_{I_2},

$$\phi_{Q_1Q_1}w_{Q_1} + \phi_{Q_1I_2}w_{I_2} = S_{Q_1} - \phi_{Q_1I_1}w_{I_1} - \phi_{Q_1Q_2}w_{Q_2}. \qquad (4.152)$$

Similarly, applying Eq. (4.149) yields the third row of the system

$$\Phi_r\mathbf{W}_r = \mathbf{S}_r. \qquad (4.153)$$

Taking the w_{I_1} and w_{Q_2} terms to the other side yields

$$\phi_{I_2 Q_1} w_{Q_1} + \phi_{I_2 I_2} w_{I_2} = S_{I_2} - \phi_{I_2 I_1} w_{I_1} - \phi_{I_2 Q_2} w_{Q_2}, \qquad (4.154)$$

which is a second equation in the unknowns w_{Q_1} and w_{I_2}.

By examining Eqs. (4.152) and (4.154), one can see what the general equation for the unconstrained weights in an N-element array will be. In general, one must solve the system of equations

$$\mathbf{\Phi}_r^R \mathbf{W}_r^R = \mathbf{S}_r^R - \sum_{\text{constrained } P_j} w_{P_j} \mathbf{\Phi}_r^{P_j}, \qquad (4.155)$$

where the notation is as follows. The matrix $\mathbf{\Phi}_r^R$ is the *reduced covariance matrix* obtained by deleting from $\mathbf{\Phi}_r$ all rows and columns associated with constrained variables. In the two-element example above, $\mathbf{\Phi}_r^R$ is obtained by striking out the first (w_{I_1}) row and column and the fourth (w_{Q_2}) row and column,

$$\mathbf{\Phi}_r^R = \begin{bmatrix} \phi_{I_1 I_1} & \phi_{I_1 Q_1} & \phi_{I_1 I_2} & \phi_{I_1 Q_2} \\ \phi_{Q_1 I_1} & \phi_{Q_1 Q_1} & \phi_{Q_1 I_2} & \phi_{Q_1 Q_2} \\ \phi_{I_2 I_1} & \phi_{I_2 Q_1} & \phi_{I_2 I_2} & \phi_{I_2 Q_2} \\ \phi_{Q_2 I_1} & \phi_{Q_2 Q_1} & \phi_{Q_2 I_2} & \phi_{Q_2 Q_2} \end{bmatrix}$$

$$= \begin{bmatrix} \phi_{Q_1 Q_1} & \phi_{Q_1 I_2} \\ \phi_{I_2 Q_1} & \phi_{I_2 I_2} \end{bmatrix}. \qquad (4.156)$$

The vector $\mathbf{W}_r^R$ is the *reduced weight vector* obtained by removing the constrained variables from the normal weight vector,

$$\mathbf{W}_r^R = \begin{bmatrix} w_{I_1} \\ w_{Q_1} \\ w_{I_2} \\ w_{Q_2} \end{bmatrix} = \begin{bmatrix} w_{Q_1} \\ w_{I_2} \end{bmatrix}. \qquad (4.157)$$

The vector $\mathbf{S}_r^R$ is the *reduced reference correlation vector* obtained from $\mathbf{S}_r$ by removing the elements associated with constrained variables,

$$\mathbf{S}_r^R = \begin{bmatrix} S_{I_1} \\ S_{Q_1} \\ S_{I_2} \\ S_{Q_2} \end{bmatrix} = \begin{bmatrix} S_{Q_1} \\ S_{I_2} \end{bmatrix}. \qquad (4.158)$$

Finally, each $\mathbf{\Phi}_r^{P_j}$ is a column vector. It is defined as the P_jth column of the matrix obtained by striking out only the *rows* of $\mathbf{\Phi}_r$ associated with constrained variables. We obtain one such column vector for each constrained weight. Thus, for example,

$$\Phi_r^{I_1} = \begin{bmatrix} \phi_{I_1 I_1} & \phi_{I_1 Q_1} & \phi_{I_1 I_2} & \phi_{I_1 Q_2} \\ \phi_{Q_1 I_1} & \phi_{Q_1 Q_1} & \phi_{Q_1 I_2} & \phi_{Q_1 Q_2} \\ \phi_{I_2 I_1} & \phi_{I_2 Q_1} & \phi_{I_2 I_2} & \phi_{I_2 Q_2} \\ \phi_{Q_2 I_1} & \phi_{Q_2 Q_1} & \phi_{Q_2 I_2} & \phi_{Q_2 Q_2} \end{bmatrix} = \begin{bmatrix} \phi_{Q_1 I_1} \\ \phi_{I_2 I_1} \end{bmatrix} \tag{4.159}$$

and

$$\Phi_r^{Q_2} = \begin{bmatrix} \phi_{I_1 I_1} & \phi_{I_1 Q_1} & \phi_{I_1 I_2} & \phi_{I_1 Q_2} \\ \phi_{Q_1 I_1} & \phi_{Q_1 Q_1} & \phi_{Q_1 I_2} & \phi_{Q_1 Q_2} \\ \phi_{I_2 I_1} & \phi_{I_2 Q_1} & \phi_{I_2 I_2} & \phi_{I_2 Q_2} \\ \phi_{Q_2 I_1} & \phi_{Q_2 Q_1} & \phi_{Q_2 I_2} & \phi_{Q_2 Q_2} \end{bmatrix} = \begin{bmatrix} \phi_{Q_1 Q_2} \\ \phi_{I_2 Q_2} \end{bmatrix}. \tag{4.160}$$

Comparison of Eqs. (4.152) and (4.154) with the general result in Eq. (4.155) shows that they are the same. A moment's reflection will convince the reader that Eq. (4.155) is the correct general result for an arbitrary number of elements with an arbitrary number of saturated weights.

Example

Now let us use this general result to determine what happens in a two-element array when some weights saturate. Consider a two-element array with half-wavelength spacing, as shown in Fig. 4.35. Assume that a CW desired signal is incident from angle θ_d and independent thermal noise is also present in the

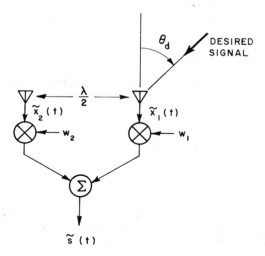

Figure 4.35   A two-element array.

element signals. The complex element signals are

$$\tilde{x}_1(t) = A_d e^{j(\omega_d t + \psi_d)} + \tilde{n}_1(t) \tag{4.161}$$

and

$$\tilde{x}_2(t) = A_d e^{j(\omega_d t + \psi_d - \phi_d)} + \tilde{n}_2(t). \tag{4.162}$$

Also, assume that the reference signal is

$$\tilde{r}(t) = \mathrm{Re}^{j(\omega_d t + \psi_d)}. \tag{4.163}$$

With these assumptions, this problem is the same as Example 1 of Chapter 2. We found in Eq. (2.124) that the optimal weight vector is given by

$$\mathbf{W} = \frac{A_d R}{2 A_d^2 + \sigma^2} \mathbf{U}_d^* = \frac{\sqrt{2 \xi_d \xi_r}}{1 + 2 \xi_d} \mathbf{U}_d^*, \tag{4.164}$$

where ξ_d, ξ_r, and $\mathbf{U}_d$ are defined in Eqs. (2.110), (4.87), and (2.113), respectively. The output SINR is [see Eq. (2.146)]

$$\mathrm{SINR} = 2 \xi_d. \tag{4.165}$$

In the absence of weight constraints, the array delivers 3 dB gain.

Now let us switch to real notation and examine the behavior of the quadrature weights as a function of ξ_d. From Eq. (4.164), we have

$$w_{I_1} = \frac{\sqrt{2 \xi_d \xi_r}}{1 + 2 \xi_d}, \tag{4.166}$$

$$w_{Q_1} = 0, \tag{4.167}$$

$$w_{I_2} = \frac{\sqrt{2 \xi_d \xi_r}}{1 + 2 \xi_d} \cos \phi_d, \tag{4.168}$$

and

$$w_{Q_2} = -\frac{\sqrt{2 \xi_d \xi_r}}{1 + 2 \xi_d} \sin \phi_d. \tag{4.169}$$

Let us arbitrarily suppose that

$$\phi_d = \frac{\pi}{4}. \tag{4.170}$$

(This value corresponds to $\theta_d \approx 14.5°$.) Also, let us assume

$$\xi_r = 10 \text{ dB}. \tag{4.171}$$

Then the four quadrature weights depend on ξ_d as shown in Fig. 4.36. Their behavior is similar to that shown in Fig. 4.33 for the single loop. All the weights peak at an intermediate value of ξ_d, in this case at -3 dB.

Now suppose none of the weights can exceed unity. In this case, we find that if $-12 \text{ dB} \leqslant \xi_d \leqslant 6 \text{ dB}$, w_{I_1} will become saturated. If ξ_d is in this

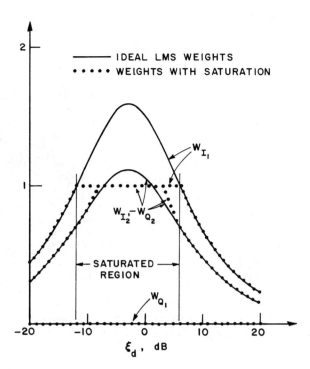

Figure 4.36 Weight behavior for a two-element array ($\phi_d = \pi/4$).

range, w_{I_1} cannot assume its ideal value, but will remain at 1. With $w_{I_1} = 1$, the solutions obtained for w_{Q_1}, w_{I_2}, and w_{Q_2} will no longer be valid in the range -12 dB $\leqslant \xi_d \leqslant 6$ dB. In this region, we must recalculate the unsaturated weights using Eq. (4.155).

To use Eq. (4.155), we must compute the covariance matrix $\boldsymbol{\Phi}_r$ and reference correlation vector $\mathbf{S}_r$ in real form. The $\tilde{x}_i(t)$ in Eqs. (4.161) and (4.162) are equivalent to the following inphase and quadrature signals:

$$x_{I_1}(t) = A_d \cos(\omega_d t + \psi_d) + n_{I_1}(t), \tag{4.172}$$

$$x_{Q_1}(t) = A_d \sin(\omega_d t + \psi_d) + n_{Q_1}(t), \tag{4.173}$$

$$x_{I_2}(t) = A_d \cos(\omega_d t + \psi_d - \phi_d) + n_{I_2}(t), \tag{4.174}$$

and

$$x_{Q_2}(t) = A_d \sin(\omega_d t + \psi_d - \phi_d) + n_{Q_2}(t). \tag{4.175}$$

The equivalent real reference signal is

$$r(t) = R \cos(\omega_d t + \psi_d). \tag{4.176}$$

Using the definitions of Φ_r and S_r in Eqs. (2.11) and (2.10), we have

$$\Phi_r = \begin{bmatrix} \alpha & 0 & \beta & -\gamma \\ 0 & \alpha & \gamma & \beta \\ \beta & \gamma & \alpha & 0 \\ -\gamma & \beta & 0 & \alpha \end{bmatrix} \tag{4.177}$$

where

$$\alpha = \frac{A_d^2}{2} + \frac{\sigma^2}{2}, \tag{4.178}$$

$$\beta = \frac{A_d^2}{2} \cos \phi_d, \tag{4.179}$$

and

$$\gamma = \frac{A_d^2}{2} \sin \phi_d, \tag{4.180}$$

and also

$$S_r = \frac{A_d R}{2} \begin{bmatrix} 1 \\ 0 \\ \cos \phi_d \\ -\sin \phi_d \end{bmatrix}. \tag{4.181}$$

Now applying Eq. (4.155) with $w_{I_1} = 1$, we find that w_{Q_1}, w_{I_2}, and w_{Q_2} must satisfy the system

$$\begin{bmatrix} \alpha & \gamma & \beta \\ \gamma & \alpha & 0 \\ \beta & 0 & \alpha \end{bmatrix} \begin{bmatrix} w_{Q_1} \\ w_{I_2} \\ w_{Q_2} \end{bmatrix} = \frac{A_d R}{2} \begin{bmatrix} 0 \\ \cos \phi_d \\ -\sin \phi_d \end{bmatrix} - \begin{bmatrix} 0 \\ \beta \\ -\gamma \end{bmatrix}. \tag{4.182}$$

We may write this equation in normalized form by dividing every term in the equation by $\sigma^2/2$. The result is

$$\begin{bmatrix} \alpha' & \gamma' & \beta' \\ \gamma' & \alpha' & 0 \\ \beta' & 0 & \alpha' \end{bmatrix} \begin{bmatrix} w_{Q_1} \\ w_{I_2} \\ w_{Q_2} \end{bmatrix} = \sqrt{2\xi_d \xi_r} \begin{bmatrix} 0 \\ \cos \phi_d \\ -\sin \phi_d \end{bmatrix} - \begin{bmatrix} 0 \\ \beta' \\ -\gamma' \end{bmatrix} \tag{4.183}$$

where

$$\alpha' = 1 + \xi_d, \tag{4.184}$$

$$\beta' = \xi_d \cos \phi_d, \tag{4.185}$$

and

$$\gamma' = \xi_d \sin \phi_d. \tag{4.186}$$

Solving this set of equations yields the solutions for w_{Q_1}, w_{I_2}, and w_{Q_2} over the region -12 dB $\leqslant \xi_d \leqslant 6$ dB. The value of w_{Q_1} turns out to be zero, the same as without saturation. However, w_{I_2} and w_{Q_2} differ from their ideal values; they grow more rapidly toward the limiting value of unity than they did without w_{I_1} saturated. The behavior of w_{I_2} and w_{Q_2} with saturation is shown as the dotted curve in Fig. 4.36.

Using this result, we find that w_{I_2} and w_{Q_2} also become saturated at $\xi_d = -8$ dB and $\xi_d = +3$ dB. (We assume each w_{P_j} is limited to the range $|w_{P_j}| \leqslant 1$, so w_{Q_2} saturates at the value $w_{Q_2} = -1$ in Fig. 4.36.) Hence for -8 dB $\leqslant \xi_d \leqslant 3$ dB, three weights will be saturated. Only w_{Q_1} remains unsaturated. To determine w_{Q_1} in this range, we must again use Eq. (4.155), this time with three variables fixed. Applying Eq. (4.155) for this case gives the single equation

$$\alpha w_{Q_1} = \gamma - \beta. \tag{4.187}$$

Since we have assumed $\phi_d = \pi/4$, the right side of this equation is zero, so

$$w_{Q_1} = 0 \tag{4.188}$$

within the range -8 dB $\leqslant \xi_d \leqslant 3$ dB. The value of w_{Q_1} remains zero for all ξ_d, even though first w_{I_1} and then w_{I_2} and w_{Q_2} all become saturated.

Now let us calculate the output signal-to-noise ratio from the array (which we still denote by SINR) as a function of ξ_d for these weights. For an arbitrary set of weights, the array output desired signal is given by

$$\tilde{s}_d(t) = A_d e^{j(\omega_d t + \psi_d)} \left[w_{I_1} - j w_{Q_1}, \; w_{I_2} - j w_{Q_2} \right] \begin{bmatrix} 1 \\ e^{-j\phi_d} \end{bmatrix}, \tag{4.189}$$

and the output desired signal power may be calculated from

$$P_d = \tfrac{1}{2} E\left\{ \left| \tilde{s}_d(t) \right|^2 \right\}. \tag{4.190}$$

The output noise power is given by

$$P_n = \frac{\sigma^2}{2} \left[w_{I_1}^2 + w_{Q_1}^2 + w_{I_2}^2 + w_{Q_2}^2 \right]. \tag{4.191}$$

These quantities may be used to determine the SINR

$$\text{SINR} = \frac{P_d}{P_n}. \tag{4.192}$$

When the SINR is calculated from the weights in Fig. 4.36, the result is shown in Fig. 4.37. In the region where the weights are saturated, the SINR is found to differ so little from the ideal result in Eq. (4.165) that there is essentially no loss in performance. (The drop is about 0.12 dB.) Thus, even though the weights saturate, there is little effect on the SINR.

Now let us add an interference signal to this example. Assume a CW interference signal arrives from angle θ_i in Fig. 4.35. The problem now is the

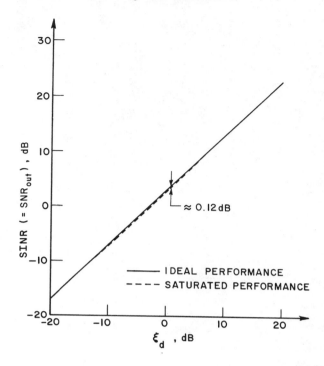

Figure 4.37 SINR with weight saturation.

same as Example 2 of Chapter 2. For this situation the complex array weights were found in Eq. (2.189). From these results, the ideal (LMS) inphase and quadrature weights may be plotted as a function of ξ_d. To be specific, let us assume $\xi_i = 40$ dB, $\xi_r = 15$ dB, $\theta_d = -10°$, and $\theta_i = 35°$. The four quadrature weights that result are plotted versus ξ_d in Fig. 4.38. We find that w_{I_1} saturates (assuming $|w_{P_j}| \leqslant 1$) for ξ_d in the range -16.3 dB $\leqslant \xi_d \leqslant 11.5$ dB. For ξ_d in this range, we solve Eq. (4.155) for the other three weights. With the interference signal added, the normalized covariance matrix is given by

$$\frac{1}{\sigma^2}\Phi_r = \begin{bmatrix} \alpha' & 0 & \beta' & -\gamma' \\ 0 & \alpha' & \gamma' & \beta' \\ \beta' & \gamma' & \alpha' & 0 \\ -\gamma' & \beta' & 0 & \alpha' \end{bmatrix} \tag{4.193}$$

where

$$\alpha' = 1 + \xi_d + \xi_i, \tag{4.194}$$

$$\beta' = \xi_d \cos \phi_d + \xi_i \cos \phi_i, \tag{4.195}$$

and

$$\gamma' = \xi_d \sin \phi_d + \xi_i \sin \phi_i. \tag{4.196}$$

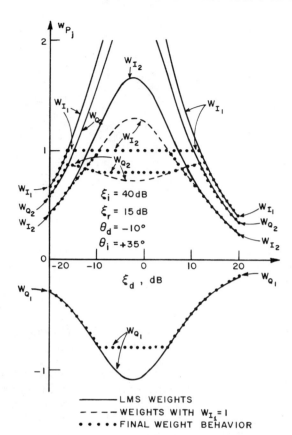

Figure 4.38 Weight behavior for a two-element array.

With w_{I_1} saturated, Eq. (4.155) yields

$$\begin{bmatrix} \alpha' & \gamma' & \beta' \\ \gamma' & \alpha' & 0 \\ \beta' & 0 & \alpha' \end{bmatrix} \begin{bmatrix} w_{Q_1} \\ w_{I_2} \\ w_{Q_2} \end{bmatrix} = \sqrt{2\xi_d\xi_r} \begin{bmatrix} 0 \\ \cos\phi_d \\ -\sin\phi_d \end{bmatrix} - \begin{bmatrix} 0 \\ \beta' \\ -\gamma' \end{bmatrix}. \qquad (4.197)$$

When these equations are solved, the dashed curves in Fig. 4.38 result. Examining these curves, we find that w_{I_2} will also saturate when ξ_d is in the range -9.5 dB $\leqslant \xi_d \leqslant 5$ dB. Within this range, with both w_{I_1} and w_{I_2} saturated, we next solve the reduced system of equations

$$\begin{bmatrix} \alpha' & \beta' \\ \beta' & \alpha' \end{bmatrix} \begin{bmatrix} w_{Q_1} \\ w_{Q_2} \end{bmatrix} = \sqrt{2\xi_d\xi_r} \begin{bmatrix} 0 \\ -\sin\phi_d \end{bmatrix} - \begin{bmatrix} 0 \\ -\gamma' \end{bmatrix}. \qquad (4.198)$$

These equations yield w_{Q_1} and w_{Q_2} that are constant over the range -9.5 dB $\leqslant \xi_d \leqslant 5$ dB where both w_{I_1} and w_{I_2} are saturated. Thus the complete weight behavior is shown dotted in Fig. 4.38.

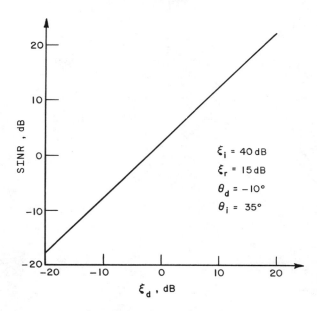

$\xi_i = 40\,dB$

$\xi_r = 15\,dB$

$\theta_d = -10°$

$\theta_i = 35°$

Figure 4.39 SINR versus ξ_d with weight saturation.

By computing the output desired signal power P_d and the output thermal noise power P_n as in Eqs. (4.190) and (4.191), and also the interference power P_i from

$$\tilde{s}_1(t) = A_i e^{j(\omega_d t + \psi_i)} \left[w_{I_1} - jw_{Q_1}, \; w_{I_2} - jw_{Q_2} \right] \begin{bmatrix} 1 \\ e^{-j\phi_i} \end{bmatrix} \qquad (4.199)$$

and

$$P_i = \tfrac{1}{2} E\left\{ |\tilde{s}_i(t)|^2 \right\}, \qquad (4.200)$$

we may find the SINR

$$\text{SINR} = \frac{P_d}{P_i + P_n}. \qquad (4.201)$$

The result, obtained from the weights in Fig. 4.38, is shown in Fig. 4.39 as a function of ξ_d. Again, we find that weight saturation causes negligible change in SINR from the ideal value.

Weight saturation does change the absolute levels of the output desired signal, interference, and thermal noise, however. Figures 4.40, 4.41, and 4.42 show the normalized powers P_d/P_r, P_i/P_r, and P_n/P_r [where P_r is the reference signal power defined in Eq. (4.143)] versus ξ_d. The figures show both the ideal output powers that would be obtained with LMS weights and those that result with the saturated weights in Fig. 4.38. It is seen that as ξ_d is reduced below 11.5 dB, where saturation begins, P_d drops much more quickly with weight

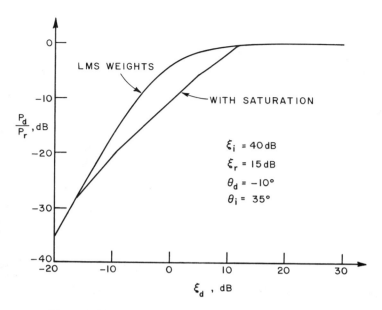

Figure 4.40 P_d/P_r versus ξ_d with weight saturation.

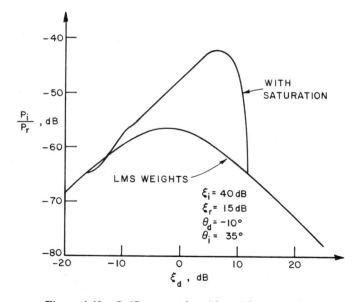

Figure 4.41 P_i/P_r versus ξ_d with weight saturation.

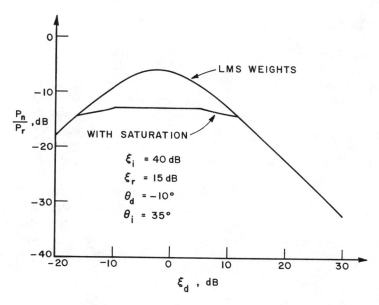

Figure 4.42 P_n/P_r versus ξ_d with weight saturation.

saturation than it does with ideal weights. (If the array output is used to generate a reference signal for the array, as discussed in Chapter 7, this drop can reduce the dynamic range of the array.) The output thermal noise power, shown in Fig. 4.42, is also lower with weight saturation than with LMS weights. Figure 4.41 shows the output interference power, which rises extremely rapidly as ξ_d drops below 11.5 dB. This change has little effect on the SINR, however, because the output interference power is far below the output thermal noise power.[‡]

These results indicate how saturation changes the absolute level of the signals at the array output. In general, the changes depend on signal arrival angles, powers, and bandwidths, as well as saturation levels. The designer will usually want to avoid weight saturation in order to make the behavior of the array output signals as well defined as possible, since the array output will be used as the input to the receiver demodulation circuitry and reference signal generation circuitry. Since the magnitude of the weights depends linearly on the reference signal amplitude [as in Eq. (4.140) or (4.164)], weight saturation is avoided simply by keeping the reference signal amplitude small enough.

[‡]Weight saturation may have a larger effect on SINR when the interference is wideband. It was shown in Chapter 3 that the interference power at the array output rises very rapidly with bandwidth [for example, see Fig. 3.11(c)]. Hence, if the bandwidth is large, the output interference power may be large enough so that weight saturation will reduce the SINR more than with narrowband signals.

4.5 WEIGHT JITTER

In section 2.1, we discussed the fact that each weight in an LMS array is actually a stochastic process. Because thermal noise is always present in the feedback loops, each weight in the array fluctuates randomly about its mean value. We shall refer to this fluctuation as "weight jitter." Weight jitter has been studied by Widrow and McCool [9] for a discrete LMS array and by Berni [10] and Koleszar [11] for an analog LMS array. In this section, we shall analyze weight jitter for the analog LMS array, using an approximate method similar to that used in [9], and shall show an example of how weight jitter depends on signal parameters.

Because a signal received by an adaptive array is multiplied by the weights, weight jitter causes a random modulation of the desired signal. In essence, the adaptive array is a dispersive channel [12] that multiplies the desired signal by a random noise process. For this reason, in practice the designer must keep weight jitter small, so that the array does not destroy the desired signal modulation.

In Chapter 2 we discussed weight transients in the LMS array. We showed that, when weight jitter is ignored, the weights vary exponentially in a transient from their initial values to their steady-state values. In this context, we used the term "steady-state" to mean that the weight transients have died out and the weights have become constant with time. In reality, however, the weights in an array are never constant, because of the weight jitter. An actual weight transient consists of an exponential behavior on which is superimposed a random fluctuation. The random fluctuation continues even after the exponential transients have died out. Hence, when weight jitter is included in the analysis, we shall use the term "steady state" to mean that the weights have become stationary random processes. In steady state, after the transients have died out, the mean and variance of each weight is a constant, but not the weight itself.

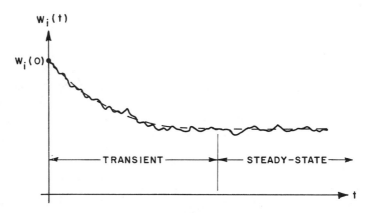

Figure 4.43 A typical weight transient.

Weight jitter occurs for the following reason. Each weight in an LMS array is derived from a feedback loop as shown in Fig. 2.8. Every signal $\tilde{x}_i(t)$ in the array and hence also $\tilde{s}(t)$ and $\tilde{\varepsilon}(t)$ are random processes. [Each $\tilde{x}_i(t)$ contains at least a thermal noise component. Usually $\tilde{x}_i(t)$ also contains a desired signal and possibly interference, both of which are random processes.] The input to the integrator in Fig. 2.8 is thus the product of two random processes, and hence w_i is a random process.

Figure 4.43 shows a typical weight transient as a function of time. During the transient period, the mean value of the weight is exponential, and the weight is a nonstationary process. After the transient has died out, the weight settles into a stationary random process. The weight has a constant mean value but varies about its mean with a certain variance. Our purpose in this section will be to study the variance of the weights in steady state.

Method of Analysis

To analyze weight jitter, we shall again use the real notation introduced in the beginning of Chapter 2 and also used in the previous section. Since the array output signal is

$$s(t) = \sum_{P,\,j} w_{P_j} x_{P_j}(t), \tag{4.202}$$

the error signal is

$$\varepsilon(t) = r(t) - \sum_{P,\,j} w_{P_j} x_{P_j}(t), \tag{4.203}$$

and the mean-square error is

$$E\{\varepsilon^2(t)\} = E\{r^2(t)\} - 2\mathbf{W}_r^T \mathbf{S}_r + \mathbf{W}_r^T \boldsymbol{\Phi}_r \mathbf{W}_r, \tag{4.204}$$

where $\mathbf{W}_r$, $\mathbf{S}_r$, and $\boldsymbol{\Phi}_r$ are defined in Eqs. (2.9) through (2.11).

The weight vector minimizing $E\{\varepsilon^2(t)\}$ is given by Eq. (2.15),

$$\mathbf{W}_{r_{\text{opt}}} = \boldsymbol{\Phi}_r^{-1} \mathbf{S}_r. \tag{4.205}$$

When $\mathbf{W}_r = \mathbf{W}_{r_{\text{opt}}}$, $E\{\varepsilon^2(t)\}$ has the value

$$\varepsilon_{\min}^2 = \min_{\mathbf{W}_r} E\left[\varepsilon^2(t)\right] = E\left[r^2(t)\right] - \mathbf{W}_{r_{\text{opt}}}^T \boldsymbol{\Phi}_r \mathbf{W}_{r_{\text{opt}}}. \tag{4.206}$$

In terms of $\mathbf{W}_{r_{\text{opt}}}$ and $\varepsilon_{\min}^2$, the mean-square error in Eq. (4.204) can be written

$$E\left[\varepsilon^2(t)\right] = \varepsilon_{\min}^2 + \left(\mathbf{W}_r - \mathbf{W}_{r_{\text{opt}}}\right)^T \boldsymbol{\Phi}_r \left(\mathbf{W}_r - \mathbf{W}_{r_{\text{opt}}}\right). \tag{4.207}$$

From this expression, we find that, for any given weight vector $\mathbf{W}_r$, the gradient of $E[\varepsilon^2(t)]$, ∇_r, is

$$\nabla_r = \nabla_{\mathbf{W}_r}\left\{E\left[\varepsilon^2(t)\right]\right\} = 2\boldsymbol{\Phi}_r\left(\mathbf{W}_r - \mathbf{W}_{r_{\text{opt}}}\right). \tag{4.208}$$

When $\mathbf{W}_r = \mathbf{W}_{r_{\text{opt}}}$, we have of course

$$\nabla_r = 0. \tag{4.209}$$

In an LMS array, the feedback loop does not use ∇_r, but an estimate of ∇_r, which we shall call $\hat{\nabla}_r$,

$$\hat{\nabla}_r = \nabla_{\mathbf{W}_r}\{\varepsilon^2(t)\} = -2\mathbf{X}_r(t)\varepsilon(t). \tag{4.210}$$

We note that $\hat{\nabla}_r$ is an unbiased estimate, since

$$E[\hat{\nabla}_r] = E\{\nabla_{\mathbf{W}_r}[\varepsilon^2(t)]\} = \nabla_{\mathbf{W}_r}\{E[\varepsilon^2(t)]\} = \nabla_r. \tag{4.211}$$

Hence if $\mathbf{W}_r = \mathbf{W}_{r_{\text{opt}}}$, we have

$$E[\hat{\nabla}_r] = 0. \tag{4.212}$$

However, if $\mathbf{W}_r = \mathbf{W}_{r_{\text{opt}}}$, we also have from Eq. (4.210)

$$E[\hat{\nabla}_r] = E\{-2\mathbf{X}_r(t)\varepsilon_0(t)\}, \tag{4.213}$$

where $\varepsilon_0(t)$ is the error signal when $\mathbf{W}_r = \mathbf{W}_{r_{\text{opt}}}$, that is,

$$\varepsilon_0(t) = r(t) - \mathbf{X}_r^T\mathbf{W}_{r_{\text{opt}}}. \tag{4.214}$$

Thus, combining Eqs. (4.212) and (4.213), we have

$$E\{\mathbf{X}_r(t)\varepsilon_0(t)\} = 0. \tag{4.215}$$

This result tells us that $\mathbf{X}_r(t)$ and $\varepsilon_0(t)$, the error signal when $\mathbf{W}_r = \mathbf{W}_{r_{\text{opt}}}$, are uncorrelated random variables. Moreover, if the element signals $x_{P_j}(t)$ are Gaussian random processes, which we shall assume, then $\mathbf{X}_r(t)$ and $\varepsilon_0(t)$ are also Gaussian. In this case Eq. (4.215) shows that $\mathbf{X}_r(t)$ and $\varepsilon_0(t)$ are also statistically independent random variables. We shall use this fact later.

Now consider the LMS algorithm,

$$\frac{d\mathbf{W}_r}{dt} = -k\hat{\nabla}_r. \tag{4.216}$$

Let us write $\hat{\nabla}_r$ as the true gradient ∇_r plus a noise term $\mathbf{G}_r$,

$$\hat{\nabla}_r = \nabla_r + \mathbf{G}_r. \tag{4.217}$$

With this notation the LMS algorithm becomes

$$\frac{d\mathbf{W}_r}{dt} = -k\nabla_r - k\mathbf{G}_r. \tag{4.218}$$

But substituting for ∇_r from Eq. (4.208), we have

$$\frac{d\mathbf{W}_r}{dt} = -2k(\mathbf{\Phi}_r\mathbf{W}_r - \mathbf{S}_r) - k\mathbf{G}_r, \tag{4.219}$$

or

$$\frac{d\mathbf{W}_r}{dt} + 2k\mathbf{\Phi}_r\mathbf{W}_r = 2k\mathbf{S}_r - k\mathbf{G}_r. \tag{4.220}$$

Next let us define $\mathbf{Z}_r$ to be the difference between $\mathbf{W}_r$ and $\mathbf{W}_{r_{\mathrm{opt}}}$:

$$\mathbf{W}_r = \mathbf{W}_{r_{\mathrm{opt}}} + \mathbf{Z}_r. \tag{4.221}$$

Then

$$\frac{d\mathbf{W}_r}{dt} = \frac{d\mathbf{Z}_r}{dt}, \tag{4.222}$$

since $\mathbf{W}_{r_{\mathrm{opt}}}$ is a constant, and Eq. (4.220) may be written

$$\frac{d\mathbf{Z}_r}{dt} + 2k\mathbf{\Phi}_r\!\left(\mathbf{W}_{r_{\mathrm{opt}}} + \mathbf{Z}_r\right) = 2k\mathbf{S}_r - k\mathbf{G}_r, \tag{4.223}$$

which, in view of Eq. (4.205), reduces to

$$\frac{d\mathbf{Z}_r}{dt} + 2k\mathbf{\Phi}_r\mathbf{Z}_r = -k\mathbf{G}_r. \tag{4.224}$$

After the exponential transients in a weight response have died out and the weights are in steady state, $\mathbf{Z}_r$ is just the weight jitter. Thus the weight jitter may be obtained by solving the linear system in Eq. (4.224) with $\mathbf{G}_r$ as the source term.

Let us consider $\mathbf{G}_r$. We have

$$\begin{aligned}
\mathbf{G}_r &= \hat{\nabla}_r - \nabla_r \\
&= -2\mathbf{X}_r(t)\varepsilon(t) + 2E\{\mathbf{X}_r(t)\varepsilon(t)\} \\
&= -2\big[\mathbf{X}_r(t)r(t) - \mathbf{S}_r\big] + 2\big[\mathbf{X}_r(t)\mathbf{X}_r^T(t) - \mathbf{\Phi}_r\big]\mathbf{W}_r.
\end{aligned} \tag{4.225}$$

Substituting Eq. (4.221) for $\mathbf{W}_r$ gives

$$\mathbf{G}_r = -2\big[\mathbf{X}_r r - \mathbf{S}_r\big] + 2\big[\mathbf{X}_r\mathbf{X}_r^T - \mathbf{\Phi}_r\big]\mathbf{W}_{r_{\mathrm{opt}}} + 2\big[\mathbf{X}_r\mathbf{X}_r^T - \mathbf{\Phi}_r\big]\mathbf{Z}_r. \tag{4.226}$$

In this equation we note that $\mathbf{X}_r r - \mathbf{S}_r$ is the instantaneous variation of $\mathbf{X}_r r$ around $\mathbf{S}_r$ and $\mathbf{X}_r\mathbf{X}_r^T - \mathbf{\Phi}_r$ is the instantaneous variation of $\mathbf{X}_r\mathbf{X}_r^T$ around $\mathbf{\Phi}_r$.

Now we make the following approximation. We suppose that the weight jitter components are small compared to the mean weights, that is,

$$\mathbf{Z}_r \ll \mathbf{W}_{r_{\mathrm{opt}}}. \tag{4.227}$$

Then

$$\big[\mathbf{X}_r\mathbf{X}_r^T - \mathbf{\Phi}_r\big]\mathbf{Z}_r \ll \big[\mathbf{X}_r\mathbf{X}_r^T - \mathbf{\Phi}_r\big]\mathbf{W}_{r_{\mathrm{opt}}}, \tag{4.228}$$

and the last term in Eq. (4.226) can be neglected in comparison with the middle term. Since $\mathbf{X}_r\mathbf{X}_r^T - \mathbf{\Phi}_r$ is the fluctuation of $\mathbf{X}_r\mathbf{X}_r^T$ around $\mathbf{\Phi}_r$ and $\mathbf{Z}_r$ is the fluctuation of $\mathbf{W}_r$ around $\mathbf{W}_{r_{\mathrm{opt}}}$, we are essentially assuming $[\mathbf{X}_r\mathbf{X}_r^T - \mathbf{\Phi}_r]\mathbf{Z}_r$ to be a second-order term that can be neglected. Thus we approximate $\mathbf{G}_r$ by

$$\mathbf{G}_r = -2\big[\mathbf{X}_r r - \mathbf{S}_r\big] + 2\big[\mathbf{X}_r\mathbf{X}_r^T - \mathbf{\Phi}_r\big]\mathbf{W}_{r_{\mathrm{opt}}}. \tag{4.229}$$

However, since $\mathbf{\Phi}_r\mathbf{W}_{r_{\text{opt}}} = \mathbf{S}_r$, this equation is just

$$\mathbf{G}_r = -2\mathbf{X}_r r + 2\mathbf{X}_r\mathbf{X}_r^T\mathbf{W}_{r_{\text{opt}}} = -2\mathbf{X}_r(t)\varepsilon_0(t), \qquad (4.230)$$

where $\varepsilon_0(t)$ is the error signal when $\mathbf{W}_r = \mathbf{W}_{r_{\text{opt}}}$, as defined in Eq. (4.214).

Now we return to Eq. (4.224). To solve this equation, we rotate coordinates. Let us define

$$\mathbf{Z}_r = \mathbf{R}_r\mathbf{Z}_r' \qquad (4.231)$$

and

$$\mathbf{G}_r = \mathbf{R}_r\mathbf{G}_r', \qquad (4.232)$$

where $\mathbf{R}_r$ is an orthogonal coordinate rotation matrix. Substituting Eqs. (4.231) and (4.232) into Eq. (4.224) and multiplying on the left by $\mathbf{R}_r^T$, we have

$$\frac{d\mathbf{Z}_r'}{dt} + 2k\mathbf{R}_r^T\mathbf{\Phi}_r\mathbf{R}_r\mathbf{Z}_r' = -k\mathbf{G}_r'. \qquad (4.233)$$

We choose $\mathbf{R}_r$ to be the matrix that diagonalizes $\mathbf{\Phi}_r$, so we have

$$\frac{d\mathbf{Z}_r'}{dt} + 2k\mathbf{\Lambda}_r\mathbf{Z}_r' = -k\mathbf{G}_r', \qquad (4.234)$$

where $\mathbf{\Lambda}_r$ is the matrix of eigenvalues of $\mathbf{\Phi}_r$. Eq. (4.234) is an uncoupled system of equations. Each component of $\mathbf{Z}_r'$ satisfies an equation of the form

$$\frac{dz_{r_j}'}{dt} + 2k\lambda_{r_j}z_{r_j}' = -kg_{r_j}', \qquad (4.235)$$

where z_{r_j}' and g_{r_j}' are the jth components of $\mathbf{Z}_r'$ and $\mathbf{G}_r'$, and λ_{r_j} is the jth eigenvalue of $\mathbf{\Phi}_r$. In this coordinate system, each component z_{r_j}' may be viewed as the output of a linear filter with transfer function

$$H_j(\omega) = \frac{-k}{j\omega + 2k\lambda_{r_j}} \qquad (4.236)$$

and with $g_{r_j}'(t)$ as the input, as shown in Fig. 4.44. It follows that the power spectral densities of $z_{r_j}'(t)$ and $g_{r_j}'(t)$ will be related by

$$S_{z_{r_j}'}(\omega) = |H_j(\omega)|^2 S_{g_{r_j}'}(\omega). \qquad (4.237)$$

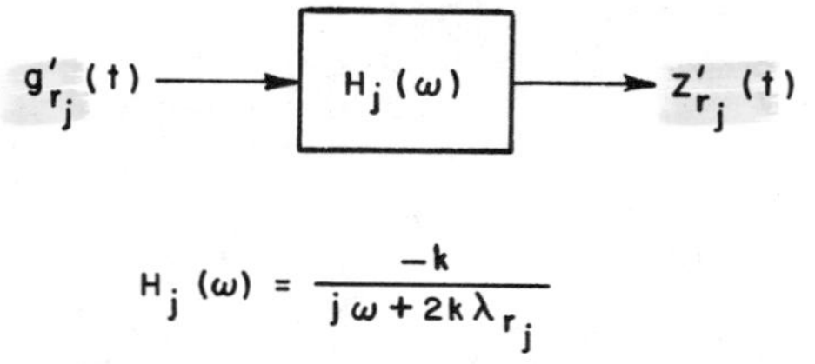

$$g_{r_j}'(t) \longrightarrow \boxed{H_j(\omega)} \longrightarrow z_{r_j}'(t)$$

$$H_j(\omega) = \frac{-k}{j\omega + 2k\lambda_{r_j}}$$

Figure 4.44   A linear filter.

Since $z'_{r_j}(t)$ is zero mean, the total power in $z'_{r_j}(t)$ is simply its variance. Therefore, the variance of $z'_{r_j}(t)$, $\sigma^2_{z'_{r_j}}$, is

$$\sigma^2_{z'_{r_j}} = \frac{1}{2\pi} \int_{-\infty}^{\infty} S_{z'_{r_j}}(\omega)\, d\omega = \frac{1}{2\pi} \int_{-\infty}^{\infty} \left| H_j(\omega) \right|^2 S_{g'_{r_j}}(\omega)\, d\omega. \qquad (4.238)$$

Thus the variance of $z'_{r_j}(t)$ can be determined from the power spectral density of $g'_{r_j}(t)$.

To determine the power spectral density of $g'_{r_j}(t)$, we proceed in two steps. First, we determine the total *power* in $g'_{r_j}(t)$, and second, we determine the *shape* of its power spectral density. To find the total power, we return to the unprimed coordinate system and consider $\mathbf{G}_r$. The covariance of $\mathbf{G}_r$ is given by

$$E\left[\mathbf{G}_r \mathbf{G}_r^T\right] = E\left\{ \left[-2\mathbf{X}_r(t)\varepsilon_0(t)\right]\left[-2\mathbf{X}_r^T(t)\varepsilon_0(t)\right] \right\} = 4E\left\{ \varepsilon_0^2(t)\mathbf{X}_r(t)\mathbf{X}_r^T(t) \right\}. \qquad (4.239)$$

However, when the array is in steady state, $\mathbf{X}_r(t)$ and $\varepsilon_0(t)$ are statistically independent random variables, as we showed in Eq. (4.215). Hence, Eq. (4.239) may be written

$$E\left[\mathbf{G}_r \mathbf{G}_r^T\right] = 4E\left\{ \varepsilon_0^2(t) \right\} E\left\{ \mathbf{X}_r(t)\mathbf{X}_r^T(t) \right\} = 4\varepsilon_{\min}^2 \mathbf{\Phi}_r. \qquad (4.240)$$

Therefore the covariance of $\mathbf{G}'_r$ is

$$E\left[\mathbf{G}'_r \mathbf{G}'^T_r\right] = \mathbf{R}_r^T E\left[\mathbf{G}_r \mathbf{G}_r^T\right]\mathbf{R}_r = 4\varepsilon_{\min}^2 \mathbf{R}_r^T \mathbf{\Phi}_r \mathbf{R}_r = 4\varepsilon_{\min}^2 \mathbf{\Lambda}_r. \qquad (4.241)$$

Since $E(\mathbf{G}'_r \mathbf{G}'^T_r)$ is diagonal, the individual $g'_{r_j}(t)$ are uncorrelated, and each $g'_{r_j}(t)$ has variance

$$\sigma^2_{g'_{r_j}} = E\left[g'^2_{r_j} \right] = 4\varepsilon_{\min}^2 \lambda_{r_j}. \qquad (4.242)$$

Because the different $g'_{r_j}(t)$ are uncorrelated, the $z'_{r_j}(t)$ will also be uncorrelated.

Now we have found the total power in $g'_{r_j}(t)$. Next we determine the shape of its spectral density. We return again to the unprimed coordinate system. Consider the power spectral density of $g_{P_j}(t)$, one of the components of $\mathbf{G}_r$. Since

$$g_{P_j}(t) = -2\varepsilon_0(t)x_{P_j}(t), \qquad (4.243)$$

the function $g_{P_j}(t)$ is the product of two Gaussian random variables. The spectral density of $g_{P_j}(t)$ can be obtained from its autocorrelation function,

$$R_{g_{P_j}}(\tau) = E\left\{ g_{P_j}(t)g_{P_j}(t+\tau) \right\} = 4E\left\{ \varepsilon_0(t)x_{P_j}(t)\varepsilon_0(t+\tau)x_{P_j}(t+\tau) \right\}. \qquad (4.244)$$

Since each factor in $R_{g_{P_j}}(t)$ is a Gaussian random variable, a well-known theorem for Gaussian random variables [13] may be invoked to write $R_{g_{P_j}}(\tau)$ as

$$R_{g_{P_j}}(\tau) = 4E\left[\varepsilon_0(t)x_{P_j}(t)\right]E\left[\varepsilon_0(t+\tau)x_{P_j}(t+\tau)\right]$$

$$+4E\left[\varepsilon_0(t)\varepsilon_0(t+\tau)\right]E\left[x_{P_j}(t)x_{P_j}(t+\tau)\right]$$

$$+4E\left[\varepsilon_0(t)x_{P_j}(t+\tau)\right]E\left[x_{P_j}(t)\varepsilon_0(t+\tau)\right]. \qquad (4.245)$$

In this expression, the first two expectations are zero by Eq. (4.215). The last four expectations all involve autocorrelation functions of the received signals in the array.

To evaluate $R_{g_{P_j}}(\tau)$, we must make some specific assumptions about the array. Let us suppose we have a two-element array, with desired signal, interference, and thermal noise present on each element signal. Suppose the inphase and quadrature signals in the array are

$$x_{I_1}(t) = d(t) + i(t) + n_{I_1}(t), \qquad (4.246)$$

$$x_{Q_1}(t) = \hat{d}(t) + \hat{i}(t) + n_{Q_1}(t), \qquad (4.247)$$

$$x_{I_2}(t) = d(t - T_d) + i(t - T_i) + n_{I_2}(t), \qquad (4.248)$$

and

$$x_{Q_2}(t) = \hat{d}(t - T_d) + \hat{i}(t - T_i) + n_{Q_2}(t), \qquad (4.249)$$

where $d(t)$, $i(t)$, and $n_{P_j}(t)$ are the desired, interference, and thermal noise signals, and where T_d and T_i are the interelement propagation time delays for the desired and interference signals, respectively. [The signals $d(t)$, $i(t)$, and $n_{P_j}(t)$ are all assumed to be zero mean and independent of each other.] For this situation, let us calculate the nonzero terms in Eq. (4.245). We shall carry out this analysis using $R_{g_{I_2}}(\tau)$ as an example. Then we shall show that the result obtained for $R_{g_{I_2}}(\tau)$ is in fact the correct result for all the $R_{g_{P_j}}(\tau)$.

The term $E[x_{I_2}(t)x_{I_2}(t+\tau)]$ is the simplest:

$$E\left[x_{I_2}(t)x_{I_2}(t+\tau)\right] = R_{x_{I_2}}(\tau)$$

$$= E\left\{\left[d(t - T_d) + i(t - T_i) + n_{I_2}(t)\right]\right.$$

$$\left.\times\left[d(t + \tau - T_d) + i(t + \tau - T_i) + n_{I_2}(t+\tau)\right]\right\}$$

$$= R_d(\tau) + R_i(\tau) + R_n(\tau), \qquad (4.250)$$

where $R_d(\tau)$, $R_i(\tau)$, and $R_n(\tau)$ are the autocorrelation functions of $d(t)$, $i(t)$, and the $n_{P_j}(t)$, respectively. Now, defining $S_{x_{I_2}}(\omega)$ to be the power spectral density of $x_{I_2}(t)$,

$$S_{x_{I_2}}(\omega) = \int_{-\infty}^{\infty} R_{x_{I_2}}(\tau)e^{-j\omega\tau}\,d\tau, \qquad (4.251)$$

we find

$$S_{x_{I_2}}(\omega) = S_d(\omega) + S_i(\omega) + S_n(\omega), \tag{4.252}$$

where $S_d(\omega)$, $S_i(\omega)$, and $S_n(\omega)$ are the power spectral densities of $d(t)$, $i(t)$, and $n_{P_j}(t)$.

Next, consider the term $E[\varepsilon_0(t)\varepsilon_0(t + \tau)]$. We have

$$\varepsilon_0(t) = r(t) - \sum_{P,j} w_{P_j} x_{P_j}(t), \tag{4.253}$$

where the w_{P_j} are the optimum weights. (To simplify the notation, we omit the subscript "opt" in each weight.) Let us assume the reference signal is a perfect replica of the desired signal,

$$r(t) = d(t). \tag{4.254}$$

Then we have

$$E\left[\varepsilon_0(t)\varepsilon_0(t + \tau)\right] = R_{\varepsilon_0}(\tau)$$

$$\begin{aligned}
= E\Big\{&\Big[d(t) - w_{I_1}\big\{d(t) + i(t) + n_{I_1}(t)\big\} \\
&- w_{Q_1}\big\{\hat{d}(t) + \hat{i}(t) + n_{Q_1}(t)\big\} \\
&- w_{I_2}\big\{d(t - T_d) + i(t - T_i) + n_{I_2}(t)\big\} \\
&- w_{Q_2}\big\{\hat{d}(t - T_d) + \hat{i}(t - T_i) + n_{Q_2}(t)\big\}\Big] \\
\times &\Big[d(t + \tau) - w_{I_1}\big\{d(t + \tau) + i(t + \tau) + n_{I_1}(t + \tau)\big\} \\
&- w_{Q_1}\big\{\hat{d}(t + \tau) + \hat{i}(t + \tau) + n_{Q_1}(t + \tau)\big\} \\
&- w_{I_2}\big\{d(t + \tau - T_d) + i(t + \tau - T_i) + n_{I_2}(t + \tau)\big\} \\
&- w_{Q_2}\big\{\hat{d}(t + \tau - T_d) + \hat{i}(t + \tau - T_i) + n_{Q_2}(t + \tau)\big\}\Big]\Big\}.
\end{aligned} \tag{4.255}$$

Evaluation of this expectation is straightforward, but tedious. After dropping all uncorrelated products, we obtain

$$R_{\varepsilon_0}(\tau)$$

$$\begin{aligned}
= &\Big[1 - 2w_{I_1} + w_{I_1}^2 + w_{Q_1}^2 + w_{I_2}^2 + w_{Q_2}^2\Big] R_d(\tau) + \Big[-w_{I_2} + w_{I_1}w_{I_2} + w_{Q_1}w_{Q_2}\Big] \\
&\times \Big[R_d(\tau - T_d) + R_d(\tau + T_d)\Big] + \Big[-w_{Q_2} + w_{I_1}w_{Q_2} - w_{Q_1}w_{I_2}\Big] \\
&\times \Big[\hat{R}_d(\tau - T_d) - \hat{R}_d(\tau + T_d)\Big] + \Big[w_{I_1}^2 + w_{Q_1}^2 + w_{I_2}^2 + w_{Q_2}^2\Big] \\
&\times \Big[R_i(\tau) + R_n(\tau)\Big] + \Big[w_{I_1}w_{I_2} + w_{Q_1}w_{Q_2}\Big] \\
&\times \Big[R_i(\tau - T_i) + R_i(\tau + T_i)\Big] + \Big[w_{I_1}w_{Q_2} - w_{I_2}w_{Q_1}\Big] \\
&\times \Big[\hat{R}_i(\tau - T_i) - \hat{R}_i(\tau + T_i)\Big], \tag{4.256}
\end{aligned}$$

where we have made use of the Hilbert transform relations in Eqs. (2.72), (2.73), and (3.47). In order to calculate the power spectral density of $\varepsilon_0(t)$,

$$S_{\varepsilon_0}(\omega) = \int_{-\infty}^{\infty} R_{\varepsilon_0}(\tau)e^{-j\omega\tau}\,d\tau, \tag{4.257}$$

we need to obtain Fourier transforms of terms of the form $\hat{R}(\tau)$. The transform of such terms may be obtained from the properties of the Hilbert transform. Since $\hat{R}(\tau)$ can be obtained by passing $R(\tau)$ through a linear filter with transfer function

$$H(\omega) = \begin{cases} -j, & \omega > 0, \\ +j, & \omega < 0, \end{cases} \tag{4.258}$$

it follows that in the frequency domain,

$$\mathscr{F}\left[\hat{R}(\tau)\right] = H(\omega)\mathscr{F}\left[R(\tau)\right]. \tag{4.259}$$

Using this result, and also using standard shifting theorems from Fourier analysis, we find

$$\begin{aligned}
S_{\varepsilon_0}(\omega) = &\left\{\left[1 - 2w_{I_1} + w_{I_1}^2 + w_{Q_1}^2 + w_{I_2}^2 + w_{Q_2}^2\right]\right.\\
&+ \left[-w_{I_2} + w_{I_1}w_{I_2} + w_{Q_1}w_{Q_2}\right]\left[2\cos\omega T_d\right]\\
&+ \left.\left[-w_{Q_2} + w_{I_1}w_{Q_2} - w_{Q_1}w_{I_2}\right]\left[-2\sin|\omega T_d|\right]\right\}S_d(\omega)\\
&+ \left\{\left[w_{I_1}^2 + w_{Q_1}^2 + w_{I_2}^2 + w_{Q_2}^2\right] + \left[w_{I_1}w_{I_2} + w_{Q_1}w_{Q_2}\right]\left[2\cos\omega T_i\right]\right.\\
&+ \left.\left[w_{I_1}w_{Q_2} - w_{Q_1}w_{I_2}\right]\left[-2\sin|\omega T_i|\right]\right\}S_i(\omega)\\
&+ \left\{w_{I_1}^2 + w_{Q_1}^2 + w_{I_2}^2 + w_{Q_2}^2\right\}S_n(\omega). \tag{4.260}
\end{aligned}$$

In a similar way, we may find the spectral densities associated with the other two expectations in Eq. (4.245). First,

$$\begin{aligned}
E\left[\varepsilon_0(t)x_{I_2}(t+\tau)\right] &= R_{\varepsilon_0 x_{I_2}}(\tau)\\
&= R_d(\tau - T_d) - w_{I_1}\left[R_d(\tau - T_d) + R_i(\tau - T_i)\right]\\
&\quad - w_{Q_1}\left[-\hat{R}_d(\tau - T_d) - \hat{R}_i(\tau - T_i)\right]\\
&\quad - w_{I_2}\left[R_d(\tau) + R_i(\tau) + R_n(\tau)\right]\\
&\quad - w_{Q_2}\left[-\hat{R}_d(\tau) - \hat{R}_i(\tau)\right]. \tag{4.261}
\end{aligned}$$

The Fourier transform of this,

$$S_{\varepsilon_0 x_{I_2}}(\omega) = \int_{-\infty}^{\infty} R_{\varepsilon_0 x_{I_2}}(\tau)e^{-j\omega\tau}\,d\tau, \tag{4.262}$$

is

$$S_{\varepsilon_0 x_{I_2}}(\omega) = S_d(\omega) e^{-j\omega T_d} - w_{I_1}\left[S_d(\omega) e^{-j\omega T_d} + S_i(\omega) e^{-j\omega T_i} \right]$$

$$+ w_{Q_1} H(\omega)\left[S_d(\omega) e^{-j\omega T_d} + S_i(\omega) e^{-j\omega T_i} \right]$$

$$- w_{I_2}\left[S_d(\omega) + S_i(\omega) + S_n(\omega) \right]$$

$$+ w_{Q_2} H(\omega)\left[S_d(\omega) + S_i(\omega) \right]. \qquad (4.263)$$

Finally, we have

$$E\left[x_{I_2}(t)\varepsilon_0(t + \tau) \right] = R_{x_{I_2}\varepsilon_0}(\tau)$$

$$= R_d(\tau + T_d) - w_{I_1}\left[R_d(\tau + T_d) + R_i(\tau + T_i) \right]$$

$$- w_{Q_1}\left[\hat{R}_d(\tau + T_d) + \hat{R}_i(\tau + T_i) \right]$$

$$- w_{I_2}\left[R_d(\tau) + R_i(\tau) + R_n(\tau) \right]$$

$$- w_{Q_2}\left[\hat{R}_d(\tau) + \hat{R}_i(\tau) \right], \qquad (4.264)$$

whose Fourier transform is

$$S_{x_{I_2}\varepsilon_0}(\omega) = \int_{-\infty}^{\infty} R_{x_{I_2}\varepsilon_0}(\tau) e^{-j\omega\tau}\, d\tau$$

$$= S_d(\omega) e^{+j\omega T_d} - w_{I_1}\left[S_d(\omega) e^{+j\omega T_d} + S_i(\omega) e^{+j\omega T_i} \right]$$

$$- w_{Q_1} H(\omega)\left[S_d(\omega) e^{+j\omega T_d} + S_i(\omega) e^{+j\omega T_i} \right]$$

$$- w_{I_2}\left[S_d(\omega) + S_i(\omega) + S_n(\omega) \right] - w_{Q_2} H(\omega)\left[S_d(\omega) + S_i(\omega) \right]. $$
$$(4.265)$$

Returning to Eq. (4.245), we now have

$$R_{g_{I_2}}(\tau) = 4 R_{\varepsilon_0}(\tau) R_{x_{I_2}}(\tau) + 4 R_{\varepsilon_0 x_{I_2}}(\tau) R_{x_{I_2}\varepsilon_0}(\tau), \qquad (4.266)$$

where $R_{\varepsilon_0}(\tau)$, $R_{x_{I_2}}(\tau)$, $R_{\varepsilon_0 x_{I_2}}(\tau)$, and $R_{x_{I_2}\varepsilon_0}(\tau)$ are defined in Eqs. (4.250), (4.256), (4.261), and (4.264), respectively. The spectral density of $g_{I_2}(t)$ is given by the Fourier transform of Eq. (4.266),

$$S_{g_{I_2}}(\omega) = \int_{-\infty}^{\infty} R_{g_{I_2}}(\tau) e^{-j\omega\tau}\, d\tau$$

$$= \frac{2}{\pi}\int_{-\infty}^{\infty} S_{\varepsilon_0}(\xi) S_{x_{I_2}}(\omega - \xi)\, d\xi + \frac{2}{\pi}\int_{-\infty}^{\infty} S_{\varepsilon_0 x_{I_2}}(\xi) S_{x_{I_2}\varepsilon_0}(\omega - \xi)\, d\xi.$$
$$(4.267)$$

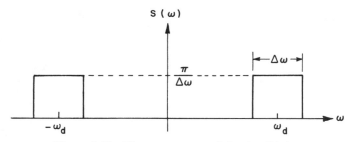

Figure 4.45 The power spectral density $S(\omega)$.

Before these convolution integrals can be carried out, it is necessary to specify the power spectral densities $S_d(\omega)$, $S_i(\omega)$, and $S_n(\omega)$. Different densities can be assumed, of course, depending on what problem is of interest. To illustrate the technique, we shall assume here that each of the signals $d(t)$, $i(t)$, and $n_{p_j}(t)$ has a flat, bandlimited power spectral density of bandwidth $\Delta\omega$. Specifically, let $S(\omega)$ be a normalized power spectral density as shown in Fig. 4.45. [The height of $S(\omega)$ has been chosen so the total power under $S(\omega)$, $(1/2\pi)\int_{-\infty}^{\infty} S(\omega)\, d\omega$, is unity.] Then we assume

$$S_d(\omega) = \frac{p_d}{2} S(\omega), \tag{4.268}$$

$$S_i(\omega) = \frac{p_i}{2} S(\omega), \tag{4.269}$$

and

$$S_n(\omega) = \frac{\sigma^2}{2} S(\omega), \tag{4.270}$$

where p_d, p_i, and σ^2 are the received desired signal, interference, and thermal noise powers per element. (The factor of $\frac{1}{2}$ is included because the power on each quadrature channel is half the element power.) Then we have

$$S_{\varepsilon_0}(\omega) = \kappa_{\varepsilon_0} S(\omega), \tag{4.271}$$

$$S_{x_{I_2}}(\omega) = \kappa_{x_{I_2}} S(\omega), \tag{4.272}$$

$$S_{\varepsilon_0 x_{I_2}}(\omega) = \kappa_{\varepsilon_0 x_{I_2}} S(\omega), \tag{4.273}$$

and

$$S_{x_{I_2}\varepsilon_0}(\omega) = \kappa_{x_{I_2}\varepsilon_0} S(\omega), \tag{4.274}$$

where

$$\kappa_{\varepsilon_0} = \left\{ \left[1 - 2w_{I_1} + w_{I_1}^2 + w_{Q_1}^2 + w_{I_2}^2 + w_{Q_2}^2 \right] + \left[-w_{I_2} + w_{I_1}w_{I_2} + w_{Q_1}w_{Q_2} \right] \right.$$

$$\times \left[2\cos\omega T_d \right] + \left[-w_{Q_2} + w_{I_1}w_{Q_2} - w_{Q_1}w_{I_2} \right] \left[-2\sin|\omega T_d| \right] \left\} \frac{P_d}{2} \right.$$

$$+ \left\{ \left[w_{I_1}^2 + w_{Q_1}^2 + w_{I_2}^2 + w_{Q_2}^2 \right] + \left[w_{I_1}w_{I_2} + w_{Q_1}w_{Q_2} \right] \left[2\cos\omega T_i \right] \right.$$

$$+ \left[w_{I_1}w_{Q_2} - w_{Q_1}w_{I_2} \right] \left[-2\sin|\omega T_i| \right] \left\} \frac{P_i}{2} \right.$$

$$+ \left\{ w_{I_1}^2 + w_{Q_1}^2 + w_{I_2}^2 + w_{Q_2}^2 \right\} \frac{\sigma^2}{2},$$

$$(4.275)$$

$$\kappa_{x_{I_2}} = \tfrac{1}{2} \left(p_d + p_i + \sigma^2 \right),$$

$$(4.276)$$

$$\kappa_{\varepsilon_0 x_{I_2}} = \frac{P_d}{2} e^{-j\omega T_d} - w_{I_1} \left[\frac{P_d}{2} e^{-j\omega T_d} + \frac{P_i}{2} e^{-j\omega T_i} \right]$$

$$+ w_{Q_1} H(\omega) \left[\frac{P_d}{2} e^{-j\omega T_d} + \frac{P_i}{2} e^{-j\omega T_i} \right]$$

$$- w_{I_2} \left[\frac{P_d}{2} + \frac{P_i}{2} + \frac{\sigma^2}{2} \right] + w_{Q_2} H(\omega) \left[\frac{P_d}{2} + \frac{P_i}{2} \right],$$

$$(4.277)$$

and

$$\kappa_{x_{I_2}\varepsilon_0} = \kappa_{\varepsilon_0 x_{I_2}}^*.$$

$$(4.278)$$

Now we will make the further assumption that the bandwidth of the signals $\Delta\omega$ is small enough that the factors $\kappa_{x_{I_2}}$, κ_{ε_0}, $\kappa_{\varepsilon_0 x_{I_2}}$, and $\kappa_{x_{I_2}\varepsilon_0}$ are essentially constant over the frequencies where $S(\omega) \neq 0$. (This condition is the same as assuming that the interelement propagation delays are negligible for the signal modulations.) In this case, the convolutions in Eq. (4.267) are easily done. The result is

$$S_{g_{I_2}}(\omega) = \kappa S_0(\omega),$$

$$(4.279)$$

where $S_0(\omega)$ is the power spectral density given by

$$S_0(\omega) = \frac{1}{2\pi} \int_{-\infty}^{\infty} S(\xi) S(\omega - \xi) \, d\xi,$$

$$(4.280)$$

and shown in Fig. 4.46, and

$$\kappa = 4 \left[\kappa_{\varepsilon_0} \kappa_{x_{I_2}} + \kappa_{\varepsilon_0 x_{I_2}} \kappa_{x_{I_2}\varepsilon_0} \right].$$

$$(4.281)$$

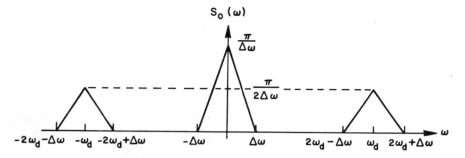

Figure 4.46　The power spectral density $S_0(\omega)$.

Note that $S_0(\omega)$ is also normalized:

$$\frac{1}{2\pi}\int_{-\infty}^{\infty} S_0(\omega)\,d\omega = 1. \tag{4.282}$$

Thus the power spectral density of $g_{I_2}(t)$ has the same shape as $S_0(\omega)$.

Now consider the spectral density of $g'_{r_j}(t)$. Since

$$\mathbf{G}'_r = \mathbf{R}^T_r \mathbf{G}_r, \tag{4.283}$$

each component $g'_{r_j}(t)$ of $\mathbf{G}'_r$ is a linear combination of the various $g_{p_j}(t)$. However, a linear combination of the $g_{p_j}(t)$ will have a power spectral density of the same shape as $S_0(\omega)$ above. To see this, suppose

$$\mathbf{R}^T_r = \begin{bmatrix} r'_{11} & r'_{12} & \cdots & r'_{1,2N} \\ r'_{21} & r'_{22} & \cdots & r'_{2,2N} \\ \vdots & & & \\ r'_{2N,1} & r'_{2N,2} & \cdots & r'_{2N,2N} \end{bmatrix} \tag{4.284}$$

and consider, for example, $g'_{r_1}(t)$,

$$g'_{r_1}(t) = r'_{11}g_{I_1}(t) + r'_{12}g_{Q_1}(t) + \cdots + r'_{1,2N}g_{Q_N}(t). \tag{4.285}$$

The autocorrelation function of $g'_{r_1}(t)$ is

$$
\begin{aligned}
R_{g'_{r_1}}(t) &= E\big[g'_{r_1}(t)g'_{r_1}(t+\tau)\big] \\
&= E\big\{\big[r'_{11}g_{I_1}(t) + \cdots + r'_{1,2N}g_{Q_N}(t)\big] \\
&\quad \times \big[r'_{11}g_{I_1}(t+\tau) + \cdots + r'_{1,2N}g_{Q_N}(t+\tau)\big]\big\} \\
&= (r'_{11})^2 E\big[g_{I_1}(t)g_{I_1}(t+\tau)\big] + r'_{12}r'_{11}E\big[g_{I_1}(t)g_{Q_1}(t+\tau)\big] \\
&\quad + r'_{12}r'_{11}E\big[g_{Q_1}(t)g_{I_1}(t+\tau)\big] + \cdots.
\end{aligned}
\tag{4.286}
$$

However, every one of the expectations in this expression is similar to that in

Eq. (4.244). For example,

$$E\left[g_{I_1}(t)g_{Q_1}(t+\tau)\right] = 4E\left\{\varepsilon_0(t)x_{I_1}(t)\varepsilon_0(t+\tau)x_{Q_1}(t+\tau)\right\}, \quad (4.287)$$

which can be expanded as in Eq. (4.245). When Eqs. (4.246) through (4.249) are then substituted for the $x_{P_1}(t)$, one finds that Eq. (4.287) has a Fourier transform with the same spectral shape as in Eq. (4.279).

Thus the power spectral density of each $g'_{r_j}(t)$ has the shape of $S_0(\omega)$ in Fig. 4.46. Moreover, in Eq. (4.242) we found that the variance in each $g'_{r_j}(t)$ is $4\varepsilon_{\min}^2\lambda_{r_j}$. It follows that the power spectral density of $g'_{r_j}(t)$, $S_{g'_{r_j}}(\omega)$, is

$$S'_{g_{r_j}}(\omega) = 4\varepsilon_{\min}^2\lambda_{r_j}S_0(\omega), \quad (4.288)$$

since, as noted in Eq. (4.282), $S_0(\omega)$ has a normalized amplitude.

Now that we have found $S'_{g_{r_j}}(\omega)$, we can apply Eq. (4.237) to determine $S'_{z_{r_j}}(\omega)$, the power spectral density of $z'_{r_j}(t)$. We have

$$S'_{z_{r_j}}(\omega) = |H_j(\omega)|^2 S'_{g_{r_j}}(\omega) = \frac{k^2}{\omega^2 + 4k^2\lambda_{r_j}^2} S'_{g_{r_j}}(\omega). \quad (4.289)$$

The variance of z'_{r_j} is then given by

$$\sigma_{z'_{r_j}}^2 = \frac{1}{2\pi}\int_{-\infty}^{\infty} S'_{z_{r_j}}(\omega)\,d\omega = \frac{1}{2\pi}\int_{-\infty}^{\infty} \frac{4k^2\varepsilon_{\min}^2\lambda_{r_j}}{\omega^2 + 4k^2\lambda_{r_j}^2} S_0(\omega)\,d\omega. \quad (4.290)$$

We can evaluate this integral easily if we make some simplifying assumptions. The most important case to consider in practice is the case where the bandwidth $\Delta\omega$ is small enough not to degrade array performance [as we assumed already in Eq. (4.279)] but still not zero [so the signals do carry modulation]. For this case, we then assume in addition that the feedback loop cutoff frequency ω_{co} associated with each eigenvalue λ_{r_j} is very small compared to the signal bandwidth,

$$\omega_{co} = 2k\lambda_{r_j} \ll \Delta\omega \quad \text{for all } j. \quad (4.291)$$

This assumption is necessary because in practice we must keep the array weights too slow to interact with the desired signal modulation. We do this by choosing the loop gain k small enough to satisfy Eq. (4.291) for the largest signal power of interest. (As we shall discuss in the next section, the eigenvalues are directly proportional to the signal powers.) Under these assumptions, the bandwidth of $|H_j(\omega)|^2$ is very small compared to that of $S_0(\omega)$, and Eq. (4.289) can be approximated by using for $S_0(\omega)$ its value at $\omega = 0$:

$$\sigma_{z'_{r_j}}^2 = \frac{2k^2\varepsilon_{\min}^2\lambda_{r_j}}{\Delta\omega}\int_{-\infty}^{\infty} \frac{d\omega}{\omega^2 + 4k^2\lambda_{r_j}^2} = \frac{\pi k\varepsilon_{\min}^2}{\Delta\omega}. \quad (4.292)$$

This result is interesting because it shows that the variance of every $z'_{r_j}(t)$ is the same. Since we found previously that the $z'_{r_j}(t)$ are uncorrelated, we therefore have

$$E\left[\mathbf{Z}'_r\mathbf{Z}'^T_r\right] = \frac{\pi k \varepsilon^2_{\min}}{\Delta\omega}\mathbf{I}, \tag{4.293}$$

where $\mathbf{I}$ is the identity matrix. Finally, transforming back to $\mathbf{Z}_r$ with Eq. (4.231), we find that the covariance matrix of $\mathbf{Z}_r$ is

$$E\left[\mathbf{Z}_r\mathbf{Z}^T_r\right] = \mathbf{R}_r E\left[\mathbf{Z}'_r\mathbf{Z}'^T_r\right]\mathbf{R}^T_r = \frac{\pi k \varepsilon^2_{\min}}{\Delta\omega}\mathbf{I}. \tag{4.294}$$

Thus the weight jitter components $z_{P_j}(t)$ are also uncorrelated and have equal variance,

$$\sigma^2_{z_{P_j}} = \frac{\pi k \varepsilon^2_{\min}}{\Delta\omega}. \tag{4.295}$$

This is the weight variance, the result we set out to obtain. It remains only to compute values of $\sigma^2_{z_{P_j}}$ for typical situations.

Note that the weight variance is proportional to the loop gain k and inversely proportional to the signal bandwidth $\Delta\omega$. The reason for this is as follows: Increasing k increases the feedback loop bandwidth and hence allows more noise power to pass through into the weight. Reducing $\Delta\omega$ also causes more noise power to fall within the feedback loop passband, because the signals have been assumed to have a fixed power, so a smaller signal bandwidth implies a higher power density within that bandwidth.

Note also that in interpreting Eq. (4.295) one must remember that k and $\Delta\omega$ are not independent. For example, one cannot infer from Eq. (4.295) that letting $\Delta\omega$ approach zero will make the variance become infinite. The reason is that if $\Delta\omega$ is reduced, k must also be reduced to satisfy Eq. (4.291). If the signal bandwidth is zero but k is not zero, Eq. (4.195) is not the correct approximation to Eq. (4.238).[‡]

Numerical Results

Now let us compute $\sigma^2_{z_{P_j}}$ for a typical situation to see how weight variance depends on signal powers and arrival angles. Specifically, suppose our two-element array (with half-wavelength spacing) receives a narrowband desired signal and a narrowband interference signal. We can obtain results for this problem immediately from our earlier examples in Chapters 2 and 3 by using complex

‡Equation (4.295) was based on the assumption that the thermal noise has the same bandwidth as the signals [see Eqs. (4.268) through (4.270)]. If we wish to determine weight jitter with zero bandwidth signals, we must still keep the thermal noise bandwidth nonzero to have a meaningful problem.

notation to compute ε^2_{min}. In general, for arbitrary weights,

$$E[\varepsilon^2(t)] = \tfrac{1}{2}E[|\tilde{\varepsilon}(t)|^2] = \tfrac{1}{2}\{E[|\tilde{r}(t)|^2] - \mathbf{W}^\dagger\mathbf{S} - \mathbf{S}^\dagger\mathbf{W} + \mathbf{W}^\dagger\mathbf{\Phi}\mathbf{W}\},$$

(4.296)

where $\tilde{r}(t)$, $\mathbf{S}$, and $\mathbf{\Phi}$ are defined in Eqs. (3.75), (3.77) (with $\eta = 0$), and (3.94). Substituting

$$\mathbf{W} = \mathbf{W}_{opt} = \mathbf{\Phi}^{-1}\mathbf{S}$$

(4.297)

in this equation yields

$$\varepsilon^2_{min} = \tfrac{1}{2}\{E[|\tilde{r}(t)|^2] - \mathbf{S}^\dagger\mathbf{W}_{opt}\}.$$

(4.298)

If we assume the signal bandwidths are small enough that the $\text{sinc}(x)$ functions in $\mathbf{S}$ and $\mathbf{\Phi}$ are essentially unity, we can then approximate $\mathbf{\Phi}$ and $\mathbf{S}$ by their CW values, which are given in Chapter 2.

Suppose first the array receives only desired signal. Then from Eq. (2.104) we have

$$E[|\tilde{r}(t)|^2] = R^2,$$

(4.299)

and from Eqs. (2.113), (2.119), and (2.124),

$$\mathbf{S} = A_d R \mathbf{U}_d^*$$

(4.300)

and

$$\mathbf{W}_{opt} = \frac{A_d R}{2A_d^2 + \sigma^2}\mathbf{U}_d^*.$$

(4.301)

Hence

$$\varepsilon^2_{min} = \tfrac{1}{2}\left[R^2 - 2\frac{A_d^2 R^2}{2A_d^2 + \sigma^2}\right]$$

$$= \frac{P_r}{1 + 2\xi_d},$$

(4.302)

where $P_r = R^2/2$ is the reference signal power and $\xi_d = A_d^2/\sigma^2$ is the input SNR per element. Then Eq. (4.295) yields

$$\sigma^2_{z_{P_j}} = \frac{\pi k P_r}{\Delta\omega}\kappa(\xi_d),$$

(4.303)

where $\kappa(\xi_d)$ is

$$\kappa(\xi_d) = \frac{1}{1 + 2\xi_d}.$$

(4.304)

Figure 4.47 shows a plot of $\kappa(\xi_d)$ as a function of ξ_d. It is seen that $\kappa(\xi_d)$ and hence $\sigma^2_{z_{P_j}}$ drops as ξ_d rises. The reason for this is easy to see. As ξ_d increases,

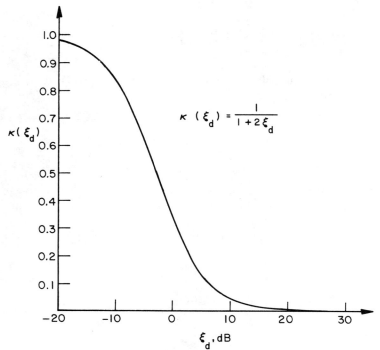

Figure 4.47 $\kappa(\xi_d)$ versus ξ_d.

the weights become smaller to keep the array output matched to the fixed amplitude reference signal. As the weights drop, there is less noise in the array output, and so there is less weight jitter produced in the error-by-signal multipliers.

Now suppose the interference is added. With interference, $E[|\tilde{r}(t)|^2]$ and $\mathbf{S}$ are the same as before, but $\mathbf{W}_{\text{opt}}$ is now given by Eq. (2.189),

$$\mathbf{W}_{\text{opt}} = \frac{\sqrt{2\xi_d\xi_r}}{D/\sigma^4}\left[\begin{array}{c}\xi_i + 1 - \xi_i e^{j(\phi_d-\phi_i)}\\ \left[\xi_i + 1 - \xi_i e^{j(\phi_i-\phi_d)}\right]e^{j\phi_d}\end{array}\right] \qquad (4.305)$$

where D/σ^4 is given in Eq. (2.190),

$$\frac{D}{\sigma^4} = 4\xi_d\xi_i\sin^2\left(\frac{\phi_d - \phi_i}{2}\right) + 2\xi_d + 2\xi_i + 1. \qquad (4.306)$$

Thus we find

$$\mathbf{S}^\dagger\mathbf{W}_{\text{opt}} = \frac{2\xi_d R^2}{D/\sigma^4}\left[\xi_i + 1 - \xi_i\cos\left(\phi_d - \phi_i\right)\right] \qquad (4.307)$$

and

$$E\left[\left|\tilde{r}(t)^2\right|\right] - \mathbf{S}^{\dagger}\mathbf{W}_{\text{opt}} = R^2\left\{1 - \frac{2\xi_d}{D/\sigma^4}\left[1 + 2\xi_i\sin^2\left(\frac{\phi_d - \phi_i}{2}\right)\right]\right\}$$

$$= R^2 \frac{1 + 2\xi_i}{1 + 2\xi_i + 2\xi_d + 4\xi_d\xi_i\sin^2\left(\dfrac{\phi_d - \phi_i}{2}\right)}. \qquad (4.308)$$

Finally,

$$\sigma_{z_{P_j}}^2 = \frac{\pi k}{2\Delta\omega}\left\{E\left[\left|\tilde{r}(t)\right|^2\right] - \mathbf{S}^{\dagger}\mathbf{W}_{\text{opt}}\right\} = \frac{\pi k P_r}{\Delta\omega}\kappa(\xi_d, \xi_i), \qquad (4.309)$$

where

$$\kappa(\xi_d, \xi_i) = \frac{1 + 2\xi_i}{1 + 2\xi_i + 2\xi_d + 4\xi_d\xi_i\sin^2\left(\dfrac{\phi_d - \phi_i}{2}\right)}. \qquad (4.310)$$

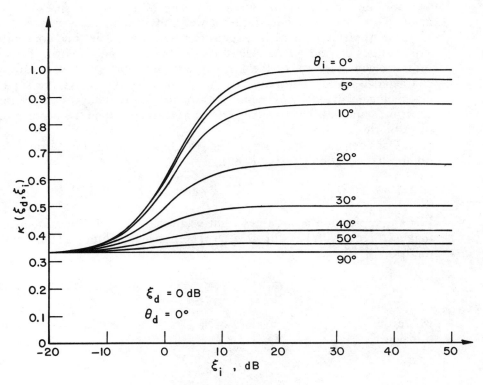

Figure 4.48 $\kappa(\xi_d, \xi_i)$ versus ξ_i.

To illustrate how $\sigma_{z_{P_j}}^2$ depends on the signal parameters, $\kappa(\xi_d, \xi_i)$ is plotted in Fig. 4.48 versus ξ_i for various θ_i and for the case $\xi_d = 0$ dB and $\theta_d = 0°$. Note that for a desired signal at $\theta_d = 0°$, the array pattern without interference would have a null at $\theta = 90°$. Hence interference at $\theta_i = 90°$ produces no change in the array weights and hence no change in the weight variance, as may be seen in the bottom curve in Fig. 4.48. However, as θ_i approaches θ_d, the weight variance grows. For a given θ_i, $\sigma_{z_{P_j}}^2$ increases with ξ_i, up to a maximum value at about $\xi_i = 20$ dB.

This concludes our study of weight jitter. Our purpose here has been to show how weight jitter may be computed and to present a numerical example. The method given assumes that the variance of the weights is small compared to the weights themselves. This assumption is usually satisfied in practice, since the array will produce too much desired signal modulation if this condition is not met.

4.6 EIGENVALUE BEHAVIOR

We now turn our attention to the problem of eigenvalue spread in adaptive arrays. We have seen that, during a weight transient, the weight vector in an LMS or Applebaum array is a sum of exponentials. The time constants of the exponentials depend on the eigenvalues of the covariance matrix. Thus changes in the eigenvalues cause the array speed of response to vary. In order to characterize speed of response variations in adaptive arrays, we shall discuss eigenvalue behavior in this section. In Chapter 5, we shall present several weight control techniques that have been developed to overcome the problem of speed of response variation.

Consider an LMS array. The weight vector in this array obeys the differential equation [see Eq. (2.86)],

$$\frac{d\mathbf{W}}{dt} + k\mathbf{\Phi W} = k\mathbf{S}. \tag{4.311}$$

For an Applebaum array, the weight vector satisfies the same equation except that $\mu\mathbf{T}^*$ replaces $\mathbf{S}$ [see Eq. (2.271)]. The transient solution of Eq. (4.311) is of the form

$$\mathbf{W}(t) = \sum_{j=1}^{N} \mathbf{C}_j e^{-k\lambda_j t} + \mathbf{\Phi}^{-1}\mathbf{S}, \tag{4.312}$$

where the λ_j are the eigenvalues of $\mathbf{\Phi}$. The time constant of jth term in this transient is

$$\tau_j = \frac{1}{k\lambda_j}. \tag{4.313}$$

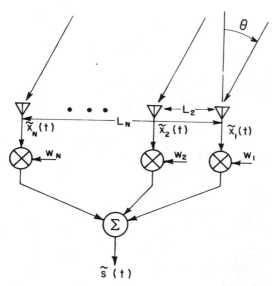

Figure 4.49   An N-element array.

Since the λ_j are the eigenvalues of $\boldsymbol{\Phi}$ and the elements of $\boldsymbol{\Phi}$ are products of the signals $\tilde{x}_j(t)$, it is clear that the eigenvalues depend on signal power. As we shall see, they also depend on the number of incident signals, the signal arrival angles, the signal bandwidths, the number of elements, the element spacings, and the element patterns.

We shall examine the eigenvalues first for CW signals and then for signals with nonzero bandwidth. This approach is useful because we can obtain the eigenvalues analytically for CW signals, whereas for nonzero bandwidth signals we must resort to numerical methods.

Eigenvalues with CW Signals

Consider an N-element array as shown in Fig. 4.49. Let the pattern of the jth element be $f_j(\theta, \phi, P)$. Suppose that the array receives a CW desired signal with parameters $(\theta_d, \phi_d, \alpha_d, \beta_d, P_d)$ and a CW interference signal with parameters $(\theta_i, \phi_i, \alpha_i, \beta_i, P_i)$. Also, assume that each element signal contains thermal noise of power σ^2, as usual. Then the covariance matrix is

$$\boldsymbol{\Phi} = \sigma^2 \mathbf{I} + A_d^2 \mathbf{U}_d^* \mathbf{U}_d^T + A_i^2 \mathbf{U}_i^* \mathbf{U}_i^T, \tag{4.314}$$

where

$$\mathbf{U}_d = \left[f_1(\theta_d, \phi_d, P_d), f_2(\theta_d, \phi_d, P_d)e^{-j\phi_{d2}}, \ldots, f_N(\theta_d, \phi_d, P_d)e^{-j\phi_{dN}} \right]^T \tag{4.315}$$

and

$$\mathbf{U}_i = \left[f_1(\theta_i, \phi_i, P_i), f_2(\theta_i, \phi_i, P_i)e^{-j\phi_{i2}}, \ldots, f_N(\theta_i, \phi_i, P_i)e^{-j\phi_{iN}} \right]^T. \tag{4.316}$$

It will be convenient to work with the normalized covariance matrix. Let

$$\Psi = \frac{1}{\sigma^2}\Phi = \mathbf{I} + \xi_d \mathbf{U}_d^* \mathbf{U}_d^T + \xi_i \mathbf{U}_i^* \mathbf{U}_i^T, \tag{4.317}$$

where $\xi_d = A_d^2/\sigma^2$ and $\xi_i = A_i^2/\sigma^2$ as usual. Let λ_j denote the jth eigenvalue of Φ and λ_j' the jth eigenvalue of Ψ. Then

$$\lambda_j = \sigma^2 \lambda_j', \qquad 1 \leqslant j \leqslant N. \tag{4.318}$$

In general, suppose λ_{max}' denotes the maximum eigenvalue and λ_{min}' the minimum eigenvalue of Ψ. We define the *eigenvalue spread S* to be the ratio

$$S = \frac{\lambda_{max}'}{\lambda_{min}'}. \tag{4.319}$$

Because of Eq. (4.313), S is also called the *time constant spread*.

Now let us consider the eigenvalues without the interference and with the interference.

Case 1. No interference When there is no interference, $\xi_i = 0$ and Ψ becomes

$$\Psi = \mathbf{I} + \xi_d \mathbf{U}_d^* \mathbf{U}_d^T. \tag{4.320}$$

By multiplying this matrix onto $\mathbf{U}_d^*$, we find that $\mathbf{U}_d^*$ is an eigenvector of Ψ with eigenvalue

$$\lambda_1' = 1 + \xi_d \mathbf{U}_d^T \mathbf{U}_d^* = 1 + \xi_d \sum_{j=1}^{N} \left| f_j(\theta_d, \phi_d, P_d) \right|^2. \tag{4.321}$$

Any other vector orthogonal to $\mathbf{U}_d^*$ is also an eigenvector, with eigenvalue unity. Since Ψ is of order $N \times N$, one can find $N - 1$ eigenvectors orthogonal to $\mathbf{U}_d^*$ and to each other, so there are $N - 1$ eigenvalues equal to unity,

$$\lambda_2', \lambda_3', \ldots, \lambda_N' = 1. \tag{4.322}$$

Because ξ_d is the input SNR, we shall say that the eigenvalue λ_1' is associated with the desired signal. The eigenvalues $\lambda_2', \lambda_3', \ldots, \lambda_N'$ are associated with the thermal noise. With only desired signal, the maximum eigenvalue is λ_1', and the minimum eigenvalue is unity. The eigenvalue spread is

$$S = \lambda_1' = 1 + \xi_d \mathbf{U}_d^T \mathbf{U}_d^* = 1 + \xi_d \sum_{j=1}^{N} \left| f_j(\theta_d, \phi_d, P_d) \right|^2. \tag{4.323}$$

Note that S depends on ξ_d, the signal arrival angle and polarization, and the element patterns, but not the element spacings. If the element patterns are isotropic, Eq. (4.323) reduces to

$$S = 1 + N\xi_d, \tag{4.324}$$

so S depends only on ξ_d.

Case 2. With interference   With both desired signal and interference present, the normalized covariance matrix is given by Eq. (4.314). The eigenvectors of this matrix may be found by noting that two of the eigenvectors must lie in the plane defined by $\mathbf{U}_d^*$ and $\mathbf{U}_i^*$. These two eigenvalues must have the form [14, 15]

$$\mathbf{e} = \alpha \mathbf{U}_d^* + \beta \mathbf{U}_i^*, \tag{4.325}$$

where α and β are constants to be determined by the requirement that

$$\mathbf{\Psi}\mathbf{e} = \lambda' \mathbf{e}, \tag{4.326}$$

where λ' is the corresponding eigenvalue. The constants α and β may be found by evaluating $\mathbf{\Psi}\mathbf{e}$ from Eqs. (4.317) and (4.325),

$$\mathbf{\Psi}(\alpha\mathbf{U}_d^* + \beta\mathbf{U}_i^*) = (\alpha\mathbf{U}_d^* + \beta\mathbf{U}_i^*) + \alpha\mathbf{U}_d^* \left(\xi_d\mathbf{U}_d^T\mathbf{U}_d^* + \frac{\beta}{\alpha}\xi_d\mathbf{U}_d^T\mathbf{U}_i^* \right)$$

$$+ \beta\mathbf{U}_i^* \left(\xi_i\mathbf{U}_i^T\mathbf{U}_i^* + \frac{\alpha}{\beta}\xi_i\mathbf{U}_i^T\mathbf{U}_d^* \right). \tag{4.327}$$

The vector $\mathbf{e}$ will be an eigenvalue if α and β are chosen so

$$\xi_d\mathbf{U}_d^T\mathbf{U}_d^* + \frac{\beta}{\alpha}\xi_d\mathbf{U}_d^T\mathbf{U}_i^* = \xi_i\mathbf{U}_i^T\mathbf{U}_i^* + \frac{\alpha}{\beta}\xi_i\mathbf{U}_i^T\mathbf{U}_d^*. \tag{4.328}$$

Therefore, from Eqs. (4.325) through (4.327), we have

$$\lambda' = 1 + \xi_d\mathbf{U}_d^T\mathbf{U}_d^* + \frac{\beta}{\alpha}\xi_d\mathbf{U}_d^T\mathbf{U}_i^*, \tag{4.329}$$

or equivalently

$$\lambda' = 1 + \xi_i\mathbf{U}_i^T\mathbf{U}_i^* + \frac{\alpha}{\beta}\xi_i\mathbf{U}_i^T\mathbf{U}_d^*. \tag{4.330}$$

By defining

$$Y = \frac{\beta}{\alpha} \tag{4.331}$$

and then transforming Eq. (4.328) into a quadratic equation, we find that

$$\xi_d\mathbf{U}_d^T\mathbf{U}_i^* Y^2 - \left(\xi_i\mathbf{U}_i^T\mathbf{U}_i^* - \xi_d\mathbf{U}_d^T\mathbf{U}_d^* \right) Y - \xi_i\mathbf{U}_i^T\mathbf{U}_d^* = 0. \tag{4.332}$$

This quadratic equation has the two solutions

$$Y_1 = \frac{1}{2\xi_d\mathbf{U}_d^T\mathbf{U}_i^*}(a + b) \tag{4.333}$$

and

$$Y_2 = \frac{1}{2\xi_d\mathbf{U}_d^T\mathbf{U}_i^*}(a - b), \tag{4.334}$$

where

$$a = \xi_i \mathbf{U}_i^T \mathbf{U}_i^* - \xi_d \mathbf{U}_d^T \mathbf{U}_d^* \qquad (4.335)$$

and

$$b = \left[a^2 + 4\xi_d \xi_i \left| \mathbf{U}_i^T \mathbf{U}_d^* \right|^2 \right]^{1/2}. \qquad (4.336)$$

From Eq. (4.329), the two eigenvalues are then

$$\lambda_1' = 1 + \xi_d \mathbf{U}_d^T \mathbf{U}_d^* + \tfrac{1}{2}(a + b) \qquad (4.337)$$

and

$$\lambda_2' = 1 + \xi_d \mathbf{U}_d^T \mathbf{U}_d^* + \tfrac{1}{2}(a - b). \qquad (4.338)$$

The remaining $N - 2$ eigenvalues are unity, because any vector $\mathbf{V}^*$ orthogonal to both $\mathbf{U}_d^*$ and $\mathbf{U}_i^*$ satisfies

$$\boldsymbol{\Psi} \mathbf{V}^* = \mathbf{V}^*. \qquad (4.339)$$

Hence such a $\mathbf{V}^*$ is an eigenvector with eigenvalue unity. Since $\boldsymbol{\Psi}$ is an $N \times N$ matrix, one can find $N - 2$ vectors orthogonal to $\mathbf{U}_d^*$ and $\mathbf{U}_i^*$ and to each other. Hence, the remaining eigenvalues associated with these eigenvectors are all unity.

Now let us make some general observations about these eigenvalues. First, we note that the eigenvalues are all real, of course, because $\boldsymbol{\Psi}$ is a Hermitian matrix. Next, we note that

$$\lambda_j' \geq 1, \qquad 1 \leq j \leq N. \qquad (4.340)$$

Equation (4.340) follows from the fact that $\xi_d \mathbf{U}_d^* \mathbf{U}_d^T$ and $\xi_i \mathbf{U}_i^* \mathbf{U}_i^T$ are both nonnegative definite matrices, so their sum is nonnegative definite. Consider $\xi_d \mathbf{U}_d^* \mathbf{U}_d^T$, for example. This matrix has rank 1, because its eigenvectors are $\mathbf{U}_d^*$, with eigenvalue $\xi_d \mathbf{U}_d^T \mathbf{U}_d^*$, and all vectors orthogonal to $\mathbf{U}_d^*$, with eigenvalue zero. Thus its only nonzero eigenvalue is $\xi_d \mathbf{U}_d^T \mathbf{U}_d^*$, which cannot be negative.

In addition, we observe that the sum of the λ_j' is

$$\sum_{j=1}^{N} \lambda_j' = N + \xi_d \mathbf{U}_d^T \mathbf{U}_d^* + \xi_i \mathbf{U}_i^T \mathbf{U}_i^*. \qquad (4.341)$$

This relation follows immediately from Eq. (4.317) and the fact that the trace of a matrix is invariant under a unitary transformation [16]. Thus the sum of the eigenvalues λ_j of $\boldsymbol{\Phi}$ in Eq. (4.314) is equal to the total power received on all the array elements. Equation (4.341) expresses the same result, except with all terms normalized to σ^2.

Finally, we note that the number of eigenvalues different from unity equals the number of signals incident on the array. We saw that with one CW signal incident (the desired signal), Ψ has one eigenvalue different from unity. With two CW signals (the desired signal and the interference), Ψ has two eigenvalues different from unity. It is clear from the method of analysis above that when several CW signals are incident, the number of eigenvalues different from unity will equal the number of signals received.[‡] For example, if three signals are incident, there will be three eigenvectors in the hyperplane defined by the three signal vectors. The remaining $N - 3$ eigenvectors perpendicular to this hyperplane will have unity eigenvalues.

Now let us examine the behavior of the eigenvalues when a desired signal and interference are present. The case of most interest is the case when the interference is much stronger than the desired signal. Suppose $\xi_i \gg \xi_d$ and suppose also that for the θ_d, ϕ_d, P_d and θ_i, ϕ_i, P_i of interest, we have[‡‡]

$$\xi_i \mathbf{U}_i^T \mathbf{U}_i^* \gg \xi_d \mathbf{U}_d^T \mathbf{U}_d^* > 1. \tag{4.342}$$

Under this condition we may approximate λ_1' and λ_2' as follows. We write Eq. (4.336) in the form

$$b = a\left[1 + \frac{4\xi_i\xi_d}{a^2}|\mathbf{U}_i^T\mathbf{U}_d^*|^2\right]^{1/2}. \tag{4.343}$$

Using the approximation $(1 + x)^{1/2} = 1 + x/2$, valid for small x, we have

$$b \simeq a + \frac{2\xi_i\xi_d}{a}|\mathbf{U}_i^T\mathbf{U}_d^*|^2 \simeq a + 2\xi_d\frac{|\mathbf{U}_i^T\mathbf{U}_d^*|^2}{\mathbf{U}_i^T\mathbf{U}_i^*}. \tag{4.344}$$

Substituting Eq. (4.335) and this equation into Eqs. (4.337) and (4.338) gives

$$\lambda_1' \simeq 1 + \xi_i\mathbf{U}_i^T\mathbf{U}_i^* + \xi_d\frac{|\mathbf{U}_i^T\mathbf{U}_d^*|^2}{\mathbf{U}_i^T\mathbf{U}_i^*} \simeq 1 + \xi_i\mathbf{U}_i^T\mathbf{U}_i^* \tag{4.345}$$

and

$$\lambda_2' = 1 + \xi_d\left[\mathbf{U}_d^T\mathbf{U}_d^* - \frac{|\mathbf{U}_i^T\mathbf{U}_d^*|^2}{\mathbf{U}_i^T\mathbf{U}_i^*}\right]. \tag{4.346}$$

We see that λ_1' is the largest eigenvalue and is associated with the interference. The middle eigenvalue, λ_2', is associated with the desired signal. The other eigenvalues $\lambda_3', \ldots, \lambda_N'$ are unity and are associated with the thermal noise.

Suppose the element patterns are isotropic. Equations (4.345) and (4.346) then become

$$\lambda_1' \simeq 1 + N\xi_i + (\xi_d/N)|\mathbf{U}_i^T\mathbf{U}_d^*|^2 \tag{4.347}$$

[‡]This statement assumes that all incoming signals produce linearly independent signal vectors. If some of the signal vectors are linearly dependent, the number of nonunity eigenvalues is reduced. Linearly dependent signal vectors occur in grating null situations, as described in section 3.3.

[‡‡]This inequality is necessary to avoid pathological cases, such as when all element patterns have a null in the interference direction.

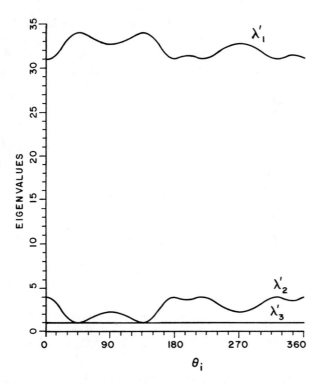

Figure 4.50   Eigenvalues versus θ_i: $N = 3$, $\xi_d = 0$ dB, $\xi_i = 10$ dB, $B_d = 0$, $B_i = 0$, $\theta_d = 45°$, half-wavelength spacing, isotropic elements.

and

$$\lambda'_2 \simeq 1 + N\xi_d - (\xi_d/N)|U_i^T U_d^*|^2. \tag{4.348}$$

Since $\lambda'_3, \ldots, \lambda'_N$ are unity, Eq. (4.341) gives

$$\sum_{j=1}^{N} \lambda'_j = N(1 + \xi_d + \xi_i). \tag{4.349}$$

To see how λ'_1 and λ'_2 vary, let us consider a specific case. Suppose the array elements are uniformly spaced along a line with half-wavelength element spacing. Let θ_d and θ_i denote the signal arrival angles relative to broadside. Then

$$|U_i^T U_d^*|^2 = |1 + e^{j(\phi_d - \phi_i)} + e^{j2(\phi_d - \phi_i)} + \cdots + e^{j(N-1)(\phi_d - \phi_i)}|^2, \tag{4.350}$$

where

$$\phi_p = \pi \sin \theta_p, \tag{4.351}$$

with $p = d$ or i. Figure 4.50 shows how the eigenvalues vary as a function of θ_i for the case $N = 3$, $\theta_d = 45°$, $\xi_d = 0$ dB, and $\xi_i = 10$ dB.[‡]

     [‡]The curves presented in this section are taken from Suen [17].

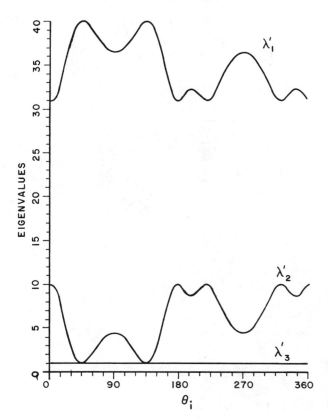

Figure 4.51 Eigenvalues versus θ_i: $N = 3$, $\xi_d = 4.77$ dB, $\xi_i = 10$ dB, $B_d = 0$, $B_i = 0$, $\theta_d = 45°$, half-wavelength spacing, isotropic elements.

Figure 4.50 illustrates several features of eigenvalue behavior. First, it is seen that λ_1' and λ_2' vary in such a way that their sum is a constant [as required by Eq. (4.349)]. Second, we see how λ_1', the eigenvalue associated with the interference, is the largest eigenvalue. The eigenvalue associated with the desired signal, λ_2', is the middle eigenvalue, and λ_3' is always unity. Third, we note from Eq. (4.350) that for a three-element array, $|\mathbf{U}_i^T \mathbf{U}_d^*|^2$ can range from 0 to 9. Hence, as may be seen from Eq. (4.348), λ_2' is bounded by $1 \leqslant \lambda_2' \leqslant 4$. Fig. 4.50 shows how λ_2' oscillates between these bounds. The eigenvalue λ_1' also undergoes the same amount of variation (the sum of λ_1' and λ_2' is constant), but because λ_1' is larger than λ_2', its fractional variation is smaller. The eigenvalue with the largest fractional change is λ_2'.

Next, suppose that we increase the SNR from 1 (0 dB) to 3 (4.77 dB). Figure 4.51 shows the eigenvalue variation for this case. Note that increasing ξ_d has increased the range of variation of both λ_1' and λ_2'.

Figures 4.50 and 4.51 are for $\xi_i = 10$ dB, a modest INR. To see how the eigenvalues depend on ξ_i, in Fig. 4.52 we show λ_1' versus θ_i for $\xi_i = 20$ dB, 30 dB, and 40 dB. As may be seen, the maximum eigenvalue is directly propor-

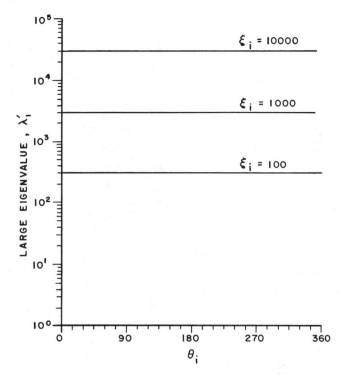

Figure 4.52 λ_1' versus θ_i for strong interference: $N = 3$, $\xi_d = 0$ dB, $B_d = 0$, $B_i = 0$, $\theta_d = 45°$, half-wavelength spacing, isotropic elements.

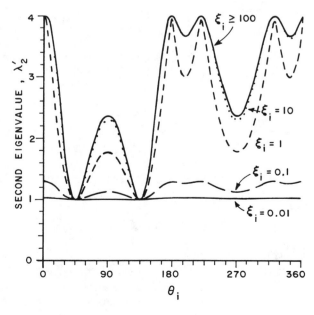

Figure 4.53 λ_2' versus θ_i for different ξ_i: $N = 3$, $\xi_d = 0$ dB, $B_d = 0$, $B_i = 0$, $\theta_d = 45°$, half-wavelength spacing, isotropic elements.

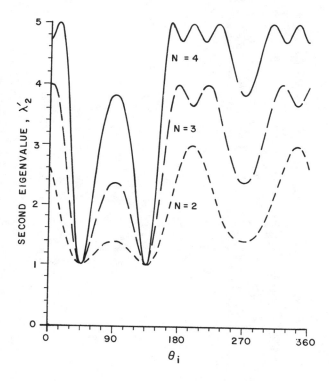

Figure 4.54 λ'_2 versus θ_i for several N: $\xi_d = 0$ dB, $\xi_i = 30$ dB, $B_d = 0$, $B_i = 0$, $\theta_d = 45°$, half-wavelength spacing, isotropic elements.

tional to ξ_i. Moreover, for these larger values of ξ_i, the variation in λ'_1 with θ_i is very small compared to λ'_1 itself.

The effect of ξ_i on λ'_2 may be seen in Fig. 4.53, which shows λ'_2 versus θ_i for values of ξ_i between 0.01 (-20 dB) and 100 ($+20$ dB). As ξ_i approaches 0, the middle eigenvalue λ'_2 becomes unity. {When $\xi_i = 0$, there is actually only one signal incident on the array. In this case the only eigenvalue different from unity is λ_1, which takes on the value $1 + 3\xi_d$ [see Eq. (4.324)]. When $\xi_i \to 0$, λ'_2 becomes one of the unity eigenvalues.}

It is clear from Eqs. (4.347) and (4.348) that increasing the number of elements N will increase both the values of λ'_1 and λ'_2 and the range over which they vary. (The quantity $|\mathbf{U}_i^T\mathbf{U}_d^*|^2$ takes on values between 0 and N^2.) Figure 4.54 shows the effect of N on the middle eigenvalue λ'_2.

Changing the spacing between elements has the effect of changing the rate at which the eigenvalues vary with signal arrival angle. Figure 4.55 shows a typical result. It shows the middle eigenvalue for a three-element array when the first two elements are separated by $L_2 = 0.3$ wavelengths and the first and third elements by L_3. In Fig. 4.55, L_3 is varied between 0.5 and 2 wavelengths.

The results in Figs. 4.50 to 4.55 are all for isotropic elements. When the elements are isotropic and $\xi_i \gg \xi_d$, the largest eigenvalue λ'_1 exhibits little variation with signal angles. When the elements are not isotropic, however, λ'_1 is

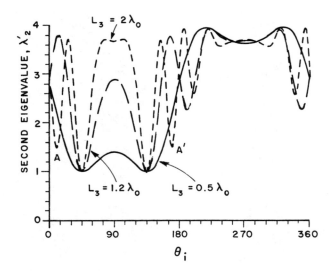

Figure 4.55 λ'_2 versus θ_i for different spacings: $L_2 = 0.5\lambda$, $N = 3$, $\xi_d = 0$ dB, $\xi_i = 30$ dB, $B_d = 0$, $B_i = 0$, $\theta_d = 45°$, isotropic elements.

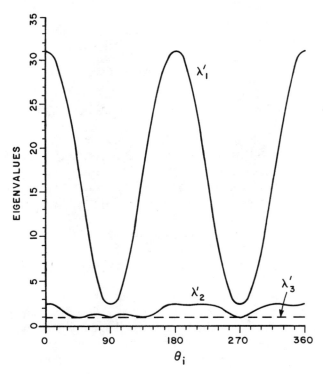

Figure 4.56 Eigenvalues versus θ_i for dipole elements: $N = 3$, $\xi_d = 0$ dB, $\xi_i = 10$ dB, $B_d = 0$, $B_i = 0$, $\theta_d = 45°$, $\alpha_1 = \alpha_2 = \alpha_3 = 0°$, half-wavelength spacing.

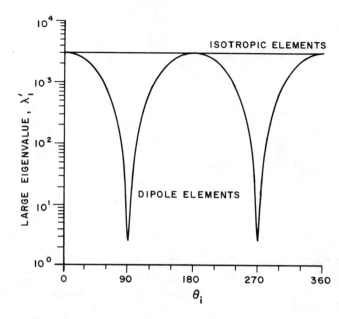

Figure 4.57 λ'_1 versus θ_i for isotropic and dipole elements: $N = 3$, $\xi_d = 0$ dB, $\xi_i = 30$ dB, $B_d = 0$, $B_i = 0$, $\theta_d = 45°$, $\alpha_1 = \alpha_2 = \alpha_3 = 0°$, half-wavelength spacing.

no longer constant. Also, the behavior of λ'_2 is changed. We shall use a three-element array of dipoles to illustrate these remarks.

Let us assume each element in the array is a short dipole with a cosine pattern.

$$f_j(\theta) = \cos(\theta - \alpha_j), \qquad 1 \leqslant j \leqslant 3. \qquad (4.352)$$

Suppose initially that all three elements have their maximum response at broadside, that is,

$$\alpha_j = 0, \qquad 1 \leqslant j \leqslant 3. \qquad (4.353)$$

Then Fig. 4.56 shows the resulting eigenvalues versus θ_i for the case $\xi_d = 0$ dB, $\xi_i = 10$ dB, and $\theta_d = 45°$. Comparing Fig. 4.56 with Fig. 4.50, we see that the most important difference is in the behavior of λ'_1, which has much greater variation than it did for isotropic elements. The reason is that the element patterns affect the amount of interference power received by the array. At $\theta_i = 0°$ or $180°$, the array receives maximum interference power, but at $\theta_i = 90°$ the interference is not seen by the array because it is in a null for every element. At $\theta_i = 90°$, λ'_1 becomes the eigenvalue due to the desired signal and λ'_2 drops to unity, because only one signal is received.

Figure 4.56 showed the eigenvalues for $\xi_i = 10$ dB. Figure 4.57 shows λ'_1 versus θ_i for $\xi_i = 30$ dB, with all other parameters the same as in Fig. 4.56. For comparison, λ'_1 is shown for isotropic elements as well as for dipole elements. Figure 4.58 shows λ'_2 for $\xi_i = 30$ dB, again for both isotropic and dipole

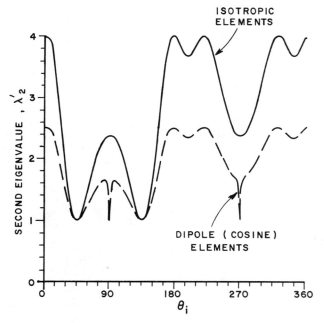

Figure 4.58 λ'_2 versus θ_i for isotropic and dipole elements: $N = 3$, $\xi_d = 0$ dB, $\xi_i = 30$ dB, $B_d = 0$, $B_i = 0$, $\theta_d = 45°$, $\alpha_1 = \alpha_2 = \alpha_3 = 0°$, half-wavelength spacing.

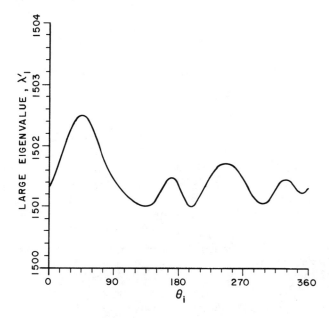

Figure 4.59 λ'_1 versus θ_i with rotated elements: $N = 3$, $\xi_d = 0$ dB, $\xi_i = 30$ dB, $B_d = 0$, $B_i = 0$, $\theta_d = 45°$, $\alpha_1 = -60°$, $\alpha_2 = 0°$, $\alpha_3 = 60°$, half-wavelength spacing.

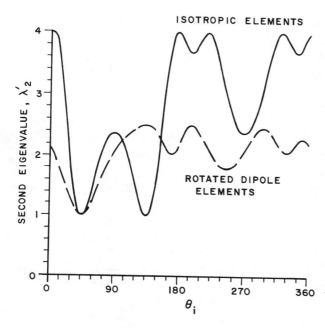

Figure 4.60 λ'_2 versus θ_i with rotated elements: $N = 3$, $\xi_d = 0$ dB, $\xi_i = 30$ dB, $B_d = 0$, $B_i = 0$, $\theta_d = 45°$, $\alpha_1 = -60°$, $\alpha_2 = 0°$, $\alpha_3 = 60°$, half-wavelength spacing.

elements. As may be seen, λ'_2 has the same general behavior for both types of elements except for θ_i near 90° and 270°. When θ_i approaches these angles, the interference is nulled by the elements, so the array receives only one signal. The eigenvalue λ'_2 then drops back to unity.

The drastic variations in λ'_1 are reduced if the dipoles are rotated so that different elements have their maxima in different directions. As an example, Fig. 4.59 shows λ'_1 versus θ_i for the case where $\alpha_1 = -60°$, $\alpha_2 = 0°$, and $\alpha_3 = 60°$. Note that the variation of λ'_1 is now much smaller. The reason is, of course, that when the interference is nulled by one element, it is still received by the other two. It turns out that for this choice of the α_j, λ'_1 is nearly constant. Figure 4.60 shows λ'_2 for the case where $\alpha_1 = -60°$, $\alpha_2 = 0°$, and $\alpha_3 = 60°$. The variation of λ'_2 is also reduced by pointing the elements in different directions. As usual, λ'_3 is always unity, regardless of the element patterns, because there are only two signals received by the array.

Eigenvalues for Nonzero Bandwidth

Next let us illustrate the effects of bandwidth on the eigenvalues. It turns out that the major effect of bandwidth is on the middle and lower eigenvalues. The maximum eigenvalue is affected very little.

To be specific, let us again consider a three-element linear array of isotropic elements a half wavelength apart. Assume the desired signal and interference have flat, bandlimited power spectral densities as shown in Figs. 3.8

and 3.9. Using the results of section 3.2, we find that the normalized covariance matrix for this case is

$$\Psi = \begin{bmatrix} 1 + \xi_d + \xi_i & \xi_d\rho_d(-T_d) + \xi_i\rho_i(-T_i) & \xi_d\rho_d(-2T_d) + \xi_i\rho_i(-2T_i) \\ \xi_d\rho_d(T_d) + \xi_i\rho_i(T_i) & 1 + \xi_d + \xi_i & \xi_d\rho_d(-T_d) + \xi_i\rho_i(-T_i) \\ \xi_d\rho_d(2T_d) + \xi_i\rho_i(2T_i) & \xi_d\rho_d(T_d) + \xi_i\rho_i(T_i) & 1 + \xi_d + \xi_i \end{bmatrix}$$

(4.354)

where T_d and T_i are the interelement time delays defined in Eqs. (3.59) and (3.80), and where

$$\rho_p(\tau) = \text{sinc}\left(\frac{\Delta\omega_p\tau}{2}\right) e^{j\Delta\omega_p\tau},$$

(4.355)

with subscript p equal to d or i.

To find the eigenvalues of this Ψ, we use a numerical technique. In general, when the covariance matrix has the form in Eq. (4.354), it is not possible to obtain the eigenvalues in closed form, as in Eqs. (4.337) and (4.338). For the particular example in Eq. (4.354), Ψ is only a 3×3 matrix, so that one could determine the eigenvalues analytically by expanding

$$|\Psi - \lambda'I| = 0.$$

(4.356)

This procedure will yield a cubic equation in λ', which can be solved in closed form. (Closed-form solutions exist for the roots of polynomials up to fourth order; for fifth and higher order polynomials it is known that closed form solutions do not exist [8].) However, the resulting solution is rather cumbersome. Instead, it appears simpler just to calculate the eigenvalues using standard computer routines. The results shown in the following figures were obtained by Suen [7] using an eigenvalue subroutine in the IBM Scientific Subroutine Package [19]. The subroutine is based on the Jacobi method as modified by Von Neumann [20, 21].

Since bandwidth has very little effect on λ'_1, we shall concentrate on λ'_2 and λ'_3. First, let us assume the interference has zero bandwidth and examine the effect of desired signal bandwidth. Figure 4.61 shows how λ'_2 varies with θ_i for several values of B_d between 0 and 1. This figure has been calculated for $\xi_d = 0$ dB, $\xi_i = 30$ dB, $\theta_d = 45°$, and $B_i = 0$. As may be seen, desired signal bandwidth has only a small effect on λ'_2.

Next, Fig. 4.62 shows the effect of B_d on λ'_3, the third eigenvalue. It is interesting to note that, with nonzero bandwidth, λ'_3 is no longer necessarily unity. (The proof that $\lambda'_3 = 1$ holds only for CW signals!)

Since we are considering isotropic elements, the sum of the eigenvalues is constant. Hence the variation of λ'_1 with θ_i is equal to the sum of the variations of λ'_2 and λ'_3 in Figs. 4.61 and 4.62. Note that this variation is very small compared to λ'_1 (which is approximately 3×10^3 for this example). This result illustrates our earlier comment that λ'_1 is essentially unaffected by B_d.

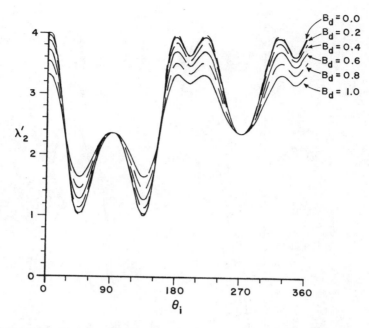

Figure 4.61 λ'_2 versus θ_i for several B_d: $N = 3$, $\xi_d = 0$ dB, $\xi_i = 30$ dB, $B_i = 0$, $\theta_d = 45°$, isotropic elements, half-wavelength spacing.

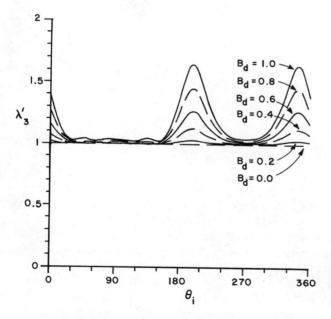

Figure 4.62 λ'_3 versus θ_i for several B_d: $N = 3$, $\xi_d = 0$ dB, $\xi_i = 30$ dB, $B_i = 0$, $\theta_d = 45°$, isotropic elements, half-wavelength spacing.

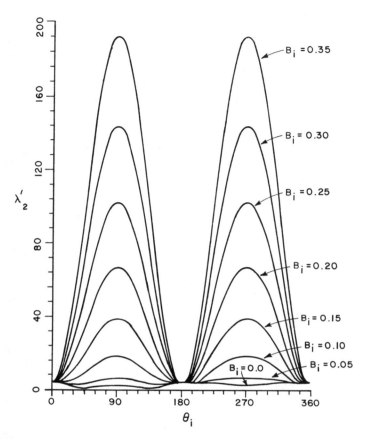

Figure 4.63 λ_2' versus θ_i for several B_i: $N = 3$, $\xi_d = 0$ dB, $\xi_i = 30$ dB, $B_d = 0$, $\theta_d = 45°$, isotropic elements, half-wavelength spacing.

Now consider the effect of B_i on the eigenvalues. Figure 4.63 shows λ_2' versus θ_i for several values of B_i. It is seen that λ_2' is much more sensitive to B_i than to B_d. A small increase in B_i causes λ_2' to increase significantly. This sensitivity occurs because the interference is much stronger than the desired signal.

The effect of B_i on the small eigenvalue, λ_3', is shown in Fig. 4.64. As B_i increases, λ_3' increases and exhibits a more complicated behavior.

Since λ_2' and λ_3' change with B_i and the sum of the eigenvalues is constant, λ_1' must change with B_i. However, because the percentage change in λ_1' due to B_i is again very small, we do not show it.

In conclusion, bandwidth does cause changes in the eigenvalues. The eigenvalues are more sensitive to B_i than to B_d (if $\xi_i \gg \xi_d$). But bandwidth affects the eigenvalues much less than signal powers or element patterns do.

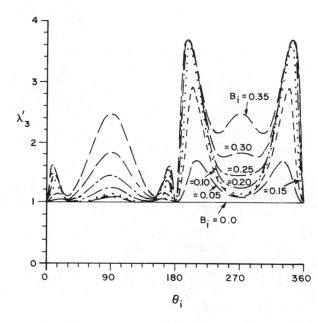

Figure 4.64 λ'_3 versus θ_i for several B_i: $N = 3$, $\xi_d = 0$ dB, $\xi_i = 30$ dB, $B_d = 0$, $\theta_d = 45°$, isotropic elements, half-wavelength spacing.

The purpose of this discussion has been to illustrate eigenvalue behavior with a few examples and to relate this behavior to the adaptive array and signal parameters. Additional information on eigenvalues may be found in Gabriel [22], Mayhan [23], and Mayhan, Simmons, and Cummings [24].

In adaptive array applications where there is a high dynamic range of signals, the eigenvalues and time constants of an LMS array usually vary over a wider range than one would like. One can either accept these variations or use another weight control technique less sensitive to eigenvalue spread. In Chapter 5 we shall describe several methods of weight control that have been developed to overcome this problem.

PROBLEMS

4.1. The purpose of this problem is to determine the effect of a quadrature hybrid phase error on the steady-state and transient behavior of LMS weights. Consider an LMS "array" with a single quadrature hybrid and two weights w_I and w_Q, as shown in Fig. 4.65. Suppose that the only signal present is a CW signal at frequency ω. Let the inphase output of the quadrature hybrid be $A \cos(\omega t)$. Suppose the quadrature output is not working properly, so that the quadrature output is $A \sin(\omega t - \chi)$, instead of $A \sin(\omega t)$. Assume the inphase and quadrature outputs are weighted, summed, and subtracted from a reference signal $R \cos(\omega t - \theta)$ as shown. Assuming the weights are driven by LMS loops that minimize the mean-square value of $\varepsilon(t)$, do the following:

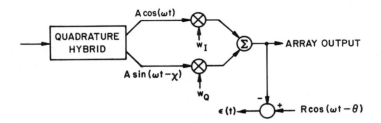

Figure 4.65 A one-element "array" with quadrature hybrid phase error.

(a) Determine the steady-state weights w_I and w_Q.
(b) Determine the steady-state array output signal. Does it match the reference signal?
(c) Determine the eigenvalues of the covariance matrix and discuss the effect of the phase error χ on the transient behavior of the weights.

4.2. Consider a two-element LMS array with isotropic elements. A CW desired signal of amplitude A_d and frequency ω_d arrives from angle $\theta_d = 30°$, where θ_d is measured from broadside as in Fig. 4.7. The array elements are a half wavelength apart at frequency ω_d. Assume each element signal contains thermal noise of power σ^2. Let the reference signal be

$$\tilde{r}(t) = \mathrm{Re}^{j\omega_r t},$$

where ω_r differs from ω_d by $\Delta\omega = \omega_r - \omega_d$.
 Assume that at $t = 0$ the weight vector is $\mathbf{W} = [w_1, w_2] = [1, 1]^T$.
(a) Determine the complete transient response of the two complex weights w_1 and w_2 in the array.
(b) Show that each weight in the element array has two time constants. For each time constant, determine the equivalent feedback loop bandwidth. Discuss how the time constants and feedback loop bandwidths are affected by the signal and thermal noise powers.
(c) Find the sinusoidal steady-state weights in the array as functions of A_d, R, $\Delta\omega$, and the LMS loop gain k. Determine the steady-state array output signal $\tilde{s}(t)$ and compare it to the reference signal. What is the effective cutoff frequency of the feedback loops? That is, how large can $\Delta\omega$ be before the array no longer makes the array output track the reference signal? Which of the two equivalent feedback loop bandwidths determines the effective cutoff frequency of the loops?

4.3. Repeat the analysis of problem 4.2 for an array with N isotropic elements. Discuss how the number of elements and the spacing between elements affects the array time constants, the feedback loop bandwidths, and the effective cutoff frequency of the array.

4.4. Show that if an input $\tilde{x}_i^*(t)\tilde{\varepsilon}(t)$ to a linear filter with transfer function k/s produces the output w_i, then an input $\tilde{x}_i^*(t)\tilde{\varepsilon}(t)e^{j\omega_0 t}$ into a filter with transfer function $k/(s - j\omega_0)$ will produce the output $w_i e^{j\omega_0 t}$.

4.5. Suppose an adaptive array has N elements spaced uniformly along a line. Let element j have element pattern $f_j(\theta, \phi)$, and suppose the signal from element j contains thermal noise of power σ_j^2.

If these elements are used in an Applebaum array, determine the proper steering vector $\mathbf{T}^*$ for the case where the desired signal arrives from direction (θ_d, ϕ_d).

4.6. Consider a single LMS loop with a real input signal $x(t)$ and one real weight w. Derive a formula for the variance of w analogous to Eq. (4.295) for the case where $x(t)$ contains a CW signal and thermal noise,

$$x(t) = A \cos(\omega t + \chi) + n(t).$$

Fig 4.45

Assume the thermal noise has power spectral density $(\sigma^2/2)S(\omega)$, where $S(\omega)$ is given in Fig. 4.25. Assume also that the loop gain k is small enough so that Eq. (4.291) holds for the strongest signal powers of interest.

Use your analytical result to obtain a curve similar to Fig. 4.47. Interpret your results.

4.7. Consider a two-element adaptive array that uses LMS feedback loops. Suppose that because of unequal cable lengths, the feedback loop for each element in the array contains unequal time delays between the reference signal hybrid and the signal-by-error multiplier. We wish to determine how different these time delays can be before the loops become unstable.

Specifically, suppose the complex feedback loop for element 1 in the array contains no time delays. But suppose the complex loop for element 2 contains a time delay $T_2 \neq 0$, where T_2 is defined in Fig. 4.6. In other words, the feedback loop behind element 1 has $T_1 = T_2 = T_3 = 0$ (in Fig. 4.6), but the loop behind element 2 has $T_1 = T_3 = 0$ and $T_2 \neq 0$.

Assume the array receives a CW desired signal of amplitude A_d and frequency ω_d from angle $\theta_d = 0$. Also let each element signal contain thermal noise of power σ^2. Assume the noise bandwidth is too small for the time delay T_2 to cause any significant decorrelation of the noise. For this situation, carry out an analysis similar to that in section 4.2 to determine the maximum value of $\omega_d T_2$ for which the array feedback is stable.

4.8. Calculate the SINR of a two-element array that has an excess time delay of T_2 in one feedback loop, as described in problem 4.7. Do this calculation for the case where there is a desired signal arriving from $\theta_d = 0°$ and an interference signal arriving from $\theta_i = 50°$. As usual, assume independent thermal noise is present on each element signal. Let the center frequency of the desired, interference, and thermal noise signals be ω_d. Assume that the SNR per element is $\xi_d = 10$ dB and the INR per element is $\xi_i = 40$ dB. Finally, assume that the bandwidths of the desired, interference, and thermal noise are all the same, equal to $\Delta\omega$.

Plot the SINR as a function of $\phi = \Delta\omega T_2/2$, as in Fig. 4.10, for representative values of fractional bandwidth $B = \Delta\omega/\omega_d$. Determine a rule of thumb for how large T_2 can be without causing serious performance degradation.

4.9. In this problem we determine how the signal level at which we balance the multiplier offset voltages in Eq. (4.69) affects the sensitivity of the array to the offset voltages.

Consider a two-element array with isotropic elements. Suppose the array signals include a desired signal of amplitude A_d arriving from angle θ_d and thermal noise, as in Eq. (4.76). Let $\theta_d = 90°$. Assume each quadrature LMS loop includes an offset voltage

$$\delta_{P_j} = \kappa_{P_j} + c_{P_j} x_{P_j}^2(t),$$

(where $P = I$ or Q and $j = 1$ or 2) as in Eq. (4.69). To simplify the problem, assume that all κ_{P_j} are equal and all c_{P_j} are equal for different quadrature loops. Specifically, assume

$$\kappa_{P_j} = \varepsilon\sigma^2\left(1 + \xi_{d_0}\right),$$

and

$$c_{P_j} = -2\varepsilon.$$

Note that with this choice, Eq. (4.69) becomes

$$\delta_{P_j} = \varepsilon\sigma^2\left(1 + \xi_{d_0}\right) - 2\varepsilon\overline{x_{P_j}^2(t)}.$$

Since the desired signal on element 1, for example, is

$$\tilde{x}_1(t) = \tilde{n}_1(t) + \tilde{d}_1(t) = \tilde{n}_1(t) + A_d e^{j(\omega_d t + \psi_d)},$$

the inphase component of $\tilde{x}_1(t)$ is

$$x_{I_1}(t) = n_{I_1}(t) + A_d \cos\left(\omega_d t + \psi_d\right),$$

and hence

$$\overline{x_{I_1}^2(t)} = \overline{n_{I_1}^2(t)} + \frac{A_d^2}{2} = \frac{\sigma^2 + A_d^2}{2}.$$

Therefore,

$$\delta_{P_j} = \varepsilon\sigma^2\left(1 + \xi_{d_0} - 2\varepsilon\left(\frac{\sigma^2 + A_d^2}{2}\right)\right)$$

$$= \varepsilon\sigma^2\left(1 + \xi_{d_0}\right) - \varepsilon\sigma^2 - \varepsilon\sigma^2\xi_d$$

$$= \varepsilon\sigma^2\left(\xi_{d_0} - \xi_d\right),$$

where $\xi_d = A_d^2/\sigma^2$. Thus, when $\xi_d = \xi_{d_0}$, the offset voltage δ_{P_j} is zero. That is, ξ_{d_0} is the "design SNR" at which the multiplier is balanced. Suppose that the δ_{P_j} is the same for each of the four quadrature loops in the array.

For this array, obtain analytic expressions for the steady-state weight vector **W** and the SINR in terms of ξ_d, ξ_r [defined in Eq. (4.87)], ξ_{d_0}, and ε. Then do the following:

(a) Make plots of the SINR in dB versus ξ_d in dB over the range -20 dB $\leqslant \xi_d \leqslant 40$ dB for the following cases:

1. $\xi_{d_0} = 0$ dB: $\varepsilon = 10^{-1}, 10^{-2}, \ldots, 10^{-5}$.
2. $\xi_{d_0} = 20$ dB: $\varepsilon = 10^{-1}, 10^{-2}, \ldots, 10^{-6}$.

(b) For the case where the loops are balanced at $\xi_{d_0} = 20$ dB, determine the largest permissible ε for which the SINR degradation below its optimal value is less than 3 dB for $\xi_d = 40$ dB.

(c) Discuss how the sensitivity of the SINR performance to ε is affected by the choice of balance point ξ_{d_0}.

4.10.   Figures 4.36 and 4.37 show the effects of weight saturation on a two-element array with desired signal and thermal noise when $\theta_d = 14.5°$ and $\xi_r = 10$ dB.

Compute a similar set of curves for the case where $\theta_d = 77°$ and $\xi_r = 20$ dB. (The arrival angle $\theta_d = 77°$ produces the largest SINR degradation for $\xi_r = 20$ dB.) Plot the weights and the SINR versus ξ_d for 0 dB $\leqslant \xi_d \leqslant$ 20 dB when every real weight w_{P_j} is limited to $|w_{P_j}| \leqslant 1$. What is the maximum SINR degradation (i.e., the SINR difference with and without saturation) when $\xi_r =$ 20 dB?

4.11. Consider a two-element adaptive array that receives a CW desired signal from broadside. Suppose as usual that there is independent thermal noise of power σ^2 on each element signal. Assume the reference signal is also CW and is perfectly correlated with the desired signal. The SNR per element is 0 dB.

Suppose that because of a circuit problem the inphase weight on element 1 saturates at ± 1. Assume that neither the quadrature weights nor the other inphase weight saturates.

Determine the SINR (output SNR) as a function of the reference signal-to-noise ratio $\xi_r = R^2/2\sigma^2$, where R is the reference signal amplitude. Show that

$$\lim_{\xi_r \to \infty} \text{SINR} = 0 \text{ dB},$$

and explain why this happens.

4.12. When applying the method in Eq. (4.155) for finding weights with constraints, the order in which the constraints are applied can make a difference. When the final constrained solution is found, one must be careful to check that the weights obtained are the correct ones.

Let us illustrate this point with a simple example. Suppose we have two real weights, and suppose the $E[\varepsilon^2(t)]$ surface has loci of constant $E[\varepsilon^2(t)]$ in the w_1, w_2-plane as shown in Fig. 4.66. Suppose further that w_1 and w_2 are each constrained to be less than unity. Assume we have solved for the optimal w_1 and w_2 without constraints, and have found the solution $w_{1_{opt}}, w_{2_{opt}}$ shown in the figure. To get to the constrained solution, we can proceed in three ways:

Method 1. Since $w_{1_{opt}}$ and $w_{2_{opt}}$ both exceed the bounds for w_1 and w_2, we can apply the constraints to w_1 and w_2 simultaneously. That is, we simply set $w_1 = 1$ and $w_2 = 1$. If we do this, we wind up at point $(1, 1)$ in Fig. 4.66.

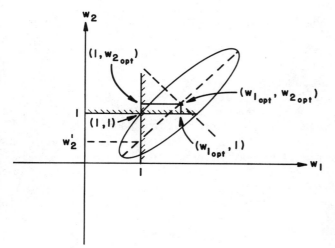

Figure 4.66 Constrained optimization with two weights.

Method 2. Since $w_{2_{opt}} > 1$, we can first apply the constraint to w_2 by setting $w_2 = 1$. This takes us to the point $(w_{1_{opt}}, 1)$ in the figure. Then we solve the remaining equation for the optimal w_1 with $w_2 = 1$. This step yields $w_1 = w_1'$, and takes us to the point $(w_1', 1)$. However, since w_1' also exceeds the bound for w_1, we apply the constraint to w_1 by setting $w_1 = 1$. Thus, with this method, we finally arrive at point $(1, 1)$, the same result as with Method 1.

Method 3. Since $w_{1_{opt}} > 1$, we can also begin by setting $w_1 = 1$. This step takes us to point $(1, w_{2_{opt}})$ in Fig. 4.66. Then, solving for the optimal w_2 with $w_1 = 1$, we find the solution $w_2 = w_2'$ shown in the figure. This value will be found because $w_2 = w_2'$ will give the lowest value of $E[\varepsilon^2(t)]$ if $w_1 = 1$. However, w_2' does not exceed the bound for w_2; thus the final solution with this method will be at the point $(1, w_2')$.

Thus we see that the solution obtained depends on the order in which the constraints are applied.

For this problem, do the following:

(a) Using this example, explain which solution is correct and why.

(b) Suppose a solution has been found by applying the constraints in an arbitrary order. Suggest a method for determining whether this solution is in fact the correct one. (Hint: Consider the gradient of $E[\varepsilon^2(t)]$.)

REFERENCES

1. J. J. DiStefano, III, A. R. Stubberud, and I. J. Williams, *Feedback and Control Systems*, Schaum's Outline Series, McGraw-Hill, New York, 1967, p. 163.

2. R. T. Compton, Jr., "The Effect of Differential Time Delays in the LMS Feedback Loops," *IEEE Transactions on Aerospace and Electronic Systems*, AES–17, no. 2 (March 1981): 222. Copyright © 1981 IEEE.

3. R. Bellman and K. L. Cooke, *Differential-Difference Equations*, Academic Press, New York, 1963.

4. R. T. Compton, Jr., "Adaptive Antennas for Aircraft Communication Systems," Report 3098–1, July 1971, ElectroScience Laboratory, Department of Electrical Engineering, Ohio State University, Columbus; prepared under Contract N00014–67–A–0232–0009 for Office of Naval Research, Arlington, Va.

5. T. W. Miller, R. Caldecott, and R. J. Huff, "A Satellite Simulator with a TDMA-System Compatible Adaptive Array," Report 3364–4, January 1976, Ohio State University ElectroScience Laboratory, Columbus; prepared under Contract F30602–72–C–0162 for Rome Air Development Center, Griffiss Air Force Base, New York 13440.

6. R. T. Compton, Jr., W. G. Swarner, and P. Palmer, "An IF Implementation of the LMS Feedback Loop," Proceedings of the 1980 Adaptive Antenna Symposium, December 1980, RADC–TR–80–378, vol. 1, p. 319, Rome Air Development Center, Air Force Systems Command, Griffiss Air Force Base, N.Y. 13441.

7. R. T. Compton, Jr., "The Effect of Integrator Pole Position on the Performance of an Adaptive Array," *IEEE Transactions on Aerospace and Electronic Systems*, AES–17, no. 4 (July 1981): 598.

8. B. S. Abrams, S. J. Harris, and A. E. Zeger, "Interference Cancellation," Final Report RADC–TR–74–225. September 1974, General Atronics Corporation, Philadelphia; prepared under Contracts F30602–72–C–0459 and F30602–73–C–0301 for Rome Air Development Center.

9. B. Widrow and J. M. McCool, "A Comparison of Adaptive Algorithms Based on the Methods of Steepest Descent and Random Search," *IEEE Transactions on Antennas and Propagations*, AP–24, no. 5 (September 1976): 615.

10. A. J. Berni, "Weight Jitter Phenomena in Adaptive Array Control Loops," *IEEE Transactions on Aerospace and Electronic Systems*, AES–13, no. 4 (July 1977): 355.

11. G. E. Koleszar, "The Stochastic Properties of the Weights in an Adaptive Antenna Array," Report 4063–1, August 1975, Ohio State University ElectroScience Laboratory, Columbus; prepared under Contract N00019–75–C–0179 for Naval Air Systems Command, Washington, D.C. 20361.

12. R. S. Kennedy, *Fading Dispersive Communication Channels*, Wiley, New York, 1969.

13. A. Papoulis, *Probability, Random Variables, and Stochastic Processes*, 2nd ed., McGraw-Hill, New York, 1984, p. 186.

14. C. A. Baird, Jr., G. P. Martin, G. G. Rassweiler, and C. L. Zahm, "Adaptive Processing for Antenna Arrays," Final Report, June 1972, Radiation Systems Division, Harris Corporation, Melbourne, FL.

15. R. T. Compton, Jr., "On Eigenvalues, SINR, and Element Patterns in Adaptive Arrays," *IEEE Transactions on Antennas and Propagation*, AP–32, no. 6 (June 1984): 643.

16. F. B. Hildebrand, *Methods of Applied Mathematics*, Prentice-Hall, Englewood Cliffs, N.J., 1952, pp. 49ff.

17. K. J. Suen, "A Study of Eigenvalue Behavior in Adaptive Arrays," Technical Report 713603–2, August 1981, Ohio State University ElectroScience Laboratory, Columbus; prepared under Contract N00019–81–C–0093 for Naval Air Systems Command, Washington, D.C. 20361.

18. S. Borofsky, *Elementary Theory of Equations*, Macmillan, 1950, p. 128.

19. System/360 Scientific Subroutine Package, Version 3, p. 164, EIGEN, IBM, New York, 1970.

20. A. S. Householder, *The Theory of Matrices in Numerical Analysis*, Dover, New York, 1964, chap. 7.

21. D. M. Young and R. T. Gregory, *A Survey of Numerical Mathematics*, Addison-Wesley, Reading, Mass., 1973, chap. 14.

22. W. F. Gabriel, "Adaptive Arrays—An Introduction," *Proceedings of the IEEE*, 64, no. 2 (February 1976): 239.

23. J. T. Mayhan, "Some Techniques for Evaluating the Bandwidth Characteristics of Adaptive Nulling Systems," *IEEE Transactions on Antennas and Propagation*, AP–27, no. 3 (May 1979): 363.

24. J. T. Mayhan, A. J. Simmons, and W. C. Cummings, "Wideband Adaptive Antenna Nulling Using Tapped Delay Lines," *IEEE Transactions on Antennas and Propagation*, AP–29, no. 6 (November 1981): 923.

5

Advanced Weight Control Techniques

As we have seen in Chapter 4, the time constants in an LMS or Applebaum array can vary over many orders of magnitude. Time-constant variation is especially large if the array must handle a wide dynamic range of signals. In many array applications, this time-constant variation is a problem. For most systems, there are both minimum and maximum time constants that are acceptable. For example, suppose an array is to be used on an aircraft. On the one hand, the slowest speed of response of the array must be fast enough that the array can track aircraft motion. One does not want the array to lose a weak desired signal when the aircraft maneuvers. On the other hand, one cannot allow the weights to become too fast. If they do, they can destroy the desired signal modulation. In practice, when an LMS array is used in a communication system, the reference signal is usually derived from the array output. (Chapter 7 describes several methods for reference signal generation.) The reference signal usually correlates well with the desired signal, but it is never an exact copy of the desired signal. If the weights are capable of changing at the signal modulation rate, they remodulate the desired signal to make it match the reference signal. An even worse situation occurs when high-power interference is present. In this case, if the weights are fast enough, they ignore the desired signal and simply modulate the interference to make it match the reference signal.

Thus system requirements usually limit the allowable time-constant spread. Because the eigenvalues depend directly on signal power, there is therefore a maximum dynamic range the system can accommodate. In practice one often finds that this range is too low. Typically one must accept a design that does not meet speed-of-response requirements in order to handle even a modest range of signal powers.

These remarks apply to a continuous LMS or Applebaum loop. However, time-constant spread causes even worse problems with a discrete loop. A discrete loop has a maximum loop gain that can be used if the loop is to be stable, as discussed in section 2.4. The fastest transient term in a discrete loop cannot be made to converge in less than a certain number of samples. With widely spread eigenvalues, an enormous number of samples is then required to get the slow transient terms to converge. For example, if the fastest term in Eq. (2.356) converges in 100 samples and the eigenvalue spread is 10^5, then 10^7 samples are required for the slowest term to converge. Normally the real-time speed of response in such a case is much too long to be useful.

For these reasons, time-constant spread is a problem. To overcome this problem, several new techniques have been developed. We describe four of these in this chapter, the modified LMS loop [1], the Gram-Schmidt preprocessor [2, 3], the recursive least-squares algorithm [4, 5], and the sample matrix inverse method [6]. The modified LMS loop is an analog feedback technique. The Gram-Schmidt preprocessor can be used in either analog or digital form. The least-squares algorithm and the sample matrix inverse method are digital techniques.

5.1 THE MODIFIED LMS LOOP‡ *(Read only)*

In this section we show how to alter the LMS feedback loop so that its time constants do not vary as the eigenvalues of the covariance matrix change. Our goal here is to obtain an analog weight control loop whose time constant is fixed. The approach we present is taken from [1].

To correct the problem of time-constant spread, it is helpful if we first examine the reason it occurs. Essentially, the reason is that the LMS algorithm is based on a gradient approach. A gradient technique causes the weight vector to move along some parts of its trajectory at a different speed than along other parts. This viewpoint will suggest a way of modifying the LMS loop to solve the problem.

We may use a simple two-dimensional example as an illustration. [We return to the real signal notation used in Eqs. (2.5) through (2.35).] From Eq. (2.21) we have

$$E\{\varepsilon^2(t)\} = \varepsilon_{\min}^2 + \left(\mathbf{W}_r - \mathbf{W}_{r_{\mathrm{opt}}}\right)^T \Phi_r \left(\mathbf{W}_r - \mathbf{W}_{r_{\mathrm{opt}}}\right), \tag{5.1}$$

where

$$\mathbf{W}_{r_{\mathrm{opt}}} = \Phi_r^{-1} \mathbf{S}_r. \tag{5.2}$$

‡Portions of this section are reprinted from the author's paper [1] with permission, © 1980 IEEE.

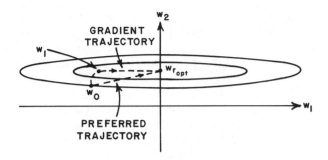

Figure 5.1 Constant $E[\varepsilon^2(t)]$ loci in the $\mathbf{W}_r$-plane (reprinted from [1] with permission, © 1980 IEEE).

The weight vector $\mathbf{W}_{r_{opt}}$ yields minimum $E\{\varepsilon^2(t)\}$, and

$$\varepsilon_{min}^2 = E\{r^2(t)\} - \mathbf{S}_r^T \Phi_r \mathbf{S}_r \qquad (5.3)$$

is the value of $E\{\varepsilon^2(t)\}$ when $\mathbf{W}_r = \mathbf{W}_{r_{opt}}$. Consider a two-dimensional $E\{\varepsilon^2(t)\}$ surface defined by

$$\mathbf{W}_{r_{opt}} = \begin{bmatrix} w_1 \\ w_2 \end{bmatrix} = \begin{bmatrix} 0 \\ 1 \end{bmatrix} \qquad (5.4)$$

and

$$\Phi_r = \begin{bmatrix} 1 & 0 \\ 0 & 100 \end{bmatrix}. \qquad (5.5)$$

The resulting $E\{\varepsilon^2(t)\}$ surface has elliptical loci of constant $E\{\varepsilon^2(t)\}$ in the $\mathbf{W}_r$ plane, as shown in Fig. 5.1. A typical trajectory traveled by a weight vector under the LMS algorithm is shown in Fig. 5.1. The weight vector starts at an arbitrary point $\mathbf{W}_0$ and travels to $\mathbf{W}_{r_{opt}}$ along the curved path shown. At each point of the trajectory, the weights move in the steepest-descent direction, which is always perpendicular to a constant $E\{\varepsilon^2(t)\}$ locus. Since the eigenvalues are unequal, the weights do not move in a straight line toward $\mathbf{W}_{r_{opt}}$, but along a curved path, as shown. Moreover, because the LMS algorithm makes the time rate change of $\mathbf{W}_r$ proportional to the slope of the $E\{\varepsilon^2(t)\}$ surface, the weight vector moves rapidly from $\mathbf{W}_0$ to $\mathbf{W}_1$ in Fig. 5.1, since the slope is large in this region, but slowly from point $\mathbf{W}_1$ to $\mathbf{W}_{r_{opt}}$ because the slope is small in this region. The movement from $\mathbf{W}_0$ to $\mathbf{W}_1$ contributes a fast term to the weight response, and the movement from $\mathbf{W}_1$ to $\mathbf{W}_{r_{opt}}$ contributes a slow term.

We observe that the spread in time constants would be eliminated if the weights were always forced to move in a straight line toward $\mathbf{W}_{r_{opt}}$ with a value of $d\mathbf{W}_r/dt$ not dependent on the slope of the surface. Such a preferred trajectory is shown in Fig. 5.1. This preferred trajectory is in the vector direction $-(\mathbf{W}_r - \mathbf{W}_{r_{opt}})$ for any given $\mathbf{W}_r$. However, the gradient of $E\{\varepsilon^2(t)\}$, as computed from Eq. (5.1), is

$$\nabla_{W_r}\{E[\varepsilon^2(t)]\} = 2\Phi_r(\mathbf{W}_r - \mathbf{W}_{r_{opt}}), \qquad (5.6)$$

so that the LMS algorithm is

$$\frac{d\mathbf{W}_r}{dt} = -2k\boldsymbol{\Phi}_r\left(\mathbf{W}_r - \mathbf{W}_{r_{\text{opt}}}\right). \tag{5.7}$$

Thus the LMS algorithm moves the weights in the direction of the vector $-\boldsymbol{\Phi}_r(\mathbf{W}_r - \mathbf{W}_{r_{\text{opt}}})$, not in the direction $-(\mathbf{W}_r - \mathbf{W}_{r_{\text{opt}}})$. Since $\boldsymbol{\Phi}_r$ has unequal eigenvalues, $-\boldsymbol{\Phi}_r(\mathbf{W}_r - \mathbf{W}_{r_{\text{opt}}})$ is usually in a different direction from $-(\mathbf{W}_r - \mathbf{W}_{r_{\text{opt}}})$. Moreover, the presence of $\boldsymbol{\Phi}_r$ in Eq. (5.7) causes the slope of the $E\{\varepsilon^2(t)\}$ surface to influence the speed of response.

Clearly, a better strategy would be to eliminate the $\boldsymbol{\Phi}_r$ from the right-hand side of Eq. (5.7), that is, to control the weights according to the equation

$$\frac{d\mathbf{W}_r}{dt} = -2k\left(\mathbf{W}_r - \mathbf{W}_{r_{\text{opt}}}\right). \tag{5.8}$$

If this control equation were used, the weights would move directly toward $\mathbf{W}_{r_{\text{opt}}}$, and the eigenvalues of $\boldsymbol{\Phi}_r$ would not influence the speed. To realize such a control law, we note from Eq. (5.6) that

$$\mathbf{W}_r - \mathbf{W}_{r_{\text{opt}}} = \tfrac{1}{2}\boldsymbol{\Phi}_r^{-1}\nabla_{W_r}\left\{E\left[\varepsilon^2(t)\right]\right\}. \tag{5.9}$$

Hence Eq. (5.8) is the same as[‡]

$$\frac{d\mathbf{W}_r}{dt} = -k\boldsymbol{\Phi}_r^{-1}\nabla_{W_r}\left\{E\left[\varepsilon^2(t)\right]\right\} \tag{5.10}$$

or, equivalently,

$$\boldsymbol{\Phi}_r\frac{d\mathbf{W}_r}{dt} = -k\nabla_{W_r}\left\{E\left[\varepsilon^2(t)\right]\right\}. \tag{5.11}$$

We will refer to this as the *ideal control law* for the adaptive array. It differs from the LMS algorithm only in the presence of the matrix $\boldsymbol{\Phi}_r$ multiplying $d\mathbf{W}_r/dt$. The differential equation satisfied by the weights with the ideal control law may be found by rearranging Eq. (5.11). From Eq. (2.13) [or from Eqs. (5.2) and (5.6)], we have

$$\nabla_{W_r}\left\{E\left[\varepsilon^2(t)\right]\right\} = 2(\boldsymbol{\Phi}_r\mathbf{W}_r - \mathbf{S}_r). \tag{5.12}$$

Substituting this into Eq. (5.11) yields

$$\boldsymbol{\Phi}_r\frac{d\mathbf{W}_r}{dt} + 2k\boldsymbol{\Phi}_r\mathbf{W}_r = 2k\mathbf{S}_r. \tag{5.13}$$

How can we obtain a feedback loop for which the weights will satisfy Eq. (5.13)? To see how, consider first the LMS algorithm. When Eq. (2.6) is

---

[‡]Equation (5.10), when expressed in discrete form, is equivalent to Newton's method in numerical analysis [7].

substituted in Eq. (2.35), the LMS algorithm becomes

$$\frac{dw_{P_i}}{dt} = 2kx_{P_i}(t)\left[r(t) - \sum_{\substack{j=1 \\ L=1,Q}}^{N} x_{L_j}(t)w_{L_j} \right]. \tag{5.14}$$

Rearranging this equation yields the vector differential equation

$$\frac{d\mathbf{W}_r}{dt} + 2k\mathbf{\Phi}_r\mathbf{W}_r = 2k\mathbf{S}_r. \tag{5.15}$$

Note that the term $\mathbf{\Phi}_r\mathbf{W}_r$ on the left side of this equation resulted from the term $x_{P_i}(t)\Sigma x_{L_j}(t)w_{L_j}$ on the right side of Eq. (5.14). To obtain the matrix $\mathbf{\Phi}_r$ in front of $d\mathbf{W}_r/dt$ as in Eq. (5.13) then, we must add a term of the form $x_{P_i}(t)\Sigma x_{L_j}(t)(dw_{L_j}/dt)$ to the right side of Eq. (5.14). It turns out that the result we want is the following control law:

$$\frac{dw_{P_i}}{dt} = 2kA\left\{ x_{P_i}(t)\left[r(t) - \sum_{\substack{j=1 \\ L=P,Q}}^{N} x_{L_j}(t)w_{L_j} - c\sum_{\substack{j=1 \\ L=P,Q}}^{N} x_{L_j}(t)\frac{dw_{L_j}}{dt} \right] \right\}. \tag{5.16}$$

In this equation, c is a gain constant and $A\{\cdot\}$ represents an averaging operation to be defined below. This equation corresponds to the feedback loop shown in Fig. 5.2, which we will call the *modified LMS loop*. It is similar to the LMS loop, except for the inclusion of the averaging operation $A\{\cdot\}$ and the extra amplifier, summer, and multipliers to form

$$c\sum_{\substack{j=1 \\ L=1,Q}}^{N} x_{L_j}(t)w_{L_j}$$

and subtract it from the reference signal.

We define the averaging operation $A\{\cdot\}$ to be a finite time average. We assume the weights are slowly varying in comparison to the signals $x_{P_i}(t)$ and $r(t)$. We let $A\{\cdot\}$ represent a time average over an interval short enough that w_{P_i} and dw_{P_i}/dt may be considered constant over this interval, but long compared to the carrier cycles of $x_{P_i}(t)$ and $r(t)$. The actual value of the time interval to be used and the reasons for including this averaging in the loop will be discussed below. For the moment, we settle for this definition, which allows us to approximate the terms on the right side of Eq. (5.16) as follows:

$$A\left\{ x_{P_i}(t)\sum_{\substack{j=1 \\ L=1,Q}}^{N} x_{L_j}(t)w_{L_j} \right\} = \sum_{\substack{j=1 \\ L=1,Q}}^{N} A\left\{ x_{P_i}(t)x_{L_j}(t) \right\}w_{L_j} \tag{5.17}$$

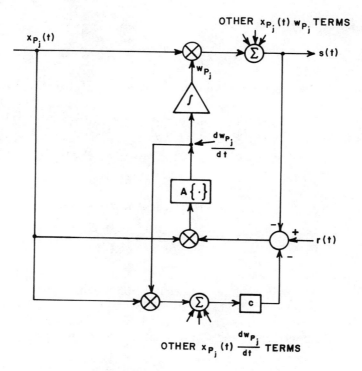

Figure 5.2   The modified LMS loop (reprinted from [1] with permission, © 1980 IEEE).

and

$$A\left\{ x_{P_i}(t) \sum_{\substack{j=1 \\ L=I,Q}}^{N} x_{L_j}(t) \frac{dw_{L_j}}{dt} \right\} = \sum_{\substack{j=1 \\ L=I,Q}}^{N} A\left\{ x_{P_i}(t) x_{L_j}(t) \right\} \frac{dw_{L_j}}{dt}. \quad (5.18)$$

Equation (5.16) may then be expressed in matrix form as

$$\left[\mathbf{I} + 2kcA\left\{ \mathbf{X}_r \mathbf{X}_r^T \right\} \right] \frac{d\mathbf{W}_r}{dt} + 2kA\left\{ \mathbf{X}_r \mathbf{X}_r^T \right\} \mathbf{W}_r = 2kA\left\{ \mathbf{X}_r r(t) \right\}. \quad (5.19)$$

Suppose temporarily that the averaging operation $A\{\cdot\}$ is good enough that

$$A\left\{ \mathbf{X}_r \mathbf{X}_r^T \right\} = \mathbf{\Phi}_r \quad (5.20)$$

and

$$A\left\{ \mathbf{X}_r r(t) \right\} = \mathbf{S}_r. \quad (5.21)$$

Then Eq. (5.19) becomes

$$[\mathbf{I} + 2kc\mathbf{\Phi}_r]\frac{d\mathbf{W}_r}{dt} + 2k\mathbf{\Phi}_r\mathbf{W}_r = 2k\mathbf{S}_r, \tag{5.22}$$

which is similar to the ideal control law in Eq. (5.13) except for the extra term $\mathbf{I}$ on the left.

Consider how the weights will behave with Eq. (5.22). A typical weight transient will be of the form

$$\mathbf{W}_r(t) = \mathbf{C}_1 e^{-[2k\lambda_1/(1+2kc\lambda_1)]t} + \mathbf{C}_2 e^{-[2k\lambda_1/(1+2kc\lambda_1)]t}$$

$$+ \cdots + \mathbf{C}_N e^{-[2k\lambda_1/(1+2kc\lambda_1)]t} + \mathbf{\Phi}_r^{-1}\mathbf{S}_r. \tag{5.23}$$

The jth time constant in this transient response is

$$\tau_j = \frac{1 + 2kc\lambda_j}{2k\lambda_j}, \tag{5.24}$$

which may be compared with Eq. (4.313) for the LMS algorithm. We find that now, as λ_j becomes large, τ_j does not become arbitrarily small as in Eq. (4.313) but is bounded below by c. By choosing c properly, we may limit the fast response speed of the array without limiting the dynamic range of the signals.

Moreover, the steady-state solution of Eq. (5.22) is

$$\mathbf{W}_r = \mathbf{\Phi}_r^{-1}\mathbf{S}_r, \tag{5.25}$$

which is the optimal solution. Thus the modified loop has the same steady-state solution as the LMS array, regardless of the value of c.

The difference between the LMS loop and the modified loop is in their transient behavior. In particular, if k is large enough that

$$2kc\lambda_j > 1 \tag{5.26}$$

for *every* eigenvalue λ_j, Eq. (5.22) may be approximated by

$$2k\mathbf{\Phi}_r\left[c\frac{d\mathbf{W}_r}{dt} + \mathbf{W}_r\right] = 2k\mathbf{S}_r, \tag{5.27}$$

or simply

$$c\frac{d\mathbf{W}_r}{dt} + \mathbf{W}_r = \mathbf{\Phi}_r^{-1}\mathbf{S}_r, \tag{5.28}$$

which is equivalent to the ideal control law in Eq. (5.8). In this case all components w_{p_i} have the same time constant, c. There is only one time constant in the array response, and it is independent of signal power.

Equation (5.22) differs from the ideal control law because of the extra term $\mathbf{I}$ on the left. This difference means that when the array receives weak signals, so $2kc\mathbf{\Phi}_r$ is small compared to $\mathbf{I}$, Eq. (5.22) becomes the LMS algorithm. With strong signals and large $2kc\Phi_r$, the **I** term is negligible and Eq. (5.22) becomes the ideal control law. For in-between cases, there will still be some spread in time constant if $2kc\lambda_j < 1$ for some λ_j. But with the loop modified as shown in Fig. 5.2, the shortest time constant is controlled by c rather than by the strongest signal.

An additional remark is helpful for understanding the control loop in Fig. 5.2. The weight vector in the LMS array satisfies Eq. (5.15). The transients in the LMS array have time constants

$$\tau_j = \frac{1}{2k\lambda_j}. \tag{5.29}$$

If Eq. (5.24) is compared with Eq. (5.29), we find that each τ_j for the new feedback loop is larger than the corresponding τ_j for the LMS loop. Therefore, when the modifications shown in Fig. 5.2 are added to the LMS loop, the result is to slow down the response time of the array. To obtain a fixed speed of response from the array, c is chosen large enough so that the fast time-constant terms in the LMS loop are slowed down until they are of the same speed as, or slower than, the slow terms in the LMS loop. The modified loop in Fig. 5.2 is thus slower than the LMS loop, but has the advantage of fixed time constants. Constancy of speed of response is much more important for system design purposes than obtaining the fastest possible response.‡ Of course, the real time speed of response of a hardware implementation would be adjusted to a suitable value by choosing gains appropriately.

We now return to the averaging operation $A\{\cdot\}$ in Eq. (5.16). $A\{\cdot\}$ was defined as a finite time average over an interval short compared to changes in w_{P_i} and dw_{P_i}/dt, but long compared to the fluctuations of $x_{P_i}(t)$ and $r(t)$. We now elaborate on this definition.

The weights in the modified loop satisfy the system

$$\left[\mathbf{I} + 2kcA\{\mathbf{X}_r\mathbf{X}_r^T\} \right] \frac{d\mathbf{W}_r}{dt} + 2kA\{\mathbf{X}_r\mathbf{X}_r^T\}\mathbf{W}_r = 2kA\{\mathbf{X}_r r(t)\}. \tag{5.30}$$

First, we observe that the matrix $A\{\mathbf{X}_r\mathbf{X}_r^T\}$ multiplying $d\mathbf{W}_r/dt$ must be nonsingular if the modified loop is to have the desired behavior. To see why, assume for the moment that the matrix $A\{\mathbf{X}_r\mathbf{X}_r^T\}$ can be approximated by a constant matrix, and make a rotation of coordinates in Eq. (5.30) into the principal axes of $A\{\mathbf{X}_r\mathbf{X}_r^T\}$. Let

$$\mathbf{W}_r = \mathbf{RV}, \tag{5.31}$$

where **R** is a $2N \times 2N$ orthogonal coordinate rotation matrix, and **V** is the

---

‡An adaptive array with continuous weight control loops can easily be made fast enough for most communication system applications. For example, an LMS array was implemented at Ohio State University [8] with time constants of the order of a few hundred nanoseconds for the strongest signals within its dynamic range. (For most applications, such a speed is much too fast.) Hence, it is entirely feasible to slow down an array response, as described here, and still have an adequately fast array.

weight vector expressed in the principal axes of $A\{\mathbf{X}_r\mathbf{X}_r^T\}$. Let

$$\Lambda^* = \mathbf{R}^T A\{\mathbf{X}_r\mathbf{X}_r^T\}\mathbf{R} \tag{5.32}$$

be the matrix of eigenvalues of $A\{\mathbf{X}_r\mathbf{X}_r^T\}$ with diagonal elements λ_j^*. After rotating coordinates, we find that the jth normal weight satisfies the differential equation

$$\left(1 + 2kc\lambda_j^*\right)\frac{dv_j}{dt} + 2k\lambda_j^* v_j = 2kq_j, \tag{5.33}$$

where q_j is the jth component of the column vector $\mathbf{Q}$:

$$\mathbf{Q} = \mathbf{R}^T A\{\mathbf{X}_r r(t)\}. \tag{5.34}$$

As long as $2kc\lambda_j^* > 1$, the time constant for v_j will be approximately c. For any given set of λ_j^*, we can assure that all transients in the array response have time constant c by choosing k large enough that $2kc\lambda_j^* > 1$ for all λ_j^*, including the smallest one. Clearly it will be possible to do so only if the smallest eigenvalue is not zero.[‡] If $A\{\mathbf{X}_r\mathbf{X}_r^T\}$ has any zero eigenvalues, the feedback loop modification in Fig. 5.2 will not have the intended effect.

These remarks make it clear that some averaging is definitely necessary. For, without averaging,

$$A\{\mathbf{X}_r\mathbf{X}_r^T\} = \mathbf{X}_r\mathbf{X}_r^T, \tag{5.35}$$

and the matrix $\mathbf{X}_r\mathbf{X}_r^T$ is always of rank 1, so all but one of its eigenvalues are zero. As the averaging time is increased, these zero eigenvalues become nonzero, finally converging to the eigenvalues of $\mathbf{\Phi}_r$ for an infinite time average.

Next, with $A\{\mathbf{X}_r\mathbf{X}_r^T\}$ defined as a finite average, we must determine what averaging time is required to make all the eigenvalues nonzero. This question is most easily answered by considering the problem in discrete form. Suppose the signals in the array are sampled every ΔT seconds. Let $\mathbf{X}_{r_j}$ denote the jth sample of vector $\mathbf{X}_r$,

$$\mathbf{X}_{r_j} = \left[x_{I_1}(j\Delta t), x_{Q_1}(j\Delta t), x_{I_2}(j\Delta t), \dots\right]^T. \tag{5.36}$$

A finite time average of $\mathbf{X}_r\mathbf{X}_r^T$ over an interval T can be approximated by an average of K samples of $\mathbf{X}_r\mathbf{X}_r^T$,

$$A\{\mathbf{X}_r\mathbf{X}_r^T\} = \frac{1}{T}\int_{t-T}^{t}\mathbf{X}_r\mathbf{X}_r^T\, dt \cong \frac{1}{K}\sum_{j=1}^{K}\mathbf{X}_{r_j}\mathbf{X}_{r_j}^T, \tag{5.37}$$

where $T = K\Delta t$. Clearly at least $2N$ samples are required to make $A\{\mathbf{X}_r\mathbf{X}_r^T\}$ nonsingular. That is, the matrix $\mathbf{X}_{r_1}\mathbf{X}_{r_1}^T$ is of rank 1, $\frac{1}{2}(\mathbf{X}_{r_1}\mathbf{X}_{r_1}^T + \mathbf{X}_{r_2}\mathbf{X}_{r_2}^T)$ is of rank 2 (if $\mathbf{X}_{r_1}$ and $\mathbf{X}_{r_2}$ are not collinear), $\frac{1}{3}(\mathbf{X}_{r_1}\mathbf{X}_{r_1}^T + \mathbf{X}_{r_2}\mathbf{X}_{r_2}^T + \mathbf{X}_{r_3}\mathbf{X}_{r_3}^T)$ is of rank 3 (if $\mathbf{X}_{r_1}$, $\mathbf{X}_{r_2}$, and $\mathbf{X}_{r_3}$ are not coplanar), and so forth. Hence to be nonsingular,

[‡] $A\{\mathbf{X}_r\mathbf{X}_r^T\}$ is nonnegative definite, so all $\lambda_j^* \geq 0$.

the matrix $(1/K)\sum_{j=1}^{K}\mathbf{X}_{r_j}\mathbf{X}_{r_j}^T$ must contain at least $2N$ samples. For $K = 2N$, the matrix will be nonsingular as long as the $\mathbf{X}_{r_j}$ are linearly independent.

To make the vectors $\mathbf{X}_{r_j}$ independent, it is sufficient that the sampling times for the $\mathbf{X}_{r_j}$ be far enough apart. Since

$$\mathbf{X}_{r_i}^T\mathbf{X}_{r_j} = \sum_{\substack{k=1 \\ L=I,Q}}^{N} x_{L_k}(i\,\Delta t)x_{L_k}(j\,\Delta t), \tag{5.38}$$

we have

$$E\left(\mathbf{X}_{r_i}^T\mathbf{X}_{r_j}\right) = \sum_{\substack{k=1 \\ L=I,Q}}^{N} R_{x_{L_k}}[(j-i)\,\Delta t], \tag{5.39}$$

where $R_{x_k}(\tau)$ is the autocorrelation function of $x_{L_k}(t)$,

$$R_{x_{L_k}}(\tau) = E\left[x_{L_k}(t)x_{L_k}(t+\tau)\right]. \tag{5.40}$$

If the sampling time Δt is large enough that all the terms $R_{x_{L_k}}[(j-i)\,\Delta t]$ are small, then $E(\mathbf{X}_{r_i}^T\mathbf{X}_{r_j})$ is small, and $\mathbf{X}_{r_i}$ and $\mathbf{X}_{r_j}$ are nearly orthogonal, on the average. The value of Δt required to make $R_{x_{L_k}}(\Delta t) \cong 0$ may be determined from the spectral density of the signals $x_{L_k}(t)$. For example, if the signals have bandlimited power spectral density $S_{x_{L_k}}(\omega)$ equal to $\pi p_0/\Delta\omega$ over a bandwidth $\Delta\omega$, as shown in Fig. 5.3, then the autocorrelation function is

$$R_{x_{L_k}}(\tau) = p_0 \operatorname{sinc}\left(\frac{\Delta\omega\tau}{2}\right)\cos\omega_d\tau, \tag{5.41}$$

and we can insure that on the average the vectors $\mathbf{X}_{r_i}$ are orthogonal by choosing

$$\Delta t \cong \frac{2\pi}{\Delta\omega} = \frac{1}{B}, \tag{5.42}$$

where $B = \Delta\omega/2\pi$ is the bandwidth in hertz. Since at least $K = 2N$ samples of $\mathbf{X}_r$ will be required to make $(1/K)\sum_{j=1}^{K}\mathbf{X}_{r_j}\mathbf{X}_{r_j}^T$ nonsingular, the time interval used in Eq. (5.37) should be no less than approximately

$$T = \frac{2N}{B}, \tag{5.43}$$

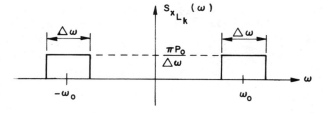

Figure 5.3   Power spectral density of $x_{L_k}(t)$.

in which case

$$A\{\mathbf{X}_r\mathbf{X}_r^T\} = \frac{B}{2N} \int_{t-2N/B}^{t} \mathbf{X}_r\mathbf{X}_r^T \, dt. \tag{5.44}$$

Of course, a longer averaging time than $2N/B$ can be used, if desired.

It is also useful to express the required averaging time in terms of carrier cycles. Since the carrier period is

$$T_0 = \frac{1}{f_0}, \tag{5.45}$$

where f_0 is the carrier frequency in hertz, we have

$$T = \frac{2N}{B/f_0} T_0. \tag{5.46}$$

Note that B/f_0 is the fractional bandwidth.

In practice, it appears that the averaging time can be somewhat smaller than this amount. The reason is that for $A\{\mathbf{X}_r\mathbf{X}_r^T\}$ to be nonsingular requires only linear independence of the $\mathbf{X}_{r_i}$, not orthogonality. The value of Δt given in Eq. (5.42) makes the $\mathbf{X}_{r_i}$ orthogonal, which is a stronger condition. In general, one finds that as the averaging time is reduced, k must be made larger to maintain $2kc\lambda_j^* > 1$ for the smallest eigenvalue. The smallest eigenvalue goes to zero as the averaging time is reduced.

The feedback loop described by Eq. (5.16) and shown in Fig. 5.2 may be described in complex notation similar to that used with the LMS loop. Using the definitions in Eqs. (2.52) through (2.57), one finds that Eq. (5.16) is equivalent to

$$\frac{dw_j}{dt} = kA\left\{ \tilde{x}_j^*(t)\left[\tilde{r}(t) - \mathbf{X}^T\mathbf{W} - c\mathbf{X}^T\frac{d\mathbf{W}}{dt} \right] \right\}. \tag{5.47}$$

Thus the modified loop in complex form is as shown in Fig. 5.4.

Now let us give an example to illustrate the behavior of the feedback loop in Fig. 5.4. Consider a two-element array of isotropic elements as shown in Fig. 2.15. Assume that a CW desired signal of amplitude A_d is incident on the array from broadside ($\theta_d = 0°$) at frequency ω_d. Assume also that a double-sideband, suppressed carrier AM interference signal of amplitude A_i, carrier frequency ω_d, and modulation frequency ω_m is incident on the array from an angle θ_i. Finally, assume that statistically independent, zero-mean random noise signals $\tilde{n}_i(t)$ with average power σ^2 are present in the signals $\tilde{x}_i(t)$. The resulting signals in the array are

$$\tilde{x}_1(t) = A_d e^{j\omega_d t} + A_i \cos \omega_m t \, e^{j\omega_d t} + \tilde{n}_1(t) \tag{5.48}$$

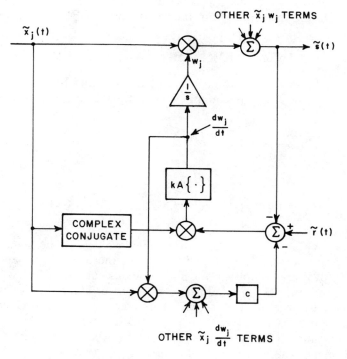

Figure 5.4 The complex modified LMS loop.

and

$$\tilde{x}_2(t) = A_d e^{j\omega_d t} + A_i \cos \omega_m t \, e^{(j\omega_d t - \phi_i)} + \tilde{n}_2(t), \qquad (5.49)$$

where

$$\phi_i = \frac{\omega_0 L}{c_0} \sin \theta_i. \qquad (5.50)$$

In Eq. (5.50), L is the element spacing and c_0 is the velocity of light. We assume the reference signal is

$$\tilde{r}(t) = e^{j\omega_d t}. \qquad (5.51)$$

The array weights satisfy Eq. (5.47). To determine typical weight transients, we have solved these equations numerically using a discrete (difference equation) approximation, as follows: All quantities in the equation are sampled every Δt seconds. We let $\mathbf{W}(j)$ be the jth sampled value of the weight vector. We approximate

$$\frac{d\mathbf{W}}{dt} \cong \frac{\Delta \mathbf{W}(j)}{\Delta t} = \frac{\mathbf{W}(j+1) - \mathbf{W}(j)}{\Delta t}. \qquad (5.52)$$

Substituting this equation in the vector form of Eq. (5.47) yields an equation for $\Delta\mathbf{W}(j)$:

$$\left[\mathbf{I} + kcA_j(\mathbf{X}^*\mathbf{X}^T)\right]\Delta\mathbf{W}(j) = k\,\Delta t\,A_j\left\{\mathbf{X}^*\left[\tilde{r}(t) - \mathbf{X}^T\mathbf{W}\right]\right\}, \qquad (5.53)$$

where $A_j\{\cdot\}$ denotes the average of the quantity in brackets at the jth sample. The average $A_j\{\cdot\}$ is computed as a moving average over the last J samples:

$$A_j(\mathbf{X}^*\mathbf{X}^T) = \frac{1}{J}\sum_{k=j-J+1}^{j}\mathbf{X}_k^*\mathbf{X}_k^T \qquad (5.54)$$

and

$$A_j\left\{\mathbf{X}^*\left[\tilde{r}(t) - \mathbf{X}^T\mathbf{W}\right]\right\} = \frac{1}{J}\sum_{k=j-J+1}^{j}\mathbf{X}_k^*\left[\tilde{r}_k - \mathbf{X}_k^T\mathbf{W}(k)\right], \qquad (5.55)$$

where $\mathbf{X}_k$ and $\tilde{r}_k$ are the kth sampled values of the signal vector $\mathbf{X}$ and the reference signal $\tilde{r}(t)$. At each iteration, the averaged quantities in Eqs. (5.54) and (5.55) are computed, the simultaneous equations for $\Delta\mathbf{W}(j)$ are solved, and the resulting $\Delta\mathbf{W}(j)$ is added to $\mathbf{W}(j)$ to produce the new value of the weight vector for the next iteration. This iterative process is continued until the transient behavior of $\mathbf{W}(j)$ is determined.[‡]

Figure 5.5 shows a typical set of weight transients, computed for the parameter values $\sigma^2 = 1$, $A_d = 10$ ($\xi_d = 10$ dB), $k = 0.025$, $c = 100$, $\Delta t = \pi/2\omega_d$ (4 samples/carrier cycle), $\omega_0 L/c_0 = \pi$ (half-wavelength element spacing), $\theta_i = 30°$, $\omega_m = 0.5\,\omega_0$, and $A_j\{\cdot\}$ an average of 8 samples ($J = 8$).

Figure 5.5(a) shows the weight transients that result when $A_i = 0$ (i.e., when there is no interference). Figure 5.5(b) shows the transients when the interference power is 30 dB above thermal noise ($\xi_i = 30$ dB), and Fig. 5.5(c) shows them when $\xi_i =$ is 60 dB. In all cases, the weight vector starts from an arbitrary value of

$$\mathbf{W} = \begin{bmatrix} 1 - j \\ 1 - j \end{bmatrix}. \qquad (5.56)$$

Comparison of Figs. 5.5(a), (b), and (c) shows that in all three cases the weight transients have the same time constant. None of the parameters in the feedback loops have been changed from one figure to the next. The only change is the interference amplitude, which is seen to have no effect on the speed of response of the loops. This constant speed of response is the behavior that we set out to obtain.

We have now found a feedback loop with the desired transient behavior. However, we shall make one further change in the loop to make it more

‡Equation (5.53) is not useful as a discrete algorithm in its own right, because it requires the solution of a set of simultaneous equations for $\Delta\mathbf{W}(j)$ at each iteration.

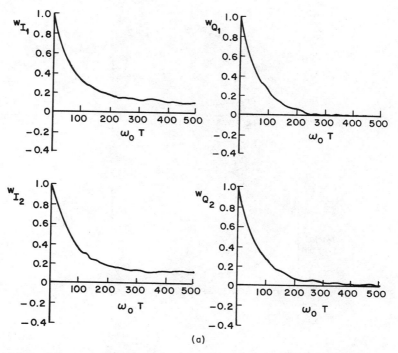

Figure 5.5   (a) Weight transients with no interference (reprinted from [1] with permission, © 1980 IEEE).

practical. Specifically, it is helpful to replace the finite time average $A\{\cdot\}$ in Fig. 5.4 with a lowpass filter. A lowpass filter is much easier to implement.

Implementing the finite time average $A\{\cdot\}$ in Eq. (5.37) would require signal processing as shown in Fig. 5.6. In practice, such a processor is difficult to build because of the time delay T. Instead, it is preferable to use a simple lowpass filter.

Suppose we replace the finite time average with a single-pole lowpass filter, that is, a filter with transfer function

$$H(s) = \frac{k}{Ts + 1}, \qquad (5.57)$$

as shown in Fig. 5.7. The impulse response of this filter is

$$h(t) = ke^{-t/T}. \qquad (5.58)$$

If the input to this filter is $f(t)$, the output $g(t)$ will be the convolution of $f(t)$ and $h(t)$:

$$g(t) = \int_{-\infty}^{\infty} h(t - \tau)f(\tau)\, d\tau. \qquad (5.59)$$

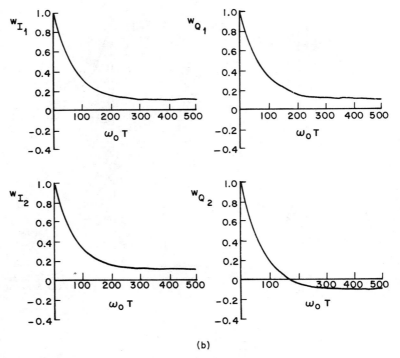

(b)

Figure 5.5 (*continued*)   (b) Weight transients with $\xi_i = 30$ dB (reprinted from [1] with permission, © 1980 IEEE).

This convolution integral essentially averages $f(t)$, with the most recent values of $f(t)$ weighted more heavily than previous values, as shown in Fig. 5.8. In Eq. (5.57), we have chosen the time constant of the filter equal to the time duration T in Eq. (5.43). In this way the averaging will involve a similar interval of time.

Suppose the finite time average in Fig. 5.4 is replaced with the lowpass filter shown in Fig. 5.7. Then the modified loop will be as shown in Fig. 5.9. Let us see how this change affects the weight transients.

Consider first the one-dimensional loop shown in Fig. 5.10. Denoting the output of the lowpass filter by u, we find that u satisfies the differential equation

$$T\frac{du}{dt} + u = k\tilde{x}^*(t)\left[\tilde{r}(t) - \tilde{x}(t)w - c\tilde{x}(t)\frac{dw}{dt}\right]. \qquad (5.60)$$

Substituting

$$u = \frac{dw}{dt} \qquad (5.61)$$

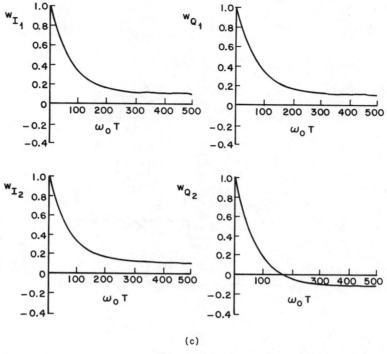

Figure 5.5 (*continued*)   (c) Weight transients with $\xi_i = 60$ dB (reprinted from [1] with permission, © 1980 IEEE).

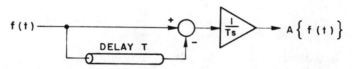

Figure 5.6   Processing for a finite time averaging.

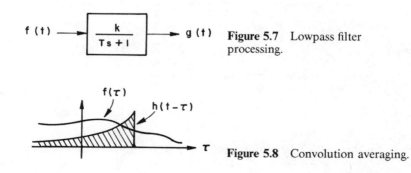

Figure 5.7   Lowpass filter processing.

Figure 5.8   Convolution averaging.

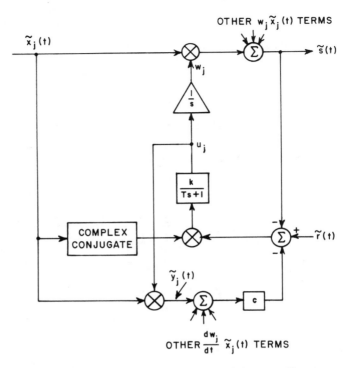

Figure 5.9 The modified loop with lowpass filter.

into Eq. (5.60) yields the differential equation for w,

$$T\frac{d^2w}{dt^2} + \left[1 + kc|\tilde{x}(t)|^2\right]\frac{dw}{dt} + k|\tilde{x}(t)|^2 w = k\tilde{x}^*(t)\tilde{r}(t). \quad (5.62)$$

Let us calculate the transients that result when $|x(t)|^2$ and $\tilde{x}^*(t)\tilde{r}(t)$ are replaced by their average values. We define

$$p = E\left[|\tilde{x}(t)|^2\right] \quad (5.63)$$

and

$$q = E\left[\tilde{x}^*(t)\tilde{r}(t)\right], \quad (5.64)$$

and, in place of Eq. (5.62), we write

$$T\frac{d^2w}{dt^2} + (1 + kcp)\frac{dw}{dt} + kpw = kq. \quad (5.65)$$

Note that the differential equation for w is now second order. The transient

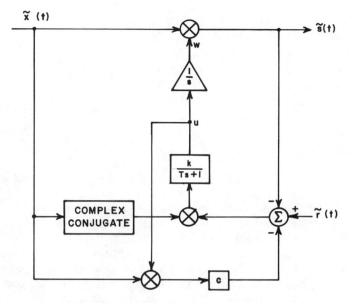

Figure 5.10 One-dimensional loop with lowpass filter.

solutions will be of the form

$$w(t) = c_1 e^{s_1 t} + c_2 e^{s_2 t} + \frac{q}{p}, \tag{5.66}$$

where s_1 and s_2 are the roots of the characteristic equation

$$Ts^2 + (1 + kcp)s + kp = 0. \tag{5.67}$$

These roots are given by

$$s_{1,2} = -\frac{1 + kcp}{2T}\left[1 \pm \sqrt{1 - \frac{4Tkp}{(1 + kcp)^2}}\right]. \tag{5.68}$$

Note that

$$\frac{4Tkp}{(1 + kcp)^2} = \frac{4kp}{1 + kcp}\frac{T}{1 + kcp} \cong 4\frac{T}{c}\frac{1}{1 + kcp} \ll 1, \tag{5.69}$$

because we assume $kcp \gg 1$ and $c \gg T$. Therefore, we may use the approximation

$$\sqrt{1 - x} = 1 - \frac{x}{2} \tag{5.70}$$

to obtain the roots in Eq. (5.68). The result is

$$s_1 = -\frac{kp}{1 + kcp} \cong -\frac{1}{c} \tag{5.71}$$

and

$$s_2 = -\frac{1}{c}\left[\frac{c}{T}(1 + kcp) - 1\right] = -\frac{\kappa}{c}, \tag{5.72}$$

where

$$\kappa = \frac{c}{T}(1 + kcp) - 1 \cong \frac{c}{T}(kcp) \gg 1. \tag{5.73}$$

Thus the root at $s = s_1$ has a fixed location in the s-plane, not dependent on signal power p. This root contributes a term with fixed time constant to the weight transient in Eq. (5.66). This term is analogous to the solution to Eq. (5.28). The second root at $s = s_2$ contributes a faster term $e^{-\kappa t/c}$ to the weight response. The speed of response of this term depends on signal power. Thus it would appear that changing to a lowpass filter has negated the advantage of the modified loop. However, it turns out that the amplitude of this fast term in the weight transient is much smaller, by the ratio κ, than the term with fixed time constant. Hence this undesired term contributes only negligibly to the weight response when κ is large.

To see that the undesired term is very small, let us compute the transient response in a typical situation. Suppose that at $t = 0$ the weight starts from a steady-state condition, that is, $w'(0) = 0$, with initial value $w(0)$. From Eq. (5.66), we find

$$w(0) = c_1 + c_2 + \frac{q}{p}, \tag{5.74}$$

and

$$w'(0) = s_1 c_1 + s_2 c_2 = 0. \tag{5.75}$$

Solving these equations for c_1 and c_2 yields

$$c_1 = \frac{\kappa[w(0) - q/p]}{\kappa - 1} \tag{5.76}$$

and

$$c_2 = -\frac{w(0) - q/p}{\kappa - 1} = -\frac{c_1}{\kappa}. \tag{5.77}$$

Thus the weight transient will be

$$w(t) = \frac{\kappa}{\kappa - 1}\left[w(0) - \frac{q}{p}\right]e^{-t/c} - \frac{1}{\kappa - 1}\left[w(0) - \frac{q}{p}\right]e^{-\kappa t/c} + \frac{q}{p}. \tag{5.78}$$

Note that the second term is smaller than the first by the ratio κ. Equation (5.73) shows that κ is greater than c/T, which is itself much greater than unity. Typically c, the array time constant, will be at least 100 times longer than the averaging time T. In this case the second term in Eq. (5.78) is smaller by a factor of at least 100 than the first term. As the signal power is increased, the amplitude of the second term becomes even smaller in proportion to the first. Thus the second term may be regarded as negligible. We can achieve the desired transient performance from the array feedback by replacing the finite time average with a lowpass filter.

For the multidimensional loop of Fig. 5.9, the weight vector obeys the differential equation

$$T\frac{d^2\mathbf{W}}{dt^2} + (\mathbf{I} + kc\mathbf{X}^*\mathbf{X}^T)\frac{d\mathbf{W}}{dt} + k\mathbf{X}^*\mathbf{X}^T\mathbf{W} = k\mathbf{X}^*\tilde{r}(t). \tag{5.79}$$

Replacing $\mathbf{X}^*\mathbf{X}^t$ by $\boldsymbol{\Phi}$ and $\mathbf{X}^*\tilde{r}(t)$ by $\mathbf{S}$ gives

$$T\frac{d^2\mathbf{W}}{dt^2} + (\mathbf{I} + kc\boldsymbol{\Phi})\frac{d\mathbf{W}}{dt} + k\boldsymbol{\Phi}\mathbf{W} = k\mathbf{S}. \tag{5.80}$$

Making a coordinate rotation

$$\mathbf{W} = \mathbf{R}\mathbf{V}, \tag{5.81}$$

multiplying on the left by $\mathbf{R}^\dagger$, and choosing $\mathbf{R}$ so $\mathbf{R}^\dagger\boldsymbol{\Phi}\mathbf{R}$ is diagonal, we find that v_i, the ith component of $\mathbf{V}$, satisfies

$$T\frac{d^2v_j}{dt^2} + (1 + kc\lambda_i)\frac{dv_i}{dt} + k\lambda_i v_i = kq_i, \tag{5.82}$$

where q_i is the ith component of the vector $\mathbf{Q} = \mathbf{R}^\dagger\mathbf{S}$. The solution of this equation is identical to Eq. (5.78) with $p \to \lambda_i$ and $q \to q_i$. Thus we see that as long as $c/T \gg 1$ and $kc\lambda_i > 1$ for all λ_i, only the $e^{-t/c}$ term will be significant in $v_i(t)$, for all i, and hence $\mathbf{W}(t)$ will have the desired fixed time constant.

Finally, we note that the modifications made to the LMS loop to obtain a fixed time constant can also be made to the Applebaum loop, where a steering vector is used instead of a reference signal. Figure 5.11 shows the modified Applebaum loop using a finite time average $A\{\cdot\}$, and Fig. 5.12 shows the loop with a lowpass filter. For the loop of Fig. 5.11, the weight vector satisfies the differential equation

$$\left[\mathbf{I} + 2kcA\{\mathbf{X}^*\mathbf{X}^T\}\right]\frac{d\mathbf{W}}{dt} + kA\{\mathbf{X}^*\mathbf{X}^T\}\mathbf{W} = \mu\mathbf{T}^*, \tag{5.83}$$

whereas in Fig. 5.12, it satisfies

$$T\frac{d^2\mathbf{W}}{dt^2} + \left[\mathbf{I} + kc\mathbf{X}^*\mathbf{X}^T\right]\frac{d\mathbf{W}}{dt} + k\mathbf{X}^*\mathbf{X}^T\mathbf{W} = \mu\mathbf{T}^*. \tag{5.84}$$

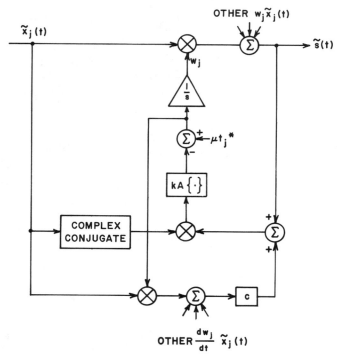

Figure 5.11 The modified Applebaum loop with averaging $A\{\cdot\}$.

The transient behavior of the weight vector with these loops is obviously the same as with the modified LMS loops.

An adaptive array using modified LMS loops as shown in Fig. 5.9 has been built and tested. This work is described by Yu [9]. He found that the transient response of the array is essentially independent of the eigenvalues, as desired. However, he also found another result: The array performance is quite sensitive to signal leakage through the derivative multiplier. Before leaving the subject of the modified LMS loop, we shall discuss this important result.

Consider the loop in Fig. 5.9 again. Let the output from the derivative multiplier by $\tilde{y}_j(t)$, as shown in Fig. 5.9. Ideally, $\tilde{y}_j(t)$ should be

$$\tilde{y}_j(t) = \tilde{x}_j(t)\frac{dw_j}{dt}. \tag{5.85}$$

In practice, however, $\tilde{y}_j(t)$ may contain a small amount of the signal $\tilde{x}_j(t)$ even when $dw_j/dt = 0$. This problem will occur if the multiplier is not properly balanced. When this leakage is present, $\tilde{y}_j(t)$ is actually given by

$$\tilde{y}_j(t) = \tilde{x}_j(t)\left[l_j + \frac{dw_j}{dt}\right], \tag{5.86}$$

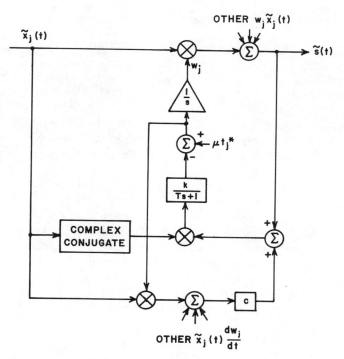

Figure 5.12   The modified Applebaum loop with lowpass filter averaging.

instead of Eq. (5.85), where l_j is a small leakage coefficient. To see how l_j affects the array weights, note that u_j in Fig. 5.9 satisfies

$$T\frac{du_j}{dt} + u_j = k\tilde{x}_j^*(t)\left[\tilde{r}(t) - \sum_{j=1}^{N} w_j\tilde{x}_j(t) - c\sum_{j=1}^{N}\tilde{y}_j(t)\right]. \qquad (5.87)$$

Substituting in $u_j = dw_j/dt$, using Eq. (5.86) for $\tilde{y}_j(t)$, and changing to vector notation, we find that the weight vector $\mathbf{W}$ satisfies

$$T\frac{d^2\mathbf{W}}{dt^2} + \frac{d\mathbf{W}}{dt} = k\mathbf{X}^*\left[\tilde{r}(t) - \mathbf{X}^T\mathbf{W} - c\mathbf{X}^T\left(\mathbf{L} + \frac{d\mathbf{W}}{dt}\right)\right], \qquad (5.88)$$

where $\mathbf{L}$ is a vector containing the leakage coefficients,

$$\mathbf{L} = [l_1, l_2, \ldots, l_N]^T. \qquad (5.89)$$

Rearranging Eq. (5.88) and taking expectations of the signal products yields the differential equation for $\mathbf{W}$,

$$T\frac{d^2\mathbf{W}}{dt^2} + (\mathbf{I} + kc\mathbf{\Phi})\frac{d\mathbf{W}}{dt} + k\mathbf{\Phi}\mathbf{W} = k(\mathbf{S} - c\mathbf{\Phi}\mathbf{L}). \qquad (5.90)$$

The steady-state **W** that results from this equation is

$$\mathbf{W} = \boldsymbol{\Phi}^{-1}(\mathbf{S} - c\boldsymbol{\Phi}\mathbf{L}) = \boldsymbol{\Phi}^{-1}\mathbf{S} - c\mathbf{L}. \tag{5.91}$$

Since $\boldsymbol{\Phi}^{-1}\mathbf{S}$ is the optimal weight vector, we see that each leakage coefficient l_j causes an error of $-cl_j$ directly to weight w_j. This error can quickly degrade the array performance, of course. The effect is identical to the effect of offset voltages, as described in section 4.3, or to the effect of steering vector errors in the Applebaum array, as will be described in section 6.3. Comparing Eqs. (5.90) and (4.73) shows that the vector $-c\boldsymbol{\Phi}\mathbf{L}$ plays the same role mathematically as the offset vector $\boldsymbol{\Delta}$ in Eq. (4.73).

Thus, if an array is to be implemented with loops as shown in Figs. 5.9 and 5.12, care must be taken to insure that signal leakage through the derivative multipliers is minimized. These multipliers must remain well balanced over the entire range of signal powers to be received by the array. If necessary, IF weights, as discussed in section 4.3 for eliminating offset voltages, may be used to overcome leakage in the derivative multiplier. The IF loop shown in Fig. 4.24 can be augmented with a derivative loop as in Fig. 5.9. With IF weights, signal leakage through the derivative multiplier is on a different frequency from the desired multiplier product, so it can be eliminated by filtering.

5.2 THE GRAM-SCHMIDT PREPROCESSOR

Another method of overcoming the problem of eigenvalue spread is the use of a Gram-Schmidt preprocessor. A Gram-Schmidt preprocessor combines the original signals from the array elements to produce a new set of uncorrelated signals. These new signals are then used as inputs to an LMS or Applebaum array processor. The technique is called a Gram-Schmidt preprocessor by analogy with the well-known Gram-Schmidt procedure for obtaining a set of mutually orthogonal vectors from a set of linearly independent vectors [10]. The Gram-Schmidt technique has been described by Brennan, Mallett, and Reed [2].

To understand this procedure, we first present a simple theorem.

Theorem. Let $\tilde{x}_1(t), \ldots, \tilde{x}_N(t)$ be a set of signals from N elements of an array. Let $\tilde{y}_1(t), \ldots, \tilde{y}_N(t)$ be a new set of N signals, each a linear combination of the $\tilde{x}_j(t)$. Assume that the transformation between the $\tilde{x}_j(t)$ and the $\tilde{y}_j(t)$ is nonsingular, that is, invertible. Then an LMS array using signals $\tilde{y}_j(t)$ as inputs will produce the same output signal and hence SINR as one using the $\tilde{x}_j(t)$ as inputs. Moreover, an Applebaum array using the $\tilde{y}_j(t)$ as inputs will also produce the same output signal and SINR as one using the $\tilde{x}_j(t)$ if the steering vector is transformed in the same way as the signals.

Proof. Let the $\tilde{y}_j(t)$ be related to the $\tilde{x}_j(t)$ by

$$\tilde{y}_1(t) = \mathbf{V}_1^T \mathbf{X},$$
$$\tilde{y}_2(t) = \mathbf{V}_2^T \mathbf{X},$$

and
$$\tilde{y}_N(t) = \mathbf{V}_N^T \mathbf{X}, \tag{5.92}$$

where

$$\mathbf{V}_1 = \begin{bmatrix} v_{11} & v_{12} & \cdots & v_{1N} \end{bmatrix}^T,$$
$$\mathbf{V}_2 = \begin{bmatrix} v_{21} & v_{22} & \cdots & v_{2N} \end{bmatrix}^T,$$
$$\vdots$$
$$\mathbf{V}_N = \begin{bmatrix} v_{N1} & v_{N2} & \cdots & v_{NN} \end{bmatrix}^T, \tag{5.93}$$

and

$$\mathbf{X} = \begin{bmatrix} \tilde{x}_1(t), \ldots, \tilde{x}_N(t) \end{bmatrix}^T. \tag{5.94}$$

Define a matrix $\mathbf{V}$ with columns $\mathbf{V}_i$,

$$\mathbf{V} = \begin{bmatrix} \mathbf{V}_1 & \mathbf{V}_2 & \cdots & \mathbf{V}_N \end{bmatrix}. \tag{5.95}$$

Then Eqs. (5.92) may be written

$$\mathbf{Y} = \mathbf{V}^T \mathbf{X}, \tag{5.96}$$

where $\mathbf{Y}$ is the signal vector associated with the $\tilde{y}_j(t)$,

$$\mathbf{Y} = \begin{bmatrix} \tilde{y}_1(t), \ldots, \tilde{y}_N(t) \end{bmatrix}^T. \tag{5.97}$$

The matrix $\mathbf{V}$ is nonsingular by assumption.

Now suppose the signals $\tilde{y}_j(t)$ are used as inputs to an LMS array with reference signal $\tilde{r}(t)$. Let $\mathbf{W}$ be the steady-state weight vector produced by this array. Then

$$\mathbf{W} = \mathbf{\Phi}_y^{-1} \mathbf{S}_y, \tag{5.98}$$

where $\mathbf{\Phi}_y$ is the covariance matrix of the signals $\tilde{y}_j(t)$,

$$\mathbf{\Phi}_y = E\begin{bmatrix} \mathbf{Y}^* \mathbf{Y}^T \end{bmatrix}, \tag{5.99}$$

and $\mathbf{S}_y$ is the reference correlation vector based on the $\tilde{y}_j(t)$,

$$\mathbf{S}_y = E\begin{bmatrix} \mathbf{Y}^* \tilde{r}(t) \end{bmatrix}. \tag{5.100}$$

With this weight vector, the array output signal will be

$$\tilde{s}(t) = \mathbf{Y}^T \mathbf{W} = \mathbf{Y}^T \mathbf{\Phi}_y^{-1} \mathbf{S}_y. \tag{5.101}$$

However, substituting Eq. (5.96) in Eqs. (5.99) and (5.100) gives

$$\mathbf{\Phi}_y = \mathbf{V}^\dagger \mathbf{\Phi}_x \mathbf{V} \tag{5.102}$$

and

$$\mathbf{S}_y = E\left[\mathbf{Y}^* \tilde{r}(t)\right] = \mathbf{V}^\dagger \mathbf{S}_x, \tag{5.103}$$

where $\mathbf{\Phi}_x$ and $\mathbf{S}_x$ are the covariance matrix and reference correlation vector associated with the signal vector $\mathbf{X}$. Since $\mathbf{V}$ is nonsingular, Eq. (5.101) may be written

$$\tilde{s}(t) = \mathbf{X}^T \mathbf{V} \mathbf{V}^{-1} \mathbf{\Phi}_x^{-1} (\mathbf{V}^\dagger)^{-1} \mathbf{V}^\dagger \mathbf{S}_x = \mathbf{X}^T \mathbf{\Phi}_x^{-1} \mathbf{S}_x. \tag{5.104}$$

This $\tilde{s}(t)$ is the same output signal that results when an LMS array has input signals $\tilde{x}_j(t)$ and reference signal $\tilde{r}(t)$. The only requirement for the theorem to hold is that $\mathbf{V}$ is invertible.

Next suppose an Applebaum array has input signals $\tilde{y}_j(t)$. Let the steering vector in the Applebaum processor be $\mathbf{Q}^*$. The steady-state weight vector in this case is

$$\mathbf{W} = \mu \mathbf{\Phi}_y^{-1} \mathbf{Q}^*, \tag{5.105}$$

where μ is an arbitrary gain constant. But because of Eq. (5.102), $\mathbf{W}$ may also be written

$$\mathbf{W} = \mu \mathbf{V}^{-1} \mathbf{\Phi}_x^{-1} (\mathbf{V}^\dagger)^{-1} \mathbf{Q}^*, \tag{5.106}$$

and the array output signal is

$$\tilde{s}(t) = \mathbf{Y}^T \mathbf{W} = \mu \mathbf{X}^T \mathbf{V} \mathbf{V}^{-1} \mathbf{\Phi}_x^{-1} (\mathbf{V}^\dagger)^{-1} \mathbf{Q}^* = \mu \mathbf{X}^T \mathbf{\Phi}_x^{-1} (\mathbf{V}^\dagger)^{-1} \mathbf{Q}^*. \tag{5.107}$$

Consider an Applebaum array with steering vector $\mathbf{T}^*$ and input signals $\tilde{x}_j(t)$. For this array the output signal would be

$$\tilde{s}(t) = \mu \mathbf{X}^T \mathbf{\Phi}_x^{-1} \mathbf{T}^*. \tag{5.108}$$

Thus the $\tilde{s}(t)$ in Eqs. (5.107) and (5.108) are the same if $\mathbf{T}^*$ and $\mathbf{Q}^*$ are related by

$$\mathbf{T}^* = (\mathbf{V}^\dagger)^{-1} \mathbf{Q}^* \tag{5.109}$$

or

$$\mathbf{Q} = \mathbf{V}^T \mathbf{T}. \tag{5.110}$$

Hence an Applebaum array will produce the same output signal in the two cases if the steering vectors are transformed in the same way as the signals, that is, according to Eq. (5.110). The proof of the theorem has now been completed.

Now let us define the Gram-Schmidt preprocessor. A Gram-Schmidt preprocessor is one that combines the signals $\tilde{x}_j(t)$ in such a way that the new

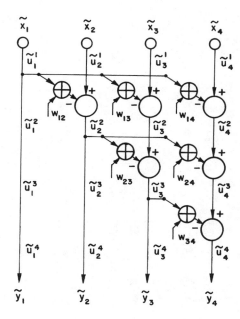

Figure 5.13 A Gram-Schmidt preprocessor.

signals $\tilde{y}_j(t)$ are mutually uncorrelated. It is simplest to explain a Gram-Schmidt preprocessor by means of an example.

Suppose there are four element signals, $\tilde{x}_1(t), \ldots, \tilde{x}_4(t)$. Assume these are combined as shown in Fig. 5.13 to produce new signals $\tilde{y}_1(t), \ldots, \tilde{y}_4(t)$. We shall choose the weights in Fig. 5.13 so that the signals $\tilde{y}_j(t)$ are mutually uncorrelated. To this end, we adopt the following notation: Let the signals $\tilde{u}_j^1(t)$ be the same as the $\tilde{x}_j(t)$. The superscript 1 indicates that these are the signals in the first row of the processor. Then, let $\tilde{u}_j^2(t)$ denote the signals in the second row of the processor, and so forth, up to $\tilde{u}_j^4(t) = \tilde{y}_j(t)$, the signals in the fourth row.

In Fig. 5.13, the signals in the second row are obtained from those in the first row as follows. For $j = 1$, we let

$$\tilde{u}_1^2(t) = \tilde{u}_1^1(t) = \tilde{x}_1(t). \tag{5.111}$$

For $j \geqslant 2$, $\tilde{u}_j^2(t)$ is obtained by subtracting a weighted version of $\tilde{u}_1^1(t)$ from $\tilde{u}_j^1(t)$. Thus,

$$\tilde{u}_2^2(t) = \tilde{u}_2^1(t) - w_{12}\tilde{u}_1^1(t) = \tilde{x}_2(t) - w_{12}\tilde{x}_1(t), \tag{5.112}$$

$$\tilde{u}_3^2(t) = \tilde{u}_3^1(t) - w_{13}\tilde{u}_1^1(t) = \tilde{x}_3(t) - w_{13}\tilde{x}_1(t), \tag{5.113}$$

and

$$\tilde{u}_4^2(t) = \tilde{u}_4^1(t) - w_{14}\tilde{u}_1^1(t) = \tilde{x}_4(t) - w_{14}\tilde{x}_1(t). \tag{5.114}$$

The weights w_{1j} for $2 \leqslant j \leqslant 4$ are chosen to decorrelate the signals $\tilde{u}_j^2(t)$ for

$2 \leqslant j \leqslant 4$ from $\tilde{u}_1^1(t) = \tilde{x}_1(t)$. Thus we choose w_{12} so that

$$E\{x_1^*(t)\tilde{u}_2^2(t)\} = E\{\tilde{x}_1^*(t)[\tilde{x}_2(t) - w_{12}\tilde{x}_1(t)]\} = 0, \qquad (5.115)$$

or

$$w_{12} = \frac{E[\tilde{x}_1^*(t)\tilde{x}_2(t)]}{E[\tilde{x}_1^*(t)\tilde{x}_1(t)]}. \qquad (5.116)$$

Similarly, we choose w_{13}, so

$$E[\tilde{x}_1^*(t)\tilde{u}_3^2(t)] = E\{x_1^*(t)[\tilde{x}_3(t) - w_{13}\tilde{x}_1(t)]\} = 0, \qquad (5.117)$$

or

$$w_{13} = \frac{E[\tilde{x}_1^*(t)\tilde{x}_3(t)]}{E[\tilde{x}_1^*(t)\tilde{x}_1(t)]}. \qquad (5.118)$$

The weight w_{14} is chosen similarly. Thus the weights in the first row are

$$w_{1j} = \frac{E[\tilde{x}_1^*(t)\tilde{x}_j(t)]}{E[\tilde{x}_1^*(t)\tilde{x}_1(t)]}, \qquad 2 \leqslant j \leqslant 4, \qquad (5.119)$$

and with these weights $\tilde{u}_1^2(t) = \tilde{x}_1(t)$ is decorrelated from $\tilde{u}_j^2(t)$ for $2 \leqslant j \leqslant 4$,

$$E[\tilde{x}_1^*(t)\tilde{u}_j^2(t)] = 0, \qquad 2 \leqslant j \leqslant 4. \qquad (5.120)$$

In the third row, we obtain the signals as follows: For the first two signals, for $j = 1, 2$, we have

$$\tilde{u}_1^3(t) = \tilde{u}_1^2(t) = \tilde{x}_1(t) \qquad (5.121)$$

and

$$\tilde{u}_2^3(t) = \tilde{u}_2^2(t). \qquad (5.122)$$

For $j \geqslant 3$, the $\tilde{u}_j^3(t)$ are obtained by decorrelating $\tilde{u}_2^2(t)$ from all signals in the third row to the right of $\tilde{u}_2^2(t)$, in the same way as in the second row. Since $\tilde{u}_1^2(t)$ is already decorrelated from $\tilde{u}_j^2(t)$ for $2 \leqslant j \leqslant 4$, the outputs $\tilde{u}_3^3(t)$ and $\tilde{u}_4^3(t)$ in the third row will necessarily be decorrelated from $\tilde{u}_1^2(t)$, because $\tilde{u}_3^3(t)$ and $\tilde{u}_4^3(t)$ are each a linear combination of two $\tilde{u}_j^2(t)$ for $2 \leqslant j \leqslant 4$. To decorrelate $\tilde{u}_3^3(t)$ and $\tilde{u}_4^3(t)$ from $\tilde{u}_2^2(t)$, we use the weights,

$$w_{2j} = \frac{E[\tilde{u}_2^{2*}(t)\tilde{u}_j^2(t)]}{E[\tilde{u}_2^{2*}(t)\tilde{u}_2^2(t)]}, \qquad 3 \leqslant j \leqslant 4. \qquad (5.123)$$

Then $\tilde{u}_3^3(t)$ and $\tilde{u}_4^3(t)$ will be decorrelated from both $\tilde{u}_1^3(t) = \tilde{u}_1^2(t)$ and $\tilde{u}_2^3(t) = \tilde{u}_2^2(t)$.

Continuing in this manner, we obtain the overall structure in Fig. 5.13, which is the Gram-Schmidt preprocessor. In this processor, all of the outputs $\tilde{y}_1(t), \ldots, \tilde{y}_4(t)$ have been decorrelated from one another. This system is called a

Gram-Schmidt preprocessor because of its obvious relation to the Gram-Schmidt procedure for orthogonalizing vectors [10]. In general, for a larger array with N signals $\tilde{x}_1(t), \ldots, \tilde{x}_N(t)$, the weights that decorrelate the outputs $\tilde{y}_1(t), \ldots, \tilde{y}_N(t)$ are

$$w_{kj} = \frac{E\left[\tilde{u}_k^{k*}(t)\tilde{u}_j^k(t)\right]}{E\left[\tilde{u}_k^{k*}(t)\tilde{u}_k^k(t)\right]}, \quad 1 \leqslant k \leqslant N - 1, \quad k + 1 \leqslant j \leqslant N. \quad (5.124)$$

Now let us show that the transformation relating the $\tilde{y}_j(t)$ to the $\tilde{x}_i(t)$ is an invertible transformation. Consider Fig. 5.13 again and note that the signals in the second row are related to those in the first row by the matrix transformation

$$\begin{bmatrix} \tilde{u}_1^2 \\ \tilde{u}_2^2 \\ \tilde{u}_3^2 \\ \tilde{u}_4^2 \end{bmatrix} = \begin{bmatrix} 1 & 0 & 0 & 0 \\ -w_{12} & 1 & 0 & 0 \\ -w_{13} & 0 & 1 & 0 \\ -w_{14} & 0 & 0 & 1 \end{bmatrix} \begin{bmatrix} \tilde{u}_1^1 \\ \tilde{u}_2^1 \\ \tilde{u}_3^1 \\ \tilde{u}_4^1 \end{bmatrix} \quad (5.125)$$

or

$$\mathbf{U}^2 = \mathbf{T}_{21}\mathbf{U}^1, \quad (5.126)$$

where $\mathbf{U}^k$ is a column vector with components $\tilde{u}_j^k(t)$, $1 \leqslant j \leqslant 4$, and where $\mathbf{T}_{21}$ is the matrix transforming $\mathbf{U}^1$ into $\mathbf{U}^2$,

$$\mathbf{T}_{21} = \begin{bmatrix} 1 & 0 & 0 & 0 \\ -w_{12} & 1 & 0 & 0 \\ -w_{13} & 0 & 1 & 0 \\ -w_{14} & 0 & 0 & 1 \end{bmatrix}. \quad (5.127)$$

Similarly, the signals in the third row are related to those in the second by

$$\mathbf{U}^3 = \mathbf{T}_{32}\mathbf{U}^2, \quad (5.128)$$

where

$$\mathbf{T}_{32} = \begin{bmatrix} 1 & 0 & 0 & 0 \\ 0 & 1 & 0 & 0 \\ 0 & -w_{23} & 1 & 0 \\ 0 & -w_{24} & 0 & 1 \end{bmatrix}. \quad (5.129)$$

Finally, those in the last row are related to those in the third row by

$$\mathbf{U}^4 = \mathbf{T}_{43}\mathbf{U}^3, \quad (5.130)$$

where

$$\mathbf{T}_{43} = \begin{bmatrix} 1 & 0 & 0 & 0 \\ 0 & 1 & 0 & 0 \\ 0 & 0 & 1 & 0 \\ 0 & 0 & -w_{34} & 1 \end{bmatrix}. \tag{5.131}$$

Altogether $\mathbf{Y} = \mathbf{U}^4$ is related to $\mathbf{X} = \mathbf{U}^1$ by

$$\mathbf{Y} = \mathbf{T}_{43}\mathbf{T}_{32}\mathbf{T}_{21}\mathbf{X} = \mathbf{V}^T\mathbf{X}. \tag{5.132}$$

The overall transformation matrix $\mathbf{V}^T$ is

$$\mathbf{V}^T = \mathbf{T}_{43}\mathbf{T}_{32}\mathbf{T}_{21}. \tag{5.133}$$

Although we could carry out the multiplication of these matrices explicitly, there is no need to do so. The matrices $\mathbf{T}_{21}$, $\mathbf{T}_{32}$, and $\mathbf{T}_{43}$ are all lower triangular matrices with unit diagonal elements. It suffices to note that the product of any two such matrices is also a lower triangular matrix with unit diagonal elements

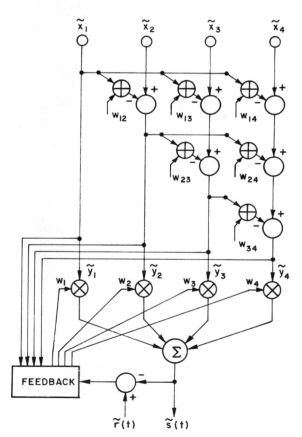

Figure 5.14 A Gram-Schmidt preprocessor followed by an LMS processor.

(try it!). Thus, $\mathbf{V}^T$ necessarily has the form

$$\mathbf{V}^T = \begin{bmatrix} 1 & 0 & 0 & 0 \\ x & 1 & 0 & 0 \\ x & x & 1 & 0 \\ x & x & x & 1 \end{bmatrix} \tag{5.134}$$

where x denotes values that may be nonzero in general. However, the determinant of any matrix of this form is unity, regardless of the values of the x's. Thus $\mathbf{V}$ cannot be singular, and the Gram-Schmidt transformation is invertible.

This proof that the Gram-Schmidt transformation is invertible for the case of four signals can be generalized in an obvious way to the case of an arbitrary number of signals. Thus we know that if a Gram-Schmidt preprocessor is inserted between the elements of an N-element array and the LMS processor, it will not affect the ultimate SINR achieved by the LMS processor.

Now let us consider what the advantage of this technique is. Suppose the Gram-Schmidt preprocessor in Fig. 5.13 is followed by an LMS array as in Fig. 5.14. By taking advantage of the decorrelation between the array input signals, we can redraw the LMS processor in Fig. 5.14 so that it is just a continuation of the Gram-Schmidt preprocessor. The first step is to note that subtracting $\sum_{j=1}^{N} w_j \tilde{y}_j(t)$ from $\tilde{r}(t)$, as in Fig. 5.14, is equivalent to subtracting each of the signals $w_j \tilde{y}_j(t)$ from $\tilde{r}(t)$ one at a time. Thus the LMS array portion of Fig. 5.14 may be redrawn as shown in Fig. 5.15. Moreover, the weight vector in the LMS array will be given by

$$\mathbf{W} = \boldsymbol{\Phi}_y^{-1} \mathbf{S}_y, \tag{5.135}$$

where

$$\mathbf{W} = [w_1, w_2, w_3, w_4]^T, \tag{5.136}$$

and $\boldsymbol{\Phi}_y$ and $\mathbf{S}_y$ are the covariance matrix and reference correlation vector associated with the signals $\tilde{y}_j(t)$, $1 \leqslant j \leqslant 4$, as defined in Eqs. (5.99) and (5.100). However, because the $\tilde{y}_j(t)$ are mutually uncorrelated, $\boldsymbol{\Phi}_y$ is a diagonal

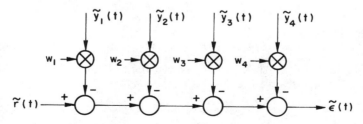

Figure 5.15   The rearranged LMS array.

matrix

$$\Phi_y = \begin{bmatrix} e[|\tilde{y}_1|^2] & 0 & 0 & 0 \\ 0 & e[|\tilde{y}_2|^2] & 0 & 0 \\ 0 & 0 & e[|\tilde{y}_3|^2] & 0 \\ 0 & 0 & 0 & e[|\tilde{y}_4|^2] \end{bmatrix}. \tag{5.137}$$

Hence Φ_y^{-1} is also diagonal with elements equal to the reciprocals of the diagonal elements of Φ_y. Combining this result with

$$\mathbf{S}_y = \begin{bmatrix} E(\tilde{y}_1^*\tilde{r}) \\ E(\tilde{y}_2^*\tilde{r}) \\ E(\tilde{y}_3^*\tilde{r}) \\ E(\tilde{y}_4^*\tilde{r}) \end{bmatrix} \tag{5.138}$$

yields the steady-state LMS weight vector

$$\mathbf{W} = \begin{bmatrix} \dfrac{E(\tilde{y}_1^*\tilde{r})}{E(|\tilde{y}_1|^2)} \\[2ex] \dfrac{E(\tilde{y}_2^*\tilde{r})}{E(|\tilde{y}_2|^2)} \\[2ex] \dfrac{E(\tilde{y}_3^*\tilde{r})}{E(|\tilde{y}_3|^2)} \\[2ex] \dfrac{E(\tilde{y}_4^*\tilde{r})}{E(|\tilde{y}_4|^2)} \end{bmatrix}. \tag{5.139}$$

Furthermore, because the $\tilde{y}_j(t)$ are uncorrelated, Eq. (5.139) can also be written in another form. Suppose we define signals $\tilde{r}_1(t)$, $\tilde{r}_2(t)$, $\tilde{r}_3(t)$, and $\tilde{r}_4(t)$ as follows. Let

$$\tilde{r}_1(t) = \tilde{r}(t), \tag{5.140}$$
$$\tilde{r}_2(t) = \tilde{r}(t) - w_1\tilde{y}_1(t), \tag{5.141}$$
$$\tilde{r}_3(t) = \tilde{r}(t) - w_1\tilde{y}_1(t) - w_2\tilde{y}_2(t), \tag{5.142}$$

and

$$\tilde{r}_4(t) = \tilde{r}(t) - w_1\tilde{y}_1(t) - w_2\tilde{y}_2(t) - w_3\tilde{y}_3(t). \tag{5.143}$$

Note that $\tilde{r}_2(t)$, $\tilde{r}_3(t)$, and $\tilde{r}_4(t)$ are the voltages after each difference in Fig. 5.15. Then, because the $\tilde{y}_j(t)$ are uncorrelated,

$$E[\tilde{y}_1^*(t)\tilde{r}(t)] = E[\tilde{y}_1^*(t)\tilde{r}_1(t)], \tag{5.144}$$
$$E[\tilde{y}_2^*(t)\tilde{r}(t)] = E[\tilde{y}_2^*(t)\tilde{r}_2(t)], \tag{5.145}$$
$$E[\tilde{y}_3^*(t)\tilde{r}(t)] = E[\tilde{y}_3^*(t)\tilde{r}_3(t)], \tag{5.146}$$

and

$$E\left[\tilde{y}_4^*(t)\tilde{r}(t)\right] = E\left[\tilde{y}_4^*(t)\tilde{r}_4(t)\right]. \tag{5.147}$$

Therefore, the steady-state weight vector in Eq. (5.139) may also be written

$$\mathbf{W} = \begin{bmatrix} \dfrac{E\left[\tilde{y}_1^* t)\tilde{r}_1(t)\right]}{E\left[|\tilde{y}_1(t)|^2\right]} \\[2ex] \dfrac{E\left[\tilde{y}_2^*(t)\tilde{r}_2(t)\right]}{E\left[|\tilde{y}_2(t)|^2\right]} \\[2ex] \dfrac{E\left[\tilde{y}_3^*(t)\tilde{r}_3(t)\right]}{E\left[|\tilde{y}_3(t)|^2\right]} \\[2ex] \dfrac{E\left[\tilde{y}_4^*(t)\tilde{r}_4(t)\right]}{E\left[|\tilde{y}_4(t)|^2\right]} \end{bmatrix}. \tag{5.148}$$

From this form we see that each weight in Fig. 5.15 may be computed solely from the two signals to be subtracted at that node. The form of each weight in Eq. (5.148) is identical to the form of each weight in the Gram-Schmidt preprocessor, as in Eq. (5.124).

Finally, with the LMS array drawn as in Fig. 5.15, we note that the entire processing structure in Fig. 5.14 may be redrawn as in Fig. 5.16. In this form, the LMS array part of the system just appears as another column in the Gram-Schmidt tree. The input to this column is $\tilde{r}(t)$ and the output is $\tilde{\varepsilon}(t)$. Since

$$\tilde{\varepsilon}(t) = \tilde{r}(t) - \sum_{j=1}^{4} w_j\tilde{y}_j(t), \tag{5.149}$$

the array output is equal to $\tilde{r}(t) - \tilde{\varepsilon}(t)$, as shown.

The most important feature of this processing structure is that the weight at each difference node is determined only by the signals at that node. Each difference node in Fig. 5.16 has the form shown in Fig. 5.17, with input signals $\tilde{a}(t)$ and $\tilde{b}(t)$. The weight on that node is to be set equal to

$$w = \frac{E\left[\tilde{a}^*(t)\tilde{b}(t)\right]}{E\left[\tilde{a}^*(t)\tilde{a}(t)\right]}. \tag{5.150}$$

This weight can be obtained in practice with either analog or digital circuitry.

To obtain the weight in analog form, one uses a single LMS loop to minimize the output power from that difference node. Such a loop is shown in Fig. 5.18. One of these loops will be needed at each weight in Fig. 5.16.

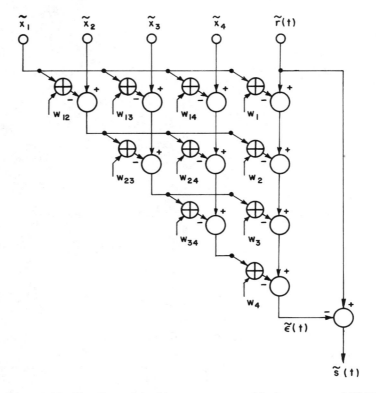

Figure 5.16 The Gram-Schmidt preprocessor with the rearranged LMS processor.

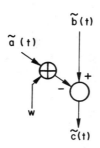

Figure 5.17
One difference
node.

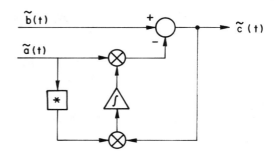

Figure 5.18 A single LMS loop at a difference node.

The differential equation for the weight in Fig. 5.18 is

$$\frac{dw}{dt} = k\tilde{a}^*(t)\tilde{c}(t), \tag{5.151}$$

where k is the loop gain. Since

$$\tilde{c}(t) = \tilde{b}(t) - w\tilde{a}(t), \tag{5.152}$$

Eq. (5.151) becomes

$$\frac{dw}{dt} + k\tilde{a}^*(t)\tilde{a}(t)w(t) = k\tilde{a}^*(t)\tilde{b}(t). \tag{5.153}$$

Assuming as usual that $w(t)$ changes slowly compared to $\tilde{a}(t)$ and $\tilde{b}(t)$, we see that the steady-state solution for $w(t)$ is

$$w(\infty) = \frac{E\left[\tilde{a}^*(t)\tilde{b}(t)\right]}{E\left[\tilde{a}^*(t)\tilde{a}(t)\right]}, \tag{5.154}$$

which is the result we need. The complete transient solution of $w(t)$ is

$$w(t) = w(\infty) + \left[w(0) - w(\infty)\right]e^{-kE[|a(t)|^2]t}, \tag{5.155}$$

where $w(0)$ is the initial value of $w(t)$. The time constant of $w(t)$ is

$$\tau = \frac{1}{kE\left[|\tilde{a}(t)|^2\right]}, \tag{5.156}$$

which depends on the average power in $\tilde{a}(t)$. However, because this is a single uncoupled LMS loop, there is only one time constant, unlike an LMS array with multiple loops. This single time constant can be normalized to a fixed value by means of an automatic gain control (AGC) in the loop. If we set

$$k = \left\{\tau_0 E\left[|\tilde{a}(t)|^2\right]\right\}^{-1}, \tag{5.157}$$

the loop time constant will be τ_0, regardless of the signal power. This form of AGC is feasible for a one-dimensional loop but not for an LMS array with coupled loops.

If the feedback loops include this AGC, then every loop in the processor of Fig. 5.16 will have the same time constant. This time constant will be independent of signal strength or of the eigenvalue spread in the original covariance matrix Φ_x. This result is the main advantage of using the Gram-Schmidt preprocessor.

The weight at each node may also be derived digitally. This method is appropriate when the signals are sampled. If digital techniques are used, each weight is simply computed from the sampled input signals at that weight. For example, suppose $\tilde{a}(j)$ and $\tilde{b}(j)$ are the jth sampled values of $\tilde{a}(t)$ and $\tilde{b}(t)$ in Fig. 5.17. Then K sequential samples may be averaged and the computed weight,

$$w = \frac{\sum_{j=1}^{K} \tilde{a}^*(j)\tilde{b}(j)}{\sum_{j=1}^{K} \tilde{a}^*(j)\tilde{a}(j)}, \tag{5.158}$$

used as an approximation to the ideal weight in Eq. (5.154). As K is increased, w more closely approximates the correct weight, but the adaptation time increases. If K samples are used, the time for each weight to adapt is just $K\Delta$, where Δ is the sampling interval, plus a fixed time to do the computations in Eq. (5.158). However, the important feature is that this adaptation time is indepen-

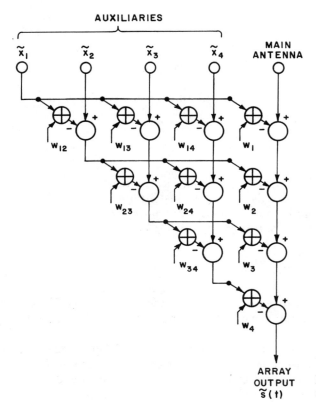

Figure 5.19   Gram-Schmidt implementation of the sidelobe canceler.

dent of the signal power or the eigenvalue spread in the covariance matrix Φ_x. Using the Gram-Schmidt technique solves the problem of time-constant spread.

The Gram-Schmidt preprocessor is not as useful with an Applebaum array as with an LMS array, because of the need to change the steering vector along with the Gram-Schmidt weights [i.e., to implement Eq. (5.110)]. However, the Gram-Schmidt preprocessor is useful with a sidelobe canceler array. We will discuss the sidelobe canceler in detail in Chapter 6 and will discuss its relationship to the Applebaum array. For the moment, we simply point out that a sidelobe canceler is an array that uses a single high-gain main-beam antenna (such as a parabolic antenna) and a few low-gain auxiliary elements. The auxiliary element signals are added to the main-beam signal after adaptive weighting. The auxiliary elements make it possible to cancel interference in the sidelobes of the main-beam antenna (hence the name). The weight on each auxiliary element is adjusted to minimize the total output power from the array.

The sidelobe canceler can be implemented with a Gram-Schmidt preprocessor as shown in Fig. 5.19. The auxiliary element signals are passed through a Gram-Schmidt preprocessor whose outputs are then subtracted from the main-beam signal. Because the preprocessor outputs are uncorrelated, they can be subtracted from the main-beam signal one at a time, as with the LMS array in Fig. 5.16.

Now let us return to the Gram-Schmidt preprocessor of Fig. 5.13. It should be noted that, if we start with a given set of element signals, there are many ways the signals can be arranged in this processor. In Fig. 5.13, the signal $\tilde{x}_1(t)$ is brought out into $\tilde{y}_1(t)$ with no change. However, any of the $\tilde{x}_j(t)$ could be selected as the signal that becomes $\tilde{y}_1(t)$. Similarly, as we proceed from left to right across the top of Fig. 5.13, the signals $\tilde{x}_j(t)$ could be arranged in any order. The output signals $\tilde{y}_j(t)$ are orthogonal regardless of how the $\tilde{x}_j(t)$ are connected. Of course, different arrangements of the $\tilde{x}_j(t)$ give different weights w_{kj}.

In general, the main advantage of a Gram-Schmidt preprocessor is that its speed of response is independent of the eigenvalues of the covariance matrix and hence of signal powers and arrival angles. However, a Gram-Schmidt preprocessor does require more weights than an LMS or Applebaum processor. Also, a practical difficulty with the Gram-Schmidt technique is that the signal-to-noise ratios become progressively smaller as the signals pass down through the processor. The coherent signal components are cancelled off in the Gram-Schmidt tree, but the thermal noise components are not. This situation can cause the lower weights in the tree to be in error in a practical system. When the Gram-Schmidt tree is implemented digitally, for example, the sampled signals are represented by only a given number of bits. As the signal-to-noise ratios drop, the coherent signal components at the bottom of the tree affect only the least significant bits of the signal samples. The resulting weights may not properly reflect the presence of the coherent signals.

5.3 A RECURSIVE LEAST-SQUARES ALGORITHM

A recursive least-squares technique can also be used to avoid eigenvalue spread problems. Recursive least-squares algorithms have been suggested by Brennan, Mallett, and Reed [5] and by Baird [4]. In this section, we describe the recursive least-squares technique as presented by Baird. It is assumed for this method of weight control that the element signals are to be sampled and the array is to be implemented in digital form. The array weights will be obtained by digital calculations from the sampled element signals. (The modified LMS loop in section 5.1 is intended only for analog weight control. The Gram-Schmidt preprocessor can be implemented in either analog or digital form.)

Suppose we let $\mathbf{X}(n)$, $\tilde{r}(n)$, and so on, denote the sampled values of the signal vector $\mathbf{X}(t)$, the reference signal $\tilde{r}(t)$, and so forth, at times $t = n\Delta t$. Assume that a given time we have collected samples 1 through n. In principle, we would like to choose the weight vector $\mathbf{W}$ in the array so that the array output matches the reference signal exactly at every sample,

$$\mathbf{X}^T(1)\mathbf{W} - \tilde{r}(1) = 0,$$
$$\mathbf{X}^T(2)\mathbf{W} - \tilde{r}(2) = 0, \tag{5.159}$$

and

$$\mathbf{X}^T(n)\mathbf{W} - \tilde{r}(n) = 0.$$

If we define the matrix $\mathbf{Q}(n)$,

$$\mathbf{Q}(n) = \begin{bmatrix} \mathbf{X}^T(1) \\ \mathbf{X}^T(2) \\ \vdots \\ \mathbf{X}^T(n) \end{bmatrix} = \begin{bmatrix} \tilde{x}_1(1) & \tilde{x}_2(1) & \cdots & \tilde{x}_N(1) \\ \tilde{x}_1(2) & \tilde{x}_2(2) & \cdots & x_N(2) \\ \vdots & & & \vdots \\ \tilde{x}_1(n) & \tilde{x}_2(n) & & \tilde{x}_N(n) \end{bmatrix} \tag{5.160}$$

and the vector $\mathbf{T}(n)$,

$$\mathbf{T}(n) = \begin{bmatrix} \tilde{r}(1) \\ \tilde{r}(2) \\ \vdots \\ \tilde{r}(N) \end{bmatrix} \tag{5.161}$$

then Eqs. (5.159) are the same as

$$\mathbf{Q}(n)\mathbf{W} - \mathbf{T}(n) = 0. \tag{5.162}$$

However, once the number of samples n exceeds the number of elements N, Eq. (5.162) will not be satisfied for any $\mathbf{W}$, because there are more equations than unknowns. Since we cannot solve Eq. (5.162) exactly, we instead choose $\mathbf{W}$ to obtain a least-squares fit between $\mathbf{Q}(n)\mathbf{W}$ and $\mathbf{T}(n)$. We define the squared error to be

$$J(\mathbf{W}) = [\mathbf{Q}(n)\mathbf{W} - \mathbf{T}(n)]^\dagger \mathbf{A}_n [\mathbf{Q}(n)\mathbf{W} - \mathbf{T}(n)], \qquad (5.163)$$

where $\mathbf{A}_n$ is a diagonal matrix used to deemphasize old data,

$$\mathbf{A}_n = \begin{bmatrix} \alpha^{n-1} & 0 & \cdots & & \\ 0 & \alpha^{n-2} & & & \\ & & \ddots & & \\ \vdots & & & \alpha & 0 \\ & & & 0 & 1 \end{bmatrix} \qquad (5.164)$$

where $0 < \alpha \leqslant 1$. To find the weight vector minimizing $J(\mathbf{W})$, we set $\partial J/\partial w_{I_i} = 0$ and $\partial J/\partial w_{Q_i} = 0$, for each i. For $\partial J/\partial w_{I_i}$, we find

$$\frac{\partial J}{\partial w_{I_i}} = [\mathbf{Q}(n)\mathbf{1}_i]^\dagger \mathbf{A}_n [\mathbf{Q}(n)\mathbf{W} - \mathbf{T}(n)]$$

$$+ [\mathbf{Q}(n)\mathbf{W} - \mathbf{T}(n)]^\dagger \mathbf{A}_n [\mathbf{Q}(n)\mathbf{1}_i] = 0, \qquad (5.165)$$

where $\mathbf{1}_i$ is a column vector whose only nonzero element is the ith element, which is unity:

$$\mathbf{1}_i = (0 \quad 0 \quad \cdots \quad 0 \quad \underset{\underset{i\text{th element}}{\uparrow}}{1} \quad 0 \quad \cdots)^T. \qquad (5.166)$$

Using the relation

$$\mathbf{X}^\dagger \mathbf{A}_n \mathbf{Y} = \mathbf{Y}^T \mathbf{A}_n \mathbf{X}^*, \qquad (5.167)$$

where $\mathbf{X}$ and $\mathbf{Y}$ are arbitrary vectors, we may rewrite Eq. (5.165) as

$$\frac{\partial J}{\partial w_{I_i}} = [\mathbf{Q}(n)\mathbf{1}_i]^\dagger \mathbf{A}_n [\mathbf{Q}(n)\mathbf{W} - \mathbf{T}(n)]$$

$$+ [\mathbf{Q}(n)\mathbf{1}_i]^T \mathbf{A}_n [\mathbf{Q}(n)\mathbf{W} - \mathbf{T}(n)]^* = 0. \qquad (5.168)$$

This equation is of the form $a + a^* = 0$, which implies $\operatorname{Re}(a) = 0$,

$$\operatorname{Re}\{[\mathbf{Q}(n)\mathbf{1}_i]^\dagger \mathbf{A}_n [\mathbf{Q}(n)\mathbf{W} - \mathbf{T}(n)]\} = 0. \qquad (5.169)$$

Similarly, we find

$$\frac{\partial J}{\partial w_{Q_i}} = j[\mathbf{Q}(n)\mathbf{1}_i]^\dagger \mathbf{A}_n [\mathbf{Q}(n)\mathbf{W} - \mathbf{T}(n)]$$

$$- j[\mathbf{Q}(n)\mathbf{W} - \mathbf{T}(n)]^\dagger \mathbf{A}_n [\mathbf{Q}(n)\mathbf{1}_i] = 0, \qquad (5.170)$$

or, after using Eq. (5.167),

$$j\left[\mathbf{Q}(n)\mathbf{1}_i\right]^\dagger \mathbf{A}_n\left[\mathbf{Q}(n)\mathbf{W} - \mathbf{T}(n)\right]$$
$$-j\left[\mathbf{Q}(n)\mathbf{1}_i\right]^T \mathbf{A}_n\left[\mathbf{Q}(n)\mathbf{W} - \mathbf{T}(n)\right]^* = 0. \qquad (5.171)$$

This is of the form $ja - ja^* = 0$, which implies $\text{Im}(a) = 0$,

$$\text{Im}\left\{\left[\mathbf{Q}(n)\mathbf{1}_i\right]^\dagger \mathbf{A}_n\left[\mathbf{Q}(n)\mathbf{W} - \mathbf{T}(n)\right]\right\} = 0. \qquad (5.172)$$

Combining Eqs. (5.169) and (5.172), we have

$$\left[\mathbf{Q}(n)\mathbf{1}_i\right]^\dagger \mathbf{A}_n\left[\mathbf{Q}(n)\mathbf{W} - \mathbf{T}(n)\right] = 0. \qquad (5.173)$$

However, $\mathbf{Q}(n)\mathbf{1}_i$ is the row vector

$$\mathbf{Q}(n)\mathbf{1}_i = \left[\tilde{x}_i^*(1), \tilde{x}_i^*(2), \ldots, \tilde{x}_i^*(n)\right], \qquad (5.174)$$

which is the ith row of $\mathbf{Q}^\dagger(n)$. Since Eq. (5.173) must hold *for every* i, we find that the value of $\mathbf{W}$ minimizing $J(\mathbf{W})$ satisfies

$$\mathbf{Q}^\dagger(n)\mathbf{A}_n\left[\mathbf{Q}(n)\mathbf{W} - \mathbf{T}(n)\right] = 0. \qquad (5.175)$$

Therefore,

$$\mathbf{W}(n) = \left[\mathbf{Q}^\dagger(n)\mathbf{A}_n\mathbf{Q}(n)\right]^{-1}\mathbf{Q}^\dagger(n)\mathbf{A}_n\mathbf{T}(n) \qquad (5.176)$$

is the least-squares weight vector. We denote it by $\mathbf{W}(n)$, to signify that it is computed from n samples.

The algorithm described by Baird [4] is a computationally efficient way of carrying out Eq. (5.176). It is assumed that, as time progresses, more and more samples are collected. As the number of samples grows, the order of the matrices in Eq. (5.176) increases. To avoid having to recompute the weight vector directly from Eq. (5.176) each time n is increased, Baird has rearranged Eq. (5.176) into a simpler form. This form allows one to update the weight vector as each new sample arrives, without the need to use Eq. (5.176) or to invert matrices.

Suppose that after n samples have been obtained, the weight vector satisfying Eq. (5.176) has been found. Now assume that sample $n + 1$ becomes available. We want to compute $\mathbf{W}(n + 1)$ from $\mathbf{W}(n)$ and the new signal sample. We proceed as follows: At sample $n + 1$, the optimal weight vector is given by

$$\mathbf{W}(n + 1) = \left[\mathbf{Q}^\dagger(n + 1)\mathbf{A}_{n+1}\mathbf{Q}(n + 1)\right]^{-1}\mathbf{Q}^\dagger(n + 1)\mathbf{A}_{n+1}\mathbf{T}(n + 1). \qquad (5.177)$$

The matrices in this equation can be written in partitioned form, as follows:

$$\mathbf{Q}(n + 1) = \left[\begin{array}{c} \mathbf{Q}(n) \\ \hline \mathbf{X}^T(n + 1) \end{array}\right], \qquad (5.178)$$

$$\mathbf{T}(n + 1) = \left[\begin{array}{c} \mathbf{T}(n) \\ \hline \tilde{r}(n + 1) \end{array}\right], \qquad (5.179)$$

and

$$\mathbf{A}_{n+1} = \left[\begin{array}{c|c} \alpha\mathbf{A}_n & 0 \\ \hline 0 & 1 \end{array}\right]. \tag{5.180}$$

We use these partitioned matrices to evaluate the matrix products appearing in Eq. (5.177). First we have

$$\mathbf{Q}^{\dagger}(n+1)\mathbf{A}_{n+1}\mathbf{T}(n+1) = \left[\begin{array}{c} \mathbf{Q}(n) \\ \hline \mathbf{X}^T(n+1) \end{array}\right]^{\dagger} \left[\begin{array}{c|c} \alpha\mathbf{A}_n & 0 \\ \hline 0 & 1 \end{array}\right] \left[\begin{array}{c} \mathbf{T}(n) \\ \hline \tilde{r}(n+1) \end{array}\right]$$

$$= \left[\begin{array}{c} \mathbf{Q}(n) \\ \hline \mathbf{X}^T(n+1) \end{array}\right]^{\dagger} \left[\begin{array}{c} \alpha\mathbf{A}_n\mathbf{T}(n) \\ \hline \tilde{r}(n+1) \end{array}\right]$$

$$= \alpha\mathbf{Q}^{\dagger}(n)\mathbf{A}_n\mathbf{T}(n) + \mathbf{X}^*(n+1)\tilde{r}(n+1). \tag{5.181}$$

Then we find

$$\mathbf{Q}^{\dagger}(n+1)\mathbf{A}_{n+1}\mathbf{Q}(n+1) = \left[\begin{array}{cc} \mathbf{Q}^{\dagger}(n) & \mathbf{X}(n+1) \end{array}\right] \left[\begin{array}{c|c} \alpha\mathbf{A}_n & 0 \\ \hline 0 & 1 \end{array}\right] \left[\begin{array}{c} \mathbf{Q}(n) \\ \hline \mathbf{X}^T(n+1) \end{array}\right]$$

$$= \left[\begin{array}{cc} \mathbf{Q}^{\dagger}(n) & \mathbf{X}^*(n+1) \end{array}\right] \left[\begin{array}{c} \alpha\mathbf{A}_n\mathbf{Q}(n) \\ \hline \mathbf{X}^T(n+1) \end{array}\right]$$

$$= \alpha\mathbf{Q}^{\dagger}(n)\mathbf{A}_n\mathbf{Q}(n) + \mathbf{X}^*(n+1)\mathbf{X}^T(n+1). \tag{5.182}$$

Now we define

$$\mathbf{P}^{-1}(n) = \mathbf{Q}^{\dagger}(n)\mathbf{A}_n\mathbf{Q}(n). \tag{5.183}$$

Then it follows that

$$\mathbf{P}^{-1}(n+1) = \mathbf{Q}^{\dagger}(n+1)\mathbf{A}_{n+1}\mathbf{Q}(n+1). \tag{5.184}$$

However, from Eq. (5.182), $\mathbf{P}^{-1}(n+1)$ is equal to

$$\mathbf{P}^{-1}(n+1) = \alpha\mathbf{Q}^{\dagger}(n)\mathbf{A}_n\mathbf{Q}(n) + \mathbf{X}^*(n+1)\mathbf{X}^T(n+1). \tag{5.185}$$

From Eq. (5.183), this may also be written

$$\mathbf{P}^{-1}(n+1) = \alpha\left[\mathbf{P}^{-1}(n) + \frac{1}{\alpha}\mathbf{X}^*(n+1)\mathbf{X}^T(n+1)\right]. \tag{5.186}$$

The weight vector in Eq. (5.177) is then

$$\mathbf{W}(n+1) = \mathbf{P}(n+1)\left[\mathbf{Q}^{\dagger}(n+1)\mathbf{A}_{n+1}\mathbf{T}(n+1)\right]. \tag{5.187}$$

The matrix $\mathbf{P}(n+1)$ can be computed from Eq. (5.186) by means of the matrix inversion lemma [see Eqs. (3.252) and (3.253)]. We find

$$\mathbf{P}(n+1) = \frac{1}{\alpha}\mathbf{P}(n) - \tau\frac{1}{\alpha^2}\mathbf{P}(n)\mathbf{X}^*(n+1)\mathbf{X}^T(n+1)\mathbf{P}(n), \qquad (5.188)$$

where

$$\tau = \left[1 + \frac{1}{\alpha}\mathbf{X}^T(n+1)\mathbf{P}(n)\mathbf{X}^*(n+1)\right]^{-1} \qquad (5.189)$$

Thus

$$\mathbf{P}(n+1) = \frac{1}{\alpha}\mathbf{P}(n) - \frac{\dfrac{1}{\alpha^2}\mathbf{P}(n)\mathbf{X}^*(n+1)\mathbf{X}^T(n+1)\mathbf{P}(n)}{1 + \dfrac{1}{\alpha}\mathbf{X}^T(n+1)\mathbf{P}(n)\mathbf{X}^*(n+1)} \qquad (5.190)$$

or

$$\mathbf{P}(n+1) = \frac{1}{\alpha}\left[\mathbf{P}(n) - \frac{\mathbf{P}(n)\mathbf{X}^*(n+1)\mathbf{X}^T(n+1)\mathbf{P}(n)}{\alpha + \mathbf{X}^T(n+1)\mathbf{P}(n)\mathbf{X}^*(n+1)}\right]. \qquad (5.191)$$

Substituting this equation and Eq. (5.181) into Eq. (5.187) gives

$$\mathbf{W}(n+1) = \frac{1}{\alpha}\left[\mathbf{P}(n) - \frac{\mathbf{P}(n)\mathbf{X}^*(n+1)\mathbf{X}^T(n+1)\mathbf{P}(n)}{\alpha + \mathbf{X}^T(n+1)\mathbf{P}(n)\mathbf{X}^*(n+1)}\right]$$
$$\times\left[\alpha\mathbf{Q}^\dagger(n)\mathbf{A}_n\mathbf{T}(n) + \mathbf{X}^*(n+1)\tilde{r}(n+1)\right]. \qquad (5.192)$$

When this expression is multiplied out and Eqs. (5.176) and (5.183) are used to replace the first product, we obtain

$$\mathbf{W}(n+1) = \mathbf{W}(n) + \mathbf{P}(n)\mathbf{X}^*(n+1)$$

$$\times\left[\frac{1}{\alpha}\tilde{r}(n+1) - \frac{\mathbf{X}^T(n+1)\mathbf{W}(n) - \dfrac{1}{\alpha}\mathbf{X}^T(n+1)\mathbf{P}(n)\mathbf{X}^*(n+1)\tilde{r}(n+1)}{\alpha + \mathbf{X}^T(n+1)\mathbf{P}(n)\mathbf{X}^*(n+1)}\right],$$
$$(5.193)$$

or, after simplifying,

$$\mathbf{W}(n+1) = \mathbf{W}(n) + \frac{\mathbf{P}(n)\mathbf{X}^*(n+1)}{\alpha + \mathbf{X}^T(n+1)\mathbf{P}(n)\mathbf{X}^*(n+1)}$$
$$\times\left[\tilde{r}(n+1) - \mathbf{X}^T(n+1)\mathbf{W}(n)\right]. \qquad (5.194)$$

Equations (5.191) and (5.194) together constitute Baird's algorithm. Equation (5.194) allows us to commute $\mathbf{W}(n+1)$ from $\mathbf{W}(n)$ and the new samples $\mathbf{X}(n+1)$ and $\tilde{r}(n+1)$. Equation (5.191) allows us to update the matrix $\mathbf{P}(n)$ at each step; $\mathbf{P}(n)$ is used to compute $\mathbf{W}(n+1)$.

To use Baird's algorithm, one starts from an arbitrary initial weight vector $\mathbf{W}(0)$ and an arbitrary choice for $\mathbf{P}(0)$, usually

$$\mathbf{P}(0) = \mathbf{I}. \tag{5.195}$$

As the signals are sampled, the weight vector and the matrix $\mathbf{P}(n)$ is computed from Eqs. (5.191) and (5.194) at each sample.

We can understand what is happening in Baird's algorithm by noting that if we set $\alpha = 1$, then $\mathbf{A}_n = \mathbf{I}$, and Eq. (5.176) becomes

$$\mathbf{W}(n) = \left[\mathbf{Q}^\dagger(n)\mathbf{Q}(n)\right]^{-1}\left[\mathbf{Q}^\dagger(n)\mathbf{T}(n)\right]. \tag{5.196}$$

But the product $\mathbf{Q}^\dagger(n)\mathbf{Q}(n)$ is

$$\mathbf{Q}^\dagger(n)\mathbf{Q}(n) = \begin{bmatrix} \tilde{x}_1^*(1) & \tilde{x}_1^*(2) & \cdots & \tilde{x}_1^*(n) \\ \tilde{x}_2^*(1) & \tilde{x}_2^*(2) & \cdots & \tilde{x}_2^*(n) \\ \vdots & & & \\ \tilde{x}_N^*(1) & \tilde{x}_N^*(2) & \cdots & \tilde{x}_N^*(n) \end{bmatrix}$$

$$\times \begin{bmatrix} \tilde{x}_1(1) & \tilde{x}_2(1) & \cdots & \tilde{x}_N(1) \\ \tilde{x}_1(2) & \tilde{x}_2(2) & \cdots & \tilde{x}_N(2) \\ \vdots & & & \\ \tilde{x}_1(n) & \tilde{x}_2(n) & \cdots & \tilde{x}_N(n) \end{bmatrix}$$

$$= \begin{bmatrix} \sum_{i=1}^n \tilde{x}_1^*(i)\tilde{x}_1(i) & \sum_{i=1}^n \tilde{x}_1^*(i)\tilde{x}_2(i) & \cdots & \sum_{i=1}^n \tilde{x}_1^*(i)\tilde{x}_N(i) \\ \sum_{i=1}^n \tilde{x}_2^*(i)\tilde{x}_1(i) & \sum_{i=1}^n \tilde{x}_2^*(i)\tilde{x}_2(i) & \cdots & \sum_{i=1}^n \tilde{x}_2^*(i)\tilde{x}_N(i) \\ \vdots & & & \\ \sum_{i=1}^n \tilde{x}_N^*(i)\tilde{x}_1(i) & \sum_{i=1}^n \tilde{x}_N^*(i)\tilde{x}_2(i) & \cdots & \sum_{i=1}^n \tilde{x}_N^*(i)\tilde{x}_N(i) \end{bmatrix}$$

$$= \sum_{i=1}^n \mathbf{X}^*(i)\mathbf{X}^T(i)$$

$$= n\hat{\boldsymbol{\Phi}}(n), \tag{5.197}$$

where

$$\hat{\boldsymbol{\Phi}}(n) = \frac{1}{n}\sum_{i=1}^n \mathbf{X}^*(i)\mathbf{X}^T(i). \tag{5.198}$$

The matrix $\hat{\boldsymbol{\Phi}}(n)$ is just an n-sample estimate of the covariance matrix.‡

‡Unfortunately, it is common to use the caret symbol (^) for both an estimate and a Hilbert transform. It should be clear from the context, however, which meaning is intended.

Also, with $\mathbf{A}_n = \mathbf{I}$, we find

$$
\mathbf{Q}^{\dagger}(n)\mathbf{T}(n) = \begin{bmatrix} \sum_{i=1}^{n} \tilde{x}_1^*(i)\tilde{r}(i) \\ \sum_{i=1}^{n} \tilde{x}_2^*(i)\tilde{r}(i) \\ \vdots \\ \sum_{i=1}^{n} \tilde{x}_N^*(i)\tilde{r}(i) \end{bmatrix} = \sum_{i=1}^{n} \mathbf{X}^*(i)\tilde{r}(i)
$$

$$
= n\hat{\mathbf{S}}(n), \tag{5.199}
$$

where

$$
\hat{\mathbf{S}}(n) = \frac{1}{n} \sum_{i=1}^{n} \mathbf{X}^*(i)\tilde{r}(i). \tag{5.200}
$$

The vector $\hat{\mathbf{S}}(n)$ is an n-sample estimate of the reference correlation vector. Thus, canceling the n's, we have from Eq. (5.196)

$$
\mathbf{W}(n) = \left[\hat{\boldsymbol{\Phi}}(n)\right]^{-1}\hat{\mathbf{S}}(n). \tag{5.201}
$$

In this form we recognize the solution for $\mathbf{W}(n)$.

More importantly, in Eq. (5.194), let us define the error signal at sample $n + 1$,

$$
\tilde{\varepsilon}(n + 1) = \tilde{r}(n + 1) - \mathbf{X}^T(n + 1)\mathbf{W}(n). \tag{5.202}
$$

Equation (5.194) is then equivalent to

$$
\mathbf{W}(n + 1) = \mathbf{W}(n) + \frac{\mathbf{P}(n)}{\alpha + \mathbf{X}^T(n + 1)\mathbf{P}(n)\mathbf{X}^*(n + 1)}\mathbf{X}^*(n + 1)\tilde{\varepsilon}(n + 1). \tag{5.203}
$$

Now suppose $\alpha = 1$. Equations (5.183) and (5.197) then give

$$
\mathbf{P}(n) = \left[\mathbf{Q}^{\dagger}(n)\mathbf{A}_n\mathbf{Q}(n)\right]^{-1} = \left[\mathbf{Q}^{\dagger}(n)\mathbf{Q}(n)\right]^{-1} = \frac{1}{n}\hat{\boldsymbol{\Phi}}^{-1}(n). \tag{5.204}
$$

Hence Eq. (5.203) is equivalent to

$$
\mathbf{W}(n + 1) = \mathbf{W}(n) + \gamma\hat{\boldsymbol{\Phi}}^{-1}(n)\mathbf{X}^*(n + 1)\tilde{\varepsilon}(n + 1), \tag{5.205}
$$

where

$$
\gamma = \left[n\{\alpha + \mathbf{X}^T(n + 1)\mathbf{P}(n)\mathbf{X}^*(n + 1)\}\right]^{-1}. \tag{5.206}
$$

Since $\mathbf{X}^*(n + 1)\tilde{\varepsilon}(n + 1)$ is just an estimate of the gradient of $E\{|\tilde{\varepsilon}^2(t)|^2\}$ at sample $n + 1$,

$$
\hat{\nabla}_W\{E[|\tilde{\varepsilon}^2(t)|]\} = \mathbf{X}^*(n + 1)\tilde{\varepsilon}(n + 1), \tag{5.207}
$$

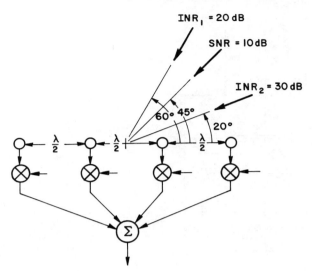

Figure 5.20 A four-element array with incident signals.

we see that Baird's algorithm is equivalent to premultiplying the gradient by the inverse of the covariance matrix. The reason that such an algorithm converges quickly should be clear from the discussion of the modified LMS loop in section 5.1.

Baird gives an example illustrating the convergence of his algorithm [4]. He considers an array of four isotropic elements a half wavelength apart as shown in Fig. 5.20. Three signals are incident on the array—a desired signal and two interference signals. The desired signal is 10 dB above thermal noise and arrives from 45° from endfire. The interference signals arrive from 20° and 60° from endfire, and are 30 dB and 20 dB above thermal noise, respectively. Each of the signals is biphase modulated with 0.1% bandwidth. The reference signal is perfectly correlated with the desired signal. The initial weight vector is $[1, 0, 0, 0]^T$, $P(0)$ is the identity matrix, and $\alpha = 1$. Figure 5.21 (from [4]) shows the array output power of the desired and interference signals as a function of the number of iterations. It may be seen that the interference power has been substantially reduced after only five samples, and the array is essentially in steady state after ten samples. If the weights in the same array were controlled with the discrete LMS algorithm, about 10^4 samples would be required to reach steady state, because the eigenvalue spread is 10^3 and a minimum of about 10 samples will be required to get the fast transient terms in the LMS algorithm to converge.

Thus Baird's algorithm converges extremely quickly compared to the LMS algorithm when convergence time is measured in terms of the number of samples required. To make a fair comparison between the two algorithms, however, it must be noted that Baird's algorithm requires several matrix multiplications at each iteration. Since forming a product such as $\mathbf{X}^T(n + 1)\mathbf{P}(n)\mathbf{X}^*(n + 1)$ requires N^3 complex multiplies (where N is the

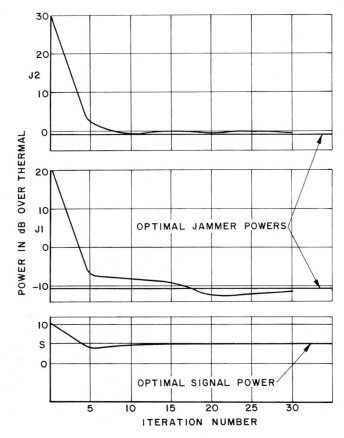

Figure 5.21 Baird's algorithm: array output signal powers versus iteration number for array in fig. 5.20 (reprinted from Baird [4] with permission).

number of array elements), the computation time for one iteration of Baird's algorithm is proportional to N^3. For the discrete LMS algorithm, the computation time for one iteration is proportional to N. Hence Baird's algorithm has the biggest advantage when N is small and the eigenvalue spread is high. Which algorithm is actually faster in real time depends on the number of elements, the eigenvalue spread, and the speed of the digital processor used.

5.4 THE SAMPLE MATRIX INVERSE METHOD

Another discrete technique for overcoming eigenvalue spread is the sample matrix inverse method, suggested by Reed, Mallett, and Brennan [11]. Their approach is very simple. Assume that an Applebaum array is to be used. Suppose the steering vector is U_d^*, where U_d is defined as in Eq. (3.236). To find the weights, we collect K samples of the signal vector $\mathbf{X}$ and form an estimate of the covariance matrix,

$$\hat{\Phi} = \frac{1}{K} \sum_{k=1}^{K} \mathbf{X}^*(k)\mathbf{X}^T(k). \tag{5.208}$$

The weight vector is then computed from

$$\hat{\mathbf{W}} = \mu \hat{\Phi}^{-1} \mathbf{U}_d^*. \tag{5.209}$$

To allow the array to adapt as the signal environment changes, this process is repeated periodically. The matrix Φ is called the *sample* covariance matrix, and the method itself is called the *sample matrix inverse*, or SMI, method.

That is all there is to the algorithm itself. However, to use the algorithm, we must know how many samples K are needed. The main contribution of Reed, Mallett, and Brennan [11] was to answer this question. We shall sketch their approach here.

The weight vector $\hat{\mathbf{W}}$ is an estimate of the optimal weight vector,

$$\mathbf{W}_{\text{opt}} = \mu \Phi_u^{-1} \mathbf{U}_d^*, \tag{5.210}$$

given in Eq. (2.222). If $\hat{\mathbf{W}}$ is used in the array, the output SINR will not be as high as if $\mathbf{W}_{\text{opt}}$ is used. With the optimal weight, the output SINR would be [see Eq. (2.221)]

$$\text{SINR}_{\text{opt}} = E\left[|a|^2\right] \frac{|\mathbf{W}_{\text{opt}}^T \mathbf{U}_d|^2}{\mathbf{W}_{\text{opt}}^T \Phi_u \mathbf{W}_{\text{opt}}}. \tag{5.211}$$

With weight vector $\hat{\mathbf{W}}$, the output SINR is

$$\text{SINR}_{\text{SMI}} = E\left[|a|^2\right] \frac{|\hat{\mathbf{W}}^T \mathbf{U}_d|^2}{\hat{\mathbf{W}}^\dagger \Phi_u \hat{\mathbf{W}}}. \tag{5.212}$$

We define

$$\rho = \frac{\text{SINR}_{\text{SMI}}}{\text{SINR}_{\text{opt}}}. \tag{5.213}$$

Clearly ρ is a real random variable in the range

$$0 \leqslant \rho \leqslant 1. \tag{5.214}$$

To determine the number of samples required, we relate the average value of ρ to K. Reed, Mallett, and Brennan [11] showed that the probability density function of ρ, $p(\rho)$, is a beta function,

$$p(\rho) = \left[\frac{K!}{(N-2)!(K+1-N)!}\right](1-\rho)^{N-2}\rho^{K+1-N}, \qquad 0 \leqslant \rho \leqslant 1. \tag{5.215}$$

In Eq. (5.215), N is the number of elements, and K is the number of samples. The derivation of this result is somewhat involved, and we shall not go through the details here. The reader is referred to Reed, Mallett, and Brennan [11] and to the references given there. From $p(\rho)$, we compute the expected value of ρ. It is found that

$$E(\rho) = \int_0^1 \rho p(\rho) \, d\rho = \frac{K + 2 - N}{K + 1}. \tag{5.216}$$

Note that if $E(\rho) = \frac{1}{2}$, the average value of SINR_{SMI} is 3 dB down from SINR_{opt}. To make $E(\rho) \geqslant \frac{1}{2}$, Eq. (5.216) shows that we must have

$$K \geqslant 2N - 3. \tag{5.217}$$

Based on this relation the rule of thumb

$$K \geqslant 2N \tag{5.218}$$

is often used. The number of samples should be twice the number of elements.

The important point about the sample matrix inverse method is that the number of samples required in computing $\hat{\mathbf{\Phi}}$ does not depend on the eigenvalue spread. Thus the convergence rate of the algorithm is independent of signal powers, arrival angles, and other parameters.

Use of the SMI technique proceeds in two steps. First, we must collect K samples of the signal vector and form the sample covariance matrix $\hat{\mathbf{\Phi}}$. The computation of $\hat{\mathbf{\Phi}}$ can be done cumulatively as the samples are collected. Then, once $\hat{\mathbf{\Phi}}$ is available, we must solve a system of linear equations[‡] for $\mathbf{W}$. The weight vector $\hat{\mathbf{W}}$ is then inserted in the array, and the process started over again.

For each weight calculation with the SMI technique, the number of multiplications required is proportional to N^3. Both the number of multiplications needed to accumulate a covariance matrix and the number needed to solve a linear system of equations increase as N^3. Thus the SMI method, like Baird's algorithm, shows its best advantage over the discrete LMS algorithm when the number of elements is small and the eigenvalue spread is high.

An adaptive array using the SMI technique can have two forms: It can be entirely digital, in which case the array output is obtained in discrete form as the dot product of the sample signal vector and the weight vector. Or, the array can be analog. In this form the element signals are still sampled, but the samples are used only to compute weights. The digitally derived weights are used to control analog multipliers behind each element. The array output signal is analog.

An advantage of the analog form is that the signals can be sampled at a rate slower than the Nyquist rate. Since the samples are used only to compute weights and not to obtain the output signals, there is no requirement for

---

[‡]Even though this method is called the sample matrix *inverse* method, we need not actually compute the inverse of $\hat{\mathbf{\Phi}}$. We only need to solve the linear system of equations $\hat{\mathbf{\Phi}}\hat{\mathbf{W}} = \mu \mathbf{U}_d^*$ for $\hat{\mathbf{W}}$. In numerical analysis, it is more efficient to solve linear equations directly—for example, with Gauss elimination methods—than to compute inverses [12].

Nyquist rate sampling. With a digital array, the sampling rate must be at the Nyquist rate. The ability to sample below the Nyquist rate is useful for applications where analog-to-digital converters with sufficient performance are unavailable.

The main disadvantage of an analog array using the SMI technique is that it is "open loop." That is, the array weights are computed strictly from the sampled element signals and do not use the array output signal to correct for errors. If one of the signal paths in the array has an amplitude or phase shift that is different from what is assumed, the computed weights do not yield the desired performance. The array output SINR is very sensitive to such errors, of course, particularly when nulling high-power interference. With such an array, performance depends critically on how well the array channels are matched.

For either a digital or an analog array, array performance is quite sensitive to weight quantization. Whenever weights are implemented in digital form, they are quantized into a finite number of bits. Each weight can have only certain discrete values. Nitzberg has studied the effects of quantization [13, 14] and has related array performance to the number of bits carried into the weights. He has shown that when an array is nulling high-power interference, the weights must carry surprisingly many bits if the performance is to be satisfactory.

In addition, in the SMI method, weight errors can occur in solving the equation $\hat{\mathbf{\Phi}}\hat{\mathbf{W}} = \mu\mathbf{U}_d^*$, because of high eigenvalue spread in $\hat{\mathbf{\Phi}}$. It is well known that the accuracy of computer solutions of linear equations deteriorates as the eigenvalue spread (or "condition number") of the matrix goes up [15]. And in many adaptive array problems the eigenvalue spread can be very high. With the SMI algorithm, care must be taken to ensure that the linear equation subroutine used gives accurate results for the eigenvalue spreads that will be encountered.

It is interesting to compare the sample matrix inverse method with the Baird algorithm. The Baird algorithm includes the matrix $\mathbf{A}_n$ in Eq. (5.164), which is used to deemphasize old data. This matrix has diagonal elements that are powers of α. However, we saw in Eqs. (5.196) through (5.201) that if $\alpha = 1$, Baird's algorithm is very similar to the SMI method. But there is a difference. For the SMI method, we use a fixed number of samples (K) in the sample covariance matrix each time the weights are computed. For the Baird algorithm in Eq. (5.201), the number of samples in the sample covariance matrix continually increases with n, the index denoting the sample number. Thus Baird's algorithm for $\alpha = 1$ corresponds to the SMI method with a longer and longer averaging time in the sample covariance matrix. For $\alpha < 1$, Baird's algorithm is equivalent to using a covariance matrix based on a continually increasing number of samples, but with the old samples gradually deemphasized.

In principle, Baird's algorithm has the advantage that it does not require the solution of a system of equations at each iteration. The algorithm simply updates the weights at each sample. However, this advantage is more illusory than real, because the number of multiplications required to carry out the matrix products in Eqs. (5.191) and (5.194) also increases as N^3 in the same way as the SMI method. Horowitz et al. [16] have implemented a four-element array using the SMI method. According to them, "For a small number of elements and a fixed level of performance, the SMI algorithm requires a lower computation rate than... [a] recursive least squares (Baird) algorithm."

This concludes our discussion of weight control techniques for overcoming eigenvalue spread problems. In the next chapter, we shall consider steered-beam adaptive arrays.

PROBLEMS

5.1. For the single feedback loop of Fig. 5.10, assume

$$\tilde{x}(t) = Ae^{j(\omega_d t + \psi_d)}$$

and

$$\tilde{r}(t) = e^{j(\omega_d t + \psi_d)},$$

where ψ_d is a random phase angle. Assume we choose $c = 10^{-3}$ to make the time constant of the loop approximate 1 millisecond. Then, suppose it is known that A can take on any value from 1 to 100. Hence, let us choose $k = 10^4$, to make $kcA^2 > 1$ for the smallest value of A. Also, assume the averaging time T is chosen to be 10^{-6} seconds.

Assume that the weight $w(t)$ has initial values $w(0) = 0$ and $w'(0) = 0$ at $t = 0$. Compute and plot the weight $w(t)$ versus t for $A = 1, 10$, and 100. How different are the time constants in the three cases?

5.2. Consider a two-element adaptive array that uses modified LMS loops of the type shown in Fig. 5.9. The weight vector **W** for this array satisfies Eq. (5.80). Assume the array receives a desired signal with bandwidth 400 kHz from broadside with an SNR per element of ξ_d. Assume the usual uncorrelated thermal noise of power σ^2 on each element.

Calculate all time constants for the weight transients in this array as a function of ξ_d over the range -20 dB $\leqslant \xi_d \leqslant 60$ dB. Perform these calculations for the following assumptions. First, suppose that all voltages in the array have been normalized so $\sigma^2 = 1$. Then choose the loop gain $k = 10^6$ so that the longest time constant in an ordinary LMS array (without the derivative loop of Fig. 5.9) will be

$$\tau_{\max} = \frac{1}{k\sigma^2} = 10^{-6} = 1 \text{ microsecond.}$$

Then, set the modified loop time constants $\tau_j = (1 + kc\lambda_j)/k\lambda_j$ equal to 1 millisecond by choosing $c = 10^{-3}$.

Now proceed as follows:

(a) Determine the required integration time T from Eq. (5.43).

(b) Determine the eigenvalues of $\mathbf{\Phi}_d$ in Eq. (5.80) in terms of the SNR ξ_d.

(c) Determine the two roots $s = s_1, s_2$ for each normal weight $v_i(t)$ in Eq. (5.82). [That is, find the values of s in $v_i(t) = e^{st}$ for which $v_i(t)$ satisfies Eq. (5.82).] This step will have to be done numerically. Note that there are four roots altogether, two for each eigenvalue.

(d) Define a time constant τ associated with each of the four roots in part (c). Plot each of the four time constants versus the SNR ξ_d over the range -20 dB $\leqslant \xi_d \leqslant$ 60 dB.

(e) Determine which of the four time constants are essentially constant and which vary with signal power. How many exponential terms will be present in the solution for each weight $w_i(t)$ in the weight transient?

5.3. The purpose of this problem is to investigate the dynamic range behavior of a Gram-Schmidt tree used in an adaptive array.

Consider a Gram-Schmidt preprocessor behind a four-element array, as shown in Fig. 5.13. Assume that the four elements lie along a straight line with half-wavelength spacing and that the elements are isotropic. Suppose there is a CW desired signal incident on the array, which produces a desired signal vector

$$\mathbf{X}_d = A_d e^{j\omega_0 t} \begin{bmatrix} 1 \\ e^{-j\phi_d} \\ e^{-j2\phi_d} \\ e^{-j3\phi_d} \end{bmatrix}$$

where

$$\phi_d = \tau \sin \theta_d,$$

and θ_d is the desired signal arrival angle. Assume a CW interference signal is also incident and produces an interference signal vector,

$$\mathbf{X}_i = A_i e^{j\omega_0 t} \begin{bmatrix} 1 \\ e^{-j\phi_i} \\ e^{-j2\phi_i} \\ e^{-j3\phi_i} \end{bmatrix}$$

with

$$\phi_i = \pi \sin \theta_i,$$

where θ_i is the interference arrival angle. Finally, assume that independent thermal noise is present on each element, with power σ^2.

Do the following:

(a) Determine the weights w_{kj} in the Gram-Schmidt tree of Fig. 5.13 for the given signals. Determine how the weight magnitudes vary down the tree.

(b) Consider the signals $\tilde{u}_j^4(t)$ defined in Fig. 5.13. Determine how $E[|\tilde{u}_j^4(t)|^2]$ varies as a function of j. (That is, investigate how the signal powers drop as we go down the tree.)

(c) Discuss the implications of your results in terms of array dynamic range.

5.4. A two-element array is to be controlled with the sample matrix inversion lemma. A steering vector $\mathbf{T}^* = (1, j)^T$ is used in the array. Four signal vectors are collected,

$$\mathbf{X}(1) = \begin{bmatrix} 1.1 \\ -j \end{bmatrix},$$

$$\mathbf{X}(2) = \begin{bmatrix} j \\ 0.9 \end{bmatrix},$$

$$\mathbf{X}(3) = \begin{bmatrix} -1 \\ j \end{bmatrix},$$

and

$$\mathbf{X}(4) = \begin{bmatrix} -j \\ -0.8 \end{bmatrix}.$$

Compute the weight vector to be used after these four samples are collected.

5.5. Write a computer program to carry out Baird's algorithm. Assume that you have a four-element array with isotropic elements. Assume that a CW desired signal at frequency ω_d arrives from $\theta_d = 0°$ with SNR per element of $\xi_d = 20$ dB. Let the elements be spaced a half wavelength apart at frequency ω_d. Assume there is uncorrelated thermal noise of power $\sigma^2 = 1$ on each element. (Note: To model the thermal noise, you will have to call a random number generator in your computer program. Be sure to scale the output from the random number routine so that it has zero mean and unit variance!) Assume that a CW interference signal also arrives, from angle $\theta_i = 50°$ with INR per element of ξ_i. In order to decorrelate the interference from the desired signal in your time-sampled simulation, assume the interference signal is on frequency $1.1\omega_d$. Let the deemphasis constant α in Eq. (5.164) be 0.9, and let all weights in the array be zero initially. Finally, let the sampling interval in Baird's algorithm be a quarter cycle at frequency ω_d.

Have your computer program print out the array weights, the output desired signal power, interference power and thermal noise power, and the SINR after each iteration, for 20 iterations. Make a plot of SINR versus sample number for two values of INR, -100 dB (i.e., no interference) and 40 dB. How many samples does it take for Baird's algorithm to converge with and without the interference?

5.6. According to the theorem in section 5.2, inserting a nonsingular transformation V between the elements of an adaptive array and an LMS processor has no effect on the output SINR from the array. Assuming a given set of signals incident on an LMS array and a given reference signal, determine what effect such a transformation will have on the steady-state array pattern.

5.7. Suppose that an array is to be controlled with the sample matrix inverse technique. Assume that each weight update will be based on $2N$ samples of the complex signal vector $\mathbf{X}$, where N is the number of array elements.

(a) Determine how many real multiplies are required to form a sample covariance matrix from $2N$ samples of the vector $\mathbf{X}$.

(b) Determine how many real multiplies are required to solve N complex linear equations with N unknowns using Gauss elimination.

(c) A common way to find the inverse of an $N \times N$ matrix $\mathbf{M}$ is to solve the linear system of equations $\mathbf{MX} = \mathbf{Y}$ N times with N different $\mathbf{Y}$-vectors, $\mathbf{Y}_1 = [1, 0, \ldots, 0]^T$, $\mathbf{Y}_2 = [0, 1, 0, \ldots, 0]^T, \ldots, \mathbf{Y}_N = [0, 0, \ldots, 1]^T$. The N solution vectors $\mathbf{X}_1, \mathbf{X}_2, \ldots, \mathbf{X}_N$ are then the columns of $\mathbf{M}^{-1}$. If this procedure is used, determine how many real multiplies are required to find the inverse of a complex sample matrix $\hat{\mathbf{\Phi}}$.

(d) According to the lemma of section 2.2, the matrix

$$\mathbf{Q} = \mathbf{B} - \beta \mathbf{Z}^* \mathbf{Z}^T,$$

has inverse

$$\mathbf{Q}^{-1} = \mathbf{B}^{-1} - \tau \mathbf{B}^{-1} \mathbf{Z}^* \mathbf{Z}^T \mathbf{B}^{-1},$$

where

$$\tau^{-1} + \beta^{-1} = \mathbf{Z}^T \mathbf{B}^{-1} \mathbf{Z}^*.$$

Assuming that $\mathbf{B}^{-1}$ is known and $\mathbf{Z}$ is a complex vector with N elements, determine how many real multiplies are required to find $\mathbf{Q}^{-1}$.

(e) In the sample inverse method, it is assumed that we accumulate the sample covariance matrix for $2N$ samples and then solve $\hat{\Phi}\mathbf{W} = \mathbf{T}^*$ for the weights. A possible alternative procedure would be to calculate an initial inverse matrix $\hat{\Phi}^{-1}$, and then update $\hat{\Phi}^{-1}$ $2N$ times using the matrix inversion lemma. At the jth sample time, when the jth sample vector $\mathbf{X}(j)$ becomes available, we could use the matrix inversion lemma to add $\mathbf{X}(j)$ to $\hat{\Phi}^{-1}$, and we could also remove the outdated sample vector $\mathbf{X}(j - 2N)$ from $\hat{\Phi}^{-1}$. Repeating this procedure $2N$ times would give $\hat{\Phi}^{-1}$ from the next block of $2N$ samples. Determine whether there would be any advantage to such a procedure over the standard sample matrix inverse technique.

5.8. The signals from a three-element array are passed through a Gram-Schmidt pre-processor, as shown in Fig. 5.22. The array receives a CW desired signal from broadside, and each element signal also contains thermal noise,

$$\tilde{x}_j(t) = A_d e^{j(\omega_d t + \psi_d)} + \tilde{n}_j(t), \qquad j = 1, 2, 3,$$

where ψ_d is a random variable uniformly distributed on $(0, 2\pi)$ and $E[\tilde{n}_j^*(t)\tilde{n}_k(t)] = \sigma^2 \delta_{jk}$.

(a) Calculate the steady-state Gram-Schmidt weights w_{12}, w_{13}, and w_{23}.

(b) Assume each weight is controlled by an analog LMS loop of the type shown in Fig. 5.18. Derive the differential equation satisfied by $w_{23}(t)$. To do so, assume that all signal products $\tilde{x}_j^*(t)\tilde{x}_k(t)$ appearing in differential equations may be replaced by their expected values $E[\tilde{x}_j^*(t)\tilde{x}_k(t)]$, and assume that the initial values of the weights at $t = 0$ are

$$w_{12}(0) = w_{13}(0) = w_{23}(0) = 0.$$

Note that one must obtain and solve the differential equations for $w_{12}(t)$ and $w_{13}(t)$ in order to obtain the differential equation for $w_{23}(t)$. Show that the value of w_{23} found in part (a) is the correct steady-state solution for $w_{23}(t)$.

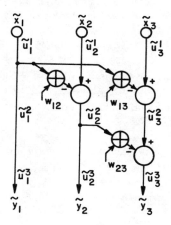

Figure 5.22 A three-element Gram-Schmidt preprocessor.

REFERENCES

1. R. T. Compton, Jr., "Improved Feedback Loop for Adaptive Arrays," *IEEE Transactions on Aerospace and Electronic Systems*, AES–16, no. 2 (March 1980): 159. Copyright © 1980 IEEE.

2. L. E. Brennan, J. D. Mallett, and I. S. Reed, "Convergence Rate in Adaptive Arrays," Report TSC–PD–A177–2, 15 July 1977, Technology Service Corporation, Santa Monica, Calif. 90403; prepared under Contract N00019–77–C–0172 for Naval Air Systems Command.

3. W. F. Gabriel, "Building Block for an Orthonormal Lattice Filter Adaptive Network," Report 8409, 10 July 1980, Naval Research Laboratory, Washington, D.C. 20375.

4. C. A. Baird, "Recursive Processing for Adaptive Arrays," Proceedings of the Adaptive Antenna Systems Workshop, March 11–13, 1974, Naval Research Laboratory, Washington, D.C., NRL Report 7803, September 1974.

5. L. E. Brennan, J. D. Mallett, and I. S. Reed, "Adaptive Arrays in Airborne MTI Radar," *IEEE Transactions on Antennas and Propagation*, AP–24, no. 5 (September 1976): 607.

6. I. S. Reed, J. D. Mallett, and L. E. Brennan, "Rapid Convergence Rate in Adaptive Arrays," *IEEE Transactions on Aerospace and Electronic Systems*, AES–10, no. 6 (November 1974): 853.

7. M. Athens, M. L. Dertouzos, R. N. Spann, and S. J. Mason, *Systems, Networks, and Computation*, McGraw-Hill, New York, 1974, p. 108.

8. T. W. Miller, R. Caldecott, and R. J. Huff, "A Satellite Simulator with a TDMA-System Compatible Adaptive Array," Report 3364–4, June 1976, Ohio State University Electro-Science Laboratory, Department of Electrical Engineering, Columbus, Ohio 43212; prepared under Contract F30602–72–C–0162 for Rome Air Development Center.

9. E. Yu, "The Performance of Adaptive Arrays with Optimum Convergence Properties," Final Report 714258–3, vol. 6, September, 1984, Ohio State University ElectroScience Laboratory, Department of Electrical Engineering, Columbus, Ohio 43212; prepared under Contract F30602–82–C–0009 for Rome Air Development Center.

10. R. Bellman, *Introduction to Matrix Analysis*, McGraw-Hill, New York, 1970.

11. I. S. Reed, J. D. Mallett, and L. E. Brennan, "Rapid Convergence Rate in Adaptive Arrays," *IEEE Transactions on Aerospace and Electronic Systems*, AES–10, no. 6 (November 1974): 853.

12. D. M. Young and R. T. Gregory, *A Survey of Numerical Mathematics*, Addison-Wesley, Reading, Mass., 1972.

13. R. Nitzberg, "Effect of Errors in Adaptive Weights," *IEEE Transactions on Aerospace and Electronic Systems*, AES–12, no. 3 (May 1976): 369.

14. R. Nitzberg, "Computational Precision Requirements for Optimal Weights in Adaptive Processing," *IEEE Transactions on Aerospace and Electronic Systems*, AES–16, no. 4 (July 1980): 418.

15. F. B. Hilderbrand, *Introduction to Numerical Analysis*, McGraw-Hill, New York, 1974.

16. L. L. Horowitz, H. Blatt, W. G. Brodsky, and K. D. Senne, "Controlling Adaptive Antenna Arrays with the Sample Matrix Inversion Algorithm," *IEEE Transactions on Aerospace and Electronic Systems*, AES–15, no. 6 (November 1979): 840.

6

Steering Vector Arrays

In this chapter we discuss adaptive arrays that use a steering vector in the weight control loops. Such arrays are often called Applebaum arrays, because of Applebaum's early work in this area [1]. (However, Griffiths appears to have been the first to publish this concept in the literature [2].) Our purpose here is to present a number of topics related to the Applebaum array. The basic Applebaum array was discussed in section 2.2.

In section 6.1, we describe the sidelobe canceler array. The sidelobe canceler was actually the first type of adaptive array [3]. Conceptually, however, it turns out to be just a special case of the general steering vector array described in section 2.2. In section 6.1 we explain the sidelobe canceler concept and show its relation to the steering vector array. In section 6.2, we show how the element signals in an Applebaum array may be linearly combined before the adaptive processor without affecting array performance. This technique is useful for conceptual purposes, such as for understanding the effects of element patterns on array performance. In section 6.3, we discuss the effect of steering vector errors on the performance of the Applebaum array. We show that the array performance is very sensitive to such errors. Also, this section serves as background for section 6.4, where we describe constrained adaptive array algorithms. Section 6.4 presents an algorithm due to Frost [4] that adapts the array response while forcing the weights to satisfy constraints. This technique is useful for reducing the sensitivity of the array to steering vector errors, for maintaining main-beam shape in the presence of interference, and for other purposes. Finally, in section 6.5, we describe the power inversion array. The power inversion array is an Applebaum array with the steering vector chosen to obtain some interference protection when neither the desired signal arrival angle nor its waveform is known.

6.1 THE SIDELOBE CANCELER

The first adaptive array concept was the sidelobe canceler [3]. A sidelobe canceler is used to reduce clutter and interference in radar. It consists of a single high-gain antenna (or main antenna) to which a number of small auxiliary elements are added. The high-gain antenna is a typical radar antenna (e.g., a parabolic dish) with a beamwidth as required by the radar system. The auxiliary elements are small, low-gain elements, with much wider beamwidths than the high-gain element. The auxiliary element outputs are multiplied by adaptive weights and then added to the high-gain antenna output. By controlling the weights on the auxiliary elements, an interference signal in the sidelobes of the high-gain element may be nulled out. Often the auxiliary elements include elements with different polarizations, so that the response of the system to cross-polarized interference may also be controlled. Figure 6.1 shows the configuration of a sidelobe canceler.

In a sidelobe canceler, there is no adaptable weight on the high-gain element. However, it turns out that the sidelobe canceler is equivalent to an Applebaum array of the type described in section 2.2. The SINR performance of a sidelobe canceler is the same as that of an Applebaum array with a controllable weight behind the high-gain element and a steering vector that turns on only the high-gain element.

Let us first show this equivalence. Consider an adaptive array using the same elements as the sidelobe canceler in Fig. 6.1, except with a weight control

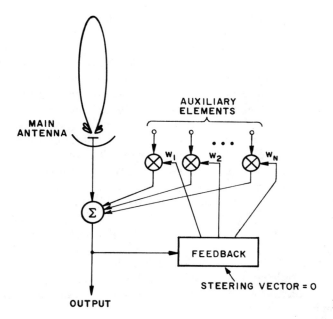

Figure 6.1 The Sidelobe Canceler.

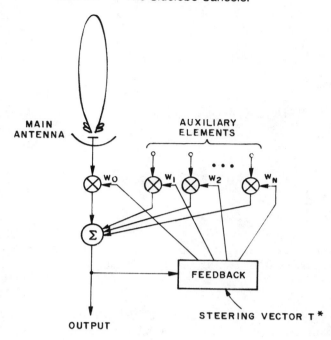

Figure 6.2 Sidelobe canceler with adjustable gain on main antenna.

loop behind the main element as well as all the auxiliary elements. Such an array is shown in Fig. 6.2. This array is an Applebaum array of the type discussed in Chapter 2. Let the weight on the high-gain element be w_0 and the weights on the auxiliary elements be $w_1, w_2, \ldots, w_N$. Assume that each weight w_k in Fig. 6.2 is controlled by an Applebaum loop with a steering weight t_k^*, as shown in Fig. 6.3.

Now consider the problem of choosing the steering vector $\mathbf{T}^* = [t_0^*, t_1^*, \ldots, t_N^*]$. As discussed in section 2.2, the steady-state weight vector in the

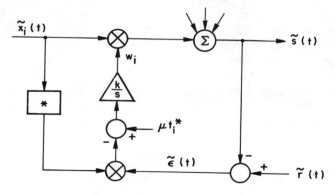

Figure 6.3 The Applebaum feedback loop.

array of Fig. 6.2 will be the solution to

$$\mathbf{W}' = \mu(\mathbf{\Phi}')^{-1}\mathbf{T}^*, \tag{6.1}$$

where $\mathbf{W}'$ is the weight vector

$$\mathbf{W}' = [w_0, w_1, w_2, \ldots, w_N]^T, \tag{6.2}$$

$\mathbf{\Phi}'$ is the covariance matrix

$$\mathbf{\Phi}' = E \begin{bmatrix} \tilde{x}_0^*\tilde{x}_0 & \tilde{x}_0^*\tilde{x}_1 & \cdots & \tilde{x}_0^*\tilde{x}_N \\ \tilde{x}_1^*\tilde{x}_0 & \tilde{x}_1^*\tilde{x}_1 & \cdots & x_1^*\tilde{x}_N \\ \vdots & & & \\ \tilde{x}_N^*\tilde{x}_0 & \tilde{x}_N^*\tilde{x}_1 & \cdots & \tilde{x}_N^*\tilde{x}_N \end{bmatrix} \tag{6.3}$$

and μ is a gain constant. As we know from Chapter 2, maximum output SINR will be obtained from the array if the steering vector is chosen to be

$$\mathbf{T}^* = \mathbf{U}_d^*, \tag{6.4}$$

where $\mathbf{U}_d$ is the desired signal vector [e.g., see Eq. (2.213)]. Moreover, because the high-gain element has much more gain than the auxiliary elements, a desired signal arriving on the main beam of the high-gain antenna produces a much larger signal on that element than on the others. Hence for this desired signal we have approximately

$$\mathbf{U}_d \simeq [1, 0, 0, \ldots, 0]^T. \tag{6.5}$$

Therefore, the optimum steering vector is simply

$$\mathbf{T}^* = [1, 0, 0, \ldots, 0]^T. \tag{6.6}$$

When this steering vector is used in Eq. (6.1), the weight vector $\mathbf{W}'$ turns out to be just a scalar multiple of the weight vector obtained with the sidelobe canceler array in Fig. 6.1. To see this relationship, suppose we solve Eq. (6.1) for $\mathbf{W}'$. Let the resulting weight on the high-gain element be w_0. Note that w_0 will not be zero, because the high-gain element has the largest desired signal component of any element in the array. (The weight vector that yields maximum array output SINR has a gain on each element proportional to the signal voltage on that element [5].) Moreover, the SINR at the array output will not be affected if all the weights in the array are multiplied by a constant. Hence, we can adjust the arbitrary coefficient μ until w_0 is equal to unity. With this value of μ, the remaining weights $w_1, w_2, \ldots, w_N$ will be the same as the weights that result in Fig. 6.1.

To see this, define the scalar

$$p_0 = E(\tilde{x}_0^*\tilde{x}_0), \tag{6.7}$$

the matrix

$$\boldsymbol{\Phi} = E \begin{bmatrix} \tilde{x}_1^* \tilde{x}_1 & \tilde{x}_1^* \tilde{x}_2 & \cdots & \tilde{x}_1^* \tilde{x}_N \\ \tilde{x}_2^* \tilde{x}_1 & \tilde{x}_2^* \tilde{x}_2 & \cdots & \tilde{x}_2^* \tilde{x}_N \\ \vdots & & & \\ \tilde{x}_N^* \tilde{x}_1 & \tilde{x}_N^* \tilde{x}_2 & \cdots & \tilde{x}_N^* \tilde{x}_N \end{bmatrix} \tag{6.8}$$

and the vector

$$\mathbf{V} = E(\tilde{x}_1^* \tilde{x}_0, \tilde{x}_2^* \tilde{x}_0, \ldots, \tilde{x}_N^* \tilde{x}_0)^T. \tag{6.9}$$

Let $\mathbf{W}$ be the weight vector associated with the auxiliary elements,

$$\mathbf{W} = [w_1, w_2, \ldots, w_N]^T. \tag{6.10}$$

Then Eq. (6.1) may be written in partitioned form as

$$\begin{bmatrix} p_0 & \vdots & \mathbf{V}^\dagger \\ \cdots & \vdots & \cdots \\ \mathbf{V} & \vdots & \boldsymbol{\Phi} \end{bmatrix} \begin{bmatrix} w_0 \\ \cdots \\ \mathbf{W} \end{bmatrix} = \begin{bmatrix} \mu \\ \cdots \\ \mathbf{0} \end{bmatrix}. \tag{6.11}$$

This equation is equivalent to a scalar equation

$$p_0 w_0 + \mathbf{V}^\dagger \mathbf{W} = \mu \tag{6.12}$$

and a vector equation

$$\boldsymbol{\Phi} \mathbf{W} = -w_0 \mathbf{V}. \tag{6.13}$$

According to the preceding discussion, we choose a value of μ in Eq. (6.1) that results in w_0 being unity. Then Eq. (6.13) reduces to

$$\boldsymbol{\Phi} \mathbf{W} = -\mathbf{V}. \tag{6.14}$$

It turns out that the weight vector for the auxiliary elements in the array of Fig. 6.1 satisfies this same equation.

To see this result, note that the weight in the ith loop of Fig. 6.1 satisfies

$$\frac{dw_i}{dt} = -k\tilde{x}_i^* [\tilde{x}_0 + w_1 \tilde{x}_1 + w_2 \tilde{x}_2 + \cdots + w_N \tilde{x}_N], \qquad 1 \leqslant i \leqslant N, \tag{6.15}$$

or in vector form

$$\frac{d\mathbf{W}}{dt} + k\mathbf{X}^* \mathbf{X}^T \mathbf{W} = -k\mathbf{X}^* \tilde{x}_0. \tag{6.16}$$

Replacing $\mathbf{X}^* \mathbf{X}^T$ and $\mathbf{X}^* \tilde{x}_0$ by their expected values gives

$$\frac{d\mathbf{W}}{dt} + k\boldsymbol{\Phi} \mathbf{W} = -k\mathbf{V}, \tag{6.17}$$

for which the steady-state solution is given by Eq. (6.14).

Thus the sidelobe canceler array is not really different from an Applebaum array with a steering vector. The SINR performance of the two will be identical for any given set of signals if the Applebaum array uses the steering vector in Eq. (6.5).

6.2 ADDITIONAL FORMS OF THE APPLEBAUM ARRAY

The Applebaum array may also be modified into other forms by using the theorem presented in section 5.2. Suppose we start with a given set of array elements. Instead of connecting the elements directly to the Applebaum processor, as in Fig. 6.4, suppose we insert a set of linear combiners between the elements and the processor. Figure 6.5 shows such an arrangement. The element signals $\tilde{x}_1(t), \ldots, \tilde{x}_N(t)$ are combined linearly to produce signals $\tilde{y}_1(t), \ldots, \tilde{y}_N(t)$, according to

$$\tilde{y}_1(t) = \mathbf{V}_1^T \mathbf{X},$$
$$\tilde{y}_2(t) = \mathbf{V}_2^T \mathbf{X},$$

and

$$\tilde{y}_N(t) = \mathbf{V}_N^T \mathbf{X}, \tag{6.18}$$

where $\mathbf{V}_1, \ldots, \mathbf{V}_N$ are a set of preweighting vectors as defined in Eqs. (5.93). Equations (6.18) may be written

$$\mathbf{Y} = \mathbf{V}^T \mathbf{X}, \tag{6.19}$$

where

$$\mathbf{V} = [\mathbf{V}_1, \mathbf{V}_2, \ldots, \mathbf{V}_N] \tag{6.20}$$

and

$$\mathbf{Y} = [\tilde{y}_1(t), \tilde{y}_2(t), \ldots, \tilde{y}_N(t)]^T. \tag{6.21}$$

According to the theorem in section 5.2, the output SINR from the system in Fig. 6.5 will be identical to that from Fig. 6.4 as long as the vectors $\mathbf{V}_i$ are linearly independent and the steering vectors in the two processors are related by

$$\mathbf{Q}^* = \mathbf{V}^\dagger \mathbf{T}^*. \tag{6.22}$$

The preweighting vectors $\mathbf{V}_i$ can be used to form any set of desired patterns from the original N elements without affecting the final SINR of the system.

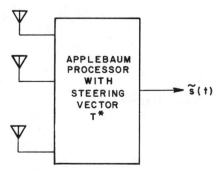

Figure 6.4   Standard Applebaum processor.

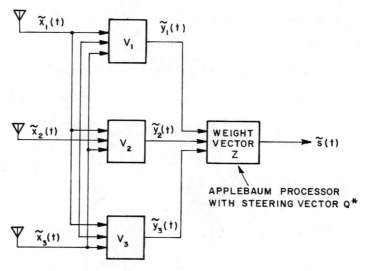

Figure 6.5   Applebaum processor with preweighting.

Consider an example. Suppose the original N elements are isotropic and a half wavelength apart. Let us choose the $\mathbf{V}_i$ to form a series of narrowbeam patterns, each in a different direction. Let

$$
\begin{aligned}
\mathbf{V}_1 &= \left[1, e^{j\phi_1}, e^{j2\phi_1}, \ldots, e^{j(N-1)\phi_1}\right]^T, \\
\mathbf{V}_2 &= \left[1, e^{j\phi_2}, e^{j2\phi_2}, \ldots, e^{j(N-1)\phi_2}\right]^T, \\
&\vdots \\
\mathbf{V}_N &= \left[1, e^{j\phi_N}, e^{j2\phi_N}, \ldots, e^{j(N-1)\phi_N}\right]^T.
\end{aligned}
\tag{6.23}
$$

As long as the ϕ_i in Eqs. (6.23) are different (modulo 2π) for different i, the vectors in Eqs. (6.23) are linearly independent,[‡] and the array output SINR will not be changed by inserting these $\mathbf{V}_i$ between the elements and the processor.

For these $\mathbf{V}_i$, the pattern for each $\tilde{y}_i(t)$ will have a beam maximum in a direction θ_i, related to ϕ_i by

$$
\phi_i = \pi \sin \theta_i.
\tag{6.24}
$$

[‡]The matrix

$$
\mathbf{V} = \begin{bmatrix}
1 & 1 & \cdots & 1 \\
e^{j\phi_1} & e^{j\phi_2} & & e^{j\phi_N} \\
e^{j2\phi_1} & e^{j2\phi_2} & & e^{j2\phi_N} \\
\vdots & \vdots & & \vdots \\
e^{j(N-1)\phi_1} & e^{j(N-1)\phi_2} & & e^{j(N-1)\phi_N}
\end{bmatrix}
$$

Since a signal propagating into the array from angle θ produces a signal vector

$$\mathbf{X} = \left[1, e^{-j\pi \sin \theta}, e^{-j2\pi \sin \theta}, \ldots\right]^T, \tag{6.25}$$

the output at port $\tilde{y}_i(t)$ from this signal will be

$$\tilde{y}_i(t) = \mathbf{V}_i^T \mathbf{X} = \sum_{k=1}^{N} e^{j(k-1)\pi(\sin \theta_i - \sin \theta)}$$

$$= e^{-j(N-1)(\pi/2)} \frac{\sin\left[N\frac{\pi}{2}(\sin \theta - \sin \theta_i)\right]}{\sin\left[\frac{\pi}{2}(\sin \theta - \sin \theta_i)\right]}. \tag{6.26}$$

The voltage pattern for each $\tilde{y}_i(t)$ is given by $|\tilde{y}_i(t)|$ as a function of θ,

$$|\tilde{y}_i(t)| = \frac{\sin\left[N\frac{\pi}{2}(\sin \theta - \sin \theta_i)\right]}{\sin\left[\frac{\pi}{2}(\sin \theta - \sin \theta_i)\right]}. \tag{6.27}$$

For example, suppose there are five elements. Let us choose the ϕ_i so that each beam maximum falls on the first null of the adjacent pattern. If $\theta_3 = 0°$, the patterns for the five signals $\tilde{y}_i(t)$ are then as shown in Fig. 6.6. (The other beam maxima for this case fall at $\theta_1 = -53.2°$, $\theta_2 = -23.8°$, $\theta_4 = 23.8°$ and $\theta_5 = 53.2°$.)

Consider what the new steering vector should be for this example. Suppose the desired signal arrives from broadside ($\theta = 0°$). Then for an Applebaum array without preweighting, as in Fig. 6.4, we would choose the steering vector

---

has the form of a Vandermonde matrix $\mathbf{M}$,

$$\mathbf{M} = \begin{bmatrix} 1 & 1 & \cdots & 1 \\ \lambda_1 & \lambda_2 & & \lambda_N \\ \lambda_1^2 & \lambda_2^2 & & \lambda_N^2 \\ \vdots & \vdots & & \\ \lambda_1^{N-1} & \lambda_2^{N-1} & & \lambda_N^{N-1} \end{bmatrix}$$

for which the determinant is [6]

$$\text{Det}(\mathbf{M}) = \prod_{1 \leqslant i < j \leqslant N} (\lambda_i - \lambda_j).$$

Since $\mathbf{M}$ is nonsingular as long as all the λ_i are different, it follows that $\mathbf{V}$ is nonsingular as long as $\phi_i \neq \phi_j \pmod{2\pi}$ for all $i \neq j$.

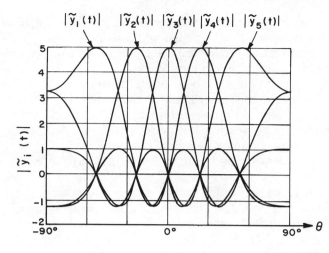

$|\tilde{y}_1(t)|$ $|\tilde{y}_2(t)|$ $|\tilde{y}_3(t)|$ $|\tilde{y}_4(t)|$ $|\tilde{y}_5(t)|$

Figure 6.6 Patterns of $|\tilde{y}_i(t)|$, $1 \leqslant i \leqslant 5$, versus θ: five-element array, $\theta_1 = -53.2°$, $\theta_2 = -23.8°$, $\theta_3 = 0°$, $\theta_4 = 23.8°$, $\theta_5 = 53.2°$.

$\mathbf{T}^*$ to be

$$\mathbf{T}^* = [1, 1, 1, 1, 1]^T \tag{6.28}$$

to point the quiescent beam at broadside. For the array of Fig. 6.5, on the other hand, we find from Eq. (6.22) that the steering vector should be

$$\mathbf{Q}^* = \mathbf{V}^\dagger \mathbf{T}^* = \begin{bmatrix} 1 & e^{-j\phi_1} & e^{-j2\phi_1} & \cdots \\ 1 & e^{-j\phi_2} & e^{-j2\phi_2} & \cdots \\ \vdots & & & \\ 1 & e^{-j\phi_5} & e^{-j2\phi_5} & \cdots \end{bmatrix} \begin{bmatrix} 1 \\ 1 \\ \vdots \\ 1 \end{bmatrix}. \tag{6.29}$$

Since by assumption a signal arriving from broadside will be in a null for all beams except beam 3, we have

$$\sum_{k=1}^{5} e^{-j(k-1)\phi_i} = 0 \quad \text{for all } i \neq 3. \tag{6.30}$$

For beam 3, $\phi_3 = 0°$, so

$$\sum_{k=1}^{5} e^{-j(k-1)\phi_3} = 5. \tag{6.31}$$

Hence Eq. (6.29) yields simply

$$\mathbf{Q}^* = [0, 0, 5, 0, 0]^T. \tag{6.32}$$

Thus the equivalent steering vector in Fig. 6.5 just turns all ports off except $\tilde{y}_3(t)$, the port whose beam points at the desired signal. With $\mathbf{T}^*$ given by Eq. (6.28) and $\mathbf{Q}^*$ by Eq. (6.32), the patterns and the SINR for the two arrays in Figs. 6.4 and 6.5 are the same for any set of signals incident on the array.

The preweighting in Eqs. (6.23) and the patterns in Fig. 6.6 are similar to what is obtained when a Butler matrix [7, 8] or a Rotman lens [9, 10] is inserted between the elements and the adaptive processor. The resulting antenna system is often referred to as a multiple-beam antenna, or MBA.

The fact that preweighting combiners can be inserted before an adaptive processor without affecting the final SINR is useful for the insight it gives into the effects that element patterns have on array performance. This point of view is often helpful, for example, for comparing the performance to be expected with different connections of elements in an array.

A word of caution is in order, however, about this result. The theorem in section 5.2 holds only when each $\tilde{y}_i(t)$ is strictly a linear sum of the $\tilde{x}_i(t)$. If the preweighting vectors $\mathbf{V}_i$ depend on frequency and if the signals have nonzero bandwidth, one cannot assume that the SINR before and after preweighting will be the same. When the $\mathbf{V}_i$ are frequency dependent, they cannot be factored out of the covariance matrix $\mathbf{\Phi}_y$ as in Eq. (5.102). In this case one must determine $\mathbf{\Phi}_y$ using the methods of section 3.2.

6.3 STEERING VECTOR ERRORS ‡

A problem with the Applebaum array is that its performance can be very sensitive to errors in the steering vector [11, 12]. The effects of these errors can be significant in array applications where the desired signal is present continuously, as in communication system applications. Steering vector errors are usually less important in radar, because the radar pulse is too short to affect the steady-state pattern. We shall examine the effect of two kinds of errors—simple pointing errors and random errors.

There are several reasons the steering vector in an Applebaum array can be in error. For example, in some design applications, the desired signal arrival angle may be known approximately but not exactly, and so a pointing error results. Or, the desired signal arrival angle may be estimated from the received signal, but because of noise in the estimation process, a pointing error results. Inaccuracies may also contribute to pointing errors. For example, the element patterns in an array may be slightly different from those assumed by the designer, because of mutual impedance effects, reflections, and the like, so the actual quiescent beam is not exactly as intended. Random steering vector errors may occur if the steering vector has been computed, because of truncation or rounding off. Or, random errors may occur because of the way the steering vector is obtained. For instance, one way to determine a steering vector in a communication system is to allow an LMS array (using a reference signal) to adapt to a desired signal during an interval when it is known that there is no

‡Portions of this section are reprinted from the author's papers [11, 12] with permission, © 1980, 1982 IEEE.

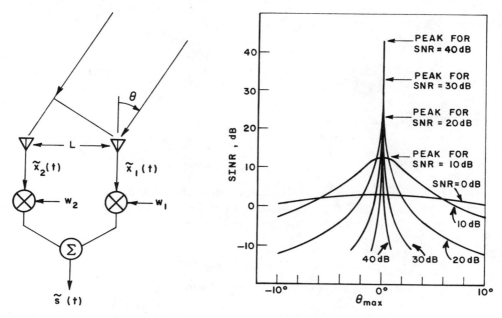

Figure 6.7 A two-element array.

Figure 6.8 SINR versus θ_{max}: two elements, $\theta_d = 0°$, $B_d = 0$, no interference.

interference. The weights obtained during this interval may then be used as steering weights during a later interval when interference may be present. However, steering weights obtained in this way will have random errors because of the noise in the array feedback loops when the weights are sampled. As we shall see, the Applebaum array performance can be very sensitive to both pointing and random errors in the steering vector.

We first show the effect of a pointing error [11]. We can use a simple two-element array to illustrate what happens. Suppose an array has two isotropic elements a half wavelength apart, as shown in Fig. 6.7. Assume that a CW desired signal is incident on the array from angle θ_d, and that thermal noise is present in each element signal. The array weight vector is then given by

$$\mathbf{W} = \mu \boldsymbol{\Phi}^{-1} \mathbf{T}^*, \tag{6.33}$$

where

$$\boldsymbol{\Phi} = \sigma^2 \mathbf{I} + A_d^2 \mathbf{U}_d^* \mathbf{U}_d^T = \sigma^2 \begin{bmatrix} 1 + \xi_d & \xi_d e^{-j\phi_d} \\ \xi e^{j\phi_d} & 1 + \xi_d \end{bmatrix}. \tag{6.34}$$

Here σ^2 is the thermal noise power per element, A_d is the desired signal voltage, and $\mathbf{U}_d$ is the vector

$$\mathbf{U}_d = [1, e^{-j\phi_d}]^T, \tag{6.35}$$

where

$$\phi_d = \pi \sin \theta_d \tag{6.36}$$

and

$$\xi_d = \frac{A_d^2}{\sigma^2}. \tag{6.37}$$

The inverse of $\mathbf{\Phi}$ is

$$\mathbf{\Phi}^{-1} = \frac{1}{\sigma^2(1 + 2\xi_d)} \begin{bmatrix} 1 + \xi_d & -\xi_d e^{-j\phi_d} \\ -\xi_d e^{j\phi_d} & 1 + \xi_d \end{bmatrix}. \tag{6.38}$$

To evaluate the effect of a pointing error, assume that the steering vector is chosen to provide a beam maximum of the quiescent pattern in a given direction θ_{max}. To determine $\mathbf{T}^*$, we note that a CW signal from angle θ_{max} will produce a signal vector

$$\mathbf{X} = \begin{bmatrix} 1, & e^{-j\pi \sin \theta_{max}} \end{bmatrix}^T e^{j\omega_0 t}. \tag{6.39}$$

The array output from a such a signal would be

$$\tilde{s}(t) = \mathbf{X}^T \mathbf{W} = \begin{bmatrix} w_1 + w_2 e^{-j\pi \sin \theta_{max}} \end{bmatrix} e^{j\omega_0 t}. \tag{6.40}$$

The array pattern will have a maximum on this signal if

$$w_1 = w_2 e^{-j\pi \sin \theta_{max}}. \tag{6.41}$$

Hence, for a given θ_{max}, we choose

$$\mathbf{T}^* = \begin{bmatrix} e^{-j\pi \sin \theta_{max}}, & 1 \end{bmatrix}^T. \tag{6.42}$$

From this $\mathbf{T}^*$, $\mathbf{W}$ may be calculated using Eq. (6.33). From $\mathbf{W}$, the array output SINR may be calculated in the usual way from Eqs. (2.135) to (2.146).

Now consider what happens to the array performance when $\theta_{max} \neq \theta_d$. Figure 6.8 shows the output SINR from the array as a function of θ_{max} when $\theta_d = 0°$. Several curves are drawn for different ξ_d. As may be seen, the SINR can drop rather precipitously when $\theta_{max} \neq \theta_d$. Figure 6.8 shows that the higher the SNR, the closer θ_{max} must be to θ_d to achieve a given SINR from the array. For example, if $\xi_d = 10$ dB, we require $-7.5° \leqslant \theta_{max} \leqslant 7.5°$ to achieve SINR $\geqslant 0$ dB. But for $\xi_d = 30$ dB, $-0.8° \leqslant \theta_{max} \leqslant 0.8°$ is necessary for SINR $\geqslant 0$ dB.

The behavior of the curves in Fig. 6.8 may be understood by examining the array patterns. Figures 6.9 and 6.10 show typical patterns under the same conditions as in Fig. 6.8. In Fig. 6.9, θ_{max} is 0°, and in Fig. 6.10, θ_{max} is 2°. For $\theta_{max} = \theta_d = 0°$, we find that, as the SNR is increased, the overall magnitude of the pattern drops, but the pattern shape does not change. The array does not form a null on the desired signal but simply reduces the pattern amplitude. As the pattern amplitude drops, both the output signal power and the output thermal noise power are lowered in proportion. Hence the output SINR remains unaffected.

For $\theta_{max} = 2°$ ($\neq \theta_d$), however, the pattern behavior is quite different, as may be seen in Fig. 6.10. Now as the SNR increases, the array increasingly nulls the desired signal. Moreover, it can do so without lowering the null overall pattern amplitude, so the result is a reduction in desired signal power without a reduction in thermal noise power. Hence the SINR drops as the SNR increases. This behavior accounts for the curves seen in Fig. 6.8.

In general, we find that the closer θ_{max} is to the desired signal direction θ_d, the stronger the desired signal power must be to move the null onto the desired signal.

A different perspective on these results may be gained by plotting the SINR versus the SNR. The result is shown in Fig. 6.11 for several values of θ_{max}. This figure is interesting because it immediately shows that the beam pointing error that can be tolerated is essentially a matter of dynamic range. For example, if $\theta_{max} = 1°$, we have SINR > 0 dB only for -3 dB $< \xi_d <$ 28 dB, whereas if $\theta_{max} = 0.1°$, SINR > 0 dB for -3 dB $< \xi_d <$ 48 dB. The greater the desired signal dynamic range we wish to accommodate, the closer θ_{max} must be to the desired signal angle.

This example illustrates the effect on array performance of one type of steering vector error, a beam-pointing error. We assumed the steering vector components were correct except that they were chosen for a beam in a slightly different direction from the desired signal. As Figs. 6.8 and 6.11 show, the array can be rather sensitive to such an error, particularly if the SNR is high.

Now let us examine the effects of random errors in the steering vector [12]. Suppose that the steering vector has been chosen to produce a beam in the proper direction, but that each component of the steering vector has a random error, uncorrelated from one element to another. Using this model, we will examine how the output SINR depends on the variance of the steering vector errors.

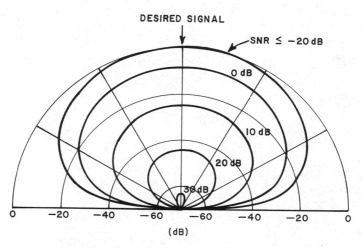

Figure 6.9   Pattern behavior for $\theta_{max} = 0°$: $\theta_d = 0°$, $B_d = 0$.

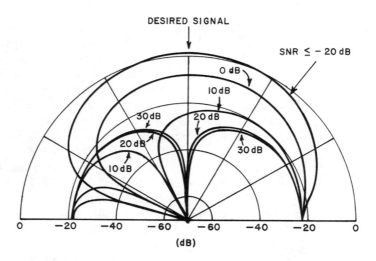

Figure 6.10 Pattern behavior for $\theta_{\max} = 2°$: $\theta_d = 0°$, $B_d = 0$.

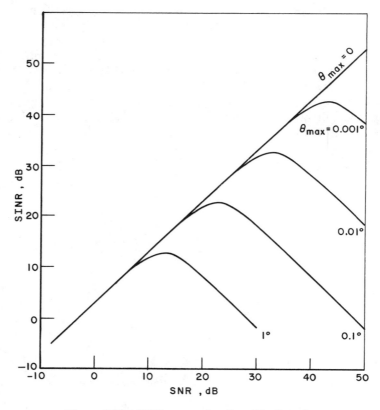

Figure 6.11 SINR versus ξ_d: $\theta_d = 0°$, $B_d = 0$.

348

To determine the effect of random errors, we shall assume an N-element array as shown in Fig. 6.12. This assumption will allow us to determine what effect the number of elements has on the results. We again assume the elements are isotropic, lie in a straight line, and have half-wavelength spacing. For this problem, we shall also assume an interference signal incident on the array as well as the desired signal and noise. Moreover, we shall allow the desired and interference signals to have nonzero bandwidth. Thus, the jth element signal is given by

$$\tilde{x}_j(t) = \tilde{d}_j(t) + \tilde{i}_j(t) + \tilde{n}_j(t), \tag{6.43}$$

where $\tilde{d}_j(t)$, $\tilde{i}_j(t)$, and $\tilde{n}_j(t)$ are the desired, interference, and noise signals, in the usual notation. The normalized covariance matrix is

$$\mathbf{\Phi}_0 = \frac{1}{\sigma^2}\mathbf{\Phi} = \mathbf{\Phi}_{d0} + \mathbf{\Phi}_{i0} + \mathbf{I}, \tag{6.44}$$

where $\mathbf{\Phi}_{d0}$ is the normalized desired signal covariance matrix,

$$\mathbf{\Phi}_{d0} = \xi_d \begin{bmatrix} \rho_d(0) & \rho_d(-T_d) & \cdots & \rho_d[-(N-1)T_d] \\ \rho_d(T_d) & \rho_d(0) & & \\ \vdots & & & \\ \rho_d[(N-1)T_d] & & \cdots & \rho_d(0) \end{bmatrix} \tag{6.45}$$

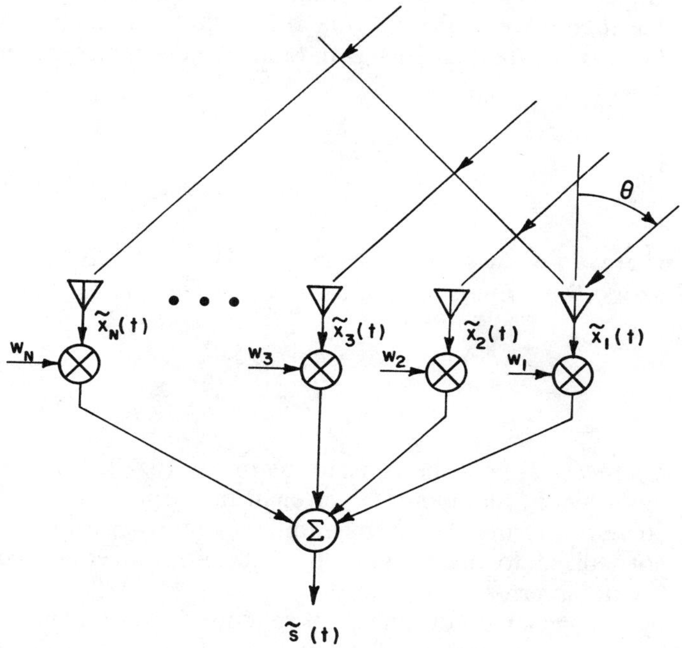

Figure 6.12 An N-element adaptive array.

and $\boldsymbol{\Phi}_{i0}$ is the normalized interference covariance matrix,

$$\boldsymbol{\Phi}_{i0} = \xi_i \begin{bmatrix} \rho_i(0) & \rho_d(-T_i) & \cdots & \rho_i[-(N-1)T_i] \\ \rho_i(T_i) & \rho_i(0) & & \\ \vdots & & & \\ \rho_i[(N-1)T_i] & & \cdots & \rho_i(0) \end{bmatrix}. \tag{6.46}$$

Here $\rho_d(\tau) = R_{\tilde{d}}(\tau)/p_d$, $\rho_i(\tau) = R_{\tilde{i}}(\tau)/p_i$, and T_d and T_i are the interelement propagation time delays defined previously in Eqs. (3.59) and (3.80). As usual, the desired and interference arrival angles are θ_d and θ_i.

The steady-state weight vector in the array (with $\mu = 1$) is

$$\mathbf{W} = \boldsymbol{\Phi}_0^{-1} \left(\frac{1}{\sigma^2} \mathbf{T}^* \right), \tag{6.47}$$

where $\mathbf{T}^*$ is the steering vector. Since our purpose here is to investigate the effects of random errors in the steering vector, let us write $\mathbf{T}^*$ in the form

$$\mathbf{T}^* = \mathbf{W}_1 + \boldsymbol{\Delta}_1, \tag{6.48}$$

where $\mathbf{W}_1$ is the ideal steering vector and $\boldsymbol{\Delta}_1$ is an error vector. The ideal steering vector is the steering vector that maximizes the array response in the direction of the desired signal. Since the desired signal arrives from angle θ_d, we choose

$$\begin{aligned} \mathbf{W}_1 &= k_s \mathbf{W}_0 \\ &= k_s \left[1, e^{j\pi \sin\theta_d}, e^{j2\pi \sin\theta_d}, \ldots, e^{j(N-1)\pi \sin\theta_d} \right]^T, \end{aligned} \tag{6.49}$$

where k_s is an arbitrary constant. The vector $\boldsymbol{\Delta}_1$ contains the steering vector errors. We write $\boldsymbol{\Delta}_1$ in the form

$$\begin{aligned} \boldsymbol{\Delta}_1 &= k_s \boldsymbol{\Delta} = k_s \left[\delta_1, \delta_2, \ldots, \delta_N \right]^T \\ &= k_s \left[\delta_{1r} + j\delta_{1i}, \delta_{2r} + j\delta_{2i}, \ldots, \delta_{Nr} + j\delta_{Ni} \right]^T, \end{aligned} \tag{6.50}$$

where k_s is the same constant as in Eq. (6.49). With $\mathbf{W}_0$ and $\boldsymbol{\Delta}$ normalized in this way, δ_k represents the error in the corresponding term $e^{j(k-1)\pi \sin\theta_d}$ of $\mathbf{W}_0$. Since this term has unit magnitude, δ_k may be regarded as the value of the error normalized to the magnitude of the ideal steering vector weight, that is, the fractional error.

To evaluate the effects of random errors, we shall assume that each real or imaginary component δ_{kr} or δ_{ki} of $\boldsymbol{\Delta}$ is a statistically independent random variable with zero mean and variance σ_w^2, that is,

$$E[\delta_{ku}] = 0 \qquad (6.51)$$

and

$$E[\delta_{ku}\delta_{lv}] = \begin{cases} \sigma_w^2, & k = l \text{ and } u = v, \\ 0, & \text{otherwise,} \end{cases} \qquad (6.52)$$

where u and v each stand for r (real) or i (imaginary).

When Eqs. (6.49) and (6.50) are substituted into Eq. (6.47), the steady-state weight vector is

$$\mathbf{W}_s = \frac{k_s}{\sigma^2}\boldsymbol{\Phi}_0^{-1}(\mathbf{W}_0 + \boldsymbol{\Delta}). \qquad (6.53)$$

For this weight vector, the desired signal component of the array output, $\tilde{s}_d(t)$, is

$$\tilde{s}_d(t) = \mathbf{X}_d^T\mathbf{W}. \qquad (6.54)$$

The output desired signal power P_d is

$$P_d = \tfrac{1}{2}E\{|\tilde{s}_d(t)|^2\} = \tfrac{1}{2}E\{\mathbf{W}^\dagger\mathbf{X}_d^*\mathbf{X}_d^T\mathbf{W}\}$$

$$= \frac{k_s^2}{2\sigma^4}E\{(\mathbf{W}_0^\dagger + \boldsymbol{\Delta}^\dagger)\boldsymbol{\Phi}_0^{-1}\mathbf{X}_d^*\mathbf{X}_d^T\boldsymbol{\Phi}_0^{-1}(\mathbf{W}_0 + \boldsymbol{\Delta})\}. \qquad (6.55)$$

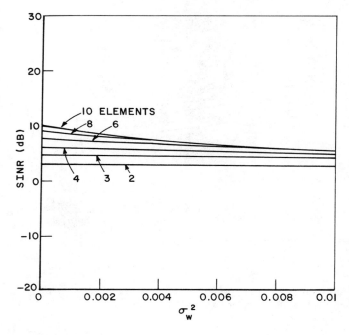

Figure 6.13 SINR versus σ_w^2: no interference, $\theta_d = 0°$, $B_d = 0$, $\xi_d = 0$ dB (reprinted from [12] with permission, © 1982 IEEE).

Here the expectation is taken over both the random components of Δ and over the signals in $\mathbf{X}_d$. Averaging $\mathbf{X}_d^* \mathbf{X}_d^T$ gives

$$P_d = \frac{k_s^2}{2\sigma^2} E\left\{ \left(\mathbf{W}_0^\dagger + \Delta^\dagger\right) \Phi_0^{-1} \Phi_{d_0} \Phi_0^{-1} \left(\mathbf{W}_0 + \Delta\right) \right\}. \tag{6.56}$$

When the expectation over Δ is carried out, the cross products between $\mathbf{W}_0$ and Δ average to zero, and we are left with

$$P_d = \frac{k_s^2}{2\sigma^2} \left[\mathbf{W}_0^\dagger \Phi_0^{-1} \Phi_{d_0} \Phi_0^{-1} \mathbf{W}_0 + E\left\{ \Delta^\dagger \Phi_0^{-1} \Phi_{d_0} \Phi_0^{-1} \Delta \right\} \right]$$

$$= \frac{k_s^2}{2\sigma^2} \left[\mathbf{W}_0^\dagger \Phi_0^{-1} \Phi_{d_0} \Phi_0^{-1} \mathbf{W}_0 + 2\sigma_w^2 \operatorname{Tr}\left\{ \Phi_0^{-1} \Phi_{d_0} \Phi_0^{-1} \right\} \right], \tag{6.57}$$

where $\operatorname{Tr}(\cdot)$ denotes the trace. A similar calculation of the output interference power P_i and output noise power P_n gives

$$P_i = \frac{k_s^2}{2\sigma^2} \left[\mathbf{W}_0^\dagger \Phi_0^{-1} \Phi_{i_0} \Phi_0^{-1} \mathbf{W}_0 + 2\sigma_w^2 \operatorname{Tr}\left\{ \Phi_0^{-1} \Phi_{i_0} \Phi_0^{-1} \right\} \right] \tag{6.58}$$

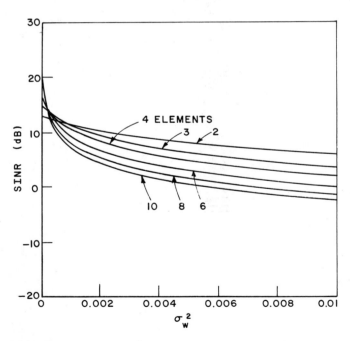

Figure 6.14   SINR versus σ_w^2: no interference, $\theta_d = 0°$, $B_d = 0$, $\xi_d = 10$ dB (reprinted from [12] with permission, © 1982 IEEE).

and

$$P_n = \frac{k_s^2}{2\sigma^2} \left[\mathbf{W}_0^\dagger \mathbf{\Phi}_0^{-1} \mathbf{\Phi}_0^{-1} \mathbf{W}_0 + 2\sigma_w^2 \, \mathrm{Tr} \left\{ \mathbf{\Phi}_0^{-1} \mathbf{\Phi}_0^{-1} \right\} \right]. \qquad (6.59)$$

The output SINR is then

$$\mathrm{SINR} = \frac{P_d}{P_i + P_n}. \qquad (6.60)$$

Note that the constant $k_s^2 / 2\sigma^2$ cancels out of this ratio and hence has no effect on the SINR.

From these equations, we may calculate how the SINR depends on the steering vector variance σ_w^2. Figures 6.13 through 6.20 show typical results for a number of cases.

First, Figs. 6.13 through 6.15 show the output SINR as a function of σ_w^2 for the case where a desired signal arrives at broadside ($\theta_d = 0$) and for no interference. The three figures are for different SNRs. Figure 6.13 is for $\xi_d = 0$ dB, Fig. 6.14 for $\xi_d = 10$ dB, and Fig. 6.15 for $\xi_d = 20$ dB. Each figure shows the SINR versus σ_w^2 for two, three, four, five, six, eight, and ten elements in the array.

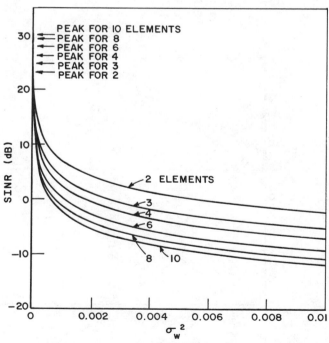

Figure 6.15   SINR versus σ_w^2: no interference, $\theta_d = 0°$, $B_d = 0$, $\xi_d = 20$ dB (reprinted from [12] with permission © 1982 IEEE).

These figures show several interesting things. First, the array output SINR can drop rather rapidly with σ_w^2. For example, Fig. 6.15 shows that when $\xi_d = 20$ dB and the array has ten elements, the SINR drops from 30 dB for $\sigma_w^2 = 0$ to 10 dB for $\sigma_w^2 = 0.0001$. The value $\sigma_w^2 = 0.0001$ corresponds to an rms fractional error in each real and imaginary part of the steering vector of $\sqrt{0.0001} = 1\%$.

Second, Figs. 6.13 through 6.15 show that the sensitivity of the SINR to σ_w^2 increases with the number of elements in the array. The more elements, the faster the SINR drops with σ_w^2. Moreover, when σ_w^2 exceeds a certain value, increasing the number of elements in the array will actually *decrease* the output SINR. If $\xi_d = 10$ dB, for example, Fig. 6.14 shows that for $\sigma_w^2 = 0.001$ the SINR is highest with two elements and drops as more elements are added. To be able to increase the SINR by adding elements to the array, one must hold σ_w^2 below a certain bound. As the SNR increases, this bound decreases.

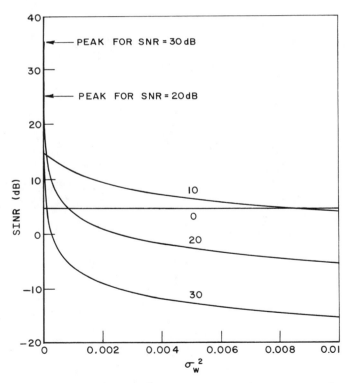

Figure 6.16   SINR versus σ_w^2: no interference, three elements, $\theta_d = 0°$, $B_d = 0$ (reprinted from [12] with permission, © 1982 IEEE).

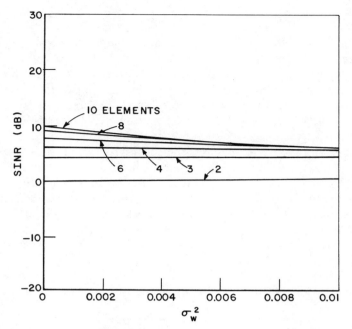

Figure 6.17 SINR versus σ_w^2: $\theta_d = 0°$, $B_d = 0$, $\xi_d = 0$ dB, $\theta_i = 30°$, $B_i = 0$, $\xi_i = 40$ dB (reprinted from [12] with permission, © 1982 IEEE).

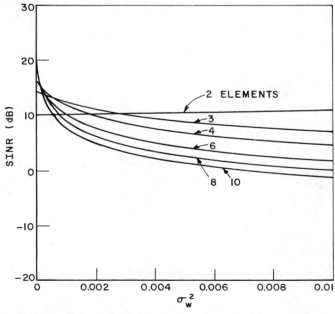

Figure 6.18 SINR versus σ_w^2: $\theta_d = 0°$, $B_d = 0$, $\xi_d = 10$ dB, $\theta_i = 30°$, $B_i = 0$, $\xi_i = 40$ dB (reprinted from [12] with permission, © 1982 IEEE).

Third, Figs. 6.13 through 6.15 show that the sensitivity of the SINR to σ_w^2 increases as the SNR increases. For $\xi_d = 0$ dB, Fig. 6.13 shows that the drop in SINR with σ_w^2 is small. But for $\xi_d = 10$ dB (Fig. 6.14) the SINR drops more quickly with σ_w^2, and for $\xi_d = 20$ dB (Fig. 6.15), the drop is even more rapid. For a fixed number of elements, the effect of the SNR may be seen by plotting the SINR versus σ_w^2 with the SNR as a parameter. Figure 6.16 shows such a plot for a three-element array and for $\xi_d = 0$, 10, 20, and 30 dB. It is again seen how increasing the SNR increases the sensitivity of the SINR to σ_w^2.

Next, we add an interference signal to the problem. Figures 6.17 through 6.20 show calculations similar to those in Figs. 6.13 through 6.16 except that now an interference signal is present at $\theta_i = 30°$ with an INR of 40 dB and zero bandwidth B_i. Figure 6.17 shows SINR versus σ_w^2 for $\xi_d = 0$ dB and for two, three, four, six, eight, and ten elements. Figure 6.18 shows similar results for $\xi_d = 10$ dB, and Fig. 6.19 shows $\xi_d = 20$ dB. Fig. 6.20 shows the SINR versus σ_w^2 for a three-element array for several SNRs.

Comparing the curves in Figs. 6.17 through 6.20 with those in Figs. 6.13 through 6.16 shows that the interference has a small influence on the sensitivity

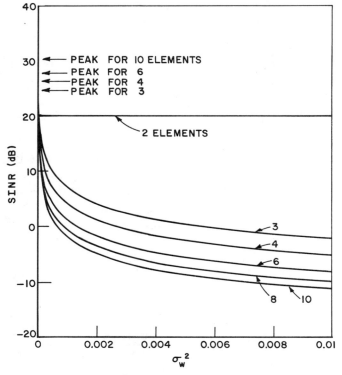

Figure 6.19 SINR versus σ_w^2: $\theta_d = 0°$, $B_d = 0$, $\xi_d = 20$ dB, $\theta_i = 30°$, $B_i = 0$, $\xi_i = 40$ dB (reprinted from [12] with permission, © 1982 IEEE).

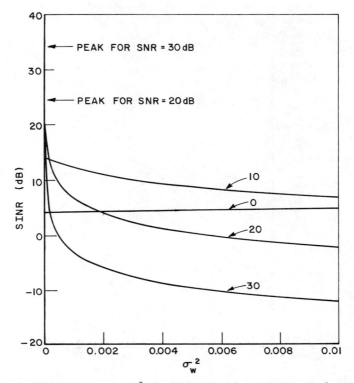

Figure 6.20   SINR versus σ_w^2: three elements, $\theta_d = 0°$, $B_d = 0$, $\theta_i = 30°$, $B_i = 0$, $\xi_i = 40$ dB (reprinted from [12] with permission, © 1982 IEEE).

of the SINR to σ_w^2. The SINR drops slightly more quickly with σ_w^2 without interference than with it. This result occurs because the interference null "uses up" one degree of freedom in the pattern. With interference present, there is less flexibility left in the pattern to null the desired signal.‡

A different perspective on these results may be gained by plotting the SINR as a function of the SNR with σ_w^2 as a parameter. Figure 6.21 shows such a plot for the case of three elements and no interference. This type of curve shows that the error variance σ_w^2 that can be tolerated again depends on the desired signal dynamic range that must be accommodated by the array. For a given σ_w^2, the SINR at first rises with SNR and then drops. The larger σ_w^2, the

‡For the special case of a two-element array, there is only one degree of freedom in the pattern to begin with. Hence, when an interference signal is present, there is no further flexibility in the pattern, other than its overall absolute magnitude, regardless of the particular error components δ_k. Since a change in pattern magnitude does not affect the SINR (it scales all signals proportionally), the SINR in Figs. 6.17 through 6.19 does not depend on σ_w^2 for the case of two elements.

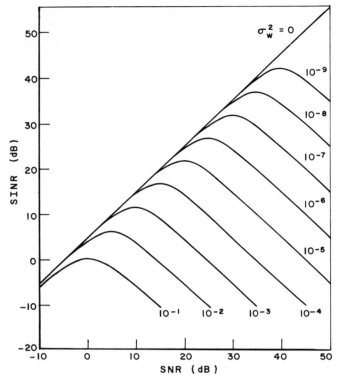

Figure 6.21 SINR versus SNR: no interference, three elements, $\theta_d = 0°$, $0 \leqslant B_d \leqslant 0.5$ (reprinted from [12] with permission, © 1982 IEEE).

smaller the range of SNR over which the SINR remains high. If $\sigma_w^2 = 10^{-6}$, for example, the SINR exceeds 10 dB for 5 dB $\leqslant$ SNR $\leqslant$ 44 dB. But if $\sigma_w^2 = 10^{-4}$, the SINR exceeds 10 dB only for 5 dB $\leqslant$ SNR $\leqslant$ 24 dB. Each order of magnitude increase in σ_w^2 decreases the available desired signal dynamic range by 10 dB.

The bandwidth of the desired signal, B_d, has no effect on the results in Fig. 6.21, because the desired signal arrives from $\theta_d = 0$. At this angle, the interelement time delay is zero, so there is no decorrelation of the signals in different array elements. However, if the desired signal arrives off broadside, B_d affects the performance. It turns out that bandwidth has the most effect when $B_d = 90°$, because this case gives the most decorrelation between element signals.

To illustrate the effect of bandwidth, we first assume there are no errors in the steering vector ($\sigma_w^2 = 0$). Under this condition, Fig. 6.22 shows the SINR plotted versus the SNR for $\theta_d = 90°$, for several values of B_d in the range $0 \leqslant B_d \leqslant 0.5$. It is seen that B_d causes a substantial degradation in SINR even for $\sigma_w^2 = 0$.

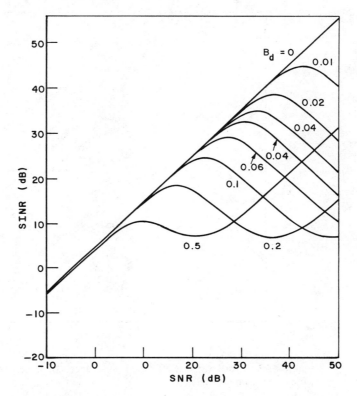

Figure 6.22   SINR versus SNR: no interference, three elements, $\theta_d = 90°$, $\sigma_w^2 = 0$ (reprinted from [12] with permission, © 1982 IEEE).

Now suppose that σ_w^2 is not equal to 0. Figure 6.23 shows the SINR versus the SNR for several values of σ_w^2 and for B_d in the range $0 \leqslant B_d \leqslant 0.05$. In these curves, the bandwidth has a large effect only for $\sigma_w^2 \leqslant 10^{-6}$. For larger values of σ_w^2, the SINR has already been suppressed far enough by the steering vector errors so that a nonzero bandwidth causes little additional degradation.

Finally, we consider the effect of an interference signal on these curves. Figure 6.24 shows typical curves of SINR versus SNR for $\theta_d = 0°$, $\theta_i = 30°$, and INR = 40 dB. Curves are shown for several values of interference bandwidth B_i in the range $0 \leqslant B_i \leqslant 0.1$. For lower values of SNR, where the steering vector errors do not affect performance (for example, for the region SNR $\leqslant$ 20 dB if $\sigma_w^2 = 10^{-6}$), increasing B_i reduces the SINR in the same way as described in Chapter 3. (For $B_i \neq 0$, the interference is not nulled as well, so that the SINR is reduced.) For higher values of SNR, however, where steering vector errors degrade performance, increasing B_i actually *increases* the SINR. This curious behavior occurs because, as B_i becomes large, the array must use more degrees of freedom to null the interference, so there are fewer left to null the

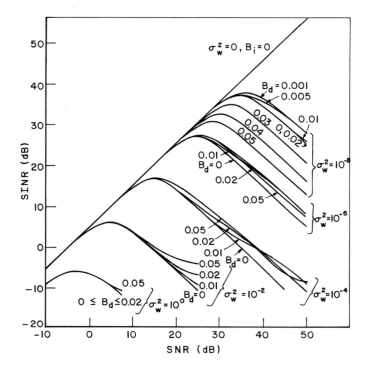

Figure 6.23 SINR versus SNR: no interference, three elements, $\theta_d = 90°$ (reprinted from [12] with permission, © 1982 IEEE).

desired signal. With a three-element array (as in Fig. 6.24), for example, there are two degrees of freedom. If $B_i = 0$, the array can null the interference with one degree of freedom and then use the other one to reduce the desired signal. But, when B_i is increased, the array must use both degrees of freedom to obtain adequate interference nulling. (It does this by providing two nulls in the frequency band occupied by the interference.) The result is that there are no degrees of freedom left to null the desired signal. Hence, the output desired signal power is suppressed less than if $B_i = 0$ and the SINR remains higher. Studies of the array patterns as σ_w^2 and B_i are varied confirm this behavior.

These results show that the performance of an Applebaum array can be quite sensitive to steering vector errors. When the steering vector is in error, the array attempts to null the desired signal. The more the steering vector is in error and the stronger the desired signal, the greater is the drop in output SINR.

To keep this issue in perspective, it should be remembered that the preceding analysis assumes that the desired signal is being received continuously by the array. Steering vector errors are of concern mostly for applications where the desired signal will be present all the time, such as in communication systems, or in cases where the desired signal power is high. Minor steering

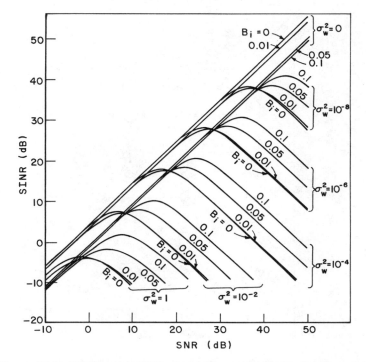

Figure 6.24   SINR versus SNR: three elements, $\theta_d = 0°$, $0 \leqslant B_d \leqslant 0.1$, $\theta_i = 30°$, $\xi_i = 40$ dB (reprinted from [12] with permission, © 1982 IEEE).

vector errors are usually not important for pulsed radar systems. In these systems, the pulse width is short compared to the array time constants, the target echos are present only a small fraction of the time, and they are usually weak, so they have little effect on the weights. In a communication system, the desired signal may be present all the time, and its power may be high. For such applications, the designer must be aware of the sensitivity of the array to steering vector errors.

6.4 CONSTRAINED ADAPTIVE ARRAY PROCESSING

The addition of constraints to adaptive array processing was first described by Frost [4] and has also been discussed by Applebaum and Chapman [13] and Takao, Fujita, and Nishi [14]. We begin with Frost's technique.

Frost presented a method of adapting the weights in an array while holding the array response fixed in a certain direction and at certain frequencies. In Frost's paper [4], it is assumed that the array processor has a tapped delay line behind each element, with a real weight at each tap, as shown in Fig. 6.25.

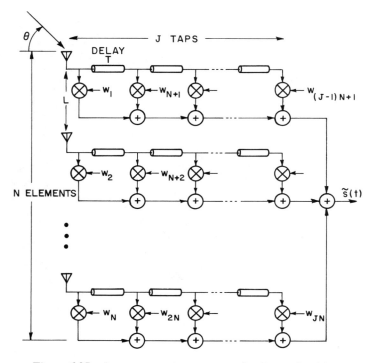

Figure 6.25   Array processing structure for Frost algorithm.

In the following discussion, we shall follow Frost's derivation, but we shall generalize it slightly by allowing the weights to be complex. We shall also consider the case where the desired signal may come from any angle. (Frost assumed the desired signal to be at broadside.)

Let a desired signal be incident on the array of Fig. 6.25 from angle θ_d from broadside. (θ is defined in Fig. 6.25.) Suppose we want to constrain the response of the array in that direction to have a fixed value. Given an arbitrary set of complex weights w_j, the frequency response of the array in the direction θ_d is

$$H(\omega) = \left(\sum_{j=1}^{N} w_j e^{-j\omega T_j} \right) + \left(\sum_{j=N+1}^{2N} w_j e^{-j\omega T_j} \right) e^{-j\omega T} + \cdots$$

$$+ \left(\sum_{j=(J-1)N+1}^{JN} w_j e^{-j\omega T_j} \right) e^{-j\omega(J-1)T}, \qquad (6.61)$$

where T is the time delay per delay-line section (assumed to be the same for every section), and T_j is the time delay between element 1 and element j,

$$T_j = \frac{L(j-1)}{c} \sin \theta_d, \qquad (6.62)$$

with L the element separation and c the velocity of light.[‡] Let the desired signal have center frequency ω_1. Then suppose we wish to constrain the weights w_j during adaptation so that, no matter how the weights change, we always have

$$H(\omega_1) = f_1, \tag{6.63}$$

where f_1 is a given constant. If we define a constraint vector $\mathbf{c}_1$ by

$$\mathbf{c}_1 = \begin{bmatrix} e^{j\omega_1 T_1} \\ e^{j\omega_1 T_2} \\ \vdots \\ e^{j\omega_1 T_N} \\ e^{j\omega_1 T_1} e^{j\omega_1 T} \\ e^{j\omega_1 T_2} e^{j\omega_1 T} \\ \vdots \\ e^{j\omega_1 T_N} e^{j\omega_1 T} \\ \vdots \\ \vdots \\ e^{j\omega_1 T_1} e^{j\omega_1 (J-1)T} \\ e^{j\omega_1 T_2} e^{j\omega_1 (J-1)T} \\ \vdots \\ e^{j\omega_1 T_N} e^{j\omega_1 (J-1)T} \end{bmatrix} \begin{matrix} \left.\vphantom{\begin{matrix}a\\a\\a\\a\end{matrix}}\right\} N \text{ terms} \\[1em] \left.\vphantom{\begin{matrix}a\\a\\a\\a\end{matrix}}\right\} N \text{ terms} \\[1em] \vdots \\[1em] \left.\vphantom{\begin{matrix}a\\a\\a\\a\end{matrix}}\right\} N \text{ terms} \end{matrix} \tag{6.64}$$

then Eq. (6.63) may be expressed

$$\mathbf{c}_1^\dagger \mathbf{W} = \mathbf{f}, \tag{6.65}$$

where $\mathbf{W}$ is the weight vector,

$$\mathbf{W} = \begin{bmatrix} w_1, w_2, \ldots, w_N, w_{N+1}, w_{N+2}, \ldots, w_{2N}, \ldots, w_{JN} \end{bmatrix}^T, \tag{6.66}$$

and $\mathbf{f}$ is the scalar (1×1 matrix),

$$\mathbf{f} = (f_1). \tag{6.67}$$

Moreover, if the desired signal occupies a frequency band around ω_1, we may wish to constrain the array response in the direction θ_d over this frequency band. We can do so by fixing the value of $H(\omega)$ at several frequencies ω_i over the band of interest. Defining

$$\mathbf{c}_i = \begin{bmatrix} e^{j\omega_i T_1}, e^{j\omega_i T_2}, \ldots, e^{j\omega_i T_N}, e^{j\omega_i (T_1 + T)}, \ldots, e^{j\omega_i [T_N + (J-1)T]} \end{bmatrix}^T, \tag{6.68}$$

we may impose additional constraints of the form

$$\mathbf{c}_i^\dagger \mathbf{W} = f_i, \tag{6.69}$$

where the f_i are a suitable set of numbers. Suppose there are K such constraint

---

[‡]T_1 is zero by definition but is used for notational convenience.

equations altogether. Then we may combine these in one equation by defining a constraint matrix,

$$\overleftarrow{\hspace{1em}K\hspace{1em}\rightarrow}$$
$$\mathbf{C} = [\mathbf{c}_1 \quad \mathbf{c}_2 \quad \cdots \quad \mathbf{c}_K] \updownarrow NJ, \tag{6.70}$$

and by defining $\mathbf{f}$ to be a K-dimensional column vector of the coefficients f_i,

$$\mathbf{f} = [f_1, f_2, \ldots, f_N]^T. \tag{6.71}$$

The constraints may then be written

$$\mathbf{C}^\dagger \mathbf{W} = \mathbf{f}. \tag{6.72}$$

We note for later use that if the vectors $\mathbf{c}_i$ are linearly independent, the matrix $\mathbf{C}$ will be of rank K. (We always have $K < JN$.)

Our task now is to adapt the weight vector $\mathbf{W}$ so that the array output power is minimized while satisfying the constraint in Eq. (6.72). As usual, we let $\mathbf{X}$ be the signal vector in the array,

$$\mathbf{X} = [\tilde{x}_1(t), \tilde{x}_2(t), \ldots, \tilde{x}_N(t), \tilde{x}_{N+1}(t), \ldots, \tilde{x}_{2N}(t), \ldots, x_{NJ}(t)]^T, \tag{6.73}$$

so the array output signal is

$$\tilde{s}(t) = \mathbf{X}^T \mathbf{W} = \mathbf{W}^T \mathbf{X}. \tag{6.74}$$

The average power of the array output signal is

$$P = \tfrac{1}{2} \mathbf{W}^\dagger E(\mathbf{X}^* \mathbf{X}^T) \mathbf{W} = \tfrac{1}{2} \mathbf{W}^\dagger \mathbf{\Phi} \mathbf{W}, \tag{6.75}$$

where, as usual,

$$\mathbf{\Phi} = E(\mathbf{X}^* \mathbf{X}^T). \tag{6.76}$$

Hence the optimization problem is to minimize $\tfrac{1}{2} \mathbf{W}^\dagger \mathbf{\Phi} \mathbf{W}$ subject to the constraint $\mathbf{C}^\dagger \mathbf{W} = \mathbf{f}$.

The problem of optimization subject to a constraint may be handled with the Lagrange multiplier method [15]. However, in order to carry out this process, we must temporarily revert to real notation.[‡] Recall that each complex weight w_j may be expressed in terms of its real and quadrature weights w_{I_j} and w_{Q_j} [see Eq. (2.53)],

$$w_j = w_{I_j} - j w_{Q_j}. \tag{6.77}$$

Since $\mathbf{\Phi}$ is Hermitian, the function $\mathbf{W}^\dagger \mathbf{\Phi} \mathbf{W}$ is a real function of the real variables w_{I_j} and w_{Q_j}. To find the optimum weight vector, we optimize with respect to both w_{I_j} and w_{Q_j} and then combine the results in complex form. To minimize $\mathbf{W}^\dagger \mathbf{\Phi} \mathbf{W}$ subject to the constraint in Eq. (6.72), we adjoin the constraint relation with unknown Lagrange multipliers to the function $\mathbf{W}^\dagger \mathbf{\Phi} \mathbf{W}$. Since satisfying the

---

[‡] We cannot do the optimization directly in complex notation because $\mathbf{W}^\dagger \mathbf{\Phi} \mathbf{W}$ is not an analytic function of the weights. The product $\mathbf{W}^\dagger \mathbf{\Phi} \mathbf{W}$ contains the conjugates w_j^*, and w_j^* is not an analytic function of w_j [16]. Hence derivatives of $\mathbf{W}^\dagger \mathbf{\Phi} \mathbf{W}$ with respect to the complex w_j are not well defined.

constraint requires that we satisfy both

$$\text{Re}\{\mathbf{C}^\dagger\mathbf{W}\} = \text{Re}\{\mathbf{f}\} \tag{6.78}$$

and

$$\text{Im}\{\mathbf{C}^\dagger\mathbf{W}\} = \text{Im}\{\mathbf{f}\}, \tag{6.79}$$

we define the performance index

$$I(\mathbf{W}) = \tfrac{1}{2}\mathbf{W}^\dagger\mathbf{\Phi}\mathbf{W} + \Lambda_r^T\,\text{Re}\{\mathbf{C}^\dagger\mathbf{W} - \mathbf{f}\} + \Lambda_i^T\,\text{Im}\{\mathbf{C}^\dagger\mathbf{W} - \mathbf{f}\}, \tag{6.80}$$

where Λ_r and Λ_i are N-dimensional column vectors of (real) Lagrange multipliers,

$$\Lambda_r = [\lambda_{r1}, \lambda_{r2}, \ldots, \lambda_{rN}]^T \tag{6.81}$$

and

$$\Lambda_i = [\lambda_{i1}, \lambda_{i2}, \ldots, \lambda_{iN}]^T. \tag{6.82}$$

By defining a complex vector Λ,

$$\Lambda = \Lambda_r + j\Lambda_i, \tag{6.83}$$

$I(\mathbf{W})$ may be written more compactly as

$$I(\mathbf{W}) = \tfrac{1}{2}\mathbf{W}^\dagger\mathbf{\Phi}\mathbf{W} + \text{Re}\{\Lambda^\dagger(\mathbf{C}^\dagger\mathbf{W} - \mathbf{f})\}. \tag{6.84}$$

The performance index $I(\mathbf{W})$ is a real function of w_{I_j} and w_{Q_j}, and we may determine the optimum weight vector by setting the derivatives of $I(\mathbf{W})$ with respect to w_{I_j} and w_{Q_j} equal to zero,

$$\frac{\partial I(\mathbf{W})}{\partial w_{P_j}} = 0, \qquad 1 < j < NJ, \qquad P = I, Q. \tag{6.85}$$

To evaluate these derivatives, it is helpful to note that $\Lambda^\dagger\mathbf{C}^\dagger\mathbf{W}$ is a scalar, so

$$\Lambda^\dagger\mathbf{C}^\dagger\mathbf{W} = (\Lambda^\dagger\mathbf{C}^\dagger\mathbf{W})^T = \mathbf{W}^T\mathbf{C}^*\Lambda^*, \tag{6.86}$$

and to note that $\text{Re}[\Lambda^\dagger\mathbf{f}]$ does not contain any weights. Hence $I(\mathbf{W})$ may be rearranged into

$$I(\mathbf{W}) = \tfrac{1}{2}\mathbf{W}^\dagger\mathbf{\Phi}\mathbf{W} + \text{Re}[\mathbf{W}^T\mathbf{C}^*\Lambda^*] + \text{additional terms}, \tag{6.87}$$

where the "additional terms" do not involve w_{I_j} or w_{Q_j}. Then, making use of the Hermitian property of $\mathbf{\Phi}$, and noting the minus sign on w_{Q_j} in Eq. (6.77), we obtain

$$\nabla_I I(\mathbf{W}) = \text{Re}[\mathbf{\Phi}\mathbf{W}] + \text{Re}[\mathbf{C}^*\Lambda^*] = 0 \tag{6.88}$$

and

$$\nabla_Q I(\mathbf{W}) = -\text{Im}[\mathbf{\Phi}\mathbf{W}] + \text{Im}[\mathbf{C}^*\Lambda^*] = 0, \tag{6.89}$$

where

$$\nabla_P = \left[\frac{\partial}{\partial w_{P1}}, \frac{\partial}{\partial w_{P2}}, \ldots, \frac{\partial}{\partial w_{PNJ}}\right]^T, \qquad P = I, Q. \tag{6.90}$$

Equations (6.88) and (6.89) may be combined into a single complex equation,

$$\mathbf{\Phi W} + \mathbf{C\Lambda} = 0. \tag{6.91}$$

The optimum weight vector is then

$$\mathbf{W}_{\text{opt}} = -\mathbf{\Phi}^{-1}\mathbf{C\Lambda}. \tag{6.92}$$

To evaluate $\mathbf{W}_{\text{opt}}$, we have to know Λ. However, since $\mathbf{W}_{\text{opt}}$ must satisfy the constraint, the following relation holds:

$$\mathbf{C}^{\dagger}\mathbf{W}_{\text{opt}} = -\mathbf{C}\mathbf{\Phi}^{-1}\mathbf{C\Lambda} = \mathbf{f}. \tag{6.93}$$

Hence,

$$\Lambda = -\left[\mathbf{C}^{\dagger}\mathbf{\Phi}^{-1}\mathbf{C}\right]^{-1}\mathbf{f}, \tag{6.94}$$

and Eq. (6.92) gives

$$\mathbf{W}_{\text{opt}} = \mathbf{\Phi}^{-1}\mathbf{C}(\mathbf{C}^{\dagger}\mathbf{\Phi}^{-1}\mathbf{C})^{-1}\mathbf{f}. \tag{6.95}$$

Now let us determine a discrete algorithm for adapting the weight vector $\mathbf{W}$ so that it will approach this $\mathbf{W}_{\text{opt}}$. Assume that at the kth iteration, we let

$$w_{I_j}(k+1) = w_{I_j}(k) - \mu\frac{\partial I(\mathbf{W})}{\partial w_{I_j}}(k) \tag{6.96}$$

and

$$w_{Q_j}(k+1) = w_{Q_j}(k) - \mu\frac{\partial I(\mathbf{W})}{\partial w_{Q_j}}(k). \tag{6.97}$$

Using the derivatives $\partial I(\mathbf{W})/\partial w_{I_j}$ and $\partial I(\mathbf{W})/\partial w_{Q_j}$ in Eqs. (6.88) and (6.89) and combining these in complex form, we have

$$\mathbf{W}(k+1) = \mathbf{W}(k) - \mu\left[\mathbf{\Phi W}(k) + \mathbf{C\Lambda}(k)\right]. \tag{6.98}$$

However, the matrix $\mathbf{\Phi} = E(\mathbf{X}^*\mathbf{X}^T)$ is not known during the adaptation process. Hence, for the adaptive algorithm, we replace it with its instantaneous estimate $\mathbf{X}^*\mathbf{X}^T$, as was done with the LMS algorithm. In place of Eq. (6.98), we write

$$\mathbf{W}(k+1) = \mathbf{W}(k) - \mu\left[\mathbf{X}^*(k)\tilde{s}(k) + \mathbf{C\Lambda}(k)\right], \tag{6.99}$$

where we have used the relation $\mathbf{X}^T(k)\mathbf{W}(k) = \tilde{s}(k)$; $\tilde{s}(k)$ is the array output signal at the kth sample. To eliminate $\Lambda(k)$, we require that $\mathbf{W}(k+1)$ satisfy the constraint,

$$\mathbf{C}^{\dagger}\mathbf{W}(k+1) = \mathbf{C}^{\dagger}\mathbf{W}(k) - \mu\left[\mathbf{C}^{\dagger}\mathbf{X}^*(k)\tilde{s}(k) + \mathbf{C}^{\dagger}\mathbf{C\Lambda}(k)\right] = \mathbf{f}. \tag{6.100}$$

Solving this equation for $\Lambda(k)$ yields

$$\Lambda(k) = (\mathbf{C}^{\dagger}\mathbf{C})^{-1}\left[\frac{1}{\mu}\mathbf{C}^{\dagger}\mathbf{W}(k) - \frac{1}{\mu}\mathbf{f} - \mathbf{C}^{\dagger}\mathbf{X}^*(k)\tilde{s}(k)\right]. \tag{6.101}$$

Inserting this equation in Eq. (6.99) gives the algorithm

$$\mathbf{W}(k+1) = \mathbf{W}(k) - \mu\big[\mathbf{I} - \mathbf{C}(\mathbf{C}^\dagger\mathbf{C})^{-1}\mathbf{C}^\dagger\big]\mathbf{X}^*(k)\tilde{s}(k)$$
$$+ \mathbf{C}(\mathbf{C}^\dagger\mathbf{C})^{-1}\big[\mathbf{f} - \mathbf{C}^\dagger\mathbf{W}(k)\big]. \tag{6.102}$$

If $\mathbf{W}(k)$ satisfies the constraint, the last term in this equation is actually zero and could be dropped. However, as Frost has pointed out [4], retaining this term makes the algorithm self-correcting; even if $\mathbf{W}(k)$ does not satisfy the constraint for some reason, the algorithm will correct for this error and make $\mathbf{W}(k+1)$ satisfy the constraint.

Equation (6.102) can be put in a more succinct form by defining

$$\mathbf{P} = \mathbf{I} - \mathbf{C}(\mathbf{C}^\dagger\mathbf{C})^{-1}\mathbf{C}^\dagger \tag{6.103}$$

and

$$\mathbf{F} = \mathbf{C}(\mathbf{C}^\dagger\mathbf{C})^{-1}\mathbf{f}. \tag{6.104}$$

Then Eq. (6.102) becomes

$$\mathbf{W}(k+1) = \mathbf{P}\big[\mathbf{W}(k) - \mu\mathbf{X}^*(k)\tilde{s}(k)\big] + \mathbf{F}. \tag{6.105}$$

This is the discrete version of Frost's algorithm in complex form.

This algorithm is not easy to interpret intuitively as it stands, because of the complicated way the constraint matrix $\mathbf{C}$ appears in Eqs. (6.103) and (6.104). However, a simple example will make clear what is happening. Suppose the array has N elements and a single complex weight behind each element, so $J = 1$. (That is, assume that there are no delay lines after the first weight in Fig. 6.25.) Then assume that a desired signal is incident on the array from angle θ_d, so the desired signal vector $\mathbf{X}_d$ is

$$\mathbf{X}_d = A_d e^{j\omega_0 t}\mathbf{U}_d, \tag{6.106}$$

with

$$\mathbf{U}_d = \big[1, e^{-j\phi_d}, e^{-j2\phi_d}, \ldots, e^{-j(N-1)\phi_d}\big]^T \tag{6.107}$$

and

$$\phi_d = \frac{2\pi L}{\lambda}\sin\theta_d, \tag{6.108}$$

where L is the interelement spacing in Fig. 6.25 and λ is the wavelength.

Assume we want the array to minimize the interference and thermal noise power at the array output while maintaining the array response in the desired signal direction constant, say, equal to unity. The constraint is then

$$\mathbf{U}_d^T\mathbf{W} = 1. \tag{6.109}$$

To express this problem in the general notation above, we let

$$\mathbf{C} = \mathbf{U}_d^*. \tag{6.110}$$

The constraint equation (6.72) is then equivalent to Eq. (6.109), where $\mathbf{f}$ is now a scalar (a 1×1 matrix),

$$\mathbf{f} = (1). \tag{6.111}$$

In this case, we find

$$\mathbf{C}^\dagger\mathbf{C} = \mathbf{U}_d^T\mathbf{U}_d^* = N, \tag{6.112}$$

so

$$(\mathbf{C}^\dagger\mathbf{C})^{-1} = \frac{1}{N}, \tag{6.113}$$

and then

$$\mathbf{C}(\mathbf{C}^\dagger\mathbf{C})^{-1}\mathbf{C}^\dagger = \frac{1}{N}\mathbf{U}_d^*\mathbf{U}_d^T. \tag{6.114}$$

Thus

$$\mathbf{P} = \mathbf{I} - \frac{1}{N}\mathbf{U}_d^*\mathbf{U}_d^T \tag{6.115}$$

and

$$\mathbf{F} = \mathbf{C}\left(\frac{1}{N}\right)(1) = \frac{1}{N}\mathbf{U}_d^*. \tag{6.116}$$

The algorithm in Eq. (6.105) becomes

$$\mathbf{W}(k+1) = \left(\mathbf{I} - \frac{1}{N}\mathbf{U}_d^*\mathbf{U}_d^T\right)[\mathbf{W}(k) - \mu\mathbf{X}^*(k)\tilde{s}(k)] + \frac{1}{N}\mathbf{U}_d^*. \tag{6.117}$$

Notice what this algorithm does. In the normal, discrete LMS algorithm, we would have

$$\mathbf{W}(k+1) = \mathbf{W}(k) - \mu\mathbf{X}^*(k)\tilde{s}(k). \tag{6.118}$$

The Frost algorithm is similar except that it first multiplies the vector $\mathbf{W}(k) - \mu\mathbf{X}^*(k)\tilde{s}(k)$ by $\mathbf{P}$, and then adds $(1/N)\mathbf{U}_d^*$ to the result. To understand what this procedure does, note that the vector $\mathbf{W}(k) - \mu\mathbf{X}^*(k)\tilde{s}(k)$ can always be written as a linear sum of a component parallel to $\mathbf{U}_d^*$ and one perpendicular to $\mathbf{U}_d^*$, that is,

$$\mathbf{W}(k) - \mu\mathbf{X}^*(k)\tilde{s}(k) = \alpha\mathbf{U}_d^* + \beta\mathbf{U}_\perp^*, \tag{6.119}$$

where α and β are two scalars and $\mathbf{U}_\perp^*$ is a vector perpendicular to $\mathbf{U}_d^*$. Then

$$\mathbf{P}[\mathbf{W}(k) - \mu\mathbf{X}^*(k)\tilde{s}(k)] = \left(\mathbf{I} - \frac{1}{N}\mathbf{U}_d^*\mathbf{U}_d^T\right)(\alpha\mathbf{U}_d^* + \beta\mathbf{U}_\perp^*)$$

$$= \alpha\mathbf{U}_d^* - \frac{\alpha}{N}(\mathbf{U}_d^T\mathbf{U}_d^*)\mathbf{U}_d^* + \beta\mathbf{U}_\perp^* = \beta\mathbf{U}_\perp^*. \tag{6.120}$$

Thus multiplication by $\mathbf{P}$ removes any component of $\mathbf{W}(k) - \mu\mathbf{X}^*(k)\tilde{s}(k)$ parallel to $\mathbf{U}_d^*$. (The operator $\mathbf{P}$ is sometimes said to "annihilate $\mathbf{U}_d^*$ on the right" [13].) Hence the Frost algorithm first eliminates any component of $\mathbf{W}(k) - \mu\mathbf{X}^*(n)\tilde{s}(k)$ parallel to $\mathbf{U}_d^*$ and then adds $(1/N)\mathbf{U}_d^*$. As a result, the component of $\mathbf{W}(k+1)$ parallel to $\mathbf{U}_d^*$ is always equal to $(1/N)\mathbf{U}_d^*$ at each step of the iteration. Moreover, since $\mathbf{P}[\mathbf{W}(k) - \mu\mathbf{X}^*(k)\tilde{s}(k)]$ is perpendicular to $\mathbf{U}_d^*$, we have

$$\mathbf{U}_d^T\mathbf{W}(k+1) = \mathbf{U}_d^T\mathbf{P}[\mathbf{W}(k) - \mu\mathbf{X}^*(k)\tilde{s}(k)] + \frac{1}{N}\mathbf{U}_d^T\mathbf{U}_d^* = 1, \qquad (6.121)$$

so the constraint is satisfied at every step of the integration.

Let us consider the steady-state weight vector $\mathbf{W}_{\text{opt}}$ to see how it compares with the weight vector in the unconstrained case. In the ordinary Applebaum array, the steady-state weight vector is equal to

$$\mathbf{W} = \mu\mathbf{\Phi}^{-1}\mathbf{T}^*, \qquad (6.122)$$

where $\mathbf{T}^*$ is the steering vector. If we choose $\mathbf{T}^* = \mathbf{U}_d^*$, $\mathbf{W}$ will be the weight vector yielding maximum SINR,

$$\mathbf{W} = \mu\mathbf{\Phi}^{-1}\mathbf{U}_d^*. \qquad (6.123)$$

Now consider the steady-state weight vector in Eq. (6.95). Since $\mathbf{C} = \mathbf{U}_d^*$ and $\mathbf{f} = (1)$, Eq. (6.95) yields

$$\mathbf{W}_{\text{opt}} = \mathbf{\Phi}^{-1}\mathbf{U}_d^*\left[\mathbf{U}_d^T\mathbf{\Phi}^{-1}\mathbf{U}_d^*\right]^{-1} = \frac{\mathbf{\Phi}^{-1}\mathbf{U}_d^*}{\mathbf{U}_d^T\mathbf{\Phi}^{-1}\mathbf{U}_d^*}, \qquad (6.124)$$

because $\mathbf{U}_d^T\mathbf{\Phi}^{-1}\mathbf{U}_d^*$ is a scalar. From this equation, we see two things. First,

$$\mathbf{U}_d^T\mathbf{W}_{\text{opt}} = \frac{\mathbf{U}_d^T\mathbf{\Phi}^{-1}\mathbf{U}_d^*}{\mathbf{U}_d^T\mathbf{\Phi}^{-1}\mathbf{U}_d^*} = 1, \qquad (6.125)$$

so the desired constraint relation is automatically satisfied. Second, we see that the weight vector in Eq. (6.124) is just a scalar multiple of the optimal weight vector in Eq. (6.123). In other words, the constrained weight vector is equal to the Applebaum weight vector but scaled in amplitude so that the response in the desired signal direction is unity.

Now let us return to the algorithm in Eq. (6.105) and make some observations about $\mathbf{P}$ and $\mathbf{F}$ in Eqs. (6.103) and (6.104). First, we observe that $\mathbf{P}$ and $\mathbf{F}$ can be simplified considerably if the constraint vectors $\mathbf{c}_j$ in Eq. (6.70) are mutually orthogonal. Suppose we have

$$\mathbf{c}_j^\dagger\mathbf{c}_k = N\delta_{jk}, \qquad (6.126)$$

where δ_{jk} is the Kronecker delta. In this case the matrix $\mathbf{C}^\dagger\mathbf{C}$ in Eq. (6.103) becomes

$$\mathbf{C}^\dagger\mathbf{C} = N\mathbf{I}_K, \qquad (6.127)$$

where $\mathbf{I}_K$ is a $K \times K$ identity matrix. Hence,

$$(\mathbf{C}^\dagger\mathbf{C})^{-1} = \frac{1}{N}\mathbf{I}_K \qquad (6.128)$$

and

$$\mathbf{P} = \mathbf{I} - \frac{1}{N}\mathbf{C}\mathbf{C}^\dagger. \qquad (6.129)$$

In general, the matrix $\mathbf{C}\mathbf{C}^\dagger$ is equal to

$$\mathbf{C}\mathbf{C}^\dagger = \mathbf{c}_1\mathbf{c}_1^\dagger + \mathbf{c}_2\mathbf{c}_2^\dagger + \cdots + \mathbf{c}_K\mathbf{c}_K^\dagger. \qquad (6.130)$$

(This equality holds for arbitrary $\mathbf{c}_j$, whether orthogonal or not.) Hence, for orthogonal $\mathbf{c}_j$, we have, from Eq. (6.129),

$$\mathbf{P} = \mathbf{I} - \frac{1}{N}\left(\mathbf{c}_1\mathbf{c}_1^\dagger + \mathbf{c}_2\mathbf{c}_2 + \cdots + \mathbf{c}_K\mathbf{c}_K^\dagger\right). \qquad (6.131)$$

Moreover, since the $\mathbf{c}_j$ are orthogonal, Eq. (6.131) may also be written

$$\mathbf{P} = \left(\mathbf{I} - \frac{1}{N}\mathbf{c}_1\mathbf{c}_1^\dagger\right)\left(\mathbf{I} - \frac{1}{N}\mathbf{c}_2\mathbf{c}_2^\dagger\right) \cdots \left(\mathbf{I} - \frac{1}{N}\mathbf{c}_K\mathbf{c}_K^\dagger\right). \qquad (6.132)$$

In this form, $\mathbf{P}$ is easy to interpret. We know that $\mathbf{I} - (1/N)\mathbf{c}_j\mathbf{c}_j^\dagger$, when it operates on a vector, removes any component of the vector parallel to $\mathbf{c}_j$. Hence the operator $\mathbf{P}$ in Eq. (6.132) successively removes all components of a vector parallel to any of the vectors $\mathbf{c}_1, \mathbf{c}_2, \ldots, \mathbf{c}_K$.

The vector $\mathbf{F}$ in Eq. (6.104) may also be simplified. When the $\mathbf{c}_j$ are orthogonal, so Eq. (6.128) holds, $\mathbf{F}$ reduces to

$$\mathbf{F} = \frac{1}{N}\mathbf{C}\mathbf{f} = \frac{1}{N}\begin{bmatrix} \mathbf{c}_1 & \mathbf{c}_2 & \cdots & \mathbf{c}_K \end{bmatrix}\begin{bmatrix} f_1 \\ f_2 \\ \vdots \\ f_K \end{bmatrix}$$

$$= \frac{1}{N}\left[f_1\mathbf{c}_1 + f_2\mathbf{c}_2 + \cdots + f_K\mathbf{c}_K\right]. \qquad (6.133)$$

In the constraint algorithm as originally presented by Frost [4], the constraint vectors $\mathbf{c}_j$ were orthogonal by definition. Frost considered the special case where the desired signal arrives from broadside. In that case the interelement time delays T_j in Eqs. (6.61) and (6.62) are all zero. The frequency response of the array to a broadside signal is then

$$H(\omega) = \left(\sum_{l=1}^{N} w_l\right) + \left(\sum_{l=N+1}^{2N} w_l\right)e^{-j\omega T} + \cdots + \left(\sum_{l=(J-1)N+1}^{JN} w_l\right)e^{-j\omega(J-1)T}.$$

$$(6.134)$$

Frost constrained $H(\omega)$ to be equal to certain values at J different frequencies by constraining

$$\sum_{l=mN+1}^{(M+1)N} w_l = f_{m+1}, \qquad (6.135)$$

or equivalently

$$\mathbf{c}_j^\dagger \mathbf{W} = f_j, \tag{6.136}$$

with

$$\mathbf{c}_j = \Big[\underbrace{0, 0, \ldots, 0}_{N \text{ terms}}, \underbrace{0, 0, \ldots, 0}_{N \text{ terms}}, \ldots, \underbrace{1, 1, \ldots, 1}_{j\text{th set of } N \text{ terms}}, \underbrace{0, 0, \ldots, 0}_{N \text{ terms}}, \ldots \Big]^T. \tag{6.137}$$

In this case $\mathbf{c}_1, \mathbf{c}_2, \ldots, \mathbf{c}_J$ are mutually orthogonal by definition because none of the $\mathbf{c}_j$ have nonzero elements in the same location.

Since the $\mathbf{c}_j$ are orthogonal in the case considered by Frost, we may use Eqs. (6.132) through (6.137) to write out the adaptation algorithm in Eq. (6.105) in scalar form. The algorithm becomes

$$w_1(k+1) = w_1(k) - \mu \tilde{x}_1^*(k)\tilde{s}(k)$$
$$- \frac{1}{N} \sum_{j=1}^{N} \big[w_j(k) - \mu \tilde{x}_j^*(k)\tilde{s}(k) \big] + \frac{f_1}{N},$$

$$w_2(k+1) = w_2(k) - \mu \tilde{x}_2^*(k)\tilde{s}(k)$$
$$- \frac{1}{N} \sum_{j=1}^{N} \big[w_j(k) - \mu \tilde{x}_j^*(k)\tilde{s}(k) \big] + \frac{f_1}{N},$$

$$\vdots$$

$$w_K(k+1) = w_K(k) - \mu \tilde{x}_K^*(k)\tilde{s}(k)$$
$$- \frac{1}{N} \sum_{j=1}^{N} \big[w_j(k) - \mu \tilde{x}_j^*(k)\tilde{s}(k) \big] + \frac{f_1}{N},$$

$$w_{K+1}(k+1) = w_{K+1}(k) - \mu \tilde{x}_{K+1}^*(k)\tilde{s}(k) \tag{6.138}$$
$$- \frac{1}{N} \sum_{j=N+1}^{2N} \big[w_j(k) - \mu \tilde{x}_j^*(k)\tilde{s}(k) \big] + \frac{f_2}{N},$$

$$\vdots$$

$$w_{2K}(k+1) = w_{2K}(k) - \mu \tilde{x}_{2K}^*(k)\tilde{s}(k)$$
$$- \frac{1}{N} \sum_{j=N+1}^{2N} \big[w_j(k) - \mu \tilde{x}_j^*(k)\tilde{s}(k) \big] + \frac{f_2}{N},$$

$$\vdots$$

$$w_{JN}(k+1) = w_{JN}(k) - \mu \tilde{x}_{JN}^*(k)\tilde{s}(k)$$
$$- \frac{1}{N} \sum_{j=(J-1)N}^{JN} \big[w_j(k) - \mu \tilde{x}_j^*(k)\tilde{s}(k) \big] + \frac{f_J}{N}.$$

In this form it is easy to see how the algorithm functions.

In the general case where the $\mathbf{c}_j$ are not orthogonal, one can use the adaptation algorithm as given in Eq. (6.105), of course. However, there is really no reason to work with nonorthogonal $\mathbf{c}_j$. As we have seen, a single constraint vector $\mathbf{c}_1$ keeps the component of $\mathbf{W}$ parallel to $\mathbf{c}_1$ fixed. With two constraint vectors $\mathbf{c}_1$ and $\mathbf{c}_2$, the constraint keeps the components of $\mathbf{W}$ in the directions of both $\mathbf{c}_1$ and $\mathbf{c}_2$ constant. Since $\mathbf{c}_1$ and $\mathbf{c}_2$ define a plane (as long as they are not collinear), the constraint keeps all components of $\mathbf{W}$ in this plane fixed. However, to keep the components of $\mathbf{W}$ in a given plane fixed, we can use any two vectors in this plane as constraint vectors. In particular, we can always choose two orthogonal vectors in this plane. Similar arguments apply when there are three or more constraint vectors. We can always choose a set of orthogonal constraint vectors that span the space defined by the original constraint vectors.

There are also other ways of using constraints. For example, Applebaum and Chapman [13] have pointed out that constraints can be used to fix not only the pattern but also one or more derivatives of the pattern in the desired direction. They suggest that such derivative constraints can be used to maintain the shape of the main beam when interference falls in the main beam. Constraints on the pattern derivatives can be imposed as follows:

Suppose we have an N-element array of isotropic elements with a single complex weight behind each element. (That is, there are no delay lines as in Fig. 6.25.) Assume the elements are a half wavelength apart. Then the voltage pattern of the array may be written

$$p(x) = \sum_{k=1}^{N} w_k e^{-j(k-1)x}, \tag{6.139}$$

where

$$x = \pi \sin \theta. \tag{6.140}$$

To fix the value of $p(x)$ at a given $x = x_d$ (corresponding to a given $\theta = \theta_d$), we impose the constraint

$$\mathbf{c}_1^\dagger \mathbf{W} = 1, \tag{6.141}$$

where

$$\mathbf{c}_1 = \begin{bmatrix} 1 & e^{jx_d} & e^{j2x_d} & \cdots & e^{j(N-1)x_d} \end{bmatrix}^T. \tag{6.142}$$

Then, since the first derivative of $p(x)$ is

$$\frac{dp(x)}{dx} = p'(x) = \sum_{k=1}^{N} [-j(k-1)] w_k e^{-j(k-1)x}, \tag{6.143}$$

we may force the first derivative to remain zero by imposing the constraint

$$\mathbf{c}_2^\dagger \mathbf{W} = 0, \tag{6.144}$$

where

$$\mathbf{c}_2 = j\begin{bmatrix} 0 & e^{jx_d} & 2e^{j2x_d} & 3e^{j3x_d} & \cdots \end{bmatrix}^T. \tag{6.145}$$

Similarly, the mth derivative is

$$p^{(m)}(x) = \sum_{k=1}^{K} [-j(k-1)]^m w_k e^{-j(k-1)x}, \tag{6.146}$$

so we may constrain the mth derivative to zero by requiring

$$\mathbf{c}_{m+1}^{\dagger} \mathbf{W} = 0, \tag{6.147}$$

where

$$\mathbf{c}_{m+1} = j^m \begin{bmatrix} 0 & e^{jx_d} & 2^m e^{j2x_d} & 3^m e^{j3x_d} & \cdots \end{bmatrix}^T. \tag{6.148}$$

Applebaum and Chapman refer to a constraint that controls the value of $p(x_d)$ and all derivatives up the mth one as an mth-order constraint. A zero-order constraint fixes the value of $p(x_d)$, a first-order constraint fixes both $p(x_d)$ and $p'(x_d)$, and so forth.

To impose a second-order constraint, for example, we do not actually use the preceding $\mathbf{c}_j$ directly. Instead, it is more convenient (in calculating the matrix $\mathbf{P}$) if we first find a set of three mutually orthogonal vectors that span the space of $\mathbf{c}_1$, $\mathbf{c}_2$, and $\mathbf{c}_3$. For example, if $\theta_d = 0$, we have from Eqs. (6.142), (6.145), and (6.148),

$$\mathbf{c}_1 = [1, 1, \ldots, 1]^T, \tag{6.149}$$

$$\mathbf{c}_2 = j[0, 1, 2, \ldots, N-1]^T, \tag{6.150}$$

and

$$\mathbf{c}_3 = -\begin{bmatrix} 0, 1, 4, 9, \ldots, (N-1)^2 \end{bmatrix}^T. \tag{6.151}$$

To construct three mutually perpendicular vectors, we define new constraint vectors $\mathbf{c}_j'$ whose kth components are given by

$$\mathbf{c}_{1k}' = a_0, \tag{6.152}$$

$$\mathbf{c}_{2k}' = b_0 + b_1 k, \tag{6.153}$$

and

$$\mathbf{c}_{3k}' = d_0 + d_1 k + d_2 k^2. \tag{6.154}$$

The coefficients a_0, b_0, b_1, d_0, d_1, and d_2 can be adjusted so that $\mathbf{c}_1'$, $\mathbf{c}_2'$, and $\mathbf{c}_3'$ are mutually orthogonal. Since the vectors $\mathbf{c}_1'$, $\mathbf{c}_2'$, and $\mathbf{c}_3'$ span the same space as $\mathbf{c}_1$, $\mathbf{c}_2$, and $\mathbf{c}_3$ in Eqs. (6.149) to (6.151), they will have the same effect on the array response.

Another way of using constraint vectors has been suggested by Takao, Fujita, and Nishi [14]. They proposed using a pair of constraint vectors to fix the array pattern response simultaneously in two closely adjacent directions. They refer to this technique as a double directional constraint. They constrain the pattern to have two fixed peaks close to each other, in a manner analogous to the double-peaked resonance of a stagger-tuned circuit. The constraint vectors appropriate for this purpose can be found by defining c_1 and c_2 for the two values of θ and constructing two orthogonal vectors in the plane defined by c_1 and c_2.

Finally, we note that a constraint could also be used to produce a fixed null in the array pattern in a certain direction, if desired. Such a constraint null might be useful if a source of interference will exist at some known angle. Moreover, one or more derivatives of the pattern in this null direction could also be fixed, to counteract the bandwidth of the interference or the fact that its arrival angle may not be known exactly.

As final topic in this section, let us briefly describe the continuous version of the constrained adaptive algorithm. The discrete constrained algorithm was given in Eq. (6.102):

$$\mathbf{W}(k+1) = \mathbf{W}(k) - \mu\left[\mathbf{I} - \mathbf{C}(\mathbf{C}^{\dagger}\mathbf{C})^{-1}\mathbf{C}^{\dagger}\right]\mathbf{X}^{*}(k)\tilde{s}(k)$$
$$+ \mathbf{C}(\mathbf{C}^{\dagger}\mathbf{C})^{-1}\left[\mathbf{f} - \mathbf{C}^{\dagger}\mathbf{W}(k)\right]. \tag{6.155}$$

As we pointed out earlier, the last term in this equation, $\mathbf{C}(\mathbf{C}^{\dagger}\mathbf{C})^{-1}[\mathbf{f} - \mathbf{C}^{\dagger}\mathbf{W}(k)]$, is zero if $\mathbf{W}(k)$ satisfies the constraint equation. However, this term has been left in, because if $\mathbf{W}(k)$ does not satisfy the constraint equation for some reason, the algorithm automatically corrects for this problem and makes $\mathbf{W}(k+1)$ satisfy it.

To obtain the equivalent continuous control loop from Eq. (6.155), one is tempted to move $\mathbf{W}(k)$ to the other side of the equation, divide by the sampling time Δt, and take the limit as $\Delta t \to 0$. This procedure gives

$$\frac{d\mathbf{W}(t)}{dt} = -\mu'\mathbf{P}[\mathbf{X}^{*}(t)\tilde{s}(t)] + \lim_{\Delta t \to 0}\frac{1}{\Delta t}\mathbf{C}(\mathbf{C}^{\dagger}\mathbf{C})^{-1}[\mathbf{f} - \mathbf{C}^{\dagger}\mathbf{W}(t)], \tag{6.156}$$

where

$$\mu' = \lim_{\Delta t \to 0}\frac{\mu}{\Delta t}. \tag{6.157}$$

However, this form has the difficulty that the last term is infinite unless $\mathbf{f} - \mathbf{C}^{\dagger}\mathbf{W}(t)$ is zero (unless $\mathbf{W}(t)$ satisfies the constraint equation). This term goes to infinity as $\Delta t \to 0$ because if $\mathbf{C}^{\dagger}\mathbf{W}(t)$ differs from $\mathbf{f}$ by a nonzero amount, then an infinite rate of change will be required to make $\mathbf{W}(t)$ satisfy the constraint an infinitesimal amount of time later. To sidestep this difficulty, we must proceed in a slightly different manner. Suppose that in the discrete algorithm

$$\mathbf{W}(k+1) = \mathbf{P}[\mathbf{W}(k) - \mu\mathbf{X}^{*}(k)\tilde{s}(k)] + \mathbf{F} \tag{6.158}$$

we use the algorithm again to express $\mathbf{W}(k)$ in terms of the earlier samples

$\mathbf{W}(k - 1)$, $\mathbf{X}^*(k - 1)$, and $\tilde{s}(k - 1)$. Substituting for $\mathbf{W}(k)$, we have

$$\mathbf{W}(k + 1) = \mathbf{P}^2[\mathbf{W}(k - 1) - \mu\mathbf{X}^*(k - 1)\tilde{s}(k - 1)]$$
$$+ \mathbf{PF} + \mathbf{P}[-\mu\mathbf{X}^*(k)\tilde{s}(k)] + \mathbf{F}. \tag{6.159}$$

However, it is easily shown from Eq. (6.103) that $\mathbf{P}$ is idempotent, that is,

$$\mathbf{P}^2 = \mathbf{P}, \tag{6.160}$$

and in addition one finds from Eqs. (6.103) and (6.104) that

$$\mathbf{PF} = 0. \tag{6.161}$$

Hence, Eq. (6.159) reduces to

$$\mathbf{W}(k + 1) = \mathbf{P}\left[\mathbf{W}(k - 1) - \mu\sum_{j=k-1}^{k} \mathbf{X}(j)\tilde{s}(j)\right] + \mathbf{F}. \tag{6.162}$$

Continuing this process back to the $k = 0$ sample, we have

$$\mathbf{W}(k + 1) = \mathbf{P}\left[\mathbf{W}(0) - \mu\sum_{j=0}^{k} \mathbf{X}^*(j)\tilde{s}(j)\right] + \mathbf{F}. \tag{6.163}$$

If we assume that the samples are separated by only a short time compared to the rate at which the variables change, we may write an equivalent relation in continuous form as

$$\mathbf{W}(t) = \mathbf{P}\left[\mathbf{W}(0) - \mu\int_0^t \mathbf{X}^*(t')\tilde{s}(t')\,dt'\right] + \mathbf{F}. \tag{6.164}$$

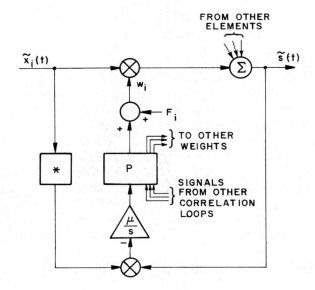

Figure 6.26 Continuous adaptive array loop with constraints.

The continuous algorithm in this form has the self-correcting property. The operator **P** will remove any components of $\mathbf{W}(0) - \int_0^t \mathbf{X}^*(t')\tilde{s}(t')\,dt'$ in the direction of **F**, and **F** is added again to insure that $\mathbf{W}(t)$ satisfies the constraint. The continuous feedback loop based on Eqs. (6.164) is shown in Fig. 6.26. Takao, Fujita, and Nishi [14] have studied the transient response of this loop.

6.5 POWER INVERSION‡

An Applebaum array may be used an additional way, in a power inversion mode [17, 18]. *Power inversion* refers to the fact that the Applebaum array can invert the power ratio of two received signals. It does so by nulling the strong signal in favor of the weak one. The power inversion technique is useful because it does not require detailed information about the desired signal waveform or arrival angle.

Normally, to receive a desired signal with an adaptive array, one must either know something about the desired signal waveform, so that a reference signal can be obtained for the LMS array (as will be discussed in Chapter 7), or one must know the desired signal arrival angle, so that a steering vector can be chosen for the Applebaum array. However, when neither the arrival angle nor the waveform is known, one may still be able to obtain some interference protection with a power inversion array. The SINR improvement of a power inversion array is not as good as that of the LMS or Applebaum array, but it may still be useful.

The power inversion array is in essence an Applebaum array. But to obtain the power inversion behavior, we make several changes in the way the array is used. First, the number of degrees of freedom in the array is chosen to equal the number of interfering signals. Second, the integrator in the Applebaum feedback loop is changed to a lowpass filter, and the loop gain is chosen in a special way. Third, a different steering vector is used.

The central idea of power inversion is as follows. Suppose we wish to protect a desired signal from interference. In general, an N-element array has $N - 1$ degrees of freedom. Let us assume that the number of degrees of freedom is chosen to equal the number of interfering signals. For example, suppose there will be one interfering signal. Then we arrange to receive the desired signal and the interference signal with a two-element array. Because this array has only one degree of freedom, it will be able to form only one null. If the weights in the array are adjusted to minimize the array output power, under the condition that not all the weights are allowed to go to zero, then the array will direct its only available null at the strong interference signal. Since the interference will be attenuated by the null, but the desired signal will not, the signal-to-interference

---

‡Portions of this section are reprinted from the author's paper [18] with permission, © 1979 IEEE.

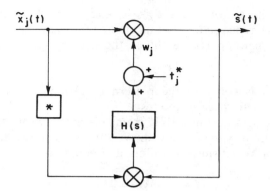

Figure 6.27 The power inversion loop.

ratio will be improved by the pattern ratio in the two directions. This is the idea of power inversion.

To achieve power inversion with an Applebaum array, we must change the feedback loop integrator to a lowpass filter. Specifically, we consider a feedback loop in which the jth weight in the array obeys the differential equation,

$$\tau \frac{dw_j}{dt} + w_j = t_j^* - k\tilde{x}_j^*(t)\tilde{s}(t), \tag{6.165}$$

where τ is a suitable constant and t_j^* is the jth component of the steering vector $\mathbf{T}^*$. The feedback loop is then as shown in Fig. 6.27, with the transfer function $H(s)$ given by

$$H(s) = \frac{k}{\tau s + 1}. \tag{6.166}$$

Changing the integrator in the Applebaum array to a lowpass filter allows us to control the dynamic range of the array with the loop gain k, as we shall see.

In addition, to use the Applebaum array in the power inversion mode, we choose the steering vector in a different way. In the normal application, the steering vector is chosen to obtain a main beam of the quiescent pattern in a specified direction with some suitable gain and sidelobe level. In a power inversion application, however, it is assumed that the desired signal arrival angle is not known in advance, so one does not know where to point the beam. Instead, the steering vector is chosen to obtain a quiescent pattern covering the sector of space from which the desired signal may arrive. Such a pattern may be obtained by using elements whose patterns cover this sector. By choosing a steering vector with only one nonzero component (so one element is on and the rest are off), we obtain a quiescent pattern equal to the element pattern of the element that is turned on. In this way, a desired signal can access the antenna from any direction within the sector.

Now let us see how to choose the loop gain in the array, by considering our two-element example. Suppose we assume that a desired signal may arrive from anywhere within the sector $-\pi \leqslant \theta_d \leqslant \pi$, and we wish to protect this signal from a single interference signal. Let us assume the elements are isotropic and spaced a half wavelength apart. We choose the steering vector to be

$$\mathbf{T}^* = [1, 0]^T, \tag{6.167}$$

so the quiescent pattern is equal to the pattern of element 1, that is, it is omnidirectional over the half space of interest.

Let us compute the steady-state SINR from this array. From this we will see how to choose the loop gain. If the jth weight in the array satisfies Eq. (6.165), the weight vector $\mathbf{W}$ satisfies the differential equation

$$\frac{d\mathbf{W}}{dt} + (\mathbf{I} + k\mathbf{\Phi})\mathbf{W} = \mathbf{T}^*. \tag{6.168}$$

The steady-state weight vector will be

$$\mathbf{W} = (\mathbf{I} + k\mathbf{\Phi})^{-1}\mathbf{T}^*. \tag{6.169}$$

Assume that each $\tilde{x}_i(t)$ consists of desired, interference, and thermal noise signals in the usual manner. The matrix $\mathbf{\Phi}$ is then

$$\mathbf{\Phi} = \sigma^2 \mathbf{I} + \begin{bmatrix} R_{\tilde{d}}(0) + R_{\tilde{\imath}}(0) & R_{\tilde{d}}^*(-T_d) + R_{\tilde{\imath}}^*(-T_i) \\ R_{\tilde{d}}(T_d) + R_{\tilde{\imath}}(T_i) & R_{\tilde{d}}(0) + R_{\tilde{\imath}}(0) \end{bmatrix} \tag{6.170}$$

where $R_{\tilde{d}}(\tau)$ and $R_{\tilde{\imath}}(\tau)$ are the autocorrelation functions of the desired and interference signals, defined in Eqs. (3.62) and (3.82). To be specific, we shall assume that the desired signal and interference have power spectral densities as shown in Figs. 3.8 and 3.9. Using the definitions in Eqs. (4.54) and (4.55) and defining

$$K = k\sigma^2, \tag{6.171}$$

we have

$$\mathbf{I} + k\mathbf{\Phi} = \begin{bmatrix} 1 + K + K\xi_d + K\xi_i & K\xi_d\rho_d^* + K\xi_i\rho_i^* \\ K\xi_d\rho_d + K\xi_i\rho_i & 1 + K + K\xi_d + K\xi_i \end{bmatrix} \tag{6.172}$$

where we omit the arguments of $\rho_d(T_d)$ and $\rho_i(T_i)$, and where ξ_d and ξ_i are the SNR and INR per element, as usual. The inverse of this matrix is

$$[\mathbf{I} + k\mathbf{\Phi}]^{-1} = \frac{1}{D}\begin{bmatrix} 1 + K + K\xi_d + K\xi_i & -K\xi_d\rho_d^* - K\xi_i\rho_i^* \\ -K\xi_d\rho_d - K\xi_i\rho_i & 1 + K + K\xi_d + K\xi_i \end{bmatrix} \tag{6.173}$$

where

$$D = (1 + K + K\xi_d + K\xi_i)^2 - |K\xi_d\rho_d + K\xi_i\rho_i|^2. \tag{6.174}$$

The steady-state weights are then given by

$$\mathbf{W} = (\mathbf{I} + k\mathbf{\Phi})^{-1}\mathbf{T}^*, \tag{6.175}$$

which yields

$$\mathbf{W} = \frac{1}{D} \begin{bmatrix} 1 + K + K\xi_d + K\xi_i \\ -K\xi_d\rho_d - K\xi_i\rho_i \end{bmatrix}. \tag{6.176}$$

With these weights the desired signal at the array output is

$$\tilde{s}_d(t) = \left[\tilde{d}(t)\tilde{d}(t - T_d) \right]\mathbf{W}$$

$$= \frac{1}{D}\left\{ \left[1 + K + K\xi_d + K\xi_i \right]\tilde{d}(t) \right. \tag{6.177}$$

$$\left. - \left[K\xi_d\rho_d + K\xi_i\rho_i \right]\tilde{d}(t - T_d) \right\},$$

and the array output desired signal power is

$$P_d = \tfrac{1}{2}E\left\{ |\tilde{s}_d|^2 \right\}$$

$$= \frac{p_d}{2D^2}\left\{ (1 + K + K\xi_d + K\xi_i)\left[1 + K + K\xi_d(1 - 2|\rho_d|^2) \right. \right.$$

$$\left. + K\xi_i(1 - 2\operatorname{Re}\{\rho_i\rho_d^*\}) \right] + |K\xi_d\rho_d + K\xi_i\rho_i|^2 \Big\}. \tag{6.178}$$

Similarly, the output interference power is

$$P_i = \frac{p_i}{2D^2}\left\{ (1 + K + K\xi_d + K\xi_i)\left[1 + K + K\xi_d(1 - 2\operatorname{Re}\{\rho_d\rho_i^*\}) \right. \right.$$

$$\left. + K\xi_i(1 - 2|p_i|^2) \right] + |K\xi_d\rho_d + K\xi_i\rho_i|^2 \Big\}, \tag{6.179}$$

and the output thermal noise power is

$$P_n = \frac{\sigma^2}{2}\mathbf{W}^\dagger\mathbf{W}$$

$$= \frac{\sigma^2}{2D}\left[(1 + K + K\xi_d + K\xi_i)^2 + |K\xi_d\rho_d + K\xi_i\rho_i|^2 \right]. \tag{6.180}$$

From these equations the SINR can be computed in the usual way.

To understand the behavior of this array we shall examine the output SINR in two cases: (1) Only desired signal and noise are present, and (2) desired, interference, and noise signals are all present. Then we shall discuss the power inversion behavior and the effects of bandwidth on the results.

Desired Signal and Noise

If only desired signal and thermal noise are present in the array, we may obtain the output desired signal power and noise power from the preceding formulas by letting $\xi_i = 0$. To be specific, let us first assume the desired signal is CW. (We shall consider the case of nonzero bandwidth later.) We have

$$\tilde{d}(t) = \sqrt{p_d}\,e^{j(\omega_d t + \psi_d)}, \tag{6.181}$$

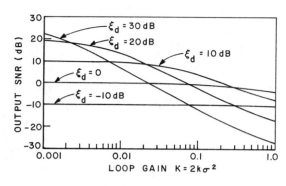

Figure 6.28 Output SNR versus loop gain K: no interference (reprinted from [18] with permission, © 1979 IEEE).

where ψ_d is uniformly distributed on $(-\pi, \pi)$. Then

$$R_{\tilde{d}}(T_d) = E\left[\tilde{d}(t + T_d)\tilde{d}^*(t)\right] = p_d e^{j\omega_d T_d} \qquad (6.182)$$

and

$$\rho_d = \frac{R_{\tilde{d}}(T_d)}{p_d} = e^{j\omega_d T_d} = e^{j\phi_d}, \qquad (6.183)$$

where ϕ_d is the interelement phase shift at the signal frequency. Substituting ρ_d into Eqs. (6.178) and (6.180), we find the output signal-to-noise ratio to be

$$\text{output SNR} = \frac{P_d}{P_n} = \xi_d \frac{(1 + K)^2}{(1 + K + K\xi_d)^2 + K^2\xi_d^2}. \qquad (6.184)$$

From this equation we may obtain an understanding of the effect of the loop gain and the input SNR on the array performance. Figure 6.28 shows a typical plot of output SNR versus K for several values of ξ_d, and Fig. 6.29 shows the output SNR versus ξ_d for several values of K.

From these curves we can see how the loop gain K should be chosen. Since the signal being received by the array is the desired signal, we do not wish to null it. When the input SNR is small, the weights in Eq. (6.176) are not much different from those with noise alone, and the array does not null the desired signal. This result may be seen in Fig. 6.28; for example, for $\xi_d = -10$ dB, K has little effect on the output SNR. With a larger input SNR, increasing K causes the array feedback to null the desired signal, and the output SNR drops. For example, in Fig. 6.28, the curve for $\xi_d = +30$ dB shows this behavior.

Figure 6.30 illustrates the effect of the desired signal on the pattern. It shows the patterns for several values of ξ_d for the case $K = 0.1$. It is seen that for $\xi_d \leqslant 0$ dB, the desired signal is not strong enough to cause a pattern null. At $\xi_d = +10$ dB, however, the array has begun to null the desired signal (which is at $0°$). The null depth increases as ξ_d increases; it is -46.1 dB when $\xi_d = +30$ dB. (In Fig. 6.30, 0 dB is defined as the array response when the weight vector equals the steering vector.)

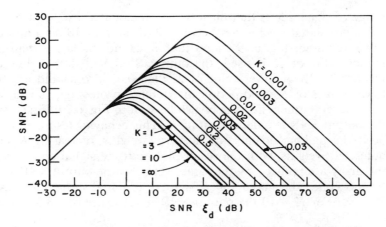

Figure 6.29   Output SNR versus input SNR: no interference (reprinted from [18] with permission, © 1979 IEEE).

Figure 6.29 shows the output SNR as a function of the input SNR for several values of the loop gain K. It is seen that for a given K, the output SNR at first increases with ξ_d (in the range where ξ_d is too small to affect the weights) and then decreases with ξ_d (when the desired signal is nulled by the array). For strong signals, a 10 dB increase in ξ_d produces a 20 dB increase in the null depth, so the output SNR drops 10 dB.

The problem we have is to prevent the array from nulling the desired signal. The optimum choice of the loop gain K depends on two factors: (1) the required minimum SNR out of the array (which depends on the receiver and the type of modulation used in the communication system), and (2) the dynamic

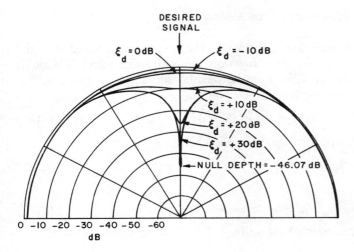

Figure 6.30   Array pattern: no interference, $K = 0.1$, $\theta_d = 0°$ (reprinted from [18] with permission, © 1979 IEEE).

range of signal levels that must be accommodated by the array. For example, if the input signal level varies between 0 dB and 20 dB, and an output SNR of 0 dB is required, Fig. 6.29 shows that K cannot be larger than about 0.07. If a higher value of K is used, the output SNR will drop below 0 dB before ξ_d reaches 20 dB. A lower value of K than 0.07 also should not be used because lower values of K yield poorer interference protection, as will be seen.

Several other effects may also be seen in Fig. 6.29. First, for $\xi_d \leqslant -10$ dB, the output SNR is independent of K. This behavior results because such a weak desired signal has no effect on the array weights. Increasing K simply lowers the quiescent weights, with the result that both the signal and noise powers out of the array are reduced by the same factor, so the output SNR is unaffected.

Second, the curve for $K = 10$ is essentially the same as the curve for $K = \infty$. For $K = 10$ the output SNR never exceeds -6.5 dB regardless of the input SNR.

Third, the larger the dynamic range of the input signal, the smaller K must be to keep the output SNR above a given minimum over the whole range. If the input SNR varies from 0 dB to $+60$ dB, for example, we must have $K \leqslant 0.002$ if the output SNR must exceed, say, 0 dB. As we shall see, such a low value of K offers little interference protection. For this reason, the power inversion technique is most effective when it is necessary to accommodate only a small dynamic range for the desired signal.

Moreover, the ideal application of the power inversion array is to a communication system where the output SNR can be less than 0 dB. One such application is in spread spectrum systems [19], which often operate with the signal below the noise because of the processing gain of the spread spectrum receiver. With the desired signal below the noise, the array does not try to null the desired signal. In this situation, one has wide latitude in the choice of K, which can then be chosen for good interference suppression.

Desired Signal, Interference, and Noise

Now assume that two signals are incident on the array, one desired and the other interference. (However, the array has no way of knowing which is which!) Assume that both signals are CW. For the desired signal, ρ_d is given in Eq. (6.183). For the interference we let

$$i(t) = \sqrt{p_i}\, e^{j(\omega_d t + \psi_i)}, \tag{6.185}$$

where ψ_i is uniformly distributed on $(-\pi, \pi)$. Then

$$R_{\tilde{i}}(T_i) = E\left[\tilde{i}(t + \tau)\tilde{i}^*(t)\right] = p_i e^{j\omega_d T_i} \tag{6.186}$$

and

$$\rho_i = e^{j\omega_d T_i} = e^{j\phi_i}. \tag{6.187}$$

As usual, ϕ_i is the interelement phase shift at the interference arrival angle.

The output SINR, given by

$$SINR = \frac{P_d}{P_i + P_n},\qquad(6.188)$$

may now be calculated by substituting ρ_d and ρ_i into Eqs. (6.178) through (6.180). A variety of curves may be computed to illustrate the behavior of the array. Figures 6.31, 6.32, and 6.33 are typical examples showing the SINR as a function of ξ_d for $K = 0.01$, 0.1, and 1, respectively. These figures assume $\theta_d = 0°$, $\theta_i = 50°$, and half-wavelength element spacing. Each figure shows the output SINR for several values of ξ_i, the input interference-to-noise ratio.

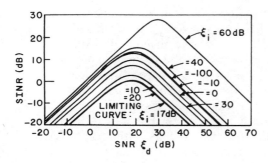

Figure 6.31   Output SINR versus input SNR: $\theta_d = 0°$, $\theta_i = 50°$, $K = 0.01$ (reprinted from [18] with permission, © 1979 IEEE).

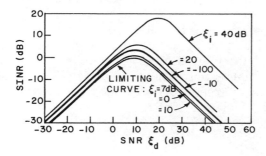

Figure 6.32   Output SINR versus input SNR: $\theta_d = 0°$, $\theta_i = 50°$, $K = 0.1$ (reprinted from [18] with permission, © 1979 IEEE).

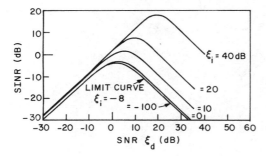

Figure 6.33   Output SINR versus input SNR: $\theta_d = 0°$, $\theta_i = 50°$, $K = 1$ (reprinted from [18] with permission, © 1979 IEEE).

Several things may be seen from these figures. First, for $\xi_i = -100$ dB the interference is virtually not present, so the SINR curves for this case are identical to the results in Fig. 6.29 for the appropriate values of K. Second, as the interference power is increased, we find that the SINR at first drops and then rises. For example, in Fig. 6.31, with $\xi_d = 10$ dB, we have SINR = 9.2 dB for $\xi_i = -100$ dB, then the SINR = -3 dB for $\xi_i = +17$ dB, and finally SINR $\rightarrow$ 12.2 dB as $\xi_i \rightarrow \infty$.

Comparing Fig. 6.31 with Figs. 6.32 and 6.33 shows that as K is increased, there is a less significant drop in the SINR for intermediate values of ξ_i. In fact, for $K = 1$ there is essentially no drop in SINR as ξ_i is increased. In this respect $K = 1$ represents the best choice of loop gain. However, $K = 1$ also results in a narrow range of acceptable desired signal levels when no interference is present, as was seen in Fig. 6.29, and also results in higher desired signal attenuation, as will be seen below. Third, for any given ξ_i there is a finite range of ξ_d over which the output SINR is above any given value. For interference power substantially less than or greater than the desired signal power, the acceptable range for ξ_d is wider. Finally, it is interesting to note that for stronger interference signals, the SINR can be substantially better than it would be without the interference. For example, consider Fig. 6.32. At $\xi_d = 20$ dB, if $\xi_i = -100$ dB we have SINR = -2.6 dB, but if $\xi_i = 40$ dB we have SINR = 17.7 dB. The reason for this behavior is that, without interference, the adaptive array devotes its single null to the desired signal. However, with strong interference, the array is forced to use its null on the interference. The desired signal is then not in a null.

Figure 6.34 shows some patterns that illustrate these remarks. It shows the array patterns for $K = 0.1$ and for $\xi_i = -100$ dB, $+7$ dB, $+20$ dB, and $+40$ dB. The shift of the null from the desired signal to the interference as ξ_i increases may be seen. It is interesting to note that during this change the array response in the desired signal direction is nearly independent of the interference power.

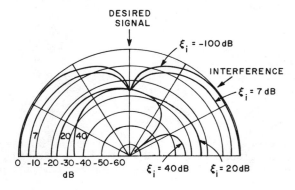

Figure 6.34 Array patterns: $\xi_d = 20$ dB, $K = 0.1$, $\theta_d = 0°$, $\theta_i = 50°$ (reprinted from [18] with permission, © 1979 IEEE).

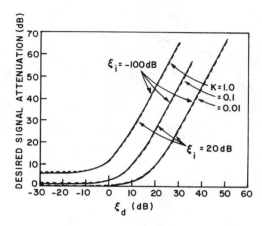

Figure 6.35   Desired signal attenuation versus input SNR: $\theta_d = 0°$, $\theta_i = 50°$ (reprinted from [18] with permission, © 1979 IEEE).

We may also compute the attenuation of the desired signal. If the array weight vector were equal to the steering vector, the desired signal output power would be

$$P_{0d} = \frac{P_d}{2}. \tag{6.189}$$

From Eq. (6.178), the desired signal output power with the array operating, P_d, will be equal to P_{0d} multiplied by a factor η

$$\eta = \left\{ (1 + K + K\xi_d + K\xi_i)\left[1 + K + K\xi_d(1 - 2|\rho_d|^2)\right.\right.$$
$$\left.\left. + K\xi_i(1 - 2\,\text{Re}\,\{\rho_i\rho_d^*\})\right] + |K\xi_d\rho_d + K\xi_i\rho_i|^2 \right\} /$$
$$\left[(1 + K + K\xi_d + K\xi_i)^2 - |K\xi_d\rho_d + K\xi_i\rho_i|^2\right]^2, \tag{6.190}$$

which we define as the attenuation of the desired signal. When $\eta = 1$, the array desired signal output power is the same as it would be with the weights given by the steering vector $\mathbf{T}^*$.

Figure 6.35 shows η in dB versus the input SNR for several values of K and ξ_i. In all cases, as ξ_d increases, the attenuation η increases. It is seen that, for a fixed K, the desired signal attenuation is almost independent of ξ_i. The reason was noted in Fig. 6.34; although the pattern changes drastically with ξ_i, the desired signal response of the array is almost independent of ξ_i.

Finally, we note that the array performance depends on the spatial separation of the desired and interfering signals. All of the curves presented so far have been for $\theta_d = 0°$ and $\theta_i = 50°$. Figures 6.36, 6.37, and 6.38 show typical plots of the output SINR as a function of θ_i for fixed θ_d. In Figs. 6.36 and 6.37 the desired signal arrives from broadside ($\theta_d = 0°$). (In Fig. 6.36, $\xi_d = 0$ dB and $\xi_i = 30$ dB; in Fig. 6.37, $\xi_d = -20$ dB and $\xi_i = +20$ dB.) In Fig. 6.38, $\theta_d = 50°$, $\xi_d = -20$ dB, and $\xi_i = +20$ dB. In all cases the SINR drops when the interference signal is near the desired signal, because the desired

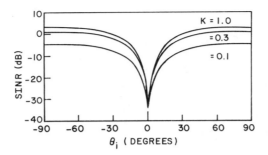

Figure 6.36 Output SINR versus interference angle θ_i: $\theta_d = 0°$, $\xi_d = 0$ dB, $\xi_i = 30$ dB (reprinted from [18] with permission, © 1979 IEEE).

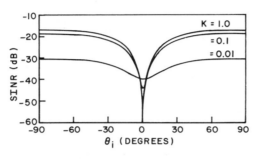

Figure 6.37 Output SINR versus interference angle θ_i: $\theta_d = 0°$, $\xi_d = -20$ dB, $\xi_i = +20$ dB (reprinted from [18] with permission, © 1979 IEEE).

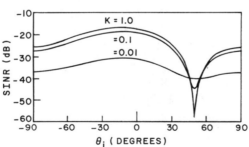

Figure 6.38 Output SINR versus interference angle θ_i: $\theta_d = 50°$, $\xi_d = -20$ dB, $\xi_i = +20$ dB (reprinted from [18] with permission, © 1979 IEEE).

signal falls in the interference null. In general, when interference is too close to the desired signal, the performance of the array will be unsatisfactory. How close the two signals may be depends on the minimum SINR the receiver can accept.

Power Inversion Behavior

Now let us assume that the noise power in the signals $\tilde{x}_j(t)$ is very small compared to the signal powers, that is, $\xi_d \gg 1$ and $\xi_i \gg 1$. Also, let us assume the array loop gain k is large enough that $kp_d \gg 1$ and $kp_i \gg 1$. [Note from Eq. (6.171) that $kp_d = K\xi_d$ and $kp_i = K\xi_i$.] Then we may drop the $1 + K$ terms in Eqs. (6.178) and (6.179) in comparison with the other terms. The output desired signal-to-interference ratio (SIR) is then

$$\text{SIR} = \frac{p_d}{p_i}$$

$$= \frac{(\xi_d + \xi_i)\{\xi_d[1 - 2|\rho_d|^2] + \xi_i[1 - 2\,\text{Re}\,(\rho_i\rho_d^*)]\} + |\xi_d\rho_d + \xi_i\rho_i|^2}{(\xi_d + \xi_i)\{\xi_i[1 - 2|\rho_i|^2] + \xi_d[1 - 2\,\text{Re}\,(\rho_d\rho_i^*)]\} + |\xi_d\rho_d + \xi_i\rho_i|^2}.$$

$$(6.191)$$

When the signals are CW (when $\rho_d = e^{j\phi_d}$ and $\rho_i = e^{j\phi_i}$), this equation simplifies to

$$\text{SIR} = \frac{p_d}{p_i} \frac{\xi_i^2}{\xi_d^2} \frac{1 - \text{Re}\,\{\rho_d\rho_i^*\}}{1 - \text{Re}\,\{\rho_d\rho_i^*\}}. \tag{6.192}$$

As long as $\phi_i \neq \phi_d \,(\text{mod}\,2\pi)$ this relation is

$$\text{SIR} = \frac{p_i}{p_d}, \tag{6.193}$$

which is the reciprocal of the SIR coming into the array. Thus an interfering signal 20 dB above the desired signal at the array input comes out 20 dB below the desired signal. This property is the reason we refer to this array as a power inversion array.

For finite gain and nonzero noise, the array approximately inverts the power ratio of two signals, as long as the noise is small and the loop gain is large. For example, Fig. 6.33 (for $K = 1$) shows that for $\xi_d = 20$ dB and $\xi_i = 40$ dB (so that the input SIR is -20 dB) the output SINR is $+18$ dB.

Bandwidth Effects

The above results were all for CW signals. For signals with nonzero bandwidth, the performance of the power inversion array is not as good as with CW signals, for the same reasons that were discussed in Chapter 3. The antenna pattern is frequency dependent, so its response varies over the signal bandwidth. Since the pattern varies much more rapidly with frequency in the nulls than elsewhere, it is primarily interference bandwidth that affects the performance. Desired signal bandwidth has only a negligible effect on the results. In this section we briefly illustrate the effects of bandwidth on a power inversion array.

Assume that the desired and interference signals are bandlimited with constant power spectral densities over bandwidths $\Delta\omega_d$ and $\Delta\omega_i$ centered at frequency ω_d. The normalized autocorrelation functions are then

$$\rho_d = \frac{\sin\frac{1}{2}(B_d\phi_d)}{\frac{1}{2}(B_d\phi_d)} e^{j\phi_d} \tag{6.194}$$

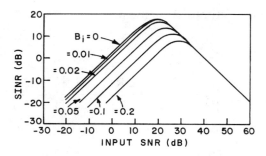

Figure 6.39 Effect of interference bandwidth on output SINR: $\theta_d = 0°$, $\theta_i = 50°$, $K = 0.1$, $\xi_i = 40$ dB, $0 \leqslant B_d \leqslant 0.2$ (reprinted from [18] with permission, © 1979 IEEE).

and

$$\rho_i = \frac{\sin \frac{1}{2}(B_i\phi_i)}{\frac{1}{2}(B_i\phi_i)} e^{j\phi_i}, \tag{6.195}$$

where B_d, B_i, ϕ_d, and ϕ_i are defined in Eqs. (3.69), (3.86), (2.100), and (2.169). The array output SINR may be calculated by substituting these ρ_d and ρ_i in Eqs. (6.178) through (6.180).

Figure 6.39 shows a typical plot of the output SINR for $\theta_d = 0°$, $\theta_i = 50°$, $K = 0.1$, $\xi_i = 40$ dB, $0 \leqslant B_d \leqslant 0.2$, and for several values of interference bandwidth in the range $0 \leqslant B_i \leqslant 0.2$. (The curve for $B_i = 0$ is the same as the $\xi_i = 40$ dB curve in Fig. 6.32.) It may be seen that as B_i increases from zero, the output SINR drops for lower values of input SNR.

The reason for this behavior may be understood from the array patterns shown in Fig. 6.40. Increasing the interference bandwidth causes the pattern magnitude to drop. This behavior occurs because the null depth varies with frequency over the interference bandwidth. As the bandwidth increases, more and more interference power appears at the array output; to compensate, the feedback lowers the value of the array weights. The result is that the pattern is reduced in all directions, including the desired signal direction.

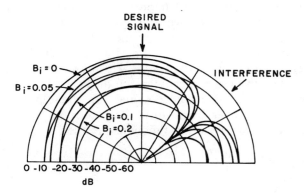

Figure 6.40 Effect of interference bandwidth on array patterns: $\theta_d = 0°$, $\theta_i = 50°$, $\xi_d = 0$ dB, $K = 0.1$, $B_d = 0$, $\xi_i = 40$ dB (reprinted from [18] with permission, © 1979 IEEE).

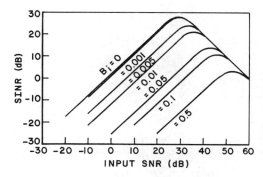

Figure 6.41 Effect of interference bandwidth on output SINR: $\theta_d = 0°$, $\theta_i = 50°$, $K = 0.1$, $\xi_i = 60$ dB, $0 \leqslant B_d \leqslant 0.5$ (reprinted from [18] with permission, © 1979 IEEE).

On the other hand, all curves in Fig. 6.39 coalesce for higher values of input SNR. The reason is that with high-input SNR, the array weights are already reduced more by the presence of both desired signal and interference than they are by bandwidth. With both strong desired signal and strong interference, the array cannot null both signals, so it turns down the weights and reduces the overall pattern magnitude. At high-input SNR, this effect is more important than the pattern reduction due to bandwidth.

We also note that the output SINR becomes more sensitive to interference bandwidth as the input interference power increases. Figure 6.41 shows a plot of output SINR similar to Fig. 6.39 except that the input interference to noise ratio is now 60 dB instead of 40 dB. It is seen that much smaller bandwidths are required to produce a given SINR degradation when $\xi_i = 60$ dB than when $\xi_i = 40$ dB.

The curves in Figs. 6.39 through 6.41 have been computed for a desired signal bandwidth $B_d = 0$. However, it is found that B_d has no noticeable effect on these curves over the range $0 \leqslant B_d \leqslant 0.2$, even if the desired signal and interference arrival angles are interchanged. The bandwidth B_d has so little effect because the pattern is much less frequency sensitive in the desired signal direction than in the null, as discussed earlier.

Note that it is the product of the interference bandwidth B_i and the interelement phase shift ϕ_i that affects ρ_i [see Eq. (6.195)]. For this reason, for interference at broadside ($\phi_i = 0$), bandwidth has no effect on array performance, but for interference at endfire ($\phi_i = \pi$), bandwidth has its greatest effect. For applications where interference bandwidth is significant, the designer may wish to minimize bandwidth effects by positioning the array so that its broadside direction is close to the interference arrival angle, if possible.

PROBLEMS

6.1.   Consider the following sidelobe canceler array. Suppose eleven isotropic elements are spaced every half wavelength along a line, as shown in Fig. 6.42. Assume that the

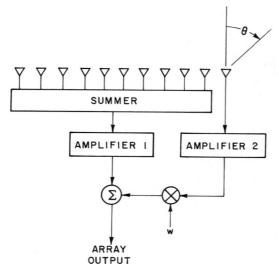

Figure 6.42 An eleven-element sidelobe canceler array.

outputs from the first ten elements are combined using equal-length cables and a summer to form a main beam pointed at broadside ($\theta = 0°$). Let the remaining element (element 11) be used as the auxiliary element to form the sidelobe canceler. The signal from this element will be multiplied by complex weight w and then added to the main-beam output, as shown.

Suppose the two amplifiers in Fig. 6.42 each contribute thermal noise of power σ^2 at their outputs. Suppose furthermore that this noise is the dominant noise in the antenna system. Next, assume that a desired signal arrives from broadside ($\theta_d = 0°$) with an SNR at the *auxiliary* amplifier output of -20 dB. (The SNR at the output of amplifier 1 will then be 0 dB.) Finally, assume that a CW interference signal arrives from angle θ_i. Let the INR at the auxiliary amplifier output be 40 dB. Now do the following:

(a) Calculate the voltage pattern of the ten-element main beam array. Plot this pattern versus θ over $-90° \leqslant \theta \leqslant 90°$.

(b) Calculate and plot the array output SINR as a function of the interference arrival angle θ_i for $-90° \leqslant \theta_i \leqslant 90°$.

(c) Now assume the noise power from the amplifier on the main beam is $10\sigma^2$, instead of σ^2. Calculate and plot the SINR versus θ_i for this case. (The signal powers are the same as before.)

(d) Next assume that the amplifier on the main beam has noise power σ^2 again, but that the noise on the auxiliary output is now $10\sigma^2$. Calculate and plot the SINR versus θ_i for this case.

(e) Explain why the curves have the behavior they do. Discuss how thermal noise levels in the main beam and the auxiliary affect the array performance.

(f) Compare the main beam pattern found in part (a) with the SINR curves found in parts (b) through (d). Discuss the relationship between these curves.

6.2. Consider a three-element Applebaum adaptive array with isotropic elements, as shown in Fig. 6.43. The desired signal is expected to arrive from broadside ($\theta_d = 0°$), and so

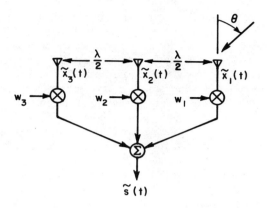

Figure 6.43 A three-element Apple-baum array.

a steering vector

$$T^* = \begin{bmatrix} 1 \\ 1 \\ 1 \end{bmatrix}$$

is chosen for use in the array feedback.

Now suppose that, because of unavoidable experimental factors, the voltage pattern $f_j(\theta_d)$ of each element j ($j = 1, 2, 3$) in the desired signal direction differs slightly from unity, say,

$$f_j(\theta_d) = g_j = (1 + \alpha_j) e^{j\beta_j},$$

where α_j and β_j are small ($\alpha_j, \beta_j \ll 1$) quantities.

Carry through an analysis of the effect of such errors on the array output SINR. Determine whether it is useful in this problem to assume that α_j and β_j are random.

For example, one could assume that α_j is uniformly distributed on $(-\varepsilon_\alpha, \varepsilon_\alpha)$ with $\varepsilon_\alpha \ll 1$, and that β_j is uniformly distributed on $(-\varepsilon_\beta, \varepsilon_\beta)$, with $\varepsilon_\beta \ll 1$. Determine whether an analysis can be carried out under these assumptions. If not, explain why not.

If the approach suggested above is not fruitful, suggest another approach and carry it out. The objective of this problem is to obtain engineering curves of SINR versus the magnitudes of α_j and β_j similar to those in Figs. 6.16 and 6.17. To this end, you should make full use of any derivations and curves in section 6.3. Carry out your calculations for a couple of representative cases, such as the following:

(a) For desired signal only, with input SNR $\xi_d = 0$ dB.

(b) For desired signal and interference, with SNR $\xi_d = 0$ dB, input INR $\xi_i = 40$ dB, $\theta_i = 50°$, both CW signals.

Describe what your results show about the effects of the random gains g_j on performance.

6.3. For the five-element beamformer shown in Fig. 6.6, find the covariance matrix $\Phi_y = E[\mathbf{Y}^*\mathbf{Y}^T]$ if the array receives a desired signal from $\theta_d = 0°$ and there is independent thermal noise present on the elements. Then, using the steering vector in Eq. (6.32), find the resulting array weights. What special property does Φ_y have in this case and why?

6.4.   In the theorem of section 5.2 and the discussion of section 6.2, it is tacitly assumed that the thermal noise levels are already established in the signals $\tilde{x}_j(t)$. In other words, no additional thermal noise is added in or after the transformation **V**.

Consider, however, the following situation. Suppose a set of N preamplifiers will be used in the array to boost signal levels, one in each channel at the input to the LMS processor. If no transformation **V** is inserted, these preamplifiers will be used directly behind the elements, so the $\tilde{x}_j(t)$ are the input signals to the preamplifiers. However, if a transformation **V** is inserted, the preamplifiers will be used after the transformation. In this case the preamplifier inputs are the signals $\tilde{y}_j(t)$. Suppose the preamplifiers are the major contributors of thermal noise in the system, and assume each preamplifier adds noise of power σ^2 to its output signal.

Does the theorem of section 5.2 hold in this situation? If so, prove it. If not, show why not.

6.5.   In section 6.3 we considered the effect of a pointing error in the steering vector of an Applebaum array. In this problem we consider what happens when the magnitude of a steering vector component is incorrectly set.

Consider an Applebaum array with two isotropic elements a half wavelength apart as in Figure 6.7. A desired signal is expected to arrive from angle θ_d. Hence, the designer chooses the steering vector **T*** equal to

$$\mathbf{T}^* = [\, e^{-j\phi_d}\ 1\,],$$

where

$$\phi_d = \pi \sin \theta_d.$$

[This relation corresponds to setting $\theta_{max} = \theta_d$ in Eq. (6.42).]

Now suppose that the desired signal does in fact arrive from angle θ_d, but that, unknown to the designer, element 2 has a voltage gain $\alpha \neq 1$. In other words, the received signal vector is actually

$$\mathbf{X}_d = A_d e^{j(\omega_d t + \psi_d)} \begin{bmatrix} 1 \\ \alpha e^{-j\phi_d} \end{bmatrix}.$$

Assume the noise power on each element is still σ^2.

For this situation, compute the output SINR achieved by the array as a function of α, over the range $0.5 \leqslant \alpha \leqslant 1.5$. For each value of α, also determine the optimal SINR that could be obtain from the array if the steering vector were correctly chosen, and calculate the dB loss in SINR that results because of the actual steering vector.

6.6.   One way of forming multiple beams from an array of elements, as discussed in section 6.2, is to combine the element signals with a Rotman Lens [9]. Fig. 6.44 shows a Rotman lens connected to an array. Each element in the array is connected to an input port of the lens, and the lens has several output ports, as shown. The lens is an electromagnetic structure that inserts different time delays between each element and each output port. The time delays are chosen so that, for each output port, a signal from a certain direction in space will undergo the same time delay in passing through every element of the array to that output port. The result is that each port has an antenna pattern with a beam maximum in a different direction in space. Such an antenna is often called a multiple-beam antenna, or MBA. In this problem we consider how such a lens affects the SINR obtained with an adaptive array.

As a simple model of a Rotman lens, consider the antenna system in Fig. 6.45. Suppose the antenna elements are isotropic and a half wavelength apart at the signal

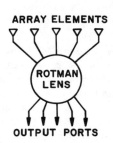

Figure 6.44   A Rotman lens array.

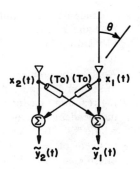

Figure 6.45   A simple model of a two-element Rotman lens array.

frequency. Assume that a desired signal arrives from $\theta_d = 0°$ with an SNR per element $\xi_d = 0$ dB, and that an interference signal arrives from θ_i with an INR of $\xi_i = 40$ dB per element. Assume that each $\tilde{x}_j(t)$ contains uncorrelated thermal noise of power σ^2, as usual. Let the desired and interference signals and the thermal noise all have relative bandwidth B. Finally, assume that the time delays T_0 in the Rotman lens are each $T_0 = \pi/\sqrt{2}$, where ω_0 is the carrier frequency of the signals.

Now do the following:

(a) Show that the antenna patterns seen at ports $\tilde{y}_1(t)$ and $\tilde{y}_2(t)$ are $\cos(\theta - \theta_0)$ patterns (i.e., "figure-8" patterns), one with a beam maximum at $\theta_0 = 45°$ and the other with a beam maximum at $\theta_0 = -45°$.

(b) Determine the condition under which this Rotman lens satisfies the theorem in section 5.2. (That is, under what condition will inserting the Rotman lens have no effect on array output SINR?)

(c) Write a computer program to evaluate the SINR achieved by the array both with and without the Rotman lens included. Compute the SINR obtained versus θ_i over the range $-90° \leqslant \theta_i \leqslant 90°$, both with and without the lens. Do these calculations for bandwidths $B = 0$ and $B = 0.05$. Plot the SINR versus θ_i for each of the four cases. Compare the curves you obtain, and explain your results in light of the theorem in section 5.2.

6.7.   Find three mutually orthogonal vectors c_1', c_2', and c_3' that span the same space as c_1, c_2, and c_3 in Eqs. (6.149) to (6.151). Use the approach suggested in Eqs. (6.152) to (6.154).

6.8.   Suppose we wish to use a power inversion array to protect a communication signal from two interference signals. For this purpose, it is necessary to use a three-element array.

Write a computer program to determine the SINR performance of a three-element power inversion array. Assume the elements are isotropic. Assume there is a desired signal at broadside ($\theta_d = 0°$) and two interference signals, one at θ_{i1} and the other at θ_{i2}. Assume all three signals are CW. Let the desired signal SNR per element be $\xi_d = 0$ dB, and let each interference signal INR per element be $\xi_{i1} = \xi_{i2} = 40$ dB. As usual, assume that independent thermal noise is present on each element signal. Let the array steering vector be $\mathbf{T}^* = [1 \quad 0 \quad 0]^T$.

Compute the output SINR from such an array as a function of θ_{i2} for $\theta_{i1} = 30°$, 60°, and 90°. Explain why your curves behave the way they do. Also, explain why the SINR drops when both interfering signals arrive from the same direction, even though this direction may be far from the desired signal direction.

6.9.   Analyze the problem of multiplier offset voltages in an analog LMS array, as described in section 4.3, under the assumption that the offset voltages are random. Assume that the real and imaginary parts δ_{I_j} and δ_{Q_j} of the offset voltage δ_j in Eq. (4.71) are all independent random variables with zero mean and variance σ_δ^2. Determine the relationship between the multiplier offset voltage problem and the steering vector problem of section 6.3 carefully, so that the curves in Figs. 6.13 to 6.24 may be interpreted for multiplier offsets. In particular, how are your σ_δ^2 and the σ_w^2 of section 6.3 related?

REFERENCES

1. S. P. Applebaum, "Adaptive Arrays," *IEEE Transactions on Antennas and Propagation*, AP–24, no. 5 (September 1976): 585.

2. L. J. Griffiths, "A Simple Adaptive Algorithm for Real-Time Processing in Antenna Arrays," *Proceedings of the IEEE*, 57, no. 10 (October 1969): 1696.

3. P. W. Howells, "Exploration in Fixed and Adaptive Resolution at GE and SURC," *IEEE Transactions on Antennas and Propagation*, AP–24, no. 5 (September 1976): 575.

4. O. L. Frost, III, "An Algorithm for Linearly Constrained Adaptive Array Processing," *Proceedings of the IEEE*, 60, no. 8 (August 1972): 926.

5. D. G. Brennan, "Linear Diversity Combining Techniques," *Proceedings of the IEEE*, 47, no. 6 (June 1959): 1075. See also problem 3.6.

6. T. Kailath, *Linear Systems*, Prentice-Hall, Englewood Cliffs, N.J., 1980.

7. J. P. Shelton and K. S. Kelleher, "Multiple Beams from Linear Arrays," *IRE Transactions on Antennas and Propagation*, AP–9, no. 1 (March 1961): 154.

8. H. J. Moody, "The Systematic Design of the Butler Matrix," *IEEE Transactions on Antennas and Propagation*, AP–12, no. 6 (November 1964): 786.

9. W. Rotman and R. F. Turner, "Wide-Angle Microwave Lens for Line Source Applications," *IEEE Transactions on Antennas and Propagation*, AP–11, no. 6 (November 1963): 623.

10. J. P. Shelton, "Focusing Characteristics of Symmetrically Configured Bootlace Lenses," *IEEE Transactions on Antennas and Propagation*, AP–26, no. 4 (July 1978): 513.

11. R. T. Compton, Jr., "Pointing Accuracy and Dynamic Range in a Steered Beam Adaptive Array," *IEEE Transactions on Aerospace and Electronic Systems*, AES–16, no. 3 (May 1980): 280. Copyright © 1980 IEEE.

12. R. T. Compton, Jr., "The Effect of Random Steering Vector Errors in the Applebaum Adaptive Array," *IEEE Transactions on Aerospace and Electronic Systems*, AES–18, no. 5 (September 1982): 392. Copyright © 1982 IEEE.

13. S. P. Applebaum and D. J. Chapman, "Adaptive Arrays with Main Beam Constraints," *IEEE Transactions on Antennas and Propagation*, AP–24, no. 5 (September 1976): 650.

14. K. Takao, M. Fujita, and T. Nishi, "An Adaptive Antenna Array under Directional

Constraint," *IEEE Transactions on Antennas and Propagation*, AP–24, no. 5 (September 1976): 662.

15. R. Weinstock, *Calculus of Variations*, Dover, New York, 1974.

16. P. M. Morse and H. Feshbach, *Methods of Theoretical Physics*, McGraw-Hill, New York, 1953; pp. 352 and 356ff.

17. C. L. Zahm, "Application of Adaptive Arrays to Suppress Strong Jammers in the Presence of Weak Signals," *IEEE Transactions on Aerospace and Electronic Systems*, AES–9, no. 2 (March 1973): 260.

18. R. T. Compton, Jr., "The Power Inversion Adaptive Array: Concept and Performance," *IEEE Transactions on Aerospace and Electronic Systems*, AES–15, no. 6 (November 1979): 803. Copyright © 1979 IEEE.

19. R. C. Dixon, *Spread Spectrum Systems*, Wiley, New York, 1976.

7

Reference Signal Generation in LMS Arrays

In this chapter we discuss methods for using adaptive arrays in communication systems. In particular, we are interested in situations where the desired signal arrival angle is not known in advance. In previous chapters, we have seen that an LMS array will automatically track the desired signal if a reference signal correlated with the desired signal is provided. Our purpose in this chapter is to show how such a reference signal may be obtained in practical communication systems.

For some communication systems, the desired signal direction is known in advance. A communication system linking two fixed locations, for example, would have a known desired-signal arrival angle. For such applications, an Applebaum or Frost array can be used, with the array beam pointed at the desired signal. Since using a steering vector is much simpler than generating a reference signal, this approach seems the most desirable when the desired signal direction is known.

However, for most communication systems, the desired signal may arrive from any direction, or at least from any direction within some sector or space. Not only will this direction be unknown to the designer, but often it will vary while the communication system operates. For this situation an LMS array is the best option, because it can automatically track the desired signal. However, to use an LMS array, one must somehow obtain a reference signal.

At first glance, the problem of obtaining a reference signal in a practical communication system does not look very promising. In a real communication system, one has no way to know the desired signal waveform in advance, of course. In fact, it is a fundamental axiom of information theory that a communication signal must be unknown in some respect if it is to convey informa-

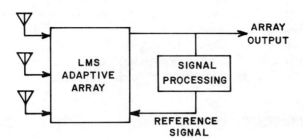

Figure 7.1   A reference signal generation loop.

tion [1]. In addition, it seems that if the desired signal were known, there would be no need for an antenna!

However, it turns out that the situation is not so hopeless. The fallacy in this reasoning is the assumption that the desired signal must be "known" to generate a reference signal. For one thing, the reference signal does not need to be an exact replica of the desired signal. It only needs to be correlated with the desired signal and uncorrelated with the interference. Such a reference signal is adequate because the steady-state array weights depend only on the correlation between the reference signal and the received signals. For another thing, the designer does not need to "know" the desired signal exactly to obtain a reference signal. For some types of modulation, a reference signal may be generated directly from the array output signal with a signal-processing loop as shown in Fig. 7.1. To design such a loop, one must know the nominal frequency of the desired signal and the basic form of its modulation, but not the precise waveform. Unknown signal parameters, such as the exact frequency or the specific modulation symbol stream, are simply passed through the loop from the array output to the reference signal.

It would be very desirable if such a reference loop could be found for any type of desired signal modulation. Unfortunately, there appears to be no general method for designing reference loops for arbitrary types of desired signal modulation. Rather, a number of specialized loops have been developed for specific signals. Each of these loops is essentially an ad hoc technique for a particular type of modulation.

In this chapter, we describe methods of generating reference signals for four types of modulation: spread spectrum with biphase modulation [2], coded amplitude modulation (AM), spread spectrum with quadriphase modulation [3], and binary frequency shift keying (FSK) [4, 5]. The first three techniques use a pseudonoise (PN) code as a tagging modulation on the desired signal. This PN code allows the reference loop to distinguish between the desired signal and interference. The fourth method is entirely different. It does not use a PN code but instead takes advantage of the internal structure of the signal modulation. We call this method a "data-derived" technique, because the reference signal is obtained directly from the desired-signal data modulation. These examples of reference signal generation will illustrate the possibilities and hopefully will suggest additional techniques to the reader.

The chapter is organized as follows: In section 7.1 we discuss certain general characteristics required of a reference signal. Then, in sections 7.2 through 7.5, we describe the four techniques we have mentioned.

7.1 REFERENCE SIGNAL REQUIREMENTS

For the array to work properly, the reference signal must be correlated with the desired signal and uncorrelated with the interference. Hence, the reference loop in Fig. 7.1 must do two things. First, it must allow the desired signal at the array output to pass through the loop without being drastically altered. (However, some distortion or delay of the desired signal modulation is acceptable, as long as the reference signal remains correlated with the desired signal.) Second, the reference loop must substantially alter the waveform of any interference, so that interference in the reference signal is decorrelated from that in the array. It is not necessary that the reference signal be free of interference; it only needs to be decorrelated.

One of the main reasons for using a reference loop as in Fig. 7.1 is that the desired signal component of the reference signal must have the same carrier frequency as the array output desired signal. In section 4.1 we examined what happens when the reference signal has a different frequency from the received signal. We showed that a frequency difference between the two signals causes the array weights to cycle at the difference frequency. The array shifts the frequency of the received signal until the array output frequency matches the reference signal frequency. Also, as the frequency difference increases, the array output amplitude drops. In general, the array retains the received signal in the array output when the frequency difference is smaller than the feedback loop bandwidth, and it rejects the signal as interference when the frequency difference is larger than the feedback loop bandwidth. Thus the reference signal frequency must not differ from the received signal frequency by more than the feedback loop bandwidth.

In practice, the easiest way to get the reference signal on the right frequency is to pass the array output signal through a processing loop as in Fig. 7.1. This technique automatically yields a reference signal on the proper frequency without the designer's having to know this frequency exactly. It is possible that for some applications, one could instead acquire the desired signal frequency with a phase-lock loop [6] or a Costas loop [7] at the array output. However, such loops complicate the signal acquisition problem for the array, particularly if interference is present along with the desired signal. The best approach appears to be to use a reference loop as in Fig. 7.1.

With such a reference loop, the next problem that occurs is that the desired signal component of the reference signal must have the same carrier phase as the array output desired signal. Otherwise, the array feedback senses a phase mismatch and changes the weights to correct for it. But with the reference signal derived from the array output, any change in the phase of the array output signal also changes the phase of the reference signal. Hence the array output phase cannot catch up with the reference signal phase but instead just chases it forever. The result is again that the array weights cycle sinusoidally with time and shift the array output frequency. This behavior has been described by DiCarlo and Compton [8, 9]. To avoid weight cycling, one must adjust the phase shift through the reference loop to the correct value at the desired-signal frequency. However, a problem exists because the reference loop phase shift always depends on frequency. When the desired-signal frequency varies over some band, as in a communication system with Doppler shifts, the reference loop phase shift must be aligned at the center of the band and the loop parameters chosen so the loop phase shift does not exceed, say, 45° at the band edges. (Phase shifts greater than 90° cause the LMS loops to become unstable.) With the loop phase shift equal to zero at the center of the band, one finds that the array pulls the array output desired signal frequency toward the center of the band [8, 9]. In other words, the Doppler frequency spread is compressed by the array.

In addition, to make the array acquire the desired signal and null the interference requires that the reference loop have the proper "gain" characteristics. In general, the array output signal $\tilde{s}(t)$ consists of a desired signal $\tilde{s}_d(t)$, interference $\tilde{s}_i(t)$, and thermal noise $\tilde{s}_n(t)$,

$$\tilde{s}(t) = \tilde{s}_d(t) + \tilde{s}_i(t) + \tilde{s}_n(t). \tag{7.1}$$

When $\tilde{s}(t)$ is passed through the loop in Fig. 7.1, the reference signal $\tilde{r}(t)$ will then be of the form,

$$\tilde{r}(t) = g_d \tilde{s}_d(t) + g_i \tilde{s}_i(t) + g_n \tilde{s}_n(t) + \tilde{r}_0(t), \tag{7.2}$$

where $g_d \tilde{s}_d(t)$, $g_i \tilde{s}_i(t)$, and $g_n \tilde{s}_n(t)$ are the components of $\tilde{r}(t)$ correlated with $\tilde{s}_d(t)$, $\tilde{s}_i(t)$, or $\tilde{s}_n(t)$, respectively, and where $\tilde{r}_0(t)$ is the part of $\tilde{r}(t)$ uncorrelated with any of $\tilde{s}_d(t)$, $\tilde{s}_i(t)$, or $\tilde{s}_n(t)$. Because the array output desired signal is $\tilde{s}_d(t)$ and the desired signal component of $\tilde{r}(t)$ is $g_d \tilde{s}_d(t)$, we call g_d the *gain* of the reference loop to the desired signal. Similarly, g_i and g_n are the gains of the reference loop to the interference and thermal noise. For a given set of signals, g_d may be found from

$$g_d = \frac{E\left[\tilde{s}_d^*(t)\tilde{r}(t)\right]}{E\left[|\tilde{s}_d(t)|\right]^2}, \tag{7.3}$$

and similarly for g_i and g_n. As the reader will see, reference loops are usually nonlinear. Hence superposition does not hold, and g_d, g_i, and g_n each depend on all the signals at the array output. However, for a given set of signals, values may be found for g_d, g_i, and g_n.

Now consider what the values of g_d, g_i, and g_n should be. Our goal is to make the array retain the desired signal in the array output while minimizing interference and thermal noise. Consider first the interference. As we commented above, it is not necessary to eliminate all interference from the reference signal. Rather, the requirement is that $|g_i| < 1$. As long as $|g_i| < 1$ for all combinations of $\tilde{s}_d(t)$, $\tilde{s}_i(t)$, and $\tilde{s}_n(t)$, the reference signal interference $g_i\tilde{s}_i(t)$ will always be smaller than the array output interference $\tilde{s}_i(t)$. The array feedback will then reduce $\tilde{s}_i(t)$ to attempt to make it match $g_i\tilde{s}_i(t)$. But as $\tilde{s}_i(t)$ becomes smaller, so will $g_i\tilde{s}_i(t)$, since $|g_i| < 1$. In steady state, the interference will be nulled as long as $|g_i|$ is always less than unity.

For the thermal noise, the requirement is the same. As long as $|g_n| < 1$ for all possible combinations of $\tilde{s}_d(t)$, $\tilde{s}_i(t)$, and $\tilde{s}_n(t)$, the thermal noise in the array output will be reduced to its minimum value.

The situation for the desired signal is slightly more complicated. To obtain proper operation from the array, the desired signal part of the reference signal, $g_d\tilde{s}_d(t)$, must have a fixed amplitude, independent of the amplitude of $\tilde{s}_d(t)$. There are several reasons for this requirement. First, the reference signal amplitude controls the steady-state weights, as discussed in Chapters 2 and 4. Because of limited dynamic range and other problems in practical weight control circuits, there is usually an optimum value for the reference signal voltage $g_d\tilde{s}_d(t)$. (For example, setting the reference signal too high will cause weight saturation, as described in section 4.4. Setting it too low exacerbates multiplier offset voltage problems, as discussed in section 4.3.) Second, one cannot allow the reference signal voltage $g_d\tilde{s}_d(t)$ to vary linearly with the array output voltage $\tilde{s}_d(t)$, because in that case the array behavior would depend critically on the value of g_d. If $|g_d| > 1$, the array weights would increase without limit, because $g_d\tilde{s}_d(t)$ would always be larger than $\tilde{s}_d(t)$. If $|g_d| < 1$, the array weights would all go to zero, because $g_d\tilde{s}_d(t)$ would always be smaller than $\tilde{s}_d(t)$. To obtain stable, nonzero weights, g_d would have to be exactly unity.[‡] Moreover, even if $g_d = 1$, the reference signal voltage in steady state would be arbitrary, since the array output could settle at any value. This situation is undesirable because the reference signal voltage must be carefully chosen for maximum dynamic range in the array.

Hence, it is preferable to operate the array with a fixed reference signal amplitude, independent of $\tilde{s}_d(t)$. In the techniques that we shall describe, the desired signals are angle modulated, and the reference loop includes a limiter to fix the reference signal voltage.

There is one further requirement when a limiter is used in the reference loop. One must take care that $|g_d| > 1$ when the voltages in the reference loop are below the clipping level of the limiter. As long as $|g_d| > 1$, the array feedback will make the amplitude of $\tilde{s}_d(t)$ increase with time until the limiter

---

[‡]With thermal noise present in the array, the reference loop gain required for stable operation is not actually unity. In section 2.2 we showed that, with thermal noise, the array output desired signal was less than the reference signal by a factor α, defined in Eq. (2.142) for a two-element array. The reference loop gain would have to be exactly $1/\alpha$ for stable operation.

takes over and sets the reference signal amplitude. The requirement that $|g_d| > 1$ for small signals is important for initial acquisition of the desired signal.

With this background, we now present specific techniques for generating reference signals in the following sections.

7.2 A BIPHASE-MODULATED SPREAD SPECTRUM SYSTEM‡

The first system we shall consider is a spread spectrum digital communication system using biphase modulation [2]. Assume that the desired signal has the form

$$\tilde{s}_d(t) = A_d e^{j[\omega_d t + \phi(t) + \psi_d]}, \tag{7.4}$$

where A_d is the amplitude, ω_d is the carrier frequency, ψ_d is the carrier phase, and $\phi(t)$ is a binary waveform whose value switches between 0 and π. The waveform $\phi(t)$ is the modulo 2π sum of two bit streams, $\phi_{\text{data}}(t)$ and $\phi_{\text{code}}(t)$,

$$\phi(t) = \phi_{\text{data}}(t) + \phi_{\text{code}}(t). \tag{7.5}$$

The waveform $\phi_{\text{data}}(t)$ is the data modulation, which is the useful information to be sent over the communication link; $\phi_{\text{code}}(t)$ is a pseudonoise (PN) code, that is, a maximal length linear shift register sequence [10, 11]. Such a code is generated with a feedback shift register as shown in Fig. 7.2. The signal in Eq. (7.4) is usually called a direct-sequence spread spectrum signal.

Let the frequency of $\phi_{\text{data}}(t)$ be f_d bits/second and that of $\phi_{\text{code}}(t)$ be f_c bits/second. The code rate is assumed to be higher than the data rate by the spreading ratio N,

$$N = \frac{f_c}{f_d}. \tag{7.6}$$

Figure 7.3 shows a typical $\phi_{\text{data}}(t)$ and $\phi_{\text{code}}(t)$ and the resulting $\phi(t)$ for a spreading ratio of 5. The details of $\phi_{\text{code}}(t)$ (the number of bits in the shift register, the feedback connections, and the clocking rate f_c) are assumed to be known at the receiving site, so that the same code can be generated for the adaptive array.

With this desired signal, a reference signal for the adaptive array can be generated with the signal-processing loop shown in Fig. 7.4. This loop first mixes the array output signal with a coded local oscillator (LO) signal $\tilde{r}_1(t)$, then filters and limits the mixer output, and finally mixes the result with $\tilde{r}_1(t)$ again. The signal $\tilde{r}_1(t)$ is biphase modulated by the same PN code as the desired

‡Portions of this section are reprinted from the author's paper [2] with permission, © 1978 IEEE.

signal,

$$\tilde{r}_1(t) = A_1 e^{j[\omega_1 t + \phi_{code}(t) + \psi_1]}, \tag{7.7}$$

where A_1, ω_1, and ψ_1 are the amplitude, frequency, and carrier phase angle of $\tilde{r}_1(t)$.

Consider what happens to the desired signal in passing through this loop. We assume that the PN code on $\tilde{r}_1(t)$ is synchronized with the code on the

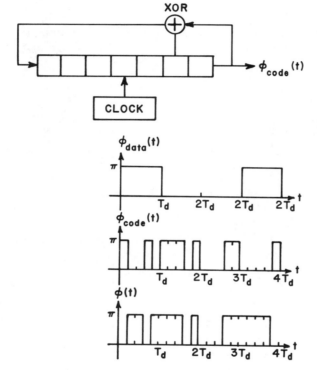

Figure 7.2 Feedback shift register.

Figure 7.3 Typical $\phi_{data}(t)$, $\phi_{code}(t)$, and $\phi(t)$ (reprinted from [2] with permission, © 1978 IEEE).

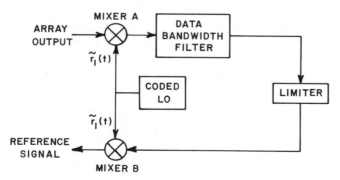

Figure 7.4 Reference signal generation loop (reprinted from [2] with permission, © 1978 IEEE).

desired signal in the array. (The method for synchronizing the local code with the received code will be discussed below.) Let Eq. (7.4) represent the desired signal at the input to Mixer A in Fig. 7.4. Then the difference product out of Mixer A is

$$\tilde{s}_d(t)\tilde{r}_1^*(t) = A_d A_1 e^{j[(\omega_d - \omega_1)t + \phi_{\text{data}}(t) + \psi_d - \psi_1]}. \tag{7.8}$$

Note that $\phi_{\text{code}}(t)$ has canceled off in this difference product. The sum product out of Mixer A is

$$\tilde{s}_d(t)\tilde{r}_1(t) = A_d A_1 \exp\left\{ j\left[(\omega_d + \omega_1)t + \phi_{\text{data}}(t) + 2\phi_{\text{code}}(t) + \psi_d + \psi_1\right]\right\}. \tag{7.9}$$

The term $2\phi_{\text{code}}(t)$ in this product is always 0 or 2π [$\phi_{\text{code}}(t)$ is always 0 or π], so that the sum product actually has no code modulation either. Thus both mixer products contain only the data modulation $\phi_{\text{data}}(t)$. Either product from Mixer A may be selected by the narrowband filter in Fig. 7.4.

Since the data modulation is slower than the code modulation by the ratio N, the desired signal bandwidth is reduced by the factor N at Mixer A. The data bandwidth filter in Fig. 7.4 has its center frequency at either the sum or difference frequency from Mixer A and has a bandwidth wide enough to pass the data modulation but not the code modulation. The desired signal passes through this filter, then through the limiter, and finally it is mixed again with $\tilde{r}_1(t)$. If the difference product is selected at Mixer A, then the sum product is used at Mixer B, or vice versa.

Assume initially that the filter makes no change to the desired signal waveform and that the limiter merely changes its amplitude. Also, assume that the difference product is selected at Mixer A. Then the limiter output is

$$\tilde{s}_l(t) = A_l \exp\left\{ j\left[(\omega_d - \omega_1)t + \phi_{\text{data}}(t) + \psi_d - \psi_1 + \psi_2\right]\right\}, \tag{7.10}$$

where A_l is the limiter output voltage and ψ_2 represents any phase shift in the reference loop up to the limiter. When $\tilde{s}_l(t)$ is mixed again with $\tilde{r}_1(t)$ in Mixer B and the sum product selected, the resulting reference signal is

$$\tilde{r}(t) = \tilde{s}_l(t)\tilde{r}_1(t) = A_l A_1 \exp\left\{ j\left[\omega_d t + \phi_{\text{data}}(t) + \phi_{\text{code}}(t) + \psi_d + \psi_0\right]\right\}, \tag{7.11}$$

where ψ_0 is the total phase shift in the loop, including ψ_2 in Eq. (7.10). To make the adaptive array work properly, ψ_0 must be adjusted to zero.[‡]

Thus the desired signal has the code removed at Mixer A and put back on at Mixer B. Note that the desired signal frequency ω_d automatically becomes the reference signal frequency. One does not have to estimate ω_d in order to generate the reference signal. As long as the filter bandwidth is wide enough to

---

[‡]If ψ_0 is not zero, the array weights oscillate sinusoidally with time and shift the output frequency ω_d of the desired signal. This problem is discussed by DiCarlo and Compton [8, 9].

accommodate any uncertainty in ω_d, the loop simply transfers the desired signal frequency through to the reference signal. In the same way, the reference loop automatically transfers the data modulation $\phi_{\text{data}}(t)$ and the carrier phase ψ_d to the reference signal. The data modulation is, of course, the information-bearing part of the desired signal, so there is no way to determine it in advance. However, by passing $\phi_{\text{data}}(t)$ through the reference loop in this way, we obtain a reference signal correlated with the desired signal without having to know $\phi_{\text{data}}(t)$.

As discussed in section 7.1, we must choose the desired signal gain of this loop correctly to get proper signal acquisition. Suppose $\tilde{s}_d(t)$ is the desired signal at the input to the reference loop and $g_d\tilde{s}_d(t)$ is the part of the reference signal correlated with $\tilde{s}_d(t)$, as given in Eqs. (7.1) and (7.2). Then when $\tilde{s}_d(t)$ is small enough that the desired signal in the reference loop is below the clipping level of the limiter, we must have $g_d > 1$. This condition will insure that $g_d\tilde{s}_d(t)$ is larger than $\tilde{s}_d(t)$ and will make $\tilde{s}_d(t)$ grow with time. When $\tilde{s}_d(t)$ becomes large enough, the limiter will take over and control the reference signal amplitude.

Now consider what happens to an interference signal in this loop. To be specific, suppose the interference is CW,

$$\tilde{s}_i(t) = A_i e^{j[\omega_d t + \psi_i]}. \tag{7.12}$$

At Mixer A, the PN code in $\tilde{r}_1(t)$ is imposed on the interference, so the interference spectrum is spread to the full code bandwidth. This bandwidth is too wide to pass through the narrowband filter. All but the center portion of the interference spectrum is suppressed by the filter. The interference remaining after the filter then passes through the limiter and finally is modulated by the PN code again at Mixer B. Thus the reference signal does contain some interference, but this interference has been spread to the full code bandwidth. As a result, the correlation between the interference in the reference signal and the original CW interference in the array is very small. In essence, most of the interference power in the reference signal ends up in the term $\tilde{r}_0(t)$ in Eq. (7.2). There is a small correlated component $g_i\tilde{s}_i(t)$ in $\tilde{r}(t)$, but because of the spectrum spreading it is possible to keep $|g_i| \ll 1$, so $\tilde{s}_i(t)$ decreases with time as the array weights adapt.

When both desired and interference signals are present in the array output, the reference signal waveform is strongly influenced by the limiter in the loop. The limiter output depends on which signal is stronger at the limiter input. The stronger signal tends to capture most of the limiter power [12, 13]. Even with the spread spectrum processing gain, an interference signal may be much stronger than the desired signal at the limiter input before it is nulled. When the dominant signal at the limiter input is interference, the limiter output and the reference signal consists mostly of interference components. But as long as $|g_i| < 1$, the array weights begin to null the interference. As the weights adapt, the interference power drops at the array output. Eventually the desired signal becomes stronger than the interference at the array output. When the array has reached steady state, the desired signal dominates both the reference signal and the array output. The essential requirement is that $|g_i| < 1$ under all signal conditions and that $|g_d| > 1$ when the desired signal is weak.

As discussed in section 7.1, the purpose of the limiter in this loop is to establish the reference signal voltage and make it independent of the array output voltage. The reference signal amplitude controls the steady-state RF voltages and weights in the array. These must be within certain ranges for proper operation of the multipliers and other circuits in the LMS feedback loops and for maximum dynamic range of the array. Also, a fixed reference signal voltage simplifies dynamic range problems in the delay lock loop used for code acquisition, as will be discussed below.

Besides generating the reference signal, the reference loop in Fig. 7.4 also yields the desired signal with the PN code removed at the filter output. The desired signal at this point is ready for data bit detection. Note that the interference suppression due to the spectrum spreading is in cascade with the interference nulling of the array. The signal-to-interference ratio is improved by both the array nulling and the spread spectrum processing gain.

Next we consider synchronization of the local PN code in the reference loop. The reference loop code must be synchronized with the received code for the reference loop to operate properly. If there is a large timing error between the two codes, the desired signal will not pass through the reference loop. The array feedback then treats the desired signal as interference and nulls it out. Experiments have shown that the array tracks the desired signal adequately for code timing errors up to about one-half bit [2]. For errors larger than one-half bit, the array nulls the desired signal.

To obtain a properly timed code for the reference loop, a delay-lock loop [14, 15] is used. The simplest form of such a loop is shown in Fig. 7.5. We shall

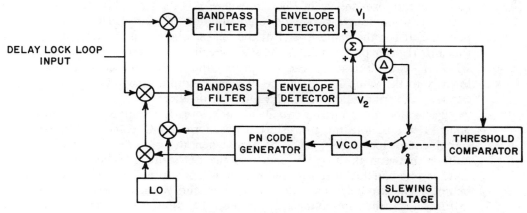

Figure 7.5 A delay-lock loop.

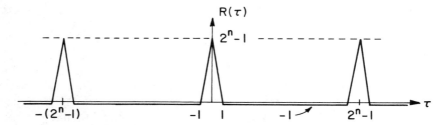

Figure 7.6 The autocorrelation function $R(\tau)$ of a PN code.

first describe the basic operation of this loop and then discuss the procedure for using it with the adaptive array.

As shown in Fig. 7.5, the input signal to a delay-lock loop is first split into two channels. The signal in each channel is mixed with an LO signal modulated by the same PN code as on the input signal. The PN codes on the two LO signals are timed one bit apart. In each channel, the sum or difference product from the mixer is selected by the filter. The filter outputs are envelope detected, and both the sum and the difference of the envelopes are derived. The sum voltage is used for timing acquisition, and the difference voltage is used for code tracking after acquisition, as described below.

Assume initially that the input signal to the delay-lock loop is modulated with code modulation, $\phi_{code}(t)$, but no data modulation. In each delay-lock loop channel, the input signal is mixed with the PN coded LO signal and then bandpass filtered and envelope detected. The result is a baseband voltage in each channel proportional to the cross-correlation between the PN code on the incoming signal and the one on the LO signal. This cross-correlation is just the autocorrelation function of the basic PN code, evaluated for the time shift between the two codes. In general, the autocorrelation function $R(\tau)$ of a PN code has the form shown in Fig. 7.6, where τ is the time shift variable [7]. The autocorrelation function is a periodic function of τ, because the PN code is periodic. It has the value $2^n - 1$ at the peaks, where n is the number of bits in the shift register that generates the PN code. The peaks occur at $\tau = k(2^n - 1)$, where k is an integer. Near the peaks, the autocorrelation function drops linearly to the value -1 at the point where τ differs from $k(2^n - 1)$ by unity. Between the triangular peaks, $R(\tau) = -1$ for all τ.

The PN codes on the two delay-lock loop LO signals are timed one bit apart. Let ε denote the time shift between these LO codes and the received signal code. Specifically, let ε be zero when the received PN code is timed halfway between the two PN codes on the LO signals. (When $\varepsilon = 0$, one LO code is one-half bit ahead of the incoming code and the other is one-half bit behind.) The two delay-lock loop voltages v_1 and v_2 then depend on ε as shown in Fig. 7.7(a); the sum voltage $v_1 + v_2$ and the difference voltage $v_1 - v_2$ are as shown in Fig. 7.7(b) and 7.7(c).

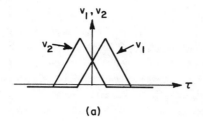

(a)

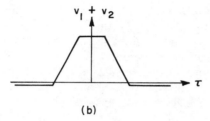

(b)

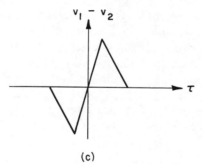

(c)

Figure 7.7 Delay-lock loop voltages: (a) voltages v_1 and v_2; (b) the sum voltages $v_1 + v_2$; (c) the difference voltage $v_1 - v_2$.

The timing of the received code is acquired with this loop by running the PN code in the delay-lock loop faster or slower than the received code. The voltage-controlled oscillator (VCO), which serves as the clock for the delay-lock loop PN code, is set to run at a faster or slower rate than the received code. This process is known as *slewing* the code. The difference in code frequencies makes the local code timing change continuously with respect to the received code. At some point the local code and the received code become aligned. When this happens, the sum voltage will rise as indicated in Fig. 7.7(b). By comparing the sum voltage to a threshold, a logic pulse can be obtained when the two codes are aligned. This logic pulse may be used to switch the loop to a tracking mode in which the difference voltage $v_1 - v_2$ is used as the VCO input. The delay-lock loop then operates as a feedback loop that tracks the code timing, with the difference voltage $v_1 - v_2$ used as the error voltage. For ε near zero, $v_1 - v_2$ depends linearly on ε, as shown in Fig. 7.7(c).

The delay-lock loop may be integrated with the reference generation loop of Fig. 7.4 as follows: The array output signal is used as the input to the delay-lock loop as well as the reference loop. The PN code generator in the delay-lock loop provides the PN code for the reference loop as well as the delay-lock loop. The reference loop code is timed halfway between the two delay-lock loop codes. When the delay-lock loop is tracking the incoming code, the code on one channel of the delay-lock loop runs one-half bit ahead of the received code and the other runs one-half bit behind. The reference loop code is then synchronized with the received signal code.

We assumed above that the input signal to the delay-lock loop contained no data modulation. However, the desired signal received by the array will have data modulation as well as code modulation. The data modulation can be handled in the delay-lock loop in two ways. If the spreading ratio N in Eq. (7.6) is high, one can use the same delay-lock loop as in Fig. 7.5 by choosing the filter bandwidths in the delay-lock loop wide enough to pass the data modulation. But if the spreading ratio is small, there may be insufficient processing gain due to spectrum despreading to establish an adequate SNR in the delay-lock loop channels. In this case one can filter each mixer output to data bandwidth and then square the signal. Squaring converts a signal with biphase modulation to a CW signal at the second harmonic. By squaring the signal, one can filter the signal to a much narrower bandwidth at the second harmonic than is possible with data modulation on the signal. Squaring allows one to improve the SNR in the delay-lock loop channels. This procedure was used in the system described in [2]. A delay-lock loop with squaring is shown in Fig. 7.8. The loop also includes a square-root operation after the envelope detectors to restore the linear relation between the difference voltage $v_1 - v_2$ and timing error ε.

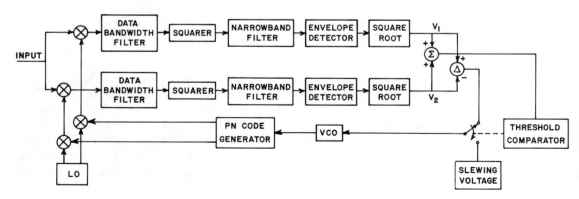

Figure 7.8 A delay-lock loop with squaring.

With the delay-lock loop added to the adaptive array, the desired signal code timing is acquired by slewing the delay-lock loop 'code generator, as discussed previously. During this process, the reference loop code is slaved to the delay-lock loop codes and hence is also slewed. Before the reference loop code is properly timed, the correlation is small between the received desired signal and the reference signal. During this time, the array nulls the desired signal. When the local code begins to align with the received code, the reference signal starts to correlate with the desired signal. As the correlation increases, the array weights change and the desired signal comes out of the null. As long as the array is fast enough, the desired signal appears at the array output just as the local code timing approaches its correct value. Hence the desired signal is present at the delay-lock loop input when it needs to be, but not before. The sum channel output rises and crosses a threshold, which terminates the slewing process and allows the loop to begin tracking.

Slewing the delay-lock loop code to acquire code timing is a well-known method of acquisition. However, because the delay-lock loop interacts with the adaptive array, there are several novel features in this adaptive array application.

First, the array provides full interference protection during the lockup phase. Interference nulling does not depend on reference loop code timing, so the array nulls interference before the local code has been aligned. Because the array removes interference during slewing, the delay-lock loop does not have to contend with interference at all. Thus the filter bandwidth in the loop, the slewing speed, and the time required for lockup do not change when interference is present.

Second, the desired signal that appears at the array output when the code timing is correct has a fixed amplitude, not dependent on received signal strength. The array forces the output desired signal amplitude to match the reference signal amplitude, which is controlled by the limiter in the reference loop. Because the desired signal amplitude is fixed, the delay-lock loop does not have to operate over a wide dynamic range of signals. This feature is helpful because it means that the threshold setting used for acquisition is independent of received signal power. Also, circuit design problems are simplified when it is not necessary to operate over a wide dynamic range. (For example, the squaring and square root operations in Fig. 7.8 are much easier to do with a fixed signal voltage.)

Third, it is interesting to see how the array pulls the desired signal out of the noise when the timing approaches the correct value. Since the desired signal starts out in a null, one may wonder how the desired signal will be present at the array output in time to generate a reference signal when the timing approaches the correct value. The answer involves two factors.

The first concerns the design of the reference loop in Fig. 7.4. When the array output signal is small, the voltage in the reference loop is too small for the limiter to clip the signal. Below the clipping level, the loop is linear; it produces a reference signal amplitude linearly proportional to the array output signal amplitude. In this low-signal region, the loop gain for the desired signal, g_d, *must* be greater than unity, so that the reference signal will be larger than the array output signal. As long as $g_d > 1$, the array weight setting that nulls the desired signal is a point of unstable equilibrium. If any weight changes away from this value slightly, so a small desired signal appears at the array output, then a correlated reference signal of larger amplitude appears. This behavior reinforces the movement of the weight away from the null. In this way, the array output signal will grow until it is large enough that the limiter clips.

The second factor is that the array weights in the adaptive array are random processes. Each weight is derived from the product of two noisy signals, the element signal and the error signal. As a result, there is always some weight jitter, as discussed in section 4.5, and the movement of each weight away from the desired signal null has no difficulty starting. (Of course, even when the desired signal is nulled at the array output, it is still present in the correlation loops for each element. If the reference signal becomes correlated with the desired signal, it has an immediate effect on the weights even if the array output desired signal is zero.) In practice, one finds no tendency for the array to keep the desired signal nulled once the code timing is nearly correct. The weight jitter always starts the weights away from this point.

Finally, we note that for this lockup procedure to work, the array speed of response must be fast enough for the desired signal to appear at the array output before the code timing has passed by. In other words, the array time constants must be compatible with the slewing speed. Also, with this slewing technique, code acquisition time is proportional to the code length. Hence this lockup procedure is most useful for short PN codes.

7.3 AN AMPLITUDE-MODULATED SIGNAL WITH PN CODING

Biphase modulation with a PN code can also be used for reference signal generation with other types of signals. For example, consider a simple amplitude-modulated (AM) signal of the form,

$$\tilde{d}(t) = A_d\big[1 + mf_d(t)\big]e^{j[\omega_d t + \psi_d]}, \tag{7.13}$$

where A_d is the amplitude, $f_d(t)$ is the modulating waveform (such as a voice signal), m is a constant controlling the percentage modulation, and ω_d and ψ_d are the carrier frequency and phase. Suppose that a PN coded biphase modulation is added to this signal, to produce a new signal of the form,

$$\tilde{d}(t) = A_d\big[1 + mf_d(t)\big]e^{j[\omega_d t + \phi_{\text{code}}(t) + \psi_d]}. \tag{7.14}$$

Here $\phi_{\text{code}}(t)$ is a binary phase modulation based on a PN code, as in Eq. (7.5). A typical desired signal waveform ($\text{Re}[\tilde{d}(t)]$) is shown in Fig. 7.9.

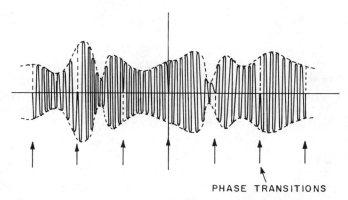

PHASE TRANSITIONS

Figure 7.9 An AM signal with PN coded phase modulation.

To receive this signal with an adaptive array, a reference signal containing only the biphase PN code modulation, but not the amplitude modulation, can be used. The reference signal

$$\tilde{r}(t) = A_r e^{j[\omega_d t + \phi_{code}(t) + \psi_d]} \tag{7.15}$$

is suitable, where A_r is the amplitude. The envelope modulation $[1 + m f_d(t)]$ is not required on $\tilde{r}(t)$ to have good correlation between $\tilde{r}(t)$ and $\tilde{d}(t)$.

Such a reference signal may be obtained with the signal-processing loop in Fig. 7.10. The array output signal is first limited and bandpass filtered, to remove the envelope modulation. Then the signal is mixed with a coded LO signal, filtered to narrow bandwidth, and remixed with the same coded LO signal to produce the reference signal. The PN code used in this loop is obtained from a delay lock loop the same way as in the system in section 7.2. The array output, after limiting and filtering, is the input to the delay lock loop. Code timing is acquired by slewing the code in the delay lock loop, as described in section 7.2. The reference loop code is slewed along with the delay-lock loop code. When the delay-lock loop acquires the code timing, the reference loop code is automatically timed properly.

A system based on this technique was built and tested by J. P. Jones at Ohio State University in 1978. This system demonstrated the feasibility of the

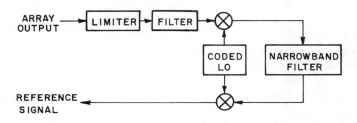

Figure 7.10 Reference signal generation for coded AM.

concept experimentally. Unfortunately, this work was not published in the literature.

The signal in Eq. (7.13) has both envelope modulation and phase modulation, but the two are independent of one another. However, when this signal is passed through a bandpass filter, the biphase modulation produces envelope modulation. We discuss the reason for this PM-AM conversion below. If $f_d(t)$ is a voice signal, one finds that the frequency of the biphase PN code modulation must be kept low compared to the frequencies in $f_d(t)$ to keep the audio distortion to an acceptable level. For example, when $f_d(t)$ contains frequencies between about 300 Hz and 3 kHz, one finds that the frequency of $\phi_{code}(t)$ must be below about 100 bits/second for good audio quality.

To see the reason for this PM-AM conversion, consider a signal biphase modulated with a square wave. Suppose $\phi(t)$ is a square wave of frequency ω_0 whose value switches between 0 and π. Also, let $p(t)$ be a square wave with values ± 1, related to $\phi(t)$ by

$$p(t) = 1 - \frac{2}{\pi}\phi(t). \tag{7.16}$$

Then consider the signal

$$\tilde{s}(t) = A_d e^{j[\omega_d t + \phi(t) + \psi_d]}. \tag{7.17}$$

This signal may also be written

$$\tilde{s}(t) = A_d p(t) e^{j[\omega_d t + \psi_d]}. \tag{7.18}$$

The square wave may be expanded in a Fourier series,

$$p(t) = \sum_{n=-\infty}^{\infty} a_n e^{jn\omega_0 t}, \tag{7.19}$$

where the Fourier coefficient a_n is

$$a_n = \frac{2}{n\pi} \sin \frac{n\pi}{2}. \tag{7.20}$$

Hence the waveform in Eq. (7.17) has the spectrum in Fig. 7.11(a). Strictly speaking, this signal has infinite bandwidth. If this signal is passed through a filter that limits the bandwidth, the filter output will contain only a finite number of spectral lines. For example, suppose the filter passes only the first three spectral lines on either side of the carrier frequency in Fig. 7.11(a). The resulting output spectrum is shown in Fig. 7.11(b), and the corresponding time-domain signal is shown in Fig. 7.11(c). It is seen how limiting the bandwidth produces envelope modulation on the signal. In essence, because of the finite filter bandwidth, the filter output signal cannot reverse phase instantaneously as in Eqs. (7.13). During a phase reversal, the filter output amplitude drops to zero. The behavior when the phase modulation on $\tilde{d}(t)$ is $\phi_{code}(t)$ instead of a square wave is similar. The only difference is that $\phi_{code}(t)$ does not

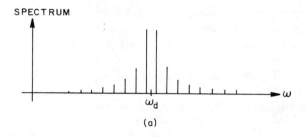

(a)

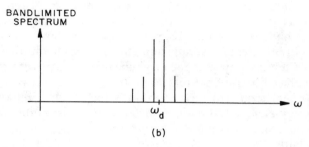

(b)

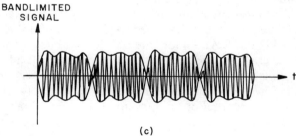

(c)

Figure 7.11 PM-AM conversion due to finite bandwidth: (a) the original spectrum; (b) the filter spectrum; (c) the time wave form.

reverse phase on every bit. Whenever it does, however, the filtered signal has AM. With voice signals, it is found that the PM-AM conversion is not objectionable when the PN code frequency is low. If the problem is important enough, PM-AM conversion may also be reduced by using quadriphase modulation instead of biphase. With quadriphase modulation, PM-AM conversion is substantially less if the phase jumps are limited to 90°.

7.4 A QUADRIPHASE-MODULATED SPREAD SPECTRUM SYSTEM

In this section we describe another direct sequence spread spectrum technique similar to that of section 7.2. This system uses quadriphase modulation, however, instead of biphase. It was designed to overcome certain limitations of the biphase system of section 7.2.

The biphase spread spectrum technique in section 7.2 has three important shortcomings. First, the system is vulnerable to repeat jamming with remodulation. Second, it is necessary to use a short PN code to obtain reasonable acquisition times. (Short codes give poor system security.) Third, the system is vulnerable to high-power CW jamming. Let us first discuss these problems before describing the quadriphase system.

The biphase-modulated system of section 7.2 is vulnerable to repeat jamming with remodulation. A repeat jammer is one that receives the desired signal and retransmits it toward the receiver.‡ This type of interference creates multipath and causes signal fading and other problems at the receiver. A repeat jammer with remodulation is one that adds extra modulation to the signal before retransmitting it. For biphase-modulated signals, remodulation by phase reversal keying with a random bit stream is simple and effective. Such additional modulation yields a signal of the same type as the original signal except with the original data modulation replaced by random bits. With the system described in section 7.2, the reference signal loop will lock onto and track such a remodulated signal just like the original signal. But since such a jammer is modulated with random bits, the communication system will be defeated by such jamming.

The second problem with the biphase system of section 7.2 is that only short PN codes can be used, because the acquisition time increases with code length. For example, the experimental system described in [2] used a 10-bit shift register to generate a 1,023-bit PN code. At a code rate of 2.5 megabits/second, signal acquisition required an average of one second. Each additional bit added to the shift register would double the average acquisition time. Thus very few additional bits can be added before the lockup time becomes unacceptably long. Moreover, short codes are not very secure. For military applications, a short PN code offers little security, because the structure of such codes is easily deduced by a listener. Thus the system described in section 7.2 does not offer much security against a smart jammer.

The third problem that we have mentioned, vulnerability to CW jamming, is a problem inherent in biphase modulation. If a strong CW signal coherent with the desired signal is received, and if any limiting occurs in the signal path, the modulation on the received signal is drastically altered. Figure 7.12 illustrates this problem. It shows the biphase desired signal as one of two phasors in the complex plane, depending on whether a 0 or a 1 is being sent. A CW interfering signal coherent with the desired signal is also shown. As may be seen, the sum of the two signals is a signal with only amplitude modulation. It has no phase modulation. Now suppose that the sum of the two signals is limited. Let the amplitude of the sum signal be limited to the value shown by the circle in Fig. 7.12. Then the limited signal will contain no modulation at all! Since

---

‡There are formidable difficulties in building such a repeat jammer, because of the difficulty of receiving and transmitting on the same frequency simultaneously. Nevertheless, repeat jamming is a commonly discussed form of jamming in communication system studies.

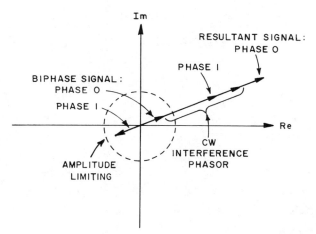

Figure 7.12   A biphase-modulated signal plus CW interference.

amplitude limiting eventually occurs to some extent in any receiver, high-power CW jamming can usually disrupt communications with biphase modulation.

To get a CW signal coherent with the desired signal, all a jammer need do is sweep the jammer frequency through the desired signal frequency band. At some time during the sweeping process the jammer phase will align with the desired signal phase as in Fig. 7.12. When the phases become aligned, the modulation is removed from the desired signal, and the timing or tracking loops in the receiver will drop out of lock. It is not necessary for the jammer to maintain coherence to disrupt the communication link.

These three difficulties with the biphase system of section 7.2 may be overcome by using quadriphase modulation and a more sophisticated reference signal generation technique. A suitable approach was developed by Winters [3] at Ohio State University. We describe his system below.

A quadriphase communication signal is equal to the sum of two biphase signals in quadrature. In Winters' technique [3], one of the biphase signals is modulated with the sum of a short PN code and the data modulation, just as in section 7.2. The other biphase signal is modulated with a very long PN code (or a nonlinear code) but no data modulation. Differential encoding is used for both.

Specifically, let a_m be the mth symbol of the short code and b_m the mth symbol of the long code. The symbols a_m and b_m have values 0 or 1 on each bit interval. Let the frequency of both codes be $f_c = T_c^{-1}$, where T_c is the code bit duration. Also, let d_k be the kth data bit symbol, also 0 or 1, of duration T_d and frequency $f_d = T_d^{-1}$. The code rate is higher than the data rate by the spreading ratio N,

$$N = \frac{f_c}{f_d}. \tag{7.21}$$

In Winters' system [3], the quadriphase signal is defined as follows:

$$\tilde{d}(t) = \tilde{d}_s(t) + \tilde{d}_l(t), \tag{7.22}$$

where

$$\tilde{d}_s(t) = \frac{A_d}{2} e^{j[\omega_d t + \zeta(t) + \psi_d - \pi/2]}, \tag{7.23}$$

$$\tilde{d}_l(t) = \frac{A_d}{2} e^{j[\omega_d t + \phi(t) + \psi_d]}, \tag{7.24}$$

$$\zeta(t) = \theta(t) + \gamma(t), \tag{7.25}$$

$$\phi(t) = \phi_m = \phi_{m-1} + \pi b_m, \qquad (m-1)T_c < t < mT_c, \tag{7.26}$$

$$\theta(t) = \theta_m = \theta_{m-1} + \pi a_m, \qquad (m-1)T_c < t < mT_c, \tag{7.27}$$

and

$$\gamma(t) = \gamma_k = \gamma_{k-1} + \pi d_k, \qquad (k-1)T_d < t < kT_d. \tag{7.28}$$

Thus $\tilde{d}_s(t)$ is modulated with the short code plus the data modulation, and $\tilde{d}_l(t)$ is modulated with the long code. A_d is the amplitude, ω_d is the carrier frequency, and ϕ_0, θ_0, and γ_0 are zero. Bit transitions for both codes and the data occur at the same times. The signal $\tilde{d}(t)$ is a quadriphase, differential phase shift keyed (DPSK) signal.

With this desired signal, a reference signal can be obtained for the adaptive array with a processing loop as shown in Fig. 7.13. This loop is similar to the one described in section 7.2, except that the LO code is changed during the acquisition process. (The short code is used initially and the long code is used after acquisition, as we shall explain.) The array output is first mixed with the coded LO signal. The mixer output is passed through a narrowband filter, hard-limited, and then remodulated with the coded LO signal at the second mixer. When the short code is used on the LO signal, the reference signal is correlated with $\tilde{d}_s(t)$, the part of the desired signal containing the short code. In this case $\tilde{d}_l(t)$ adds to the self-noise [14, 16] in the reference signal but does not

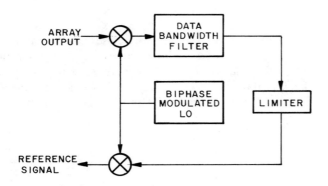

Figure 7.13 Reference signal generation for quadriphase system.

destroy the correlation between the reference signal and $\tilde{d}_s(t)$. Similarly, when the long code is used on the LO signal, the reference signal correlates with $\tilde{d}_l(t)$, and $\tilde{d}_s(t)$ contributes to the self-noise.

Code timing is acquired with this signal in a three-step process. The first step is similar to that described in section 7.2 for the biphase system. Initially, the short code is used to modulate the LO in the reference loop. The timing of this code is controlled by a delay-lock loop, which slews the code until correlation is obtained and the loop has locked on $\tilde{d}_s(t)$. The behavior of the array and the delay-lock loop during this initial phase is similar to that of the biphase system, except that now the signal being acquired is a quadriphase signal.

After the short code timing has been acquired, the second step is to acquire the long code timing. During this step, the short code is used to generate a reference signal for the array. Note that once the short code has been acquired, the interference is nulled at the array output, so the array output consists mostly of desired signal. Moreover, since bit transitions on the two codes occur simultaneously, the clock tracking the short code is synchronized with the bit intervals in the long code. Hence, the long code bits can be detected. During the second step of the acquisition process, the long code timing is derived by a method known as RASE (Rapid Acquisition by Sequential Estimation) due to Ward [17]. In this method, the current bits in the long code shift register are estimated by detecting the long code bits on the received signal and loading them into the shift register. When the shift register has been fully loaded, it is connected in its feedback mode and used to generate a PN code. If the bits loaded into the shift register are correct (if there were no bit detection errors), the code generated by the feedback shift register will match the code on $\tilde{d}_l(t)$. If one or more bits in the shift register are in error, the codes will not match. To determine whether the codes match, the feedback shift register output is correlated against the received signal for a short time. If the correlation is high, then the correct code timing has been obtained. If the correlation is low, a

TABLE 1   EXPERIMENTAL FOUR-PHASE SYSTEM PARAMETERS

LMS adaptive array	4 antenna elements
Code modulation frequency	175.2 kbits/s
Spreading ratio	16
Data rate	10.95 kbits/s
Minimum received E_Δ/N_0	0 dB
Average acquisition time	0.23 s
Maximum allowed acquisition time	0.55 s
Short code length	255 symbols
Long code length	1.72×10^{10} symbols (34 bit shift register)

Source: Reprinted from [3] with permission, © 1982 IEEE.

bit error was made in detecting the long code bits. In this case the entire process is repeated. Another sequence of long code bits is detected, the shift register is reloaded, and the measurement of correlation is performed again. Typically, several attempts are needed before the correct shift register loading is obtained. However, the total acquisition time is very much less with this technique than with slewing [17].

Once the long code timing is acquired, the final step is to change the LO code in the reference loop to the long code. After this change, the reference signal correlates with $\tilde{d}_l(t)$, the part of $\tilde{d}(t)$ derived from the long code.

To protect this system against a repeat jammer with remodulation, a special technique is incorporated in the acquisition process. Note that because the long code is modulated on $\tilde{d}_l(t)$ with no data, jammer remodulation will alter the bit stream of the long code. Hence the long code acquisition circuitry will not lock if the signal has been remodulated with a random bit stream. However, the jammer signal may be inadvertently acquired during the first step of the acquisition process. Therefore, the following technique is used: If the long code is not acquired within a given time after the short code delay-lock loop has locked, the clock timing for the delay-lock loop is advanced one bit. This step unlocks the delay-lock loop and causes the short code acquisition process to begin again, starting from where it left off. If the delay-lock loop locks initially on a repeat jammer with remodulation, it will be bumped off and will lock the

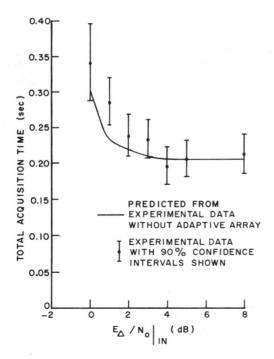

Figure 7.14 Total acquisition time versus received energy-to-noise density ratio (reprinted from [3] with permission, © 1982 IEEE).

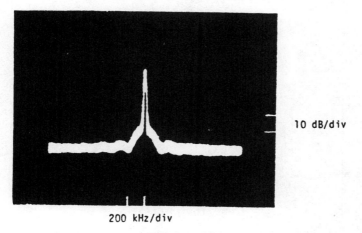

10 dB/div

200 kHz/div

Figure 7.15   Received power density spectrum at array input: $E_\Delta/N_0 = 8$ dB, $J/S = 20$ dB (reprinted from [3] with permission, © 1982 IEEE).

next time on the desired signal. Thus a jammer with remodulation can interrupt the acquisition process, but only temporarily. It cannot prevent acquisition of the direct signal. It is to take advantage of this feature that the long code is used without data modulation in this system.

Winters designed and built an experimental system to test this concept [3]. Table 1 (from [3]) lists some of the important parameters used in this system. "Maximum allowed acquisition time" in this table refers to the time allowed for

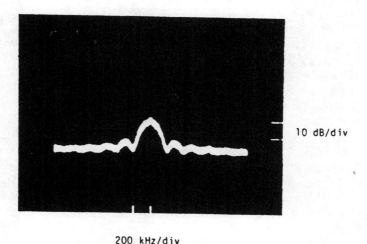

10 dB/div

200 kHz/div

Figure 7.16   Array output power density spectrum for input in Fig. 7.15 (reprinted from [3] with permission, © 1982 IEEE).

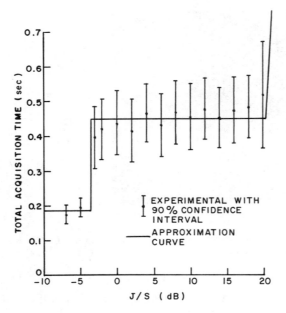

Figure 7.17 Total acquisition time versus jammer-to-signal ratio for a repeat jammer with remodulation (reprinted from [3] with permission, © 1982 IEEE).

acquisition of the long code. If the long code is not acquired after this length of time, the short code generator is bumped ahead and the entire lockup procedure restarted. This is the feature described above for overcoming the repeat jammer with remodulation.

For this system, Fig. 7.14 shows the average total acquisition time versus E_Δ/N_0, where E_Δ is the received energy per bit and N_0 is the noise power density, each measured per array element. It may be seen that the signal is acquired in less than $\frac{1}{3}$ second even when $E_\Delta/N_0 = 0$ dB. Since a four-element array has 6 dB gain in the absence of interference, $E_\Delta/N_0 = 0$ dB in Fig. 7.14 corresponds to $E_\Delta/N_0 = +6$ dB at the array output.

Figures 7.15 and 7.16 show typical power spectral densities at the array input (per element) and output, that is, before and after adaptation. These figures show typical CW jammer suppression. At the array input, the jammer-to-signal ratio (J/S) is 20 dB, but at the array output very little jammer power is discernible.

Figure 7.17 shows measured acquisition times when a repeat jammer with remodulation is present. When J/S increases above -1 dB, the jammer is often acquired temporarily by the short code delay-lock loop. This situation increases the average acquisition time but does not prevent the array from ultimately acquiring the desired signal. In general, a jammer with remodulation is no more effective in preventing lockup than a CW jammer.

This completes our discussion of the quadriphase system. Further details on this system may be found in Winters [3].

7.5 A DATA-DERIVED REFERENCE GENERATION TECHNIQUE

All of the reference signal techniques discussed so far use pseudonoise codes. These PN codes give the desired signal a structure that can be exploited by the signal-processing circuitry. In this section we describe an entirely different technique, one that does not use a PN code. In this method we choose the desired-signal modulation so that the reference signal may be obtained from the data modulation itself. For this reason, we refer to this approach as a data-derived reference signal technique. The method was first studied by Hudson [4] and was subsequently tested experimentally by Ganz [5]. The method could be used with different types of digital modulation, but here we describe its use with binary FSK (frequency shift keyed) signals.

Consider a binary FSK desired signal of the form

$$\tilde{s}(t) = A_d e^{j[\omega_n t + \psi_d]} \quad \text{for} \quad (n-1)T_d \leqslant t < T_d, \tag{7.29}$$

where A_d is the amplitude, ψ_d is the carrier phase angle, T_d is the symbol duration, and n is an integer denoting the symbol interval. The frequency of $\tilde{s}(t)$ for symbol interval n, ω_n, is either ω_0 or ω_1 on each symbol interval,

$$\omega_n = \begin{cases} \omega_0, & \text{binary } 0, \\ \omega_1, & \text{binary } 1. \end{cases} \tag{7.30}$$

The frequency ω_n conveys the data modulation.

In this technique, we assume that the symbol stream from which $\tilde{s}(t)$ is derived is a first-order Markov source. (A kth-order Markov source is one in which each symbol depends statistically on preceding k symbols [1].) Thus we assume that the probability of obtaining a 0 or a 1 on symbol $n+1$ depends on which symbol occurred on the nth symbol. Such a source may be represented by a transition diagram as in Fig. 7.18, which shows the probability of each type of transition from one symbol to the next. For example, if the nth symbol is a 0, symbol $n+1$ will be a 1 with probability p and a 0 with probability $1-p$. We

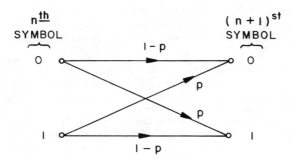

Figure 7.18 Markov source transition diagram.

assume the symbol stream is stationary and symmetric.[‡] As will be seen, this Markov property is useful because it allows us to predict symbols.

In generating a reference signal, we have the following problem: To obtain a reference signal correlated with $\tilde{s}(t)$ in real time, we must know the data symbols on $\tilde{s}(t)$ at the *beginning* of each symbol interval. However, when $\tilde{s}(t)$ is demodulated in the receiver, each data symbol becomes known only at the end of that symbol interval. (The detector integrates over the symbol interval and makes a decision at the *end* of the interval [18].) Thus the detected symbol stream is available too late for use in the reference signal. But if the symbol stream is Markov, and if $p \neq \frac{1}{2}$, then we can *predict* each symbol in the stream *from the preceding symbol*. For example, if $p = 0.9$ in Fig. 7.18, each 0 will be followed by a 1 with probability 0.9. Therefore, when a 0 is detected for one symbol, we can predict that the next symbol will be a 1 and get the correct result with probability 0.9. This predicted symbol stream is available early enough to generate a reference signal. The closer p is to zero or unity, the greater the accuracy with which we can predict the symbols and the greater the correlation between the reference signal and the desired signal.

Of course, there is a penalty for setting $p \neq \frac{1}{2}$ in a Markov symbol stream. Doing so will reduce the entropy of the symbol stream to less than its maximum value. (The entropy is the average amount of information carried per symbol by the symbol stream [1].) The entropy of a binary, first-order Markov source H in bits/symbol, is [1],

$$H = -p \log_2 p - (1 - p) \log_2 (1 - p). \tag{7.31}$$

The entropy H has a maximum value of 1 bit/symbol for $p = \frac{1}{2}$ and drops to zero as p approaches zero or unity. Thus, with $p \neq \frac{1}{2}$, we transmit less than the maximum amount of information per symbol. If information must be transmitted at a certain rate, a symbol stream with $H < 1$ bit/symbol will require a higher symbol rate and hence a wider bandwidth than one with $H = 1$. Thus, with this technique, we compromise on information rate, or bandwidth, in order to generate a reference signal for the array.

If the symbol stream we wish to transmit over the communication link does not have the desired Markov property to begin with, it may be mapped into one that does. Although we shall not discuss the general problem of such mappings here, we present a simple example to show that it is possible. Suppose the original message stream has no statistical dependence between symbols. (Or, equivalently, suppose it is a Markov source with $p = \frac{1}{2}$.) A new symbol stream

---

[‡]If $P_n(0)$ and $P_n(1)$ are the probabilities of 0 and 1 on the nth symbol, respectively, a stationary sequence is one for which $P_n(0)$ and $P_n(1)$ do not depend on n. A symmetric sequence is one for which the transition probability from 0 to 1 is the same as that from 1 to 0. Figure 7.18 depicts a symmetric Markov source with these probabilities equal to p. For a symmetric Markov source, it is easily shown that for any value of p in the range $0 < p < 1$, the probabilities $P_n(0)$ and $P_n(1)$ converge to the steady-state values $P_n(0) = P_n(1) = \frac{1}{2}$ as n increases, regardless of the initial probabilities $P_0(0)$ and $P_0(1)$. Thus a symmetric Markov source becomes stationary in the steady state.

4 BIT WORDS	NUMBER OF TRANSITIONS
0000	0
0001	1
0010	2 ✓
0011	1
0100	2 ✓
0101	3 ✓
0110	2 ✓
0111	1
1000	1
1001	2 ✓
1010	3 ✓
1011	2 ✓
1100	1
1101	2 ✓
1110	1
1111	0

(a)

MESSAGE BITS	TRANSMITTED BITS
000	0010
001	0100
010	0101
011	0110
100	1001
101	1010
110	1011
111	1101

(b)

Figure 7.19   Markov encoding.

that is Markov with $p \neq \frac{1}{2}$ may be formed from the original symbol stream by means of a simple block code as shown in Fig. 7.19. In this figure we map each group of three symbols from the original source into a new group of four symbols with the desired Markov property. The four-symbol groups are chosen as follows. First, we list all possible words containing four symbols, as shown in Fig. 7.19(a). For each word on this list, we count the number of symbol changes (i.e., from 0 to 1 or from 1 to 0) during the word. This number is shown in the second column of Fig. 7.19(a). Then, from the 16 possible words, we select the eight that have the highest number of symbol changes. These eight words are marked with a check in Fig. 7.19(a). Finally, we map each three-symbol word from the original message into one of the four-symbol words marked with a check in Fig. 7.19(a). This mapping is shown in Fig. 7.19(b). Since the words checked have the highest number of symbol changes among four-symbol words, we have biased the transition probability in the resulting symbol stream so that symbol changes are more likely than nonchanges. For this particular set of words (and for independent symbols in the original message) we find that $p = 0.69$. Using the new symbol stream instead of the original one will necessi-

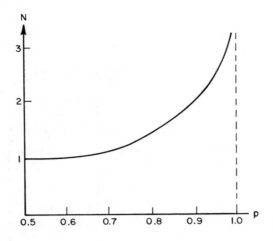

Figure 7.20 Spreading ratio N versus transition probability p.

tate increasing the bandwidth by the ratio $\frac{4}{3}$ if we must transmit the original bits at the same rate.

In general, if we reduce the entropy of the symbol stream by a mapping such as the one above, but keep the information rate constant, the bandwidth required after coding B_c is related to the original message bandwidth B_m by

$$B_c = NB_m, \tag{7.32}$$

where N is the *spreading ratio* (now not necessarily an integer),

$$N = H_m/H_c, \tag{7.33}$$

H_m is the entropy of the original message symbol stream, and H_c is the entropy of the new coded symbol stream. For $H_m = 1$ bit/symbol and H_c as given in Eq. (7.31), N is

$$N = \left[-p \log_2 p - (1 - p) \log_2 (1 - p) \right]^{-1}, \tag{7.34}$$

which is plotted versus p in Fig. 7.20. Note, for example, that doubling the bandwidth allows symbol predictions with a probability of being correct of about 0.9.‡

Although doubling the bandwidth may seem an excessive penalty, one should bear in mind that other approaches for generating a reference signal, such as those in sections 7.2 and 7.4, involve spread spectrum signals. For these methods, the spread bandwidth is also larger than the information bandwidth, usually by much more than a factor of 2.

If the desired signal symbol stream has this Markov property, a reference signal may be generated as shown in Fig. 7.21. First, the desired signal symbol

---

‡In the example of Fig. 7.19, a bandwidth spreading ratio of $\frac{4}{3}$ resulted in $p = 0.69$. Figure 7.20 shows that for $N = \frac{4}{3}$, $p = 0.77$. This difference occurs because the Markov stream produced by the mapping in Fig. 7.19 is actually higher than first order. The entropy for higher order Markov sources is discussed in Abramson [1].

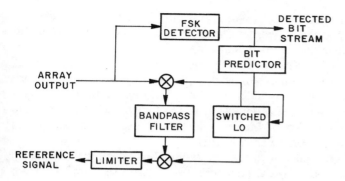

Figure 7.21 Reference generation loop for FSK signals.

stream is detected from the array output signal. Then, from each detected symbol, the next symbol is predicted, one symbol in advance. This predicted symbol switches the LO frequency to the proper value so that the desired signal will pass through the bandpass filter (if the predicted symbol is correct). The filter output is then limited, to fix the amplitude, and used for the reference signal.

The operation of this reference loop is very simple. When a symbol is predicted correctly, the desired signal passes through the bandpass filter and into the reference signal essentially unchanged.[‡] When a symbol is predicted incorrectly, the desired signal does not appear in the reference signal, because the LO is on the wrong frequency for the signal to pass through the bandpass filter. Averaged over many symbols, the correlation between the reference signal and the desired signal is proportional to the probability of correct symbol prediction, that is, to the Markov transition probability.

To make this system reject CW interference, one should choose $p > \frac{1}{2}$ in Fig. 7.18. With $p > \frac{1}{2}$, the desired signal alternates symbols more often than not. The predicted symbol for each interval is then just the opposite of the one detected for the preceding interval. CW interference on one of the two FSK frequencies will then cause the LO in Fig. 7.21 to consistently pick the wrong frequency to pass the interference.

With $p > \frac{1}{2}$, however, the array is vulnerable to two other types of interference: (1) an FSK signal consisting of alternate 0's and 1's, and (2) a signal consisting of the two frequencies ω_0 and ω_1 simultaneously (i.e., a comb jammer). The simple strategy described here is not intended to combat these types of interference.

In general, one must recognize that any method of reference signal generation will be fooled by some type of interference. In particular, a signal of the same form as the desired signal will always be a problem. The spread spectrum techniques in sections 7.2 and 7.4 rely on the assumption that the

---

[‡]Note that the reference signal automatically has the right frequency and (if the loop phase shift is properly adjusted) the right carrier phase angle.

interference does not have the same modulation and PN code as the desired signal. For FSK signaling as described here, it appears possible to overcome the problem of an FSK jammer that transmits alternate 0's and 1's by using M-ary FSK based on a higher order Markov source and a more elaborate prediction strategy. On the other hand, comb jamming is a problem for any FSK system, regardless of how the reference signal is derived. If comb jamming is anticipated, one should not choose FSK modulation in the first place. Note that the symbol prediction technique described here could also be used with other types of digital modulation, such as phase shift keying.

The initial acquisition behavior of the array with this reference generation technique may be understood with the concepts discussed in section 7.1. If g_d, g_i, and g_n are the reference loop gains for the desired signal, interference, and thermal noise, then desired signal acquisition requires $|g_i| < 1$ and $|g_n| < 1$

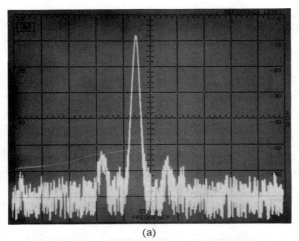

(a)

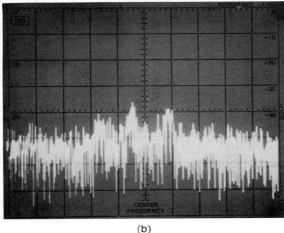

(b)

Figure 7.22   Suppression of CW jammer: (a) array output—fixed array; (b) array output after adaptation (reprinted from Ganz [5] with permission).

under all signal conditions and requires $|g_d| > 1$ when the desired signal is weak. If these conditions are always met, the array will lock on the desired signal and minimize interference and thermal noise. For the reference loop described, it can be shown that the loop gains g_d, g_i, and g_n all have suitable behavior if the loop is properly designed. For example, when the dominant signal at the array output is CW interference, the bit predictor consistently chooses the wrong LO frequency to pass the interference through the filter. The interference then suffers a large attenuation in passing through the loop because it is out of the filter passband. Hence, g_i is very low in this case. When the desired signal is dominant at the array output, the bit predictor usually chooses the correct LO frequency so that the desired signal passes the filter with little attenuation. Since g_d is the desired signal gain averaged over many symbols, it is possible to choose the electronic gain of the loop so that $g_d > 1$. Additionally,

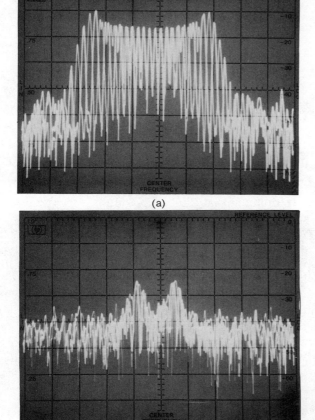

(a)

(b)

Figure 7.23 Suppression of an FM jammer: (a) array outputs with fixed weights; (b) array output after adaptation (reprinted from Ganz [5] with permission).

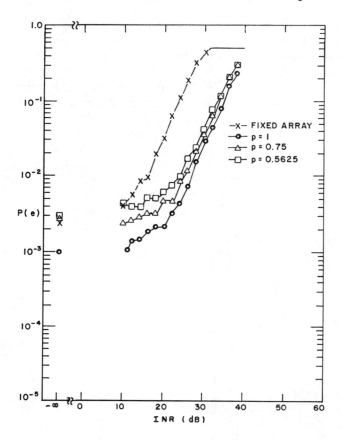

Figure 7.24 Bit error probability versus INR for $E_b/N_0 = 12$ dB (reprinted from Ganz [5] with permission).

when the desired signal is dominant at the array output, the weak signal suppression of the limiter helps to keep g_i and g_n small.

An experimental system was designed and built by Ganz to test these concepts [5]. He used a three-element LMS adaptive processor. A typical measurement of power spectral density at the array output is shown in Fig. 7.22. The output spectrum with the array weights frozen to form a beam in the broadside direction is shown in Fig. 7.22(a). The desired signal arrives from broadside, and a CW interference signal arrives from 66° off broadside (with elements a half wavelength apart at the center frequency). The CW interference is coherent with the lower FSK frequency. Figure 7.22(a) shows the output spectrum when the weights are frozen,‡ and Fig. 7.22(b) shows it after adaptation. It may be seen how the adaptive array removes the undesired CW signal.

---

‡The spectral component to the left of the CW interference in Fig. 7.22(a) is an intermodulation product. Since this component falls outside the filter passbands in the FSK demodulator, it is of little importance.

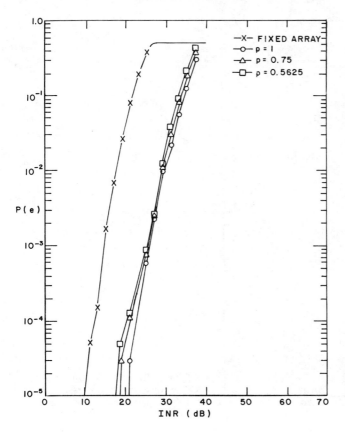

Figure 7.25 Bit error probability versus INR for $E_b/N_0 = 17$ dB (reprinted from Ganz [5] with permission).

Figure 7.23 shows similar measured spectral densities obtained with a modulated interfering signal. The interference is a sinusoidally modulated FM signal 20 dB stronger than the desired signal. Fig. 7.23(a) shows the spectrum at the array output with the array weights fixed, and Fig. 7.23(b) shows the output after adaptation.

Figures 7.24 through 7.27 show some additional experimental results for measured bit error probabilities with fixed and adapted weights. Each figure shows the bit error probability as a function of the INR (interference-to-noise ratio). These curves were obtained by varying the interference power and holding the noise power constant. Each figure is for a fixed SNR. Four curves are shown in each figure. The first, labeled "fixed array," shows the measured bit error probability with the array weights fixed. The other three curves show the measured bit error probability when the array is adapting but with different Markov transition probabilities. It may be seen that $p = 1$ gives the best performance, as one would expect, but the change in performance between $p = 1$ and $p = 0.56$ is small.

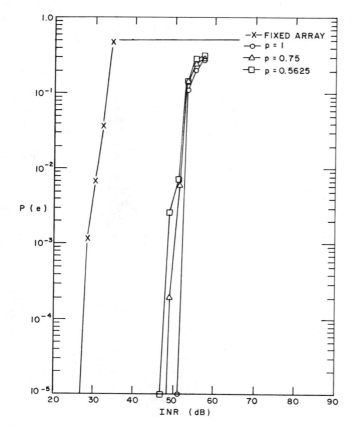

Figure 7.26 Bit error probability versus INR for $E_b/N_0 = 27$ dB (reprinted from Ganz [5] with permission).

Figure 7.24 shows the performance for a desired signal with E_b/N_0 equal to 12 dB, a low value. (E_b is the signal energy per bit, measured per element of the array.) Ganz defined the AJ (antijam) margin as the difference in INR that can be tolerated by the fixed and adaptive arrays for a BEP (bit error probability) of 10^{-3} [5]. In Fig. 7.24, AJ margins are approximately 9 dB for $p = 0.56$, 10 dB for $p = 0.75$, and 12 dB for $p = 1$.

Figure 7.25 shows similar measurements for $E_b/N_0 = 17$ dB. AJ margins for this case are similar to those in Fig. 7.24. Figure 7.26 shows the results for $E_b/N_0 = 27$ dB. The AJ margin is larger in this case and varies between about 20 dB and 24 dB. Finally, Fig. 7.27 shows the results for $E_b/N_0 = 37$ dB. The input SNR in this case is near the upper end of the dynamic range for the adaptive array electronics. For this case, the AJ margin is about 18 dB when $p = 1$ and drops to about 12 dB for transition probabilities less than 1. As E_b/N_0 was increased further, the system performance deteriorated because the useful dynamic range of the adaptive array had been exceeded.

Ganz's results show that this bit prediction technique for generating a reference signal is promising for practical applications. The transition probabili-

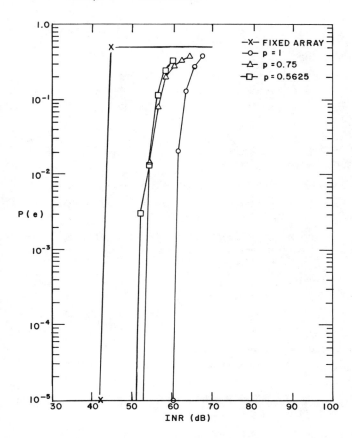

Figure 7.27 Bit error probability versus INR for $E_b/N_0 = 37$ dB (reprinted from Ganz [5] with permission).

ties needed require only a modest increase in bandwidth over a conventional FSK system for a given information rate.

Thus we conclude our discussion of reference signal generation techniques for LMS adaptive arrays. The author hopes that these examples will illustrate the possibilities to the reader and will perhaps suggest additional techniques. Although generating a reference signal is not trivial, it is certainly not impossible. To design a communication system using an adaptive array, it seems clear that the signal modulation must be chosen not only to fulfill communication objectives but also to allow reference signal generation.

REFERENCES

1. N. Abramson, *Information Theory and Coding*, McGraw-Hill, New York, 1963.
2. R. T. Compton, Jr., "An Adaptive Array in a Spread-Spectrum Communication System," *Proceedings of the IEEE*, 66, no. 3 (March 1978): 289. Copyright © 1978 IEEE.

3. J. H. Winters, "Spread Spectrum in a Four-Phase Communication System Employing Adaptive Antennas," *IEEE Transactions on Communications*, COM–30, no. 5 (May 1982): 929. Copyright © 1982 IEEE.

4. E. C. Hudson, "Use of an Adaptive Array in a Frequency-Shift Keyed Communication System," Technical Report 712684–1, August 1980, Ohio State University ElectroScience Laboratory, Columbus, Ohio 43212; prepared under Contract N00019-80-C-0181 for Naval Air Systems Command.

5. M. W. Ganz, "On the Performance of an Adaptive Array in a Frequency Shift Keyed Communication System," M.Sc. thesis, August 1982, Department of Electrical Engineering, Ohio State University, Columbus, Ohio 43210.

6. A. J. Viterbi, *Principles of Coherent Communication*, McGraw-Hill, New York, 1966.

7. R. E. Ziemer and R. L. Peterson, *Digital Communications and Spread Spectrum Systems*, Macmillan, New York, 1985.

8. D. M. DiCarlo and R. T. Compton, Jr., "Reference Loop Phase Shift in Adaptive Arrays," *IEEE Transactions on Aerospace and Electronic Systems*, AES–14, no. 4 (July 1978): 599.

9. D. M. DiCarlo, "Reference Loop Phase Shift in an *N*-element Adaptive Array," *IEEE Transactions on Aerospace and Electronic Systems*, AES–15, no. 4 (July 1979): 576.

10. R. E. Ziemer and W. H. Tranter, *Principles of Communications*, Houghton Mifflin, Boston, 1976.

11. S. W. Golomb, *Shift Register Sequences*, Holden-Day, San Francisco, 1967.

12. W. B. Davenport, Jr., "Signal-to-Noise Ratios in Band-Pass Limiters," *Journal of Applied Physics*, 24, no. 6 (June 1953): 720.

13. J. J. Jones, "Hard Limiting of Two Signals in Random Noise," *IEEE Transactions on Information Theory*, IT–9, no. 1 (January 1963): 34.

14. J. J. Spilker, "Delay-Lock Tracking of Binary Signals," *IEEE Transactions on Space Electronics and Telemetry*, SET–9 (March 1963): 1.

15. W. J. Gill, "A Comparison of Binary Delay-Lock Tracking-Loop Implementations," *IEEE Transactions on Aerospace and Electronic Systems*, AES–2, no. 4 (July 1966): 415.

16. W. J. Gill and J. J. Spilker, Jr., "An Interesting Decomposition for the Self-Products of Random and Pseudorandom Binary Sequences," *IEEE Transactions on Communications Systems*, CS–11 (June 1963): 246.

17. R. B. Ward, "Acquisition of Pseudonoise Signals by Sequential Estimation," *IEEE Transactions on Communications*, COM–13, no. 4 (December 1965): 475.

18. H. L. Van Trees, *Detection, Estimation, and Modulation Theory*, part 1, Wiley, New York, 1968.

Appendix A

Hilbert Transforms and Analytic Signals

Suppose $f(t)$ is a real, zero-mean signal. We define the Hilbert transform of $f(t)$ to be

$$\hat{f}(t) = \frac{1}{\pi} \int_{-\infty}^{+\infty} \frac{f(\tau)}{t - \tau} \, d\tau. \tag{A.1}$$

The integral in Eq. (A.1) is actually a Cauchy principal value integral, that is,

$$\hat{f}(t) = \frac{1}{\pi} P \int_{-\infty}^{+\infty} \frac{f(\tau)}{t - \tau} \, d\tau, \tag{A.2}$$

where P denotes the operation

$$P \int_{-\infty}^{+\infty} \frac{f(\tau)}{t - \tau} \, d\tau = \lim_{\varepsilon \to 0^+} \left[\int_{-\infty}^{t-\varepsilon} \frac{f(\tau)}{t - \tau} \, d\tau + \int_{t+\varepsilon}^{+\infty} \frac{f(\tau)}{t - \tau} \, d\tau \right]. \tag{A.3}$$

Because both integrals on the right side of Eq. (A.3) involve the same ε, the integral in Eq. (A.3) is well-defined in the limit as $\varepsilon \to 0^+$. In the following discussion, we will omit the symbol P for the Cauchy principal value, but the reader should understand that this interpretation is assumed.

The Hilbert transform in Eq. (A.1) may be viewed as a convolution integral, that is,

$$\hat{f}(t) = f(t) \otimes \frac{1}{\pi t}, \tag{A.4}$$

where $\otimes$ denotes convolution. Thus taking the Hilbert transform of $f(t)$ is

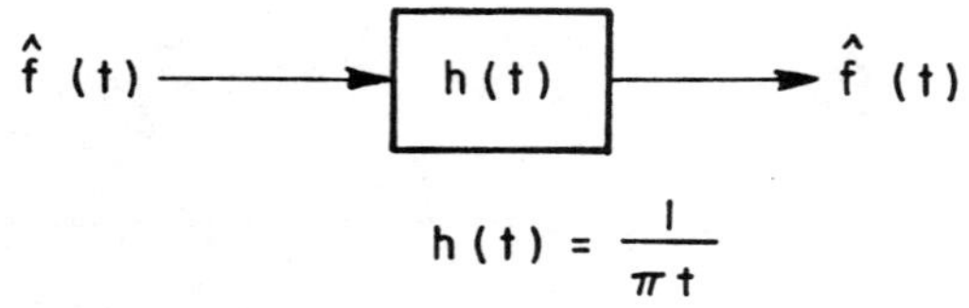

$$\hat{f}(t) \longrightarrow \boxed{h(t)} \longrightarrow \hat{\hat{f}}(t)$$

$$h(t) = \frac{1}{\pi t}$$

Figure A.1 The Hilbert transform filter.

equivalent to passing $f(t)$ through a linear filter with impulse response

$$h(t) = \frac{1}{\pi t}, \tag{A.5}$$

as shown in Fig. A.1. The transfer function $H(\omega)$ associated with $h(t)$ is

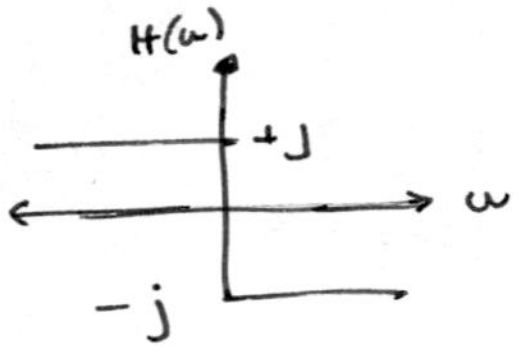

$$H(\omega) = \mathscr{F}[h(t)]$$

$$= \int_{-\infty}^{+\infty} h(t) e^{-j\omega t}\, dt$$

$$= \begin{cases} -j, & \omega > 0, \\ +j, & \omega < 0. \end{cases} \tag{A.6}$$

A simple way to prove Eq. (A.6) is to consider the transform $H_\alpha(\omega)$,

$$H_\alpha(\omega) = \begin{cases} -je^{-\alpha\omega}, & \omega > 0, \\ +je^{\alpha\omega}, & \omega < 0. \end{cases} \tag{A.7}$$

The inverse transform $h_\alpha(t)$ of $H_\alpha(\omega)$ is easily shown to be

$$h_\alpha(t) = \frac{1}{2\pi} \int_{-\infty}^{+\infty} H_\alpha(\omega) e^{j\omega t}\, d\omega$$

$$= \frac{4\pi t}{\alpha^2 + (2\pi t)^2}. \tag{A.8}$$

Then, since

$$\lim_{\alpha \to 0} H_\alpha(\omega) = H(\omega) = \begin{cases} -j, & \omega > 0, \\ +j, & \omega < 0, \end{cases} \tag{A.9}$$

and

$$\lim_{\alpha \to 0} h_\alpha(t) = h(t), \tag{A.10}$$

we interpret $h(t)$ and $H(\omega)$ as a Fourier transform pair.

Now let $F(\omega)$ be the Fourier transform of $f(t)$,

$$F(\omega) = \mathscr{F}[f(t)] = \int_{-\infty}^{+\infty} f(t) e^{-j\omega t}\, dt, \tag{A.11}$$

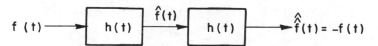

Figure A.2 The double Hilbert transform.

and $\hat{F}(\omega)$ be the Fourier transform of $\hat{f}(t)$,[‡]

$$\hat{F}(\omega) = \mathscr{F}\left[\hat{f}(t)\right] = \int_{-\infty}^{+\infty} \hat{f}(t) e^{-j\omega t}\, dt. \qquad (A.12)$$

Then Eq. (A.4) is equivalent to the frequency domain relation,

$$\hat{F}(\omega) = H(\omega)F(\omega) = \begin{cases} -jF(\omega), & \omega > 0, \\ +jF(\omega), & \omega < 0. \end{cases} \qquad (A.13)$$

Thus the Fourier transform of $\hat{f}(t)$ is found by multiplying $F(\omega)$ by $-j$ at positive frequencies and $+j$ at negative frequencies.

From these definitions, we can obtain several useful properties of Hilbert transforms.

Theorem 1

$$\hat{\hat{f}}(t) = -f(t). \qquad (A.14)$$

Proof. Since $\hat{f}(t)$ is obtained by passing $f(t)$ through the filter $H(\omega)$ in Fig. A.1, we can obtain $\hat{\hat{f}}(t)$ by passing $f(t)$ through such a filter twice, as in Fig. A.2. However, the two filters $H(\omega)$ in cascade in Fig. A.2 are equivalent to a single filter with transfer function $H^2(\omega) = (\pm j)^2 = -1$ at all frequencies. Hence the output $\hat{\hat{f}}(t)$ is just $-f(t)$.

From Theorem 1, we also have the following:

Corollary 1A.   The inverse Hilbert transform is

$$f(t) = -\frac{1}{\pi} \int_{-\infty}^{+\infty} \frac{\hat{f}(\tau)}{t - \tau}\, d\tau. \qquad (A.15)$$

Proof. The signal between the two filters in Fig. A.2 is $\hat{f}(t)$, and the output is $\hat{\hat{f}}(t) = -f(t)$. Hence an input $\hat{f}(t)$ applied to a filter $-H(\omega)$ would produce an output $f(t)$. Thus, in the time domain, we have

$$f(t) = \hat{f}(t) \otimes \left(-\frac{1}{\pi t}\right), \qquad (A.16)$$

which is equivalent to Eq. (A.15).

[‡]Note that $\hat{F}(\omega)$ is *not* the Hilbert transform of $F(\omega)$!

Theorem 2. If $f_1(t)$ and $f_2(t)$ are two real, zero-mean, stationary random processes, then

$$E[\hat{f}_1(t_1)\hat{f}_2(t_2)] = E[f_1(t_1)f_2(t_2)], \tag{A.17}$$

where $E[\cdot]$ denotes the expectation.

Proof. From the definitions of $\hat{f}_1(t)$ and $\hat{f}_2(t)$, we have

$$E[\hat{f}_1(t_1)\hat{f}_2(t_2)] = E\left[\frac{1}{\pi^2}\int_{-\infty}^{+\infty}\frac{f_1(\tau_1)}{t_1-\tau_1}\,d\tau_1\int_{-\infty}^{+\infty}\frac{f_2(\tau_2)}{t_2-\tau_2}\,d\tau_2\right]. \tag{A.18}$$

Making the change of variables $\tau_1 = t_1 - \xi_1$ and $\tau_2 = t_2 - \xi_2$ gives

$$E[\hat{f}_1(t_1)\hat{f}_2(t_2)] = E\left[\frac{1}{\pi^2}\int_{-\infty}^{+\infty}\frac{f_1(t_1-\xi_1)}{\xi_1}\,d\xi_1\int_{-\infty}^{+\infty}\frac{f_2(t_2-\xi_2)}{\xi_2}\,d\xi_2\right]$$

$$= \frac{1}{\pi^2}\int_{-\infty}^{+\infty}\int_{-\infty}^{+\infty}E[f_1(t_1-\xi_1)f_2(t_2-\xi_2)]\frac{d\xi_1}{\xi_1}\frac{d\xi_2}{\xi_2}. \tag{A.19}$$

Because $f_1(t)$ and $f_2(t)$ are stationary, this equation may be written

$$E[\hat{f}_1(t_1)\hat{f}_2(t_2)] = \frac{1}{\pi^2}\int_{-\infty}^{+\infty}\int_{-\infty}^{+\infty}E[f_1(t_1)f_2(t_2+\xi_1-\xi_2)]\frac{d\xi_1}{\xi_1}\frac{d\xi_2}{\xi_2}$$

$$= E\left[\frac{1}{\pi^2}\int_{-\infty}^{+\infty}\int_{-\infty}^{+\infty}f_1(t_1)f_2(t_2+\xi_1-\xi_2)\frac{d\xi_1}{\xi_1}\frac{d\xi_2}{\xi_2}\right]$$

$$= E\left[f_1(t_1)\frac{1}{\pi}\int_{-\infty}^{+\infty}\left\{\frac{1}{\pi}\int_{-\infty}^{+\infty}f_2(t_2+\xi_1-\xi_2)\frac{d\xi_2}{\xi_2}\right\}\frac{d\xi_1}{\xi_1}\right]$$

$$= E\left[f_1(t_1)\frac{1}{\pi}\int_{-\infty}^{+\infty}\hat{f}(t_2+\xi_1)\frac{d\xi_1}{\xi_1}\right]. \tag{A.20}$$

However, substituting $\alpha = t_2 + \xi_1$ in the last integral gives

$$\frac{1}{\pi}\int_{-\infty}^{+\infty}\hat{f}_2(t_2+\xi_1)\frac{d\xi_1}{\xi_1} = \frac{1}{\pi}\int_{-\infty}^{+\infty}\frac{\hat{f}(\alpha)}{\alpha-t_2}\,d\alpha$$

$$= -\frac{1}{\pi}\int_{-\infty}^{+\infty}\frac{\hat{f}_2(\alpha)}{t_2-\alpha}\,d\alpha$$

$$= f_2(t_2), \tag{A.21}$$

according to Eq. (A.15). Using Eq. (A.21) in Eq. (A.20) then gives Eq. (A.17).

From this theorem, we have the following corollaries:

Corollary 2A

$$E\left[\hat{f}_1(t_1)f_2(t_2)\right] = -E\left[f_1(t_1)\hat{f}_2(t_2)\right].$$ (A.22)

Proof. Replace $f_2(t_2)$ in Eq. (A.17) by $\hat{f}_2(t_2)$. Then use Eq. (A.14) of Theorem 1 to replace $\hat{\hat{f}}_2(t_2)$ by $-f_2(t_2)$.

Corollary 2B

$$E\left[\hat{f}^2(t)\right] = E\left[f^2(t)\right].$$ (A.23)

Proof. Let $t_1 = t_2 = t$ and $f_1(t) = f_2(t) = f(t)$ in Eq. (A.17).

Corollary 2C

$$E\left[f(t)\hat{f}(t)\right] = 0.$$ (A.24)

Proof. Let $t_1 = t_2 = t$ and $f_1(t) = f_2(t) = f(t)$ in Eq. (A.22). This gives $E[\hat{f}(t)f(t)] = -E[f(t)\hat{f}(t)]$, from which Eq. (A.24) follows.

Given a signal $f(t)$ and its Hilbert transform $\hat{f}(t)$, we define the *analytic signal $\tilde{f}(t)$* to be

$$\tilde{f}(t) = f(t) + j\hat{f}(t).$$ (A.25)

The signal $\tilde{f}(t)$ is a useful representation because its Fourier transform has nonzero values only for positive ω. To see this result let $\tilde{F}(\omega)$ be the Fourier transform of $\tilde{f}(t)$,

$$\tilde{F}(\omega) = \mathcal{F}\left[\tilde{f}(t)\right] = \int_{-\infty}^{+\infty} \tilde{f}(t)e^{-j\omega t}\, dt.$$ (A.26)

Then we have the following:

Theorem 3

$$\tilde{F}(\omega) = \begin{cases} 2F(\omega), & \omega > 0, \\ 0, & \omega < 0. \end{cases}$$ (A.27)

Proof. Since $F(\omega)$ and $\hat{F}(\omega)$ are the Fourier transforms of $f(t)$ and $\hat{f}(t)$, respectively, it follows from Eq. (A.25) that

$$\tilde{F}(\omega) = F(\omega) + j\hat{F}(\omega).$$ (A.28)

The result in Eq. (A.27) may be obtained by substituting Eq. (A.13) into Eq. (A.28).

Now let us consider a simple example. Suppose $f(t)$ is a sinusoid with amplitude A, frequency ω_0, and phase θ,

$$f(t) = A\cos(\omega_0 t + \theta).$$ (A.29)

Let us find the Hilbert transform and analytic signal associated with $f(t)$. It is easiest to find $\hat{f}(t)$ in the frequency domain. The Fourier transform of $f(t)$ is

$$F(\omega) = \mathscr{F}[f(t)]$$
$$= \int_{-\infty}^{+\infty} f(t)e^{-j\omega t}\, dt$$
$$= A\pi[e^{j\theta}\delta(\omega - \omega_0) + e^{-j\theta}\delta(\omega + \omega_0)]. \tag{A.30}$$

Then $\hat{F}(\omega)$ may be found from Eq. (A.13), that is, by multiplying $F(\omega)$ by the $H(\omega)$ in Eq. (A.6),

$$\hat{F}(\omega) = A\pi[-je^{j\theta}\delta(\omega - \omega_0) + je^{-j\theta}\delta(\omega + \omega_0)]$$
$$= Aj\pi[e^{-j\theta}\delta(\omega + \omega_0) - e^{j\theta}\delta(\omega - \omega_0)]. \tag{A.31}$$

However, Eq. (A.31) is just the Fourier transform of $A\sin(\omega_0 t + \theta)$, so we find

$$\hat{f}(t) = \mathscr{F}^{-1}[\hat{F}(\omega)] = A\sin(\omega_0 t + \theta). \tag{A.32}$$

From this result it follows that the analytic signal associated with $f(t)$ is

$$\tilde{f}(t) = f(t) + j\hat{f}(t) = Ae^{j\omega_0 t + \theta}. \tag{A.33}$$

The Fourier transform $\tilde{F}(\omega)$ of $\tilde{f}(t)$ is then

$$\tilde{F}(\omega) = \mathscr{F}[\tilde{f}(t)] = 2A\pi e^{j\theta}\delta(\omega - \omega_0). \tag{A.34}$$

It is a common practice in electrical engineering to use an exponential such as Eq. (A.33) to represent the sinusoid in Eq. (A.29). From the preceding discussion, it is clear that this procedure amounts to using the analytic signal to represent the corresponding real signal.

Several useful relationships for analytic signals can be derived from Theorems 1 and 2 and Corollaries 2A through 2C. For example,

Theorem 4. For any two analytic signals $\tilde{f}_1(t)$ and $\tilde{f}_2(t)$,

$$E[\tilde{f}_1(t_1)\tilde{f}_2(t_2)] = 0. \tag{A.35}$$

Proof. Replacing $\tilde{f}_1(t_1)$ and $\tilde{f}_2(t_2)$ by their definitions gives

$$E[\tilde{f}_1(t_1)\tilde{f}_2(t_2)] = E[\{f_1(t_1) + j\hat{f}_1(t_1)\}\{f_2(t_2) + j\hat{f}_2(t_2)\}]$$
$$= E[f_1(t_1)f_2(t_2)] - E[\hat{f}_1(t_1)\hat{f}_2(t_2)]$$
$$+ jE[f_1(t_1)\hat{f}_2(t_2)] + jE[\hat{f}_1(t_1)f_2(t_2)]. \tag{A.36}$$

The result in Eq. (A.36) is zero because of Eqs. (A.17) and (A.22).

Similarly, we also have

Theorem 5

$$E[\tilde{f}_1^*(t_1)\tilde{f}_2(t_2)] = 2E[f_1(t_1)f_2(t_2)] + 2jE[f_1(t_1)\hat{f}_2(t_2)]. \tag{A.37}$$

Proof. The proof is similar to that in Theorem 4. Because of the conjugate on $\tilde{f}_1(t_1)$, the real and imaginary parts double, instead of canceling.

When we represent a real signal with its analytic signal, we shall need to have an autocorrelation function and a power spectral density defined in terms of the analytic signal. Before presenting these definitions, however, let us first consider the conventional autocorrelation function and power spectral density for a real signal, and see how these may be arranged in analytic form. For a real, random process $f(t)$, the autocorrelation function $R_f(\tau)$ is defined as

$$R_f(\tau) = E[f(t)f(t + \tau)] \tag{A.38}$$

and the power spectral density $S_f(\omega)$ as

$$S_f(\omega) = \mathscr{F}[R_f(\tau)]. \tag{A.39}$$

It is possible to take Hilbert transforms and define analytic forms not only for $f(t)$, but also for $R_f(\tau)$. Suppose we define $\hat{R}_f(\tau)$ to be the Hilbert transform of $R_f(\tau)$,

$$\hat{R}_f(\tau) = \frac{1}{\pi} \int_{-\infty}^{+\infty} \frac{R_f(\tau)}{\tau - \xi} \, d\xi. \tag{A.40}$$

Then we find the following:

Theorem 6

$$\hat{R}_f(\tau) = E[f(t)\hat{f}(t + \tau)]. \tag{A.41}$$

Proof. We have

$$\begin{aligned}
\hat{R}_f(\tau) &= \frac{1}{\pi} \int_{-\infty}^{+\infty} \frac{R_f(\xi)}{\tau - \xi} \, d\xi \\
&= \frac{1}{\pi} \int_{-\infty}^{+\infty} \frac{E[f(t)f(t + \xi)]}{\tau - \xi} \, d\xi \\
&= E\left\{ f(t) \frac{1}{\pi} \int_{-\infty}^{+\infty} \frac{f(t + \xi)}{\tau - \xi} \, d\xi \right\}.
\end{aligned} \tag{A.42}$$

If we substitute $t + \xi = \alpha$ in the last integral, we find,

$$\begin{aligned}
\frac{1}{\pi} \int_{-\infty}^{+\infty} \frac{f(t + \xi)}{\tau - \xi} \, d\xi &= \frac{1}{\pi} \int_{-\infty}^{+\infty} \frac{f(\alpha)}{\tau - (\alpha - t)} \, d\alpha \\
&= \frac{1}{\pi} \int_{-\infty}^{+\infty} \frac{f(a)}{(t + \tau) - \alpha} \, d\alpha \\
&= \hat{f}(t + \tau).
\end{aligned} \tag{A.43}$$

Putting Eq. (A.43) in Eq. (A.42) then gives Eq. (A.41).

Moreover, suppose $\hat{S}_f(\omega)$ is the Fourier transform of $\hat{R}_f(\tau)$. Then we have

Theorem 7

$$\hat{S}_f(\omega) = \mathscr{F}\left[\hat{R}_f(\tau)\right] = \begin{cases} -jS_f(\omega), & \omega > 0, \\ +jS_f(\omega), & \omega < 0. \end{cases} \tag{A.44}$$

Proof. This result follows from Eq. (A.13).

From $R_f(\tau)$ and its Hilbert transform $\hat{R}_f(\tau)$, we can define $\tilde{R}_f(\tau)$ to be the *analytic* form of the autocorrelation function of $R_f(\tau)$,

$$\tilde{R}_f(\tau) = R_f(\tau) + j\hat{R}_f(\tau). \tag{A.45}$$

Also, suppose we let $\tilde{S}_f(\omega)$ be the Fourier transform of $\tilde{R}_f(\tau)$,

$$\tilde{S}_f(\omega) = \mathscr{F}\left[\tilde{R}_f(\tau)\right]. \tag{A.46}$$

Then $\tilde{S}_f(\omega)$ is related to $S_f(\omega)$ by

$$\tilde{S}_f(\omega) = \begin{cases} 2S_f(\omega), & \omega > 0, \\ 0, & \omega < 0, \end{cases} \tag{A.47}$$

as may be seen from Eq. (A.27).

Now let us return to the analytic signal $\tilde{f}(t)$ and consider how to define its autocorrelation function and power spectral density. We shall define the auto-correlation function of $\tilde{f}(t)$ to be

$$R_{\tilde{f}}(\tau) = E\left[\tilde{f}^*(t)\tilde{f}(t+\tau)\right]. \tag{A.48}$$

The relationship between $R_{\tilde{f}}(\tau)$ and the autocorrelation functions defined previously is as follows. First, we have

Theorem 8

$$R_{\tilde{f}}(\tau) = 2\tilde{R}_f(\tau), \tag{A.49}$$

where $\tilde{R}_f(\tau)$ is defined in Eq. (A.45).

Proof. Applying Eqs. (A.37), (A.41), and (A.45), we have

$$\begin{aligned} R_{\tilde{f}}(\tau) &= 2E\left[f(t)f(t+\tau)\right] + j2E\left[f(t)\hat{f}(t+\tau)\right] \\ &= 2\left[R_f(\tau) + j\hat{R}_f(\tau)\right] \\ &= 2\tilde{R}_f(\tau). \end{aligned} \tag{A.50}$$

Next, we define $S_{\tilde{f}}(\omega)$, the power spectral density of $\tilde{f}(t)$, to be the Fourier transform of $R_{\tilde{f}}(\tau)$,

$$S_{\tilde{f}}(\omega) = \mathscr{F}\left[R_{\tilde{f}}(\tau)\right] = \int_{-\infty}^{+\infty} R_{\tilde{f}}(\tau)e^{-j\omega\tau}\,d\tau. \tag{A.51}$$

Of course, $R_{\tilde{f}}(\tau)$ is then the inverse transform of $S_{\tilde{f}}(\omega)$,

$$R_{\tilde{f}}(\tau) = \mathscr{F}^{-1}\left[S_{\tilde{f}}(\omega)\right] = \frac{1}{2\pi}\int_{-\infty}^{+\infty}S_{\tilde{f}}(\omega)e^{j\omega\tau}\,d\omega. \tag{A.52}$$

The relationship between $S_{\tilde{f}}(\omega)$ and the power spectral density of $f(t)$ is as follows:

Theorem 9

$$S_{\tilde{f}}(\omega) = \begin{cases} 4S_f(\omega), & \omega > 0, \\ 0, & \omega < 0. \end{cases} \tag{A.53}$$

Proof. Since $R_{\tilde{f}}(\tau) = 2\tilde{R}_f(\tau)$ from Eq. (A.49), it follows that

$$S_{\tilde{f}}(\omega) = 2\tilde{S}_f(\omega), \tag{A.54}$$

where $\tilde{S}_f(\omega)$ is defined in Eq. (A.46). Equation (A.53) then follows from Eq. (A.47).

Note that since $S_{\tilde{f}}(\omega) = 0$ for $\omega < 0$, Eq. (A.52) could also be written

$$R_{\tilde{f}}(\tau) = \frac{1}{2\pi}\int_0^{+\infty}S_{\tilde{f}}(\omega)e^{j\omega\tau}\,d\omega. \tag{A.55}$$

To represent signals in analytic form, we shall work with the transform pair $R_{\tilde{f}}(\tau) \leftrightarrow S_{\tilde{f}}(\omega)$ as defined previously. These are the definitions used in Chapters 2 and 3.

When calculating the average power in a signal represented by its analytic form, one must be careful about factors of 2. Let us see why.

Suppose we are considering a real signal $f(t)$. The average power in $f(t)$ is

$$P_f = E\left[f^2(t)\right]. \tag{A.56}$$

Using the real autocorrelation function in Eq. (A.38), we may write P_f as

$$P_f = R_f(0). \tag{A.57}$$

Since $R_f(\tau)$ is the inverse transform of $S_f(\omega)$, we also have

$$P_f = R_f(0) = \frac{1}{2\pi}\int_{-\infty}^{+\infty}S_f(\omega)\,d\omega. \tag{A.58}$$

Moreover, because $R_f(\tau)$ is real, $S_f(\omega)$ is an even function of ω. Therefore, Eq. (A.58) may also be written

$$P_f = R_f(0) = \frac{1}{\pi}\int_0^{+\infty}S_f(\omega)\,d\omega. \tag{A.59}$$

[Note that since $f(t)$ was assumed to be zero-mean, $S_f(\omega)$ does not contain an impulse at $\omega = 0$.]

To express P_f in terms of $R_{\tilde{f}}(\tau)$ and $S_{\tilde{f}}(\omega)$, we note from Eq. (A.53) that $S_f(\omega) = \frac{1}{4} S_{\tilde{f}}(\omega)$ for $\omega > 0$. Hence Eq. (A.59) may also be written

$$P_f = \frac{1}{4\pi} \int_0^{+\infty} S_{\tilde{f}}(\omega)\, d\omega. \qquad (A.60)$$

From Eq. (A.55) it then follows that P_f is also

$$P_f = \tfrac{1}{2} R_{\tilde{f}}(0). \qquad (A.61)$$

Hence, when we have a real signal $f(t)$ and we represent this signal by its associated analytic form $\tilde{f}(t)$, the average power in $f(t)$ may be calculated from $R_{\tilde{f}}(\tau)$ or $S_{\tilde{f}}(\omega)$ by Eq. (A.60) or Eq. (A.61). This is the method used in Chapters 2 and 3 when $f(t)$ is the output signal from an adaptive array. The array output power is the power in $f(t)$, and this is calculated from Eq. (A.60) or Eq. (A.61).

However, suppose we are discussing the signal received on a single element of an adaptive array. The signal from an array element is passed through a quadrature hybrid (see Appendix B), and each quadrature output is separately weighted. In this case we let $f(t)$ and $\hat{f}(t)$ represent the inphase and quadrature outputs from the quadrature hybrid, respectively. Now the total signal power available from that element includes the powers in *both* $f(t)$ and $\hat{f}(t)$. We showed in Eq. (A.23) that these powers are equal. Therefore, the total power from an element—that is, the power in both quadrature hybrid outputs—is $2P_f$, or

$$\text{element power} = 2P_f = R_{\tilde{f}}(0) = \frac{1}{2\pi} \int_{-\infty}^{+\infty} S_{\tilde{f}}(\omega)\, d\omega. \qquad (A.62)$$

Note that Eq. (A.62) differs from Eqs. (A.60) and (A.61) by a factor of 2.

When calculating the power in a signal represented by its analytic form, one must be careful to distinguish between the two situations above. If the power we wish to compute is $E[f^2(t)]$, we use Eq. (A.60) or Eq. (A.61). But if the power desired is $E[f^2(t)] + E[\hat{f}^2(t)]$, then we use Eq. (A.62).

REFERENCES

Additional information on Hilbert transforms and analytic signals may be found in the following:

1. R. Arens, "Complex Processes for Envelopes of Normal Noise," *IRE Transactions on Information Theory*, IT-3, no. 3 (September 1957): 204.

2. J. Dugundji, "Envelopes and Pre-Envelopes of Real Waveforms," *IRE Transactions on Information Theory*, IT-4, no. 1 (March 1958): 53.

3. E. Bedrosian, "The Analytic Signal Representation of Modulated Waveforms," *Proceedings of the IEEE*, 50, no. 10 (October 1962): 2071.

Appendix B

Quadrature Hybrids

A quadrature hybrid is a commonly used three-port device. It has one input and two outputs, as shown in Fig. B.1. As long as the ports are properly terminated and the device is used within its design frequency range, an RF signal applied to the input produces two equal-amplitude output signals whose carriers are in time quadrature. In this appendix, we describe how to characterize a quadrature hybrid mathematically.

Since a quadrature hybrid has one input and two outputs, it can be represented by two transfer functions $H_I(\omega)$ and $H_Q(\omega)$, as shown in Fig. B.2. If $H_I(\omega)$ and $H_Q(\omega)$ are measured for a typical quadrature hybrid, one finds that $H_I(\omega)$ and $H_Q(\omega)$ are similar to the curves shown in Fig. B.3. Within the design frequency range of the hybrid, the amplitudes $|H_I(\omega)|$ and $|H_Q(\omega)|$ are essentially constant, and the phase shifts $\angle H_I(\omega)$ and $\angle H_Q(\omega)$ vary linearly with frequency. Moreover, at a given frequency, $\angle H_I(\omega)$ and $\angle H_Q(\omega)$ differ by 90°. Inside the operating bandwidth of the hybrid, $H_I(\omega)$ and $H_Q(\omega)$ may be written

$$
H_I(\omega) = \begin{cases} \dfrac{1}{\sqrt{2}} e^{-j\phi_0} e^{-j(\omega-\omega_0)T_0}, & \omega > 0, \\[2ex] \dfrac{1}{\sqrt{2}} e^{+j\phi_0} e^{-j(\omega+\omega_0)T_0}, & \omega < 0, \end{cases} \tag{B.1}
$$

and

$$
H_Q(\omega) = \begin{cases} -j\dfrac{1}{\sqrt{2}} e^{-j\phi_0} e^{-j(\omega-\omega_0)T_0}, & \omega > 0, \\[2ex] +j\dfrac{1}{\sqrt{2}} e^{+j\phi_0} e^{-j(\omega+\omega_0)T_0}, & \omega < 0, \end{cases} \tag{B.2}
$$

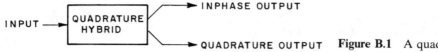

Figure B.1   A quadrature hybrid.

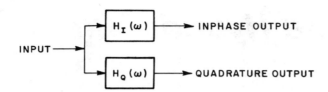

Figure B.2   Transfer function equivalent of a quadrature hybrid.

where ω_0 is the center frequency of the operating bandwidth and ϕ_0 is the phase shift of $H_I(\omega)$ at $\omega = \omega_0$. Figure B.3 shows $H_I(\omega)$ and $H_Q(\omega)$ only for $\omega > 0$, but the values of $H_I(\omega)$ and $H_Q(\omega)$ for $\omega < 0$ may be determined from the symmetry properties

$$H_I(-\omega) = H_I^*(\omega) \tag{B.3}$$

and

$$H_Q(-\omega) = H_Q^*(\omega), \tag{B.4}$$

which hold for any linear filter with a real impulse response.

Thus passing an input signal through a quadrature hybrid is equivalent to passing it through two filters as shown in Fig. B.4, where $\mathrm{sgn}(\omega)$ denotes the function,

$$\mathrm{sgn}(\omega) = \begin{cases} +1, & \omega > 0, \\ -1, & \omega < 0, \end{cases} \tag{B.5}$$

and $H(\omega)$ is the transfer function

$$H(\omega) = \begin{cases} -j, & \omega > 0, \\ +j, & \omega < 0. \end{cases} \tag{B.6}$$

To model a quadrature hybrid mathematically in an adaptive array, we usually omit the first two boxes in the block diagram of Fig. B.4, except for the factor $1/\sqrt{2}$. The first box with transfer function $e^{-j\omega T_0}$ may be omitted because it is equivalent to a time delay T_0. This time delay is the same for every element of an array. Hence, leaving out this term is just equivalent to redefining the time origin of the signals. The phase factor $e^{j\,\mathrm{sgn}(\omega)[\omega_0 T_0 - \phi_0]}$ in the second box may be omitted because its only effect is to shift the carrier phase of every signal[‡] in the array by $\omega_0 T_0 - \phi_0$. However, we usually assume that the phase

---

[‡]The phase factor $e^{j\,\mathrm{sgn}(\omega)[\omega_0 T_0 - \phi_0]}$ is similar to the phase factor $e^{j\,\mathrm{sgn}(\omega)[\theta]}$ in Eq. (A.30), corresponding to the phase shift θ in Eq. (A.29) (of Appendix A).

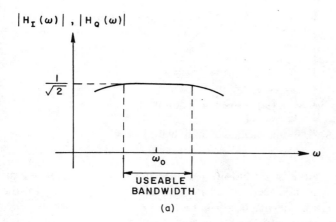

(a)

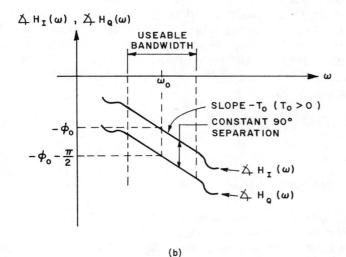

Figure B.3 Quadrature hybrid transfer functions: (a) magnitudes; (b) phase shifts.

(b)

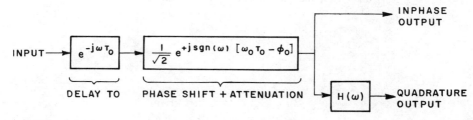

Figure B.4 The quadrature hybrid model.

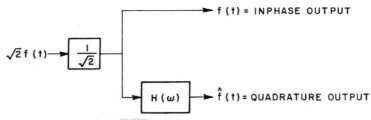

Figure B.5 The simplified quadrature hybrid model.

angle of each incoming signal is a random variable uniformly distributed on $(0, 2\pi)$ anyway, so there is no need to carry this phase term along in the analysis. On the other hand, the attenuation factor $1/\sqrt{2}$ in the second box must be retained in order to satisfy the requirement for conservation of power in the quadrature hybrid.

With the delay and phase factors omitted, we model the quadrature hybrid as shown in Fig. B.5. Note that the transfer function $H(\omega)$ is the same as the Hilbert transform transfer function defined in Eq. (A.6) of Appendix A. Therefore, if we denote the inphase output of the quadrature hybrid by $f(t)$, the quadrature output will be $\hat{f}(t)$, the Hilbert transform of $f(t)$. In addition, the input to the quadrature hybrid will be $\sqrt{2} f(t)$, as shown in Fig. B.5. This is the notation used in Chapters 2 and 3.

REFERENCES

Additional information about quadrature hybrids may be found in the following:

1. R. E. Fisher, "Broadband Twisted-Wire Quadrature Hybrids," *IEEE Transactions on Microwave Theory and Techniques*, MTT–21, no. 5 (May 1973): 355.

2. C. L. Ruthroff, "Some Broad-Band Transformers," *Proceedings of the IRE*, 47, no. 8 (August 1959): 1337.

3. J. Lange, "Interdigitated Stripline Quadrature Hybrid," *IEEE Transactions on Microwave Theory and Techniques*, MTT–17, no. 12 (December 1969): 1150.

Index